PHYTOCHROME

A bibliography with author, biological materials, taxonomic, and subject indexes of publications prior to 1975

PHYTOCHROME

A bibliography with author, biological materials, taxonomic, and subject indexes of publications prior to 1975

BY

DAVID L. CORRELL

JOHN L. EDWARDS

AND

W. SHROPSHIRE, JR.

*Published for
Radiation Biology Laboratory,
Smithsonian Institution
by the
Smithsonian Institution Press
1977*

Library of Congress Catalog Card Number: 77-80216
ISBN: 0-87474-840-2

Smithsonian Institution Press
Washington, D.C. 20560

Radiation Biology Laboratory
Smithsonian Institution
12441 Parklawn Drive
Rockville, Maryland 20852

PREFACE

Introduction

Phytochrome is a chromoprotein of widespread occurrence in plants, the chromophore of which undergoes a photoreversible reaction. This reaction results in absorption maxima of the chromoprotein shifting reversibly between 660 nm for the red absorbing form and 730 nm for the far red absorbing form. This pigment mediates a variety of photomorphogenic responses. The characteristics of many of these responses involve its ability to undergo photoreversal. The term phytochrome was first coined by Warren Butler (p. 17 of Ref. 246) and introduced into the literature in 1960; references: Borthwick and Hendricks (229), Butler (336), and Hendricks (1059). However, this bibliography also includes those reports of phytochrome research which were carried out before the name was used. Although a number of reviews of phytochrome research have been published, no bibliographies have been published.

Guidelines Used in Constructing this Bibliography

In order to construct a bibliography certain limitations of coverage had to be established for a topic so broad and diffuse. These are sometimes rather arbitrary, but if they were not adherred to the project would have become too large to cope with. Included are: I. Reports of research in which the molecular properties of phytochrome were studied. II. Reports of research in which responses of plants which had been exposed to restricted spectral regions are mediated by phytochrome. a. Experiments performed with white light were arbitrarily eliminated. b. Plant response studies carried out with light of restricted spectral quality were only included if the response involved has been reported to involve either antagonistic or synergistic effects between near UV, blue, red, and far red (700-760 nm) spectral bands. c. In addition, reports of studies of photosynthesis were excluded unless an interaction with phytochrome was specifically claimed by the authors. III. Reviews of phytochrome research which met the above three major criteria.

Construction of this Bibliography

All references are listed alphabetically by first author and are numbered consecutively. These numbers are for convenience in compiling indexes. Complete references are given where obtainable. In those cases where the original publication was not obtained, the reference is followed by a notation that it was obtained from a secondary source and the source of this reference. All abbreviations follow the recommendations of the Bibliographic Guide for Editors and Authors, American Chemical Society, 1974, where appropriate. Those citations of journals not included in that publication are given in full. Reports which are reviews, abstracts, or reviews with some new research data are designated as such immediately following the reference (R, A, R-D; respectively). Reports have been referenced in the original language. If not practical, the titles have been translated to English with the original language indicated. Errors in the published titles have not been corrected. Author surnames and initials are cited but all author names are included in the index. The taxonomic index includes entries for both the scientific names and common names. Variety names were not indexed. The following references were used in preparing the taxonomic index:

Genera Siphonogamarum. C. D. De Dalla Torrne and H. Harms. Sumtibus Guilelmi Engelmann, 1900-1907.

Gray's Manual of Botany Eighth Edition. M. L. Fernald. D. Van Nostrand Company, New York, Corrected Printing, 1970.

The Mosses and Liverworts. H. S. Conard. Wm. C. Brown Company, Dubuque, Iowa, 1956.

Manual of Cultivated Plants. L. H. Bailey. The MacMillan Company, Collier-MacMillan Canada Ltd., Toronto, Ontario, Eleventh Printing, 1969.

The Standard Cyclopedia of Horticulture. L. H. Bailey. The MacMillan Company, New York, 1947.

The taxonomic index is a listing of the names of all plants reported used in phytochrome research. To find citation of a specific plant the biological materials index must be used.

The subject index is divided into four major sections: I. Types of irradiance, II. Phytochrome molecular properties, III. Biological responses, IV. Reviews. If articles in a rather specific topic area are desired a comparison of references listed in several sections should allow the reader to quickly select the relevant literature (e.g., to search for references on action spectra for chloroplast orientation in *Mougeotia* one need only check for references common to those three sections). Indexed enzyme names have been made to conform with those in *Enzyme Nomenclature, Recommendations (1972) of the International Union of Pure and Applied Chemistry and the International Union of Biochemistry*, Elsevier, Amsterdam (1973). Where the enzyme name was not listed the author's original designation has been used.

Sources

References listed in this bibliography were gathered by many techniques. The most important were complete searches of numerous Plant Science Journals, Biological

Abstracts and Chemical Abstracts, personal contacts with scientists who are actively doing research related to phytochrome, and the cross-indexing of all references cited in those reports which were obtained. The authors would appreciate notification of errors and omissions, including copies or reprints of pertinent omitted or unobtained publications for future inclusion.

Acknowledgments

In order to complete this bibliography, extensive help was obtained from the Smithsonian Libraries both in obtaining many difficult to obtain reports and in helping to arrange for the translation of many of these reports. Special thanks are given to Mr. Jack Marquardt, Miss Jean Smith, and Miss Mary Clare Cahill of the Smithsonian Library. We would also like to thank the many scientists who have responded to our requests for reprints over the years.

Thanks are also extended to Mrs. Patricia Burleigh-McDougal and to Miss Leslie Ann Killeen for their assistance in translating a large number of French reports and in obtaining, sorting, and filing some of the reports. The authors also thank Mr. Norman B. Jaffee of the Smithsonian Botany Department for his help and suggestions in constructing the taxonomic index. For typing, the authors are indebted to Mrs. Karen Applestein.

Preparation of the bibliography was funded entirely by the Smithsonian Radiation Biology Laboratory.

Rockville, Maryland   November 13, 1976

CONTENTS

BIBLIOGRAPHY

0001. Abeles, F.B.; Holm, R.E.; Gahagan, H.E. 1967. PHOTOCONTROL OF ETHYLENE PRODUCTION. Plant Physiol. 42: Suppl.-9 (A).

0002. Abeles, F.B.; Lonski, J. 1969. STIMULATION OF LETTUCE SEED GERMINATION BY ETHYLENE. Plant Physiol. 44: 277-280.

0003. Åberg, B. 1943. PHYSIOLOGISCHE UND ÖKOLOGISCHE STUDIEN ÜBER DIE PFLANZLICHE PHOTOMORPHOSE. Symb. Bot. Ups. VIII (1): 1-189 (R-D).

0004. Abrami, G. 1972. HOMEOSTATIC MECHANISM IN LIGHT-CONTROLLED GERMINATION OF SEEDS. Proc. VI Int. Congr. Photobiol. Abstr. No. 196 (A).

0005. Acton, G.J. 1971. INDUCTION OF RIBONUCLEASE ACTIVITY BY RED AND FAR-RED LIGHT. Proc. Eur. Annu. Symp. Plant Photomorphogenesis, (Athens), p. 10 (A).

0006. Acton, G.J. 1972. PHYTOCHROME CONTROL OF THE LEVEL OF EXTRACTABLE RIBONUCLEASE ACTIVITY IN ETIOLATED HYPOCOTYLS. Nature (London), New. Biol. 236: 255-256.

0007. Acton, G.J. 1974. PHYTOCHROME CONTROL OF BOUND RIBONUCLEASE. Proc. Eur. Annu. Symp. Plant Photomorphogenesis, (Antwerpen), p. 53 (A).

0008. Acton, G.J. 1974. PHYTOCHROME CONTROLLED ACID RNASE: AN "ATTACHED" PROTEIN OF RIBOSOMES. Phytochemistry 13: 1303-1310.

0009. Acton, G.J.; Drumm, H.; Mohr, H. 1974. CONTROL OF SYNTHESIS DE NOVO OF ASCORBATE OXIDASE IN THE MUSTARD SEEDLING (SINAPIS ALBA L.) BY PHYTOCHROME. Planta 121: 39-50.

0010. Acton, G.J.; Murray, P.B. 1974. THE ROLES OF AUXIN AND GIBBERELLIN IN REVERSING RADIATION INHIBITION OF HYPOCOTYL LENGTHENING. Planta 117: 219-226.

0011. Acton, G.J.; Schopfer, P. 1974. PHYTOCHROME-INDUCED SYNTHESIS OF RIBONUCLEASE DE NOVO IN LUPIN HYPOCOTYL SECTIONS. Biochem. J. 142: 449-455.

0011.5 Addicott, F.T.; Lyon, J.L. 1973. PHYSIOLOGICAL ECOLOGY OF ABSCISSION. Shedding of Plant Parts. Ed. T.T. Kozlowski, Academic Press, New York and London, pp. 85-124 (R).

0012. Adrianowsky, A. 1884. WIRKUNG DES LICHTES AUF DAS ERSTE KEIMUNGS-STADIUM DER SAMEN. Bot. Centralbl. 29: 73-75.

0013. Aghion, C.C.; Mancinelli, A.L. 1969. SYNTHESIS AND DECAY OF PHYTO-CHROME IN CUCUMBER COTYLEDONS. Plant Physiol. 44: Suppl.-19 (A).

0014. Aghion, J.; Jouglard, C.; Lourtioux, A. 1962. CONTRIBUTION À L'ÉTUDE DES PROPRIÉTÉS PHOTOCHIMIQUES DU PHYTOCHROME. C.R. Acad. Sci. Ser. D. 255: 1465-1466.

0015. Aghion, J.; Jouglard, C.; Lourtioux, A. 1962. EFFETS D'ÉCLAIREMENTS, COLORÉS DE FAIBLES ÉNERGIES SUR LA CROISSANCE DE COLÉOPTILES D'AVOINES *IN VITRO*. Physiol. Plant 15: 452-456 (ENG Summary).

0016. Aghion, J.; Jacques, R.; Jouglard, C.; Lourtioux, A. 1966. PHOTO-CROISSANCE DE SEGMENTS DE COLEOPTILES D'AVOINE MAINTENUS EN SUR-VIESPECTRES D'ACTION. Photochem. Photobiol. 5: 169-175.

0017. Ahmed, A.M.M.; Ries, E. 1969. THE PATTERN OF $^{14}CO_2$ FIXATION IN DIFFERENT PHASES OF THE LIFE CYCLE AND UNDER DIFFERENT WAVELENGTHS IN *CHLORELLA PYRENOIDOSA*. Prog. in Photosynthesis Res. 3: 1662-1668. Ed. H. Metzner; Munich: Goldmann-Verlag.

0018. Ahmed, E.O.S. 1961. A COMPARATIVE STUDY OF THE INFLUENCE OF FAR-RED IRRADIATION AND OF GIBBERELLIC ACID ON THE GROWTH OF TOMATO PLANTS. M. Sc. Thesis, Univ. London (not obtained). (Referred to by Selman, J.W.; Ahmed, E.O.S. 1962. Ann. Appl. Biol. 50: 479-485).

0019. Ahmed, S.I.; Swain, T. 1970. THE EFFECT OF LIGHT ON THE ACTIVITY OF ENZYMES OF THE AROMATIC PATHWAY IN PEAS AND MUNG BEANS. Phytochemistry 9: 2287-2290.

0020. Aimi, R.; Shibasaki, S. 1972. CIRCADIAN RHYTHM AND LIGHT CONTROL OF THE DIURNAL LEAF MOVEMENT OF *PHASEOLUS* IN RELATION TO BIOELECTRIC RESPONSES. Proc. VI Int. Congr. Photobiol. Abstr. No. 193 (A).

0021. Akoyunoglou, G.A. 1968. THE EFFECT OF RED AND FAR-RED LIGHT ON CHLOROPHYLL BIOSYNTHESIS IN DARK-GROWN BEAN LEAVES AT VARIOUS AGES. Proc. V Int. Congr. Photobiol. p. 86 (A).

0022. Akoyunoglou, G. 1970. THE EFFECT OF AGE ON THE PHYTOCHROME-MEDIATED CHLOROPHYLL FORMATION IN DARK-GROWN BEAN LEAVES. Physiol. Plant 23: 29-37.

0023. Akoyunoglou, G. 1971. EFFECT OF RED AND FAR-RED LIGHT ON THE LATE STAGES OF CHLOROPHYLL SYNTHESIS. Proc. Eur. Annu. Symp. Plant Photomorphogenesis, (Athens), p. 11 (A).

0024. Aksenova, N.P. 1965. EFFECT OF 2,4-DINITROPHENOL ON THE UPTAKE OF OXYGEN IN LIGHT AND IN DARKNESS BY LEAVES OF COCKLEBUR AND *RUDBECKIA*. Dokl. Akad. Nauk SSSR. 162: 1194-1197 (Rus).

0025. Akulovich, N.K.; Godnev, T.N.; Domash, V.I. 1966. DETERMINATION OF PHYTOCHROME IN GREEN PLANTS. Dokl. Akad. Nauk B. SSR 10: 601-603 (Rus).

0026. Alcorn, S.M.; Kurtz, E.B. Jr. 1959. SOME FACTORS AFFECTING THE GERMINATION OF SEED OF THE SAGUARO CACTUS *(CARNEGIEA GIGANTEA)*. Am. J. Bot. 46: 526-529.

0027. Alfermann, W. 1972. INDUCTION OF ANTHOCYANIN SYNTHESIS BY LIGHT AND AUXINS IN TISSUE CULTURES OF *DAUCUS CAROTA*. Proc. VI Int. Congr. Photobiol. Abstr. No. 187 (A).

0028. Amen, R.D. 1968. A MODEL OF SEED DORMANCY. Bot. Rev. 34: 1-31 (R-D).

0029. Anand, R.; Maheshwari, S.C. 1966. GERMINATION AND FLOWERING IN *ARABIDOPSIS THALIANA* IN STERILE CULTURE. Physiol. Plant. 19: 1011-1019.

0030. Anand, R.; Galston, A.W. 1968. STUDIES ON PRIMARY PHYTOCHROME REACTIONS REGULATING SUCROSE UPTAKE IN ETIOLATED PEA SEEDLINGS. Plant Physiol. 43: Suppl.-22 (A).

0031. Anand, R. 1969. INVESTIGATIONS ON PHYTOCHROME REGULATION OF SUCROSE UTILIZATION IN ETIOLATED PEA SEEDLINGS. Ph.D. Thesis Yale Univ., New Haven.

0032. Anand, R.; Galston, A.W. 1971. FURTHER INVESTIGATIONS ON PHYTOCHROME-CONTROLLED SUCROSE UPTAKE INTO APICAL BUDS OF ETIOLATED PEAS. Plant Physiol. 47: Suppl.-11 Abstr. No. 66 (A).

0033. Anand, R.; Galston, A.W. 1972. FURTHER INVESTIGATIONS ON PHYTOCHROME-CONTROLLED SUCROSE UPTAKE INTO APICAL BUDS OF ETIOLATED PEAS. Am. J. Bot. 59: 327-336.

0034. Anderson, G.R.; Jenner, E.L.; Mumford, F.E. 1968. TEMPERATURE AND PH STUDIES ON PHYTOCHROME *IN VITRO*. Proc. V Int. Congr. Photobiol. p. 94 (A).

0035. Anderson, G.R.; Jenner, E.L.; Mumford, F.E. 1968. LOW-TEMPERATURE SPECTRA OF PHYTOCHROME *IN VITRO*. Plant Physiol. 43: Suppl.-15 (A).

0036. Anderson, G.R.; Jenner, E.L.; Mumford, F.E. 1969. TEMPERATURE AND PH STUDIES ON PHYTOCHROME *IN VITRO*. Biochemistry 8: 1182-1187.

0037. Anderson, G.R.; Jenner, E.L.; Mumford, F.E. 1970. OPTICAL ROTATORY DISPERSION AND CIRCULAR DICHROISM SPECTRA OF PHYTOCHROME. Biochim. Biophys. Acta 221: 69-73.

0038. Andreae, S.A.; Hopkins, W.G. 1973. INTERACTION OF ABSCISIC ACID AND RED LIGHT DURING INDUCTION OF FLOWERING OF *CHENOPODIUM RUBRUM*. Plant Physiol. 51: Suppl.-29 Abstr. No. 158 (A).

0039. Anonymous. 1953. NEW LIGHT ON PLANTS. Agric. Res. 1: 3-5 (R).

0040. Anonymous. 1961. PLANT LIGHT-GROWTH DISCOVERIES---FROM PHOTOPERIODISM TO PHYTOCHROME. ARS Special Report 22-64: 1-17 (R).

0041. Anonymous. 1972. SEED ECOLOGY. Nature (London) 237: 74-75 (R).

0042. Anonymous. 1972. PHYTOCHROME INTERMEDIATES *IN VIVO*. Nature (London) 237: 429 (R).

0043. Appleman, D.; Pyfrom, H.T. 1955. CHANGES IN CATALASE ACTIVITY AND OTHER RESPONSES INDUCED IN PLANTS BY RED AND BLUE LIGHT. Plant Physiol. 30: 543-549.

0044. Applewhite, P.B.; Satter, R.L.; Galston, A.W. 1973. PROTEIN SYNTHESIS DURING ENDOGENOUS RHYTHMIC LEAFLET MOVEMENT IN *ALBIZZIA*. J. Gen. Physiol. 62: 707-713.

0045. Arias, I.; Wulff, R. 1972. GERMINACION EN *JUSSIAEA SUFFRUTICOSA*: EFECTOS DE INTENSIDAD DE LUZ Y ESTADOS FOTOESTACIONARIOS DEL FITOCROMO. Acta Cient. Venez. 23: 50 (A).

0046. Arthur, J.M. 1929. SOME EFFECTS OF RADIANT ENERGY ON PLANTS. J. Opt. Soc. Am. Rev. Sci. Instrum. 18: 253-263.

0047. Arthur, J.M. 1932. ARTIFICIAL LIGHT AND PLANT GROWTH. Agric. Eng. 13: 228-291 (R-D).

0048. Arthur, J.M. 1932. RED PIGMENT PRODUCTION IN APPLES BY MEANS OF ARTIFICIAL LIGHT SOURCES. Contrib. Boyce Thompson Inst. 4: 1-18.

0049. Arthur, J.M.; Stewart, W.D. 1933. TRANSPIRATION OF TOBACCO PLANTS IN RELATION TO RADIANT ENERGY IN THE VISIBLE AND INFRA-RED. Contrib. Boyce Thompson Inst. 5: 483-501.

0050. Arthur, J.M.; Stewart W.D. 1935. RELATIVE GROWTH AND DRY WEIGHT PRODUCTION OF PLANT TISSUE UNDER MAZDA, NEON, SODIUM, AND MERCURY VAPOR LAMPS. Contrib. Boyce Thompson Inst. 7: 119-130.

0051. Arthur, J.M. 1936. PLANT GROWTH IN CONTINUOUS ILLUMINATION. *BIOLOGICAL EFFECTS OF RADIATION,* Ed. B.M. Duggar, McGraw-Hill, New York, II: pp. 715-726 (R).

0052. Arthur, J.M. 1936. SOME INFRA-RED EFFECTS ON GREEN PLANTS. *BIOLOGICAL EFFECTS OF RADIATION,* Ed. B.M. Duggar, McGraw-Hill, New York, II: pp. 841-852 (R).

0053. Arthur, J.M. 1936. RADIATION AND ANTHOCYANIN PIGMENTS. *RADIATION EFFECTS IN BIOLOGY,* Ed. B.M. Duggar, McGraw-Hill, New York, II: pp. 1109-1118 (R).

0054. Asakawa, S.; Inokuma, T. 1961. LIGHT-SENSITIVITY IN THE GERMINATION OF *PINUS THUNBERGII* AND *PICEA GLEHNII* SEEDS. Nippon Ringakkai-Shi 43: 331-335.

0055. Asakawa, S.; Nagao, A. 1963. GERMINATION BEHAVIOR OF *ALNUS INOKUMAI* SEEDS. Nippon Ringakkai-Shi 45: 331-334.

0056. Asakawa, S.; Sasaki, S. 1972. EFFECT OF MONOCHROMATIC LIGHTS ON THE GERMINATION OF *PINUS THUNBERGII* SEEDS. Nippon Ringakkai-Shi 54: 350-355.

0057. Asomaning, E.J.A.; Galston, A.W. 1959. THE EFFECTS OF PREIRRADIATION WITH RED AND BLUE LIGHT ON PIGMENT CONTENT AND PHOTOTROPIC SENSI-TIVITIES OF OAT AND BARLEY COLEOPTILES. Proc. IX Int. Bot. Congr. 2: 10-11 (A).

0058. Asomaning, E.J.A.; Galston, A.W. 1961. COMPARATIVE STUDY OF PHOTO-TROPIC RESPONSE AND PIGMENT CONTENT IN OAT AND BARLEY COLEOPTILES. Plant Physiol. 36: 453-464.

0059. Aspinall, D. 1969. THE EFFECTS OF DAY LENGTH AND LIGHT INTENSITY ON THE GROWTH OF BARLEY. VI. INTERACTIONS BETWEEN THE EFFECTS OF TEMPERATURE, PHOTOPERIOD, AND THE SPECTRAL COMPOSITION OF THE LIGHT SOURCE. Aust. J. Biol. Sci. 22: 53-67.

0060. Attridge, T.H.; Smith, H. 1967. A PHYTOCHROME-MEDIATED INCREASE IN THE LEVEL OF PHENYLALANINE AMMONIA-LYASE ACTIVITY IN THE TERMINAL BUDS OF *PISUM SATIVUM*. Biochim. Biophys. Acta 148: 805-807.

0061. Attridge, T.H. 1969. ENZYME CONTROL OF FLAVONOID BIOSYNTHESIS. Ph.D. Thesis, Univ. London, England (not obtained).

0062. Attridge, T.H.; Smith, H. 1973. EVIDENCE FOR A POOL OF INACTIVE PHENYLALANINE AMMONIA-LYASE IN *CUCUMIS SATIVUS* SEEDLINGS. Phytochemistry 12: 1569-1574.

0063. Attridge, T.H. 1974. PHYTOCHROME-MEDIATED ENZYME SYNTHESIS AND ENZYME ACTIVATION IN MUSTARD COTYLEDONS. Proc. Eur. Annu. Symp. Plant Photomorphogenesis, (Antwerpen), pp. 67-69 (A).

0064. Attridge, T.H. 1974. PHYTOCHROME-MEDIATED SYNTHESIS OF ASCORBIC ACID OXIDASE IN MUSTARD COTYLEDONS. Biochim. Biophys. Acta 362: 258-265.

0065. Attridge, T.H.; Johnson, C.B.; Smith, H. 1974. DENSITY-LABELLING EVIDENCE FOR THE PHYTOCHROME-MEDIATED ACTIVATION OF PHENYLALANINE AMMONIA-LYASE IN MUSTARD COTYLEDONS. Biochim. Biophys. Acta 343: 440-451.

0066. Attridge, T.H.; Smith, H. 1974. DENSITY-LABELLING EVIDENCE FOR THE BLUE-LIGHT-MEDIATED ACTIVATION OF PHENYLALANINE AMMONIA-LYASE IN *CUCUMIS SATIVUS* SEEDLINGS. Biochim. Biophys. Acta 343: 452-464.

0067. Audus, L.J. 1969. GEOTROPISM. *Physiology of Plant Growth and Development*. Ed. M.B. Wilkins, McGraw-Hill, New York, pp. 204-242 (R).

0068. Augustinussen, E. 1964. ON THE FORMATION OF CHLOROPHYLL-A AND CHLORO-PHYLL-B IN ETIOLATED LEAVES. Physiol. Plant. 17: 403-406.

0069. Augustinussen, E.; Madsen, A. 1965. REGENERATION OF PROTOCHLOROPHYLL IN ETIOLATED BARLEY SEEDLINGS FOLLOWING DIFFERENT LIGHT TREATMENTS. Physiol. Plant. 18: 828-837.

0070. Augustinussen, E. 1966. THE EFFECTS OF RED AND FAR-RED LIGHT ON RESPI-RATION IN ETIOLATED BARLEY SEEDLINGS. K. Vet. Landbohoejsk. Arsskr. pp. 157-170.

0071. Avery, G.S., Jr.; Burkholder, P.R.; Creighton, H.B. 1937. GROWTH HOR-MONE IN TERMINAL SHOOTS OF *NICOTIANA* IN RELATION TO LIGHT. Am. J. Bot. 24: 666-673.

0072. Avery, G.S., Jr.; Burkholder, P.R.; Creighton, H.B. 1937. POLARIZED GROWTH AND CELL STUDIES IN THE FIRST INTERNODE AND COLEOPTILE OF *AVENA* IN RELATION TO LIGHT AND DARKNESS. Bot. Gaz. (Chicago) 99: 125-143.

0073. Avery, G.S., Jr.; Burkholder, P.R.; Creighton, H.B. 1938. GROWTH AND CELL STRUCTURE IN THE FIRST INTERNODE AND COLEOPTILE OF *AVENA* AS AFFECTED BY RED, GREEN, BLUE, AND VIOLET RADIATION. Am. J. Bot. 25: 10S (A).

0074. Ayers, J.; Mancinelli, A.L. 1969. PHYTOCHROME CONTROL OF ANTHOCYANIN SYNTHESIS IN TOMATO SEEDLINGS. Plant Physiol. 44: Suppl.-19 Abstr. No. 88 (A).

0075. Baar, H. 1912. ÜBER DEN EINFLUSS DES LICHTES AUF DIE SAMENKEIMUNG UND SEINE ABHÄNGIGKEIT VON ANDEREN FAKTOREN. Sitzungsber. Akad. Wiss. Wein. Math. Naturw. Kl. Abt. 1: 121: 667-705.

0076. Babenko, V.I.; Kvasnyuk, A.K. 1970. AN ATTEMPT TO PENETRATE INTO THE NATURE OF THE RESPONSE OF PHYTOCHROME TO IRRADIATION WITH RED AND FAR RED LIGHT. Dokl. Akad. Nauk SSSR 195: 229-231 (RUS).

0077. Babenko, V.I.; Kvasnyuk, A.K. 1971. DYNAMICS OF PHYTOCHROME ACCUMULATION IN THE APEX OF WINTER WHEAT PLANTS DURING VERNALIZATION. Dopov. Akad. Nauk Ukr. RSR Ser. B. 33: 265-268 (UKR) (ENG Summary).

0078. Babuskin, L.N. 1955. THE SPECTRUM OF PHOTOTAXIS OF THE CHLOROPLASTS. Dokl. Akad. Nauk SSSR 103: 333-335 (RUS).

0079. Balangé, A.P.; Rollin, P. 1973. PURIFICATION OF PHOTOREVERSIBLE PHYTOCHROME FROM AVENA SEEDLINGS BY ISOELECTRIC FOCUSING. Plant Sci. Lett. 1: 59-64.

0080. Balangé, A.P. 1974. SPECTRAL CHANGES OF PHYTOCHROME IN GLYCEROL SOLUTIONS. Physiol. Veg. 12: 95-105.

0081. Ball, N.G. 1936. THE EFFECT OF NOCTURNAL ILLUMINATION BY DIFFERENT REGIONS OF THE SPECTRUM ON THE SUBSEQUENT OPENING OF FLOWER-BUDS. New Phytol. 35: 101-116.

0082. Ball, N.G.; Dyke, I.J. 1954. AN ENDOGENOUS 24-HOUR RHYTHM IN THE GROWTH RATE OF THE AVENA COLEOPTILE. J. Exp. Bot. 5: 421-433.

0083. Ball, N.G. 1969. NASTIC RESPONSES. PHYSIOLOGY OF PLANT GROWTH AND DEVELOPMENT, Ed. M.B. Wilkins, McGraw-Hill, New York, pp. 276-300 (R).

0084. Baradat, Ph. 1968. EFFET DE LUMIÈRES COLORÉES DE DIVERSES LONGUEURS D'ONDES SUR L'OUVERTURE DU CROCHET HYPOCOTYLAIRE DE PICEA ABIES. Mem. Soc. Bot. Fr. 1966: 67-75.

0085. Barceló-Coll, J. 1972. BIOSÍNTESIS DE NICOTINA Y METABOLISMO NITROGENADO EN "NICOTIANA RUSTICA L." BAJO EL INFLUJO DE CIERTAS LUCES MONOCROMÁTICAS Y DEL FRÍO. Circ. Farm. 236: 257-308 (ENG Summary).

0086. Barrett, J. 1967. PHOTO-OXIDATION OF MAGNESIUM PORPHYRINS AND FORMATION OF PROTOBILIVIOLIN. Nature (London) 215: 733-735.

0087. Barthe, F. 1969. CONTRIBUTION Á LA CONNAISSANCE DES PROPRIÉTÉS DU PHYTOCHROME, PAR SPECTROPHOTOMÉTRIE IN VIVO ET DE SOU D'ACTION, PAR L'ÉTUDE DE DEUX OXYDASES, CHEZ LA MONTARDE BLANCHE (SINAPIS ALBA L.). Ph.D. Thesis, Univ. Rouen, France (not obtained).

0088. Barz, W.; Adamek, Ch. 1970. ÜBER DEN EINFLUSS VON LICHT AUF DEN UMSATZ DER ISOFLAVONE FORMONONETIN UND BIOCHANIN A IN CICER ARIETINUM L. Planta 90: 191-202 (ENG Summary).

0089. Barz, W.; Hösel, W.; Adamek, Ch. 1971. ÜBER DEN EINFLUSS VON LICHT AUF DEN UMSATZ VON FLAVONOLEN UND ISOFLAVONEN IN *CICER ARIETINUM*. Phytochemistry 10: 343-349 (ENG Summary).

0090. Barzilai, E.; Mayer, A.M. 1964. KININS IN GERMINATING LETTUCE SEED. Aust. J. Biol. Sci. 17: 798-800.

0091. Bass, L.N. 1950. EFFECT OF WAVE LENGTH BANDS OF FILTERED LIGHT ON GERMINATION OF SEEDS OF KENTUCKY BLUEGRASS *(POA PRATENSIS)* J. Iowa Agric. Exp. St. 57: 61-71.

0092. Bassi, P.K.; Purohit, A.N.; Tregunna, E.B. 1974. CARBON DIOXIDE AND PHYTOCHROME ACTION. Plant Physiol. 53: Suppl.-3 Abstr. No. 9 (A).

0093. Bauer, L.; Mohr, H. 1959. DER NACHWEIS DES REVERSIBLEN HELLROT-DUNKEL-ROT-REAKTIONSSYSTEMS BEI LAUBMOOSEN. Planta 54: 68-73 (ENG Summary).

0094. Bavrina, T.V. 1969. PHYTOCHROME AND ITS ROLE IN THE PHOTOPERIODIC REACTION OF PLANT'S FLOWERING. Izv. Akad. Nauk SSSR Ser. Biol. No. 3, pp. 371-385 (R) (RUS) (ENG Summary).

0094.5 Baxter, P. 1972. THE FLOWERING PROCESS - A NEW THEORY. *Plant Growth Substances 1970,* Proc. VII Int. Conf. Plant Growth Substances. Ed. D.J. Carr, Springer-Verlag, Berlin, Heidelberg, New York, pp. 775-779 (R).

0095. Beauchesne, G.; Poulain, M.C. 1966. INFLUENCE DES ÉCLAIREMENTS APPROXIMATIVEMENT MONOCHROMATIQUES SUR LE DEVELOPPEMENT DES TISSUS DE MOELLE DE TABAC CULTIVÉS *IN VITRO* EN PRESENCE D'AUXINE ET DE KINETINE. Photochem. Photobiol. 5: 157-167 (ENG Summary).

0096. Beauchesne, G.; Poulain, C.; Letouzé, R. 1970. LES CULTURES *IN VITRO* DE TISSU DE MOËLLE DE TABAC W. 38, EN ÉCLAIREMENTS MONOCHROMATIQUES. PHOTOINACTIVATION DES AUXINES INDOLIQUES. Physiol. Plant. 23: 1101-1109.

0097. Becker, K. 1971. UNTERSUCHUNGEN ÜBER DEN PIGMENT- UND LIPOCHINOSTOFF-WECHSEL BEI DER ENTWICKLUNG FUNKTIONS-TÜCHTIGER CHLOROPLASTEN. Ph.D. Thesis, Univ. Münster, Germany (not obtained).

0098. Beevers, L.; Loveys, B.; Pearson, J.A.; Wareing, P.F. 1970. PHYTOCHROME AND HORMONAL CONTROL OF EXPANSION AND GREENING OF ETIOLATED WHEAT LEAVES. Planta 90: 286-294.

0099. Bellini, E.; Van Poucke, M. 1970. DISTRIBUTION OF PHENYLALANINE AMMONIA-LYASE IN ETIOLATED AND FAR-RED IRRADIATED RADISH SEEDLINGS. Planta 93: 60-70.

0100. Bellini, E.; Hillman, W.S. 1971. RED AND FAR RED EFFECTS ON PHENYLALA-NINE AMMONIA-LYASE IN *RAPHANUS* AND *SINAPIS* SEEDLINGS DO NOT CORRE-LATE WITH PHYTOCHROME SPECTROPHOTOMETRY. Plant Physiol. 47: 668-671.

0101. Bellini, E. 1972. PHYTOCHROME AND FAR RED EFFECTS ON RADISH SEEDLINGS. Proc. VI Int. Congr. Photobiol. Abstr. No. 173 (A).

0102. Bellini, E.; Martelli, M. 1973. ANTHOCYANIN SYNTHESIS IN RADISH SEED-LINGS: EFFECTS OF CONTINUOUS FAR RED IRRADIATION AND PHYTOCHROME TRANSFORMATIONS. Z. Pflanzenphysiol. 70: 12-21.

0103. Bellini, E.; Molteni, E. 1974. EFFECTS OF LIGHT ON MOVEMENTS OF *OXALIS ACETOSELLA* LEAFLETS. Proc. Eur. Annu. Symp. Plant Photomorphogene-sis, (Antwerpen) p. 90.

0104. Bennet-Clark, T.A.; Ball, N.G. 1951. THE DIAGEOTROPIC BEHAVIOUR OF RHIZOMES. J. Exp. Bot. 2: 169-203.

0104.5 Bentrup, F.W. 1974. LICHTABHÄNGIGE MEMBRANPOTENTIALE BEI PFLANZEN. Ber. Dtsch. Bot. Ges. 87: 515-528.

0105. Bergann, F. 1930. UNTERSUCHUNGEN ÜBER LICHTWACHSTUM LICHTKRÜMMUNG UND LICHTABFALL BEI *AVENA SATIVA* MIT HILFE MONOCHROMATISCHEN LICHTES. Planta 10: 666-743.

0106. Berger, C.; Bergmann, L. 1967. FARBLICHT UND PLASTIDENDIFFERENZIERUNG IM SPEICHERGEWEBE VON *SOLANUM TUBEROSUM* L. Z. Pflanzenphysiol. 56: 439-445 (ENG Summary).

0107. Bergfeld, V.R. 1963. DIE WIRKUNG VON HELLROTER UND BLAUER STRAHLUNG AUF DIE CHLOROPLASTENAUSBILDUNG. Z. Naturforsch. 18b: 328-331 (ENG Summary).

0108. Bergfeld, V.R. 1963. DIE BEEINFLUSSUNG DER ZELLKERNE IN DEN VORKEIMEN VON *DRYOPTERIS FILIX-MAS* DURCH ROTE UND BLAUE STRAHLUNG. Z. Natur-forsch. 18b: 557-562 (ENG Summary).

0109. Bergfeld, V.R. 1964. DER EINFLUSS ROTER UND BLAUER STRAHLUNG AUF DIE AUSBILDUNG DER CHLOROPLASTEN BEI GEHEMMTER PROTEINSYNTHESE. Z. Naturforsch. 19b: 1076-1078 (ENG Summary).

0110. Bergfeld, V.R. 1964. DIE LICHTABHÄNGIGE AUSBILDUNG DER ZELLKERNE IN DEN VORKEIMEN VON *DRYOPTERIS FILIX-MAS* BEI HEMMUNG DER PROTEINSYN-THESE. Z. Naturforsch. 19b: 1142-1146 (ENG Summary).

0111. Bergfeld, R. 1965. ZELLTEILUNG UND MORPHOGENESE DER VORKEIME VON
    DRYOPTERIS FILIX-MAS (L.) SCHOTT IN HELLROTER UND BLAUER STRAHLUNG
    BEI HEMMUNG DER PROTEINSYNTHESE. Z. Naturforsch. 20b: 591-594
    (ENG Summary).

0112. Bergfeld, R. 1965. DIE AUSBILDUNG DER CHLOROPLASTEN UND KERNE IN DEN
    GAMETOPHYTEN-ZELLEN VON *DRYOPTERIS FILIX-MAS* (L.) SCHOTT UNTER DER
    EINWIRKUNG HELLROTER UND BLAUER STRAHLUNG. Ber. Dtsch. Bot. Ges. 78:
    69-73.

0113. Bergfeld, R. 1967. KERN-UND NUCLEOLUSAUSBILDUNG IN DEN GAMETOPHYTENZEL-
    LEN VON *DRYOPTERIS FILIX-MAS* (L.) SCHOTT BEI UMSTEUERUNG DER MORPHO-
    GENESE. Z. Naturforsch. 22b: 972-976 (ENG Summary).

0114. Bergfeld, R. 1968. CHLOROPLASTENAUSBILDUNG UND MORPHOGENESE DER GAME-
    TOPHYTEN VON *DRYOPTERIS FILIX-MAS* (L.) SCHOTT NACH APPLIKATION VON
    CHLORAMPHENICOL UND ACTIDION (CYCLOHEXIMID). Planta 81: 274-279
    (ENG Summary).

0115. Bergfeld, R. 1970. FEINSTRUKTUR DER CHLOROPLASTEN IN DEN GAMETOPHYTEN-
    ZELLEN VON *DRYOPTERIS FILIX-MAS* (L.) SCHOTT NACH EINWIRKUNG HELL-
    ROTER UND BLAUER STRAHLUNG. Z. Pflanzenphysiol. 63: 55-64 (ENG
    Summary).

0116. Bergmann, L.; Berger, Ch. 1966. FARBLICHT UND PLASTIDENDIFFERENZIERUNG
    IN ZELLKULTUREN VON *NICOTIANA TABACUM* VAR. "SAMSUN". Planta 69:
    58-69 (ENG Summary).

0116.5 Bergmann, L.; Van Steveninck, R.F.M. 1974. ROUND TABLE DISCUSSION 9.
    Membrane Transport in Plants. Ed. U. Zimmerman and J. Dainty.
    Springer-Verlag; Berlin, Heidelberg, New York. pp 462-463 (R).

0117. Berrie, A.M.M. 1966. THE EFFECT OF TEMPERATURE AND LIGHT ON THE GER-
    MINATION OF LETTUCE SEEDS. Physiol. Plant. 19: 429-436.

0118. Berrie, A.M.M.; Robertson, J. 1973. GROWTH RETARDANTS AND THE GERMINA-
    TION OF LIGHT SENSITIVE LETTUCE SEED. Physiol. Plant. 28: 278-283.

0119. Berrie, A.M.M.; Paterson, J.; West, H.R. 1974. WATER CONTENT AND THE
    RESPONSIVITY OF LETTUCE SEEDS TO LIGHT. Physiol. Plant. 31: 90-96.

0120. Berry, D.R.; Smith, H. 1971. RED LIGHT STIMULATION OF PROLAMELLAR BODY
    RECRYSTALLIZATION AND THYLAKOID FORMATION IN BARLEY ETIOPLASTS. J.
    Cell Sci. 8: 185-200.

0121. Bert, P. 1870. RECHERCHES SUR LES MOUVEMENTS DE LA SENSITIVE *(MIMOSA
    PUDICA* LINN). Mem. Soc. Sci. Phys. Nat. Bordeaux 8: 1-58.

0122. Bert, M.P. 1878. INFLUENCE DE LA LUMIÈRE SUR LES ÈTRES VIVANTS. Revue
Sci. 14: 2e Séries Numéro 42, pp. 981-986 (R-D).

0123. Bertsch, W.F. 1958. EFFECTS OF COMPOSITION OF THE MEDIUM ON THE LIGHT
SENSITIVITY OF ETIOLATED PEA SECTION GROWTH. Plant Physiol. 33:
Suppl.-32-33 (A).

0124. Bertsch, W.F. 1959. FAR-RED REVERSIBILITY OF BLUE LIGHT EFFECTS IN
ETIOLATION. Proc. IX Int. Bot. Congr. 2: 29 (A).

0125. Bertsch, W.F. 1959. ON THE PHOTOINHIBITION OF ETIOLATED PEA STEM SEC-
TION GROWTH. Ph.D. Thesis, Yale Univ. New Haven.

0126. Bertsch, W.F. 1961. THE PROMOTION OF PHOTOSENSITIVE GROWTH BY SUGARS
AND COBALT IN ETIOLATED PEA STEM SECTIONS. Prog. Photobiol. Proc.
Int. Congr. 3rd Copenhagen 1960, pp. 398-400.

0127. Bertsch, W.F.; Hillman, W.S. 1961. THE PHOTOINHIBITION OF GROWTH IN
ETIOLATED STEM SEGMENTS. I. GROWTH CAUSED BY SUGARS IN *PISUM*. Am.
J. Bot. 48: 504-511.

0128. Bertsch, W.F. 1963. THE PHOTOINHIBITION OF GROWTH IN ETIOLATED STEM
SEGMENTS. II. GROWTH CAUSED BY COBALT IN *PISUM*. Am. J. Bot. 50:
213-219.

0129. Bertsch, W.F. 1963. THE PHOTOINHIBITION OF GROWTH IN ETIOLATED STEM
SEGMENTS. III. FAR-RED REVERSIBILITY OF BLUE LIGHT EFFECTS IN *PISUM*.
Am. J. Bot. 50: 754-760.

0130. Bertsch, W.; Mohr, H. 1965. DIE UNABHÄNGIGKEIT DER LICHTINDUZIERTEN
ANTHOCYANSYNTHESE VON DER PHOTOSYNTHESE. Planta 65: 17-26 (ENG
Summary).

0131. Bertsch, W.; Mohr, H. 1965. EIN BEITRAG ZUR INTERPRETATION DER DUNKEL-
ROTBANDE DER HOCHENERGIEREAKTION BEI DER PHOTOMORPHOGENESE (LICHT-
ABHÄNGIGE ANTHOCYANSYNTHESE BEI SENFKEIMLINGEN, *(SINAPIS ALBA* L.).
Planta 65: 245-258 (ENG Summary).

0132. Bertsch, W. 1966. EIN BEITRAG ZUR INTERPRETATION DER DUNKELROTBANDE
DER HOCHENERGIEREAKTION BEI DER PHOTOMORPHOGENESE (LICHTABHÄNGIGE
ANTHOCYANSYNTHESE BEI SENFKEIMLINGEN, *SINAPIS ALBA* L.). Ph.D.
Thesis, Univ. Freiburg, Germany.

0133. Betria, A.I.; Montaldi, E.R. 1974. LIGHT EFFECTS ON BULB DIFFERENTIA-
TION AND LEAF GROWTH IN *CYPERUS ROTUNDUS* L. Phyton (Buenos Aires)
32: 1-8.

0134. Bewley, J.D.; Black, M.; Negbi, M. 1967. IMMEDIATE ACTION OF PHYTO-
CHROME IN LIGHT-STIMULATED LETTUCE SEEDS. Nature (London) 215:
648-649.

0135. Bewley, J.D.; Negbi, M.; Black, M. 1968. IMMEDIATE PHYTOCHROME ACTION
IN LETTUCE SEEDS AND ITS INTERACTION WITH GIBBERELLINS AND OTHER
GERMINATION PROMOTERS. Planta 78: 351-357.

0136. Bhandari, M.C.; Sen, D.N. 1973. PHYTOCHROME AND SEED GERMINATION IN
CITRULLUS COLOCYNTHIS (LINN.) SCHRAD. Sci. Cult. 39: 458-459.

0137. Bhargava, S.C. 1964. PHOTOPERIODISM, FLORAL INDUCTION AND FLORAL INHI-
BITION IN *SALVIA OCCIDENTALIS*. Meded. Landbouwhogesch. Wageningen
64-12: 1-74.

0138. Bianco, J. 1972. ÉTUDE DE LA GERMINATION DE *RUMEX ALPINUS* L. Trav. Sci.
Parc. Nat. Vanoise II: 27-34 (ENG, GER, ITA Summary).

0139. Bianco, J.; Pellegrin, M. Ch. 1973. PHYSIOLOGIE DE LA GERMINATION D'UNE
PLANTE ALPINE: *LOISELEURIA PROCUMBENS* (L.)DESV. Trav. Sci. Parc. Nat.
Vanoise III: 43-51.

0140. Bianco, J. 1973. PHYTOCHROME ET GERMINATION DES SEMENCES DE *RUMEX*.
Physiol. Plant. 28: 61-66 (ENG Summary).

0141. Bianco, J.; Bulard, C. 1974. ÉTUDE DE LA GERMINATION DES GRAINES DE
RHODODENDRON FERRUGINEUM L. ET DE *TOFIELDEA CALYCULATA* (L.) WAHLNB.
Trav. Sci. Parc. Nat. Vanoise V: 121-130 (ENG, GER, ITA Summary).

0142. Bickford, E.D.; Dunn, S. 1972. PHOTOPERIODISM AND PHOTOMORPHOGENESIS,
Lighting for Plant Growth. The Kent State Univ. Press, Ohio
pp. 81-100 (R).

0143. Biebel, J.P. 1942. SOME EFFECTS OF RADIANT ENERGY IN RELATION TO ETIO-
LATION. Plant Physiol. 17: 377-396.

0144. Bienger, I. 1970. KINETISCHE STUDIEN ZUR PHYTOCHROM-ABHÄNGIGEN ASCOR-
BAT-AKKUMULATION UND EXPERIMENTE ZU EINER MOLEKULAREN DEUTUNG DER
REGULATION. Ph.D. Thesis, Univ. Freiburg, Germany.

0145. Bienger, I.; Schopfer, P. 1970. DIE PHOTOMODULATION DER AKKUMULATIONS-
RATE VON ASCORBINSÄURE BEIM SENFKEIMLING *(SINAPIS ALBA* L.) DURCH
PHYTOCHROM. Planta 93: 152-159 (ENG Summary).

0146. Birth, G.S. 1960. AGRICULTURAL APPLICATIONS OF THE DUAL-MONOCHROMATOR
SPECTROPHOTOMETER. Agric. Eng. 41: 432-435.

0147. Birth, G.S.; Norris, K.H.   1965.   THE DIFFERENCE METER FOR MEASURING
        INTERIOR QUALITY OF FOODS AND PIGMENTS IN BIOLOGICAL TISSUES.   Tech.
        Bull. No. 1341, U.S. Dept. of Agric. 1-20.

0148. Björn, L.O.; Virgin, H.I.   1958.   THE INFLUENCE OF RED LIGHT ON THE
        GROWTH OF PEA SEEDLINGS. AN ATTEMPT TO LOCALIZE THE PERCEPTION.
        Physiol. Plant. 11: 363-373.

0149. Björn, L.O.; Suzuki, Y.; Nilsson, J.   1963.   INFLUENCE OF WAVE LENGTH ON
        THE LIGHT RESPONSE OF EXCISED WHEAT ROOTS.   Physiol. Plant 16: 132-
        141.

0150. Björn, L.O.   1965.   CHLOROPHYLL FORMATION IN EXCISED WHEAT ROOTS.
        Physiol. Plant. 18: 1130-1142.

0151. Björn, L.O.   1967.   THE EFFECT OF LIGHT ON THE DEVELOPMENT OF PLASTIDS
        IN PLANT ROOTS.   Proc. Eur. Annu. Symp. Plant Photomorphogenesis
        (Hvar), pp. 3-4 (A).

0152. Björn, L.O.   1967.   SOME EFFECTS OF LIGHT ON EXCISED WHEAT ROOTS WITH
        SPECIAL REFERENCE TO PEROXIDE METABOLISM.   Physiol. Plant. 20: 149-
        170.

0153. Björn, L.O.   1967.   THE LIGHT REQUIREMENT FOR DIFFERENT STEPS IN THE
        DEVELOPMENT OF CHLOROPLASTS IN EXCISED WHEAT ROOTS.   Physiol. Plant.
        20: 483-499.

0154. Björn, L.O.   1967.   THE EFFECT OF BLUE AND RED LIGHT ON NADP-LINKED GLY-
        CERALDEHYDEPHOSPHATE DEHYDROGENASES IN EXCISED ROOTS.   Physiol.
        Plant. 20: 519-527.

0155. Björn, L.O.   1967.   THE EFFECT OF LIGHT ON THE DEVELOPMENT OF ROOT PLAS-
        TIDS.   Ph.D. Thesis, Univ. Lund, Sweden (A,R).

0156. Blaauw, O.H.   1961.   THE INFLUENCE OF BLUE, RED AND FAR RED LIGHT ON
        GEOTROPISM AND GROWTH OF THE *AVENA* COLEOPTILE.   Acta Bot Neerl. 10:
        397-450.

0157. Blaauw, O.H.   1963.   EFFECTS OF RED LIGHT ON GEOTROPISM OF *AVENA* AND
        THEIR POSSIBLE RELATIONS TO PHOTOTROPIC PHENOMENA.   Acta Bot Neerl.
        12: 424-432.

0158. Blaauw, O.H.; Blaauw-Jansen, G.   1964.   THE INFLUENCE OF RED LIGHT ON THE
        PHOTOTROPISM OF *AVENA* COLEOPTILES.   Acta Bot. Neerl. 13: 541-552.

0159. Blaauw, O.H.; Blaauw-Jansen, G.; van Leeuwen, W.J.   1968.   AN IRREVERSI-
        BLE RED-LIGHT-INDUCED GROWTH RESPONSE IN *AVENA*.   Planta 82: 87-104.

0160. Blaauw, O.H.; Blaauw-Jansen, G. 1970. THE PHOTOTROPIC RESPONSES OF
AVENA COLEOPTILES. Acta Bot. Neerl. 19: 755-763.

0161. Blaauw, O.H.; Blaauw-Jansen, G. 1970. THIRD POSITIVE (C-TYPE) PHOTO-
TROPISM IN THE *AVENA* COLEOPTILE. Acta Bot. Neerl. 19: 764-776.

0162. Blaauw, O.H.; Blaauw-Jansen, G. 1974. THE INFLUENCE OF RED LIGHT ON
THE GEOTROPIC RESPONSES OF *AVENA* COLEOPTILES. Z. Pflanzenphysiol.
71: 57-62.

0163. Blaauw-Jansen, G. 1959. THE INFLUENCE OF RED AND FAR RED LIGHT ON
GROWTH AND PHOTOTROPISM OF THE *AVENA* SEEDLING. Ph.D. Thesis, Univ.
Utrecht, Netherlands.

0164. Blaauw-Jansen, G. 1962. THE LOWER LIMIT OF SENSITIVITY OF THE *AVENA*
STRAIGHT-GROWTH TEST. Proc. K. Ned. Akad. Wet. Ser. C. 65: 59-65.

0165. Blaauw-Jansen, G.; Blaauw, O.H. 1966. EFFECT OF RED LIGHT ON IRREVERS-
IBLE AND REVERSIBLE EXPANSION OF *AVENA* COLEOPTILE SECTIONS. Planta
71: 291-304.

0166. Blaauw-Jansen, G.; Blaauw, O.H. 1968. GEOTROPIC CURVATURE OF *AVENA*
COLEOPTILES IN SOLUTIONS OF VARIOUS OSMOTIC VALUES. Acta Bot. Neerl.
17: 273-280.

0167. Blaauw-Jansen, G. 1974. DOSE-RESPONSE CURVES FOR PHYTOCHROME-MEDIATED
ANTHOCYANIN SYNTHESIS IN THE MUSTARD SEEDLING *(SINAPIS ALBA* L.).
Acta Bot. Neerl. 23: 513-519.

0168. Black, M.; Wareing, P.F. 1954. PHOTOPERIODIC CONTROL OF GERMINATION
IN SEED OF BIRCH *(BETULA PUBESCENS* EHRH). Nature (London) 174:
705-706.

0169. Black, M.; Wareing, P.F. 1955. GROWTH STUDIES IN WOODY SPECIES VII.
PHOTOPERIODIC CONTROL OF GERMINATION IN *BETULA PUBESCENS* EHRH.
Physiol. Plant. 8: 300-316.

0170. Black, M.; Wareing, P.F. 1957. SENSITIVITY OF LIGHT-INHIBITED SEEDS
TO CERTAIN SPECTRAL REGIONS. Nature (London) 180: 395.

0171. Black, M.; Wareing, P.F. 1959. THE INHIBITION OF GERMINATION OF SEEDS
BY RADIATION. Proc. IX Int. Bot. Congr. 2: 2-3 (A).

0172. Black, M.; Wareing, P.F. 1959. THE ROLE OF GERMINATION INHIBITORS AND
OXYGEN IN THE DORMANCY OF THE LIGHT-SENSITIVE SEED OF *BETULA* SPP.
J. Exp. Bot. 10: 134-145.

0173. Black, M.; Wareing, P.F. 1960. PHOTOPERIODISM IN THE LIGHT-INHIBITED
SEED OF *NEMOPHILA INSIGNIS*. J. Exp. Bot. 11: 28-39.

0174. Black, M.; Richardson, M. 1965. PROMOTION OF GERMINATION IN LIGHT-
REQUIRING SEED BY CHLORAMPHENICOL. Nature (London) 208: 1114-1115.

0175. Black, M. 1969. LIGHT-CONTROLLED GERMINATION OF SEEDS. Symp. Soc.
Exp. Biol. 23: 193-217 (R).

0176. Black, M. 1970. SEED GERMINATION AND DORMANCY. Sci. Prog. (London)
58: 379-393 (R).

0177. Black, M.; Vlitos, A.J. 1972. POSSIBLE INTERRELATIONSHIPS OF PHYTO-
CHROME AND PLANT HORMONES. *Phytochrome*. Ed. K. Mitrakos and
W. Shropshire, Jr. Academic Press, London and New York, pp. 517-550
(R).

0178. Black, M.; Bewley, J.D.; Fountain, D. 1974. LETTUCE SEED GERMINATION
AND CYTOKININS: THEIR ENTRY AND FORMATION. Planta 117: 145-152.

0179. Black, M.; Shuttleworth, J. 1974. THE ROLE OF THE COTYLEDONS IN PHOTO-
CONTROL OF HYPOCOTYL ELONGATION IN *CUCUMIS SATIVUS* L. Proc. Eur.
Annu. Symp. Plant Photomorphogenesis, (Antwerpen) p. 117 (A).

0180. Black, M.; Shuttleworth, J.E. 1974. THE ROLE OF THE COTYLEDONS IN THE
PHOTOCONTROL OF HYPOCOTYL ENTENSION IN *CUCUMIS SATIVUS* L. Planta
117: 57-66.

0181. Blondon, F.; Jacques, R. 1970. ACTION DE LA LUMIÈRE SUR L'INITIATION
FLORALE DU *LOLIUM TEMULENTUM* L.: SPECTRE D'ACTION ET RÔLE DU PHYTO-
CHROME. C.R. Acad. Sci. Ser. D. 270: 947-950.

0182. Bock, G.; Haupt, W. 1961. DIE CHLOROPLASTENDREHUNG BEI *MOUGEOTIA* III.
DIE FRAGE DER LOKALISIERUNG DES HELLROT-DUNKELROT-PIGMENTSYSTEMS IN
DER ZELLE. Planta 57: 518-530 (ENG Summary).

0183. Bogorad, L.; McIlrath, W.J. 1960. EFFECT OF LIGHT QUALITY ON AXILLARY
BUD DEVELOPMENT IN *XANTHIUM*. Plant Physiol. 35: Suppl.-32 (A).

0184. Bogorad, L. 1967. BIOSYNTHESIS AND MORPHOGENESIS IN PLASTIDS. *Biochemistry of Chloroplasts,* Ed. T.W. Goodwin, Academic Press, New
York and London II: 615-631 (R).

0185. Bogorad, L. 1967. THE ROLE OF CYTOPLASMIC UNITS. CONTROL MECHANISMS IN
PLASTID DEVELOPMENT. Develop. Biol. Suppl. 1: 1-31 (R).

0186. Böhm, J.A. 1859. ÜBER DEN EINFLUSS DER SONNENSTRAHLEN AUF DIE CHLORO-
PHYLLBILDUNG UND DAS WACHSTUM DER PFLANZEN ÜBERHAUPT. Sitzungsber.
Akad. Wiss. Wien. Math. Naturwiss. Kl. Abt. 1 37: 435-476.

0187. Boisard, J. 1968. LA PHOTOSENSIBILITÉ DES AKENES DE LAITUDE VARIÉTÉ "REINE DE MAI" ET SON INTERPRETATION PAR SPECTROPHOTOMETRIE *IN VIVO* DU PHOTORÉCEPTEUR. Ph.D. Thesis, Univ. Rouen, France (not obtained).

0188. Boisard, J.; Spruit, C.J.P.; Rollin, P. 1968. PHYTOCHROME IN SEEDS AND AN APPARENT DARK REVERSION OF P_r TO P_{fr}. Meded. Landbouwhogesch. Wageningen 68-17: 1-5.

0189. Boisard, J. 1969. RÔLE DU PHYTOCHROME DANS LA PHOTOSENSIBILITÉ DES AKÈNES DE LAITUE VARIÉTÉ "REINE DE MAI". Physiol. Veg. 7: 119-133 (ENG Summary).

0190. Boisard, J.; Malcoste, R. 1970. ANALYSE SPECTROPHOTOMÉTRIQUE DU PHYTO-CHROME DANS L'EMBRYON DE COURGE *(CUCURBITA PEPO)* ET DE POTIRON *(CUCURBITA MAXIMA)*. Planta 91: 54-67 (ENG Summary).

0191. Boisard, J.; Malcoste, R. 1970. APPLICATIONS DE LA SPECTROPHOTOMÉTRIE DIFFÉRENTIELLE *IN VIVO* A L'ÉTUDE DU PHYTOCHROME DES GRAINES. Physiol. Veg. 8: 530 (A).

0192. Boisard, J.; Malcoste, R. 1970. PHYTOCHROME ACTIF (P_{730}) ET RÉVERSION INVERSE DANS LES GRAINES DE QUELQUES CUCURBITACÉES. Physiol. Veg. 8: 565-572 (ENG Summary).

0193. Boisard, J.; Malcoste, R. 1970. LE PHOTOCONTRÔLE DE LA GERMINATION DES GRAINES DE *CUCURBITA PEPO* L. (COURGE) ET LE SITE DE LA PHOTOSENSIBI-LITÉ. C.R. Acad. Sci. Ser. D 271: 304-307.

0194. Boisard, J.; Marmé, D.; Schäfer, E. 1971. EVIDENCE FOR MORE THAN ONE FORM OF P_{fr} IN PUMPKIN SEEDLINGS. Proc. Eur. Annu. Symp. Plant Photomorphogenesis, (Athens), p. 12 (A).

0195. Boisard, J.; Marmé, D.; Schäfer, E. 1971. THE DEMONSTRATION *IN VIVO* OF MORE THAN ONE FORM OF P_{fr}. Planta 99: 302-310.

0196. Boisard, J.; Balange, A.P. 1972. DISPARITION DU PHYTOCHROME EN LUMIÈRE ROUGE LOINTAIN. C.R. Acad. Sci. Ser. D 275: 2655-2658.

0197. Boisard, J.; Gabriac-Marchal, B.; Rollin, P. 1974. RELATIONS ENTRE DESTRUCTION ET SYNTHÈSE DU PHYTOCHROME DANS L'HYPOCOTYLE DE COURGE. Physiol. Veg. 12: 601-616 (ENG Summary).

0198. Boisard, J.; Marmé, D.; Briggs, W.R. 1974. *IN VIVO* PROPERTIES OF MEMBRANE-BOUND PHYTOCHROME. Plant Physiol. 54: 272-276.

0199. Bokura, T. 1967. PHOTO-GROWTH REACTION OF LEAF IN RICE PLANTS *(ORYZA SATIVA* L.). Bot. Mag. 80: 272-278.

0200. Bonner, B.A. 1959. THE EFFECT OF MODIFIED ATMOSPHERES ON THE PHOTO-
CONTROL OF PEA-EPICOTYL SECTION GROWTH. Proc. IX Int. Bot. Congr. 2:
39 (A).

0201. Bonner, B.A. 1960. PARTIAL PURIFICATION OF THE PHOTOMORPHOGENIC PIGMENT
FROM PEA SEEDLINGS. Plant Physiol. 35: Suppl.-32 (A).

0202. Bonner, B.A. 1961. PROPERTIES OF PHYTOCHROME FROM PEAS. Plant Physiol.
36: Suppl.-43 (A).

0203. Bonner, B.A. 1962. *IN VITRO* DARK CONVERSION AND OTHER PROPERTIES OF
PHYTOCHROME. Plant Physiol. 37: Suppl.-27 (A).

0204. Bonner, B. 1966. PHYTOCHROME AND THE RED, FAR-RED SYSTEM. In: Meetings
of the American Association for the Advancement of Science: Plant
Biology today: Advances and Challenges, Wadsworth Publishing Co. Inc.
Belmont, Calif., pp. 185-208 (R).

0205. Bonner, B.A. 1967. INCORPORATION OF DELTA AMINOLEVULINIC ACID INTO THE
CHROMOPHORE OF PHYTOCHROME. Plant Physiol. 42: Suppl.-11 (A).

0206. Bonner, B.A.; Reed, W.A. 1968. A CLOSE COUPLING BETWEEN PHYTOCHROME
P_{fr} AND GEOTROPIC CURVATURE RATE IN *TROPAEOLUM*. Plant Physiol. 43:
Suppl.-14 (A).

0207. Bonner, J. 1959. THE PHOTOPERIODIC PROCESS. *Photoperiodism and
Related Phenomena in Plants and Animals,* Ed. R.B. Withrow, A.A.A.S.,
Washington, D.C., pp. 245-254 (R).

0208. Bonner, J. 1959. CHEMICAL NATURE OF THE INDUCTIVE PROCESSES. *Photoperiodism and Related Phenomena in Plants and Animals,* Ed. R.B.
Withrow, A.A.A.S., Washington, D.C.; pp. 411-421 (R).

0209. Bonnett, H.T. 1972. PHYTOCHROME REGULATION OF ENDOGENOUS BUD DEVELOP-
MENT IN ROOT CULTURES OF *CONVOLVULUS ARVENSIS*. Planta 106: 325-330.

0210. Boresch, K. 1922. PHOTOKATALYSEN IN PFLANZEN. Naturwissenschaften 10:
505-512 (R).

0211. Borodin, J. 1868. ÜBER DIE WIRKUNG DES LICHTES AUF EINIGE HÖHERE
KRYPTOGAMEN. Bull. Acad. Imp. Sci. St. Petersbourg 12: 432-447.

0212. Borodin, J. 1869. ÜBER DIE WIRKUNG DES LICHTES AUF DIE VERTHEILUNG DER
CHLOROPHYLLKÖRNER IN DEN GRÜNEN THEILEN DER PHANEROGAMEN. Bull.
Acad. Imp. Sci. St. Petersbourg 13: 567-586.

0213. Borthwick, H.A. 1947. DAY LENGTH AND FLOWERING. Yearb. Agric. 1943-
1947 pp. 273-283 (R). Also published in GER [Landwirtsch. 1948,
15/16: 221-223.]

0214. Borthwick, H.A.; Hendricks, S.B.; Parker, M.W. 1947. ACTION SPECTRUM
FOR THE CONTROL OF FLOWERING IN WINTER BARLEY, A LONG-DAY PLANT.
Am. J. Bot. 34: 598 (A).

0215. Borthwick, H.A.; Hendricks, S.B.; Parker, M.W. 1948. ACTION SPECTRUM
FOR PHOTOPERIODIC CONTROL OF FLORAL INITIATION OF A LONG-DAY PLANT,
WINTEX BARLEY *(HORDEUM VULGARE)*. Bot. Gaz. (Chicago) 110: 103-118.

0216. Borthwick, H.A.; Parker, M.W.; Hendricks, S.B. 1948. WAVELENGTH DEPEND-
ENCE AND THE NATURE OF PHOTOPERIODISM. *Vernalization and Photo-
periodism*: a symposium. Lotsya 1: 71-78 Chronica Botanica Co.,
Waltham, Mass. (R).

0217. Borthwick, H.A.; Parker, M.W.; Hendricks, S.B. 1950. REPRODUCTION IN
PLANTS. RECENT DEVELOPMENTS IN THE CONTROL OF FLOWERING BY PHOTO-
PERIOD. Am. Nat. 84: 117-134 (R).

0218. Borthwick, H.A.; Hendricks, S.B.; Parker, M.W. 1951. ACTION SPECTRUM
FOR INHIBITION OF STEM GROWTH IN DARK-GROWN SEEDLINGS OF ALBINO AND
NONALBINO BARLEY *(HORDEUM VULGARE)*. Proc. Annu. Meeting Am. Soc.
Plant Physiol. Sept. 9-12 Minneapolis, Minn. p. 30 (A).

0219. Borthwick, H.A.; Hendricks, S.B.; Parker, M.W. 1951. ACTION SPECTRUM
FOR INHIBITION OF STEM GROWTH IN DARK-GROWN SEEDLINGS OF ALBINO AND
NONALBINO BARLEY *(HORDEUM VULGARE)*. Bot. Gaz. (Chicago) 113: 95-105.

0220. Borthwick, H.A.; Hendricks, S.B.; Parker, M.W.; Toole, E.H.; Toole, V.K.
1952. A REVERSIBLE PHOTOREACTION CONTROLLING SEED GERMINATION.
Proc. Nat. Acad. Sci. USA 38: 662-666.

0221. Borthwick, H.A.; Hendricks, S.B.; Parker, M.W. 1952. THE REACTION CON-
TROLLING FLORAL INITIATION. Proc. Nat. Acad. Sci. USA 38: 929-934.

0222. Borthwick, H.A.; Parker, M.W. 1952. LIGHT IN RELATION TO FLOWERING AND
VEGETATIVE DEVELOPMENT. Proc. XIII Int. Hortic. Congr. II 801-810
(R).

0223. Borthwick, H.A.; Hendricks, S.B.; Toole, E.H.; Toole, V.K. 1954. ACTION
OF LIGHT ON LETTUCE-SEED GERMINATION. Bot. Gaz. (Chicago) 115:
205-225.

0224. Borthwick, H.A. 1955. LIGHT AND SOME PLANT RESPONSES. Proc. Plant
Propagators Soc. V Annu. Meet. pp. 63-72 (R).

0225. Borthwick, H.A.; Hendricks, S.B.; Parker, M.W. 1956. "PHOTOPERIODISM".
RADIATION BIOLOGY: VISIBLE AND NEAR-VISIBLE LIGHT. Ed.
A. Hollaender, III: 479-517 (R).

0226. Borthwick, H.A. 1957. LIGHT EFFECTS ON TREE GROWTH AND SEED GERMINA-
       TION. Ohio J. Sci. 57: 357-364 (R).
0227. Borthwick, H.A. 1959. PHOTOPERIODIC CONTROL OF FLOWERING. *Photo-*
       periodism and Related Phenomena in Plants and Animals, Ed.
       R.B. Withrow, A.A.A.S. Washington, D.C., pp. 275-287 (R).
0228. Borthwick, H.A. 1959. HOW LIGHT CONTROLS PLANT DEVELOPMENT. Agriç.
       Res. 8: 3-5 (R).
0229. Borthwick, H.A.; Hendricks, S.B. 1960. PHOTOPERIODISM IN PLANTS.
       Science 132: 1223-1228 (R).
0230. Borthwick, H.A. 1961. THE LIFE PROCESSES OF SEEDS. Yearb. Agric. 1961,
       U.S. Gov't. Printing Press, Washington, D.C., pp. 37-45 (R).
0231. Borthwick, H.A. 1961. PHOTOPERIODIC CONTROL OF FLOWERING. Bull.
       Torrey Bot. Club. 88: 337-338 (R).
0232. Borthwick, H.A.; Cathey, H.M. 1961. DEPENDENCE OF PHOTOPERIOD CONTROL
       OF FLOWERING IN CHRYSANTHEMUM ON DARK REVERSION OF PHYTOCHROME.
       Plant Physiol. 36: Suppl.-52 (A).
0233. Borthwick, H.A.; Hendricks, S.B. 1961. EFFECTS OF RADIATION ON GROWTH
       AND DEVELOPMENT. *Handbuch der Pflanzenphysiologie.* Ed. W. Ruhland,
       Berlin-Göttingen Heidelberg, Springer XVI: 299-330 (R).
0234. Borthwick, H.A.; Nakayama, S.; Hendricks, S.B. 1961. FAILURE OF REVERS-
       IBILITY OF THE PHOTOREACTION CONTROLLING PLANT GROWTH. Prog. Photo-
       biol. Proc. Int. Congr. 3rd. Copenhagen, 1960, pp. 394-398.
0235. Borthwick, H.A. 1962. PLANTS AND LIGHT. Yearb. Agric. 1962, U.S.
       Gov't. Printing Office, Washington, D.C., pp. 116-123 (R).
0236. Borthwick, H.A. 1962. EFFECTS OF LIGHT INTENSITY AND QUALITY ON
       FLOWERING AND FRUIT SET. Proc. Campbell Soup Co. Plant Sci. Symp.
       pp. 189-199 (R).
0237. Borthwick, H.A.; Cathey, H.M. 1962. SIGNIFICANCE OF DARK REVERSION OF
       PHYTOCHROME IN FLOWERING OF SHORT-DAY PLANTS. Science 136: 324 (A).
0238. Borthwick, H.A.; Cathey, H.M. 1962. ROLE OF PHYTOCHROME IN CONTROL OF
       FLOWERING OF CHRYSANTHEMUM. Bot. Gaz. (Chicago) 123: 155-162.
0239. Borthwick, H.A. 1964. CONTROL OF PHOTOMORPHOGENESIS BY PHYTOCHROME.
       Proc. X Int. Bot Congr. p. 197 (A) (R).
0240. Borthwick, H.A. 1964. PHYTOCHROME ACTION AND ITS TIME DISPLAYS. Am.
       Nat. 98: 347-355 (R).

0241. Borthwick, H.A.; Downs, R.J. 1964. ROLES OF ACTIVE PHYTOCHROME IN CONTROL OF FLOWERING OF *XANTHIUM PENSYLVANICUM*. Bot. Gaz. (Chicago) 125: 227-231.

0242. Borthwick, H.A.; Toole, E.H.; Toole, V.K. 1964. PHYTOCHROME CONTROL OF *PAULOWNIA* SEED GERMINATION. Isr. J. Bot 13: 122-133.

0243. Borthwick, H.A. 1965. WHAT LIGHT CAN DO TO PLANTS. Electromagn. Radiat. Agric., pp. 67,68,69,70 (R).

0244. Borthwick, H.A. 1965. LIGHT EFFECTS WITH PARTICULAR REFERENCE TO SEED GERMINATION. Proc. Int. Seed Test. Assoc. 30: 15-27 (R).

0245. Borthwick, H.A.; Hendricks, S.B.; Schneider, M.J.; Taylorson, R.B.; Toole, V.K. 1969. THE HIGH-ENERGY LIGHT ACTION CONTROLLING PLANT RESPONSES AND DEVELOPMENT. Proc. Nat. Acad. Sci. USA 64: 479-486.

0246. Borthwick, H. 1972. HISTORY OF PHYTOCHROME. *Phytochrome,* Ed. K. Mitrakos and W. Shropshire, Jr., Academic Press: London and New York pp 3-23 (R).

0247. Borthwick, H. 1972. THE BIOLOGICAL SIGNIFICANCE OF PHYTOCHROME. *Phytochrome,* Ed. K. Mitrakos and W. Shropshire, Jr., Academic Press: London and New York, pp. 27-44 (R).

0248. Bose, J.C. 1918. LIFE MOVEMENTS IN PLANTS. Transactions of the Bose Research Institute, Calcutta. Vol. 1, pp. 205-212 and 242-248.

0249. Bottomley, W.; Smith, H.; Galston, A.W. 1965. A PHYTOCHROME MEDIATED EFFECT OF LIGHT ON THE HYDROXYLATION PATTERN OF FLAVONOIDS IN *PISUM SATIVUM* VAR. 'ALASKA'. Nature (London) 207: 1311-1312.

0250. Bottomley, W.; Smith, H.; Galston, A.W. 1966. FLAVONOID COMPLEXES IN *PISUM SATIVUM* - III. THE EFFECT OF LIGHT ON THE SYNTHESIS OF KAEM-PFEROL AND QUEROCETIN COMPLEXES. Phytochemistry 5: 117-123.

0251. Bottomley, W. 1970. DEOXYRIBONUCLEIC ACID-DEPENDENT RIBONUCLEIC ACID POLYMERASE ACTIVITY OF NUCLEI AND PLASTIDS FROM ETIOLATED PEAS AND THEIR RESPONSE TO RED AND FAR RED LIGHT *IN VIVO*. Plant Physiol. 45: 608-611.

0252. Boutin, M.E.; Klein, R.M. 1972. ABSENCE OF PHYTOCHROME PARTICIPATION IN CHLOROPHYLL SYNTHESIS IN *EUGLENA*. Plant Physiol. 49: 656-657.

0253. Bradbeer, J.W. 1971. PLASTID DEVELOPMENT IN PRIMARY LEAVES OF *PHASEOLUS VULGARIS* THE EFFECTS OF SHORT BLUE, RED, FAR-RED, AND WHITE LIGHT TREATMENTS ON DARK-GROWN PLANTS. J. Exp. Bot. 22: 382-390.

0254. Bradbeer, J.W.; Ireland, H.M.M.; Gyldenholm, A.O.; Haslett, B.G.;
Murray, D.R.; Whatley, F.R. 1971. THE BIOSYNTHESIS OF THE ENZYMES
OF THE PHOTOSYNTHETIC CARBON CYCLE IN *PHASEOLUS VULGARIS*. Proc. Int.
Congr. Photosynth. Res. 2nd Stresa 1971, pp. 2383-2389.

0255. Bradbeer, J.W.; Gyldenholm, A.O.; Smith, J.W.; Rest, J.; Edge, H.J.W.
1974. PLASTID DEVELOPMENT IN PRIMARY LEAVES OF *PHASEOLUS VULGARIS*.
IX. THE EFFECTS OF SHORT LIGHT TREATMENTS ON PLASTID DEVELOPMENT.
New Phytol. 73: 281-290.

0256. Bradley, M.O.; Hillman, W.S. 1966. INSENSITIVITY OF PHYTOCHROME DECAY
IN VIVO TO RESPIRATORY UNCOUPLING BY 2,4-DINITROPHENOL. Nature
(London) 210: 838.

0257. Brandt, A.B. 1958. CAROTENOID SYNTHESIS AND ACCUMULATION AS FUNCTIONS
OF LIGHT INTENSITY AND SPECTRAL COMPOSITION. Biofizika 3: 659-662.

0258. Brauner, L.; Brauner, M. 1947. UNTERSUCHUNGEN ÜBER DEN MECHANISMUS DER
PHOTOTROPISCHEN REAKTION DER BLATTFIEDERN VON *ROBINIA PSEUDOACACIA*.
Rev. Fac. Sci. Univ. Istanbul, Ser. B., 12: 35-79 (ENG, TURK
Summary).

0259. Brauner, L. 1948. UNTERSUCHUNGEN ÜBER DIE PHOTOTROPISCHEN REAKTIONEN
DES PRIMÄRBLATTGELENKS VON *PHASEOLUS MULTIFLORUS* IN WEISSEM UND IN
FARBIGEM LICHT. Rev. Fac. Sci. Univ. Istanbul Ser. B.; 13: 211-267
(ENG, TURK Summary).

0260. Bregeaut, J.; Rollin, P. 1965. INFLUENCE DE LA LUMIÈRE SUR LA SYNTHESE
DES ANTHOCYANES CHEZ *PHACELIA TANACETIFOLIA* (HYDROPHYLLACEES). Isr.
J. Bot. 14: 59-68 (ENG Summary).

0261. Brett, D.W. 1970. SHOOT AUXIN AND LIGHT IN THE MECHANISM MAINTAINING
THE POSTURE OF THE COTYLEDONS OF *LINUM USITATISSIMUM*. J. Exp. Bot.
21: 432-445.

0262. Brian, P.W. 1958. ROLE OF GIBBERELLIN-LIKE HORMONES IN REGULATION OF
PLANT GROWTH AND FLOWERING. Nature (London) 181: 1122-1123.

0263. Brian, P.W. 1959. EFFECTS OF GIBBERELLINS ON PLANT GROWTH AND DEVELOP-
MENT. Biol. Rev. 34: 37-84 (R).

0264. Briggs, W.R. 1960. RED LIGHT, AUXIN PRODUCTION, AND PHOTOTROPIC
CURVATURE OF CORN COLEOPTILES. Plant Physiol. 35: Suppl.-31-32 (A).

0265. Briggs, W.R. 1963. RED LIGHT, AUXIN RELATIONSHIPS AND THE PHOTOTROPIC
RESPONSES OF CORN AND OAT COLEOPTILES. Am. J. Bot. 50: 196-207.

0266. Briggs, W.R. 1963. THE PHOTOTROPIC RESPONSES OF HIGHER PLANTS. Annu.
       Rev. Plant Physiol. 14: 311-352 (R).

0267. Briggs, W.R.; Siegelman, H.W. 1963. PHYTOCHROME DISTRIBUTION IN ETIO-
       LATED SEEDLINGS. Plant Physiol. 38: Suppl.-5 (A).

0268. Briggs, W.R. 1964. PHOTOTROPISM IN HIGHER PLANTS. *Photophysiology,*
       Ed. A.C. Giese, Academic Press, New York and London I: 223-271 (R).

0269. Briggs, W.R.; Fork, D.C. 1965. THE BEHAVIOR OF INTERMEDIATES DURING
       PHYTOCHROME TRANSFORMATION. Plant Physiol. 40: Suppl.-53 (A).

0270. Briggs, W.R.; Fork, D.C. 1965. STUDIES ON PHYTOCHROME TRANSFORMATION
       IN VITRO. Carnegie Inst. Washington Yearb. 64, pp. 406-412.

0271. Briggs, W.R.; Siegelman, H.W. 1965. DISTRIBUTION OF PHYTOCHROME IN
       ETIOLATED SEEDLINGS. Plant Physiol. 40: 934-941.

0272. Briggs, W.R.; Chon, H.P. 1966. THE PHYSIOLOGICAL VERSUS THE SPECTRO-
       PHOTOMETRIC STATUS OF PHYTOCHROME IN CORN COLEOPTILES. Plant
       Physiol. 41: 1159-1166.

0273. Briggs, W.R. 1968. SOME PHYSICAL PROPERTIES OF PHYTOCHROME. Proc. V
       Int. Congr. Photobiol., p. 99 (A).

0274. Briggs, W.R.; Fork, D.C. 1968. INTERMEDIATES IN PHYTOCHROME TRANSFOR-
       MATION *IN VIVO* AND *IN VITRO.* Carnegie Inst. Washington Yearb.
       66: 203-208.

0275. Briggs, W.R.; Zollinger, W.D.; Platz, B.B. 1968. SOME PROPERTIES OF
       PHYTOCHROME ISOLATED FROM DARK-GROWN OAT SEEDLINGS (*AVENA SATIVA*
       L.). Plant Physiol. 43: 1239-1243.

0276. Briggs, W.R. 1969. A COMPARATIVE STUDY OF PHYTOCHROME PROPERTIES *IN
       VIVO* AND *IN VITRO.* Proc. XI Int. Bot. Congr., p. 22 (A) (R).

0277. Briggs, W.R.; Fork, D.C. 1969. LONG-LIVED INTERMEDIATES IN PHYTOCHROME
       TRANSFORMATION I: *IN VITRO* STUDIES. Plant Physiol. 44: 1081-1088.

0278. Briggs, W.R.; Fork, D.C. 1969. LONG-LIVED INTERMEDIATES IN PHYTOCHROME
       TRANSFORMATION II: *IN VITRO* AND *IN VIVO* STUDIES. Plant Physiol. 44:
       1089-1094.

0279. Briggs. W.R.; Tobin, E.M.; Wright, W.E. 1971. ORIENTATION OF PHYTO-
       CHROME IN DRIED GELATIN FILMS. Plant Physiol. 47: Suppl.-1 (A).

0280. Briggs, W.R. 1972. SOME PHOTOCHEMICAL AND PHOTOBIOLOGICAL PROPERTIES
       OF THE PLANT PHOTORECEPTOR PHYTOCHROME. Abstr. of Papers 163rd Nat.
       Meeting Am. Chem. Soc. Boston, Massachusetts, April 9-14, 1972 (A)
       (R).

0281. Briggs, W.R. 1972. PHYTOCHROME I: MOLECULAR PROPERTIES AND PHOTOCHEM-
ISTRY. Proc. VI Int. Congr. Photobiol. Abstr. No. 020 (A).

0282. Briggs, W.R.; Gardner, G.; Hopkins, D.W. 1972. SOME TECHNICAL PROBLEMS
IN THE PURIFICATION OF PHYTOCHROME. *Phytochrome,* Ed. K. Mitrakos
and W. Shropshire, Jr., Academic Press: London and New York,
pp. 145-158 (R).

0283. Briggs, W.R.; Rice, H.V. 1972. PHYTOCHROME: CHEMICAL AND PHYSICAL
PROPERTIES AND MECHANISM OF ACTION. Annu. Rev. Plant Physiol. 23:
293-334 (R).

0284. Briggs, W.R.; Rice, H.V.; Gardner, G.; Pike, C.S. 1972. THE NATURE OF
PURIFIED PHYTOCHROME. *Structural and Functional Aspects of Phytochemistry. Recent Advances in Phytochemistry,* Ed. V.C. Runeckles
and T.C. Tso, Academic Press, New York and London 5: 35-50 (R).

0285. Briggs, W.R. 1973. PHYTOCHROME: PLANT LIGHT SENSOR AND PHOTOSWITCH.
An. Acad. Bras. Cienc. 45: 85-92 (R).

0286. Brook, P.J. 1969. STIMULATION OF ASCOSPORE RELEASE IN *VENTURIA
INAEQUALIS* BY FAR RED LIGHT. Nature (London) 222: 390-392.

0287. Brooker, J.D.; Russell, D.W. 1974. SOME PROPERTIES OF 3-HYDROXY-3-
METHYLGLUTARYL COENZYME A REDUCTASE FROM *PISUM SATIVUM*. R. Soc.
N.Z. Bull. 12: 365-370.

0288. Brown, J.A.M.; Klein, W.H. 1968. ACTION SPECTRUM FOR FLORAL INDUCTION
IN *ARABIDOPSIS THALIANA* L. HEYNH GROWN IN CONTINUOUS LIGHT. Proc.
Can. Soc. Plant Physiol. 9: 22-23 (A).

0289. Brown, J.A.M. 1969. PHOTOMORPHOGENESIS IN *ARABIDOPSIS THALIANA*
Arabidopsis Info. Serv. 6: 16.

0290. Brown, J.A.M.; Klein, W.H. 1969. PHOTOMORPHOGENESIS IN *ARABIDOPSIS,*
THRESHOLD INTENSITIES AND BLUE FAR-RED SYNERGISM IN FLORAL INDUCTION.
Proc. XI Int. Bot. Congr., p. 23 (A).

0291. Brown, J.A.M.; Klein, W.H. 1971. PHOTOMORPHOGENESIS IN *ARABIDOPSIS
THALIANA* (L.) HEYNH. THRESHOLD INTENSITIES AND BLUE-FAR-RED
SYNERGISM IN FLORAL INDUCTION. Plant Physiol. 47: 393-399.

0292. Brown, T.J.; Geen, G.H. 1974. THE EFFECT OF LIGHT QUALITY ON THE
CARBON METABOLISM AND EXTRACELLULAR RELEASE OF *CHLAMYDOMONAS REIN-
HARDTII* DANGEARD. J. Phycol. 10: 213-220.

0293. Brulfert, J.; Guerrier, D.; Queiroz, O. 1973. PHOTOPERIODISM AND
ENZYME ACTIVITY: BALANCE BETWEEN INHIBITION AND INDUCTION OF THE
CRASSULACEAN ACID METABOLISM. Plant Physiol. 51: 220-222.

0294. Buchholz, J.T. 1936. THE EFFECTS OF VISIBLE AND ULTRAVIOLET RADIATION
ON THE HISTOLOGY OF PLANT TISSUES. *Biological Effects of Radiation*.
Ed. B.M. Duggar, McGraw-Hill, New York II: 829-840 (R).

0295. Buck, J. 1953. MEETING OF THE SOCIETY OF GENERAL PHYSIOLOGISTS:
SYMPOSIUM ON PHOTOPERIODISM. Science 118: 768-769 (A).

0296. Bulakh, A.A.; Guminetsky, S.G.; Grodzinsky, D.M. 1967. DEPENDENCE BE-
TWEEN PHOTOSENSITIVITY OF SEEDS OF SOME VARIETIES OF LETTUCE AND
THEIR OPTICAL CHARACTERISTICS. Uk. Bot. Zh. 24: 25-29 (UKR) (ENG
Summary).

0297. Bulakh, A.A.; Grodzinsky, D.M. 1970. RED-FAR RED EFFECT AND FORMATION
OF ANTHOCYANINS IN PLANTS. Fiziol. Biokhim. Kult. Rast. 2: 21-26
(RUS) (ENG Summary).

0298. Bulakh, A.A.; Guminetsky, S.G.; Grodzinsky, D.M.; Rvachez, V.P. 1971.
SPECTRAL MEASUREMENTS OF THE DYNAMICS OF THE PHYTOCHROME SYSTEM IN
ETIOLATED PLANT SPROUTS. Biofizika 16: 379-380 (RUS) (A).

0299. Bulard, C. 1973. INTERACTION BETWEEN ABSCISIC ACID AND GIBBERELLINS
(GA_3 OR GA_4) ON LETTUCE SEEDS GERMINATION. Plant Physiol. 51:
Suppl.-36 Abstr. No. 197 (A).

0300. Bünning, E.; Stern, K. 1930. ÜBER DIE TAGESPERIODISCHEN BEWEGUNGEN DER
PRIMÄRBLÄTTER VON *PHASEOLUS MULTIFLORUS* II DIE BEWEGUNGEN BEI THER-
MOKONSTANZ. Ber. Dtsch. Bot. Ges. 48: 227-252.

0301. Bünning, E. 1931. UNTERSUCHUNGEN ÜBER DIE AUTONOMEN TAGESPERIODISCHEN
BEWEGUNGEN DER PRIMÄRBLÄTTER VON *PHASEOLUS MULTIFLORUS*. Jahrb. Wiss.
Bot. 75: 439-480.

0302. Bünning, E. 1941. ÜBER DIE VERHINDERUNG DES ETIOLEMENTS. Ber. Dtsch.
Bot. Ges. 59: 2-9.

0303. Bünning, E. 1952. MORPHOGENESIS IN PLANTS. Surv. Biol. Prog. 2: 104-
140 (R).

0304. Bünning, E.; Mohr, H. 1955. DAS AKTIONSSPEKTRUM DES LICHTEINFLUSSES
AUF DIE KEIMUNG VON FARNSPOREN. Naturwissenschaften 42: 212.

0305. Bünning, E.; Könitz, W. 1957. DIURNALE ANTAGONISTISCHE SCHWANKUNGEN
VON HELL-UND DUNKELROT-EMPFINDLICHKEIT EINER KURZTAGPFLANZE.
Naturwissenschaften 44: 568.

0306. Bünning, E.; Lörcher, L. 1957. REGULIERUNG UND AUSLÖSUNG ENDOGEN-TAGES-
PERIODISCHER BLATTBEWEGUNGEN DURCH VERSCHIEDENE LICHTQUALITÄTEN.
Naturwissenschaften 44: 472.

0307. Bünning, E.; Etzold, H. 1958. ÜBER DIE WIRKUNG VON POLARISIERTEM LICHT
AUF KEIMENDE SPOREN VON PILZEN, MOOSEN UND FARNEN. Ber. Dtsch. Bot.
Ges. 71: 304-306.

0308. Bünning, E. 1959. DIURNAL CHANGES IN PIGMENT CONTENT AND IN THE PHOTO-
PERIODIC EFFICIENCY OF RED AND FAR RED. *Photoperiodism and Related
Phenomena in Plants and Animals*. Ed. R.B. Withrow, A.A.A.S. Washing-
ton, D.C., pp. 537-540 (R-D).

0309. Bünning, E. 1960. OPENING ADDRESS: BIOLOGICAL CLOCKS. Cold Spring
Harbor Symp. Quant. Biol. 25: 1-9 (R).

0310. Bünning, E. 1960. CIRCADIAN RHYTHMS AND THE TIME MEASUREMENT IN PHOTO-
PERIODISM. Cold Spring Harbor Symp. Quant. Biol. 25: 249-256 (R).

0311. Bünning, E.; Engelmann, W. 1960. ENDOGEN-TAGESPERIODISCHE SCHWANKUNGEN
DER PHOTOPERIODISCHEN HELLROT-EMPFINDLICHKEIT BEI *KALANCHOË BLOSS-
FELDIANA*. Naturwissenchaften 47: 332.

0312. Bünning, E. 1961. ENDOGENOUS RHYTHMS AND MORPHOGENESIS. Can. J. Bot.
39:461-467 (R).

0313. Bünning, E.; Moser, I. 1966. RESPONSE-KURVEN BEI DER CIRCADIANEN
RHYTHMIK VON *PHASEOLUS*. Planta 69: 101-110 (ENG Summary).

0314. Bürcky, K.; Kauss, H. 1974. VERÄNDERUNG IM GEHALT AN ATP UND ADP IN
WURZELSPITZEN DER MUNGOBOHNE NACH HELLROTBELICHTUNG. Z. Pflanzenphysiol. 73: 184-186 (ENG Summary).

0315. Burden, R.S.; Firn, R.D.; Hiron, R.W.P.; Taylor, H.F.; Wright, S.T.C.
1971. INDUCTION OF PLANT GROWTH INHIBITOR XANTHOXIN IN SEEDLINGS
BY RED LIGHT. Nature (London) New Biol. 234: 95-96.

0316. Burdett, A.N.; Vidaver, W.E. 1971. SYNERGISTIC ACTION OF ETHYLENE WITH
GIBBERELLIN OR RED LIGHT IN GERMINATING LETTUCE SEEDS. Plant
Physiol. 48: 656-657.

0317. Burdett, A.N. 1972. TWO EFFECTS OF PROLONGED FAR RED LIGHT ON THE
RESPONSE OF LETTUCE SEEDS TO EXOGENOUS GIBBERELLIN. Plant Physiol.
49: 531-534.

0318. Burdett, A.N. 1972. ANTAGONISTIC EFFECTS OF HIGH AND LOW TEMPERATURE
PRETREATMENTS ON THE GERMINATION AND PREGERMINATION ETHYLENE SYNTHE-
SIS OF LETTUCE SEEDS. Plant Physiol. 50: 201-204.

0319. Burger, W.C. 1965. EFFECT OF LIGHT ON THE GERMINATION OF BARLEY AND ITS RELATION TO DORMANCY. J. Inst. Brew. 71: 244-250.

0320. Burger, W.C. 1967. PHOTOCONTROL OF PLANT GROWTH AND DEVELOPMENT. Wallerstein Lab. Commun. 30: 109-122 (R).

0321. Burgerstein, A. 1908. EINFLUSS DES LICHTES VERSCHIEDENER BRECHBARKEIT AUF DIE BILDUNG VON FARN-PROTHALLIEN. Ber. Dtsch. Bot. Ges 26: 449-451.

0322. Burkart, S.; Sánchez, R.A. 1969. INTERACTION BETWEEN AN INHIBITOR PRESENT IN THE SEEDS OF *DATURA FEROX* L. AND LIGHT IN THE CONTROL OF GERMINATION. Bot. Gaz. (Chicago) 130: 42-47.

0323. Burke, M.J.; Pratt, D.C.; Moscowitz, A. 1972. LOW TEMPERATURE ABSORPTION AND CIRCULAR DICHROISM SPECTRA OF PHYTOCHROME. Plant Physiol. 49: Suppl.-53 Abstr. No. 296 (A).

0324. Burke, M.J.; Pratt, D.C.; Moscowitz, A. 1972. LOW TEMPERATURE ABSORPTION AND CIRCULAR DICHROISM STUDIES OF PHYTOCHROME. Biochemistry 11: 4025-4031.

0325. Burkholder, P.R.; Pratt, R. 1934. THE PHOTEOLIC MOVEMENTS OF *MIMOSA PUDICA* IN RELATION TO INTENSITY AND WAVE-LENGTH. Am. J. Bot. 21: 704 (A).

0327. Burkholder, P.R. 1936. THE ROLE OF LIGHT IN THE LIFE OF PLANTS I. LIGHT AND PHYSIOLOGICAL PROCESSES. Bot. Rev. 2: 1-52 (R).

0328. Burkholder, P.R. 1936. THE ROLE OF LIGHT IN THE LIFE OF PLANTS II. THE INFLUENCE OF LIGHT UPON GROWTH AND DIFFERENTIATION. Bot. Rev. 2: 97-172 (R).

0329. Burkholder, P.R.; Pratt, R. 1936. LEAF-MOVEMENTS OF *MIMOSA PUDICA* IN RELATION TO THE INTENSITY AND WAVE LENGTH OF THE INCIDENT RADIATION. Am. J. Bot. 23: 212-220.

0330. Burkholder, P.R.; Johnston, E.S. 1937. INACTIVATION OF PLANT GROWTH SUBSTANCE BY LIGHT. Smithson. Misc. Collect. 95: 1-14.

0331. Burström, H. 1961. PHYSICS OF CELL ELONGATION. *Handbuch der Pflanzenphysiologie*. Ed. W. Ruhland, Berlin-Göttingen Heidelberg, Springer, XIV: 285-310 (R).

0332. Butala, S.S. 1970. THE EFFECT OF FAR-RED AND BLUE LIGHT ON MALEIC HYDRAZIDE-INDUCED CHROMOSOMAL ABERRATIONS IN *VICIA FABA*. Ph.D. Thesis, Washington State Univ., Pullman (not obtained except Diss. abstract Int. B, 31: 3190-3191).

0333. Butler, L.G.; Bennett, V. 1969. PHYTOCHROME CONTROL OF MAIZE LEAF IN-ORGANIC PYROPHOSPHATASE AND ADENYLATE KINASE. Plant Physiol. 44: 1285-1290.

0334. Butler, W.L.; Norris, K.H.; Siegelman, H.W.; Hendricks, S.B. 1959. DETECTION, ASSAY, AND PRELIMINARY PURIFICATION OF THE PIGMENT CON-TROLLING PHOTORESPONSIVE DEVELOPMENT OF PLANTS. Proc. Nat. Acad. Sci. USA 45: 1703-1708.

0335. Butler, W.L.; Downs, R.J. 1960. LIGHT AND PLANT DEVELOPMENT. Sci. Am. 203: 56-63 (R).

0336. Butler, W.L.; Hendricks, S.B.; Siegelman, H.W. 1960. *IN VIVO* AND *IN VITRO* PROPERTIES OF PHYTOCHROME. Plant Physiol. 35: Suppl.-32 (A) (R).

0337. Butler, W.L.; Norris, K.H. 1960. THE SPECTROPHOTOMETRY OF DENSE LIGHT-SCATTERING MATERIAL. Arch. Biochem. Biophys. 87: 31-40.

0338. Butler, W.L. 1961. SOME PHOTOCHEMICAL PROPERTIES OF PHYTOCHROME. Prog. Photobiol., Proc. Int. Congr. 3rd Copenhagen, pp. 569-571.

0339. Butler, W.L.; Siegelman, H.W.; Hendricks, S.B. 1961. SOME PHOTOCHEMICAL PROPERTIES OF PHYTOCHROME. Plant Physiol. 36: Suppl.-42-43 (A).

0340. Butler, W.L.; Downs, R.J. 1962. LIGHT AND PLANT DEVELOPMENT. Priroda Moscow 8: 48-54 (Translation of 335) (RUS) (R).

0341. Butler, W.L. 1963. CONTROL OF PLANT DEVELOPMENT BY RED AND FAR-RED LIGHT. Bull. Philos. Soc. Washington 16: 225-240 (R).

0342. Butler, W.L.; Lane, H.C.; Siegelman, H.W. 1963. NONPHOTOCHEMICAL TRANS-FORMATION OF PHYTOCHROME *IN VIVO*. Plant Physiol. 38: 514-519.

0343. Butler, W.L.; Norris, K.H. 1963. EFFECTS OF LIGHT ON PLANTS. Agric. Eng. July: 368-369 (R).

0344. Butler, W.L. 1964. ACTION SPECTRA OF PHYTOCHROME *IN VITRO*. Proc. Conf. Molecular Mechanisms in Photobiol., Wakulla Springs, Florida, Feb. 1964 (A) (not obtained).

0345. Butler, W.L. 1964. SYMPOSIUM ON PHOTOMORPHOGENESIS IN PLANTS I. INTRODUCTION. Q. Rev. Biol. 39: 1-5 (R).

0346. Butler, W.L. 1964. SYMPOSIUM ON PHOTOMORPHOGENESIS IN PLANTS II. DARK TRANSFORMATION OF PHYTOCHROME *IN VIVO*. Q. Rev. Biol. 39: 6-10 (R).

0347. Butler, W.L.; Hendricks, S.B.; Siegelman, H.W. 1964. ACTION SPECTRA OF PHYTOCHROME *IN VITRO*. Photochem. Photobiol. 3: 521-528.

0348. Butler, W.L.; Siegelman, H.W.; Miller, C.O. 1964. DENATURATION OF PHY-
TOCHROME. Biochemistry 3: 851-857.

0349. Butler, W.L.; Hendricks, S.B.; Siegelman, H.W. 1965. PURIFICATION AND
PROPERTIES OF PHYTOCHROME. *Chemistry and Biochemistry of Plant
Pigments,* Ed. T.W. Goodwin, Academic Press, New York and London,
pp. 197-210 (R).

0350. Butler, W.L.; Lane, H.C. 1965. DARK TRANSFORMATIONS OF PHYTOCHROME *IN
VIVO* II. Plant Physiol. 40: 13-17.

0351. Butler, W.L.; Linschitz, H.; Siegelman, H.W.; Norris, K.H. 1965. FLASH
PHOTOLYSIS OF PHYTOCHROME. Plant Physiol. 40: Suppl.-53 (A).

0352. Butler, W.L. 1972. PHOTOCHEMICAL PROPERTIES OF PHYTOCHROME *IN VITRO*.
Phytochrome, Ed. K. Mitrakos and W. Shropshire, Jr., Academic Press,
New York and London, pp. 185-192 (R).

0353. Butt, A.M. 1968. VEGETATIVE GROWTH, MORPHOGENESIS AND CARBOHYDRATE
CONTENT OF THE ONION PLANT AS A FUNCTION OF LIGHT AND TEMPERATURE
UNDER FIELD AND CONTROLLED CONDITIONS. (Ph.D. Thesis, Univ.
Wageningen, Netherlands) Meded. Landbouwhogesch. Wageningen 68-10:
1-211.

0354. Camm, E.L.; Towers, G.H.N. 1973. REVIEW ARTICLE PHENYLALANINE AMMONIA
LYASE. Phytochemistry 12: 961-973 (R).

0355. Carceller, M.S.; Sánchez, R.A. 1972. THE INFLUENCE OF PHYTOCHROME IN
THE WATER EXCHANGE OF EPIDERMAL CELLS OF *TARAXACUM OFFICINALE*.
Experientia 28: 364.

0356. Carlin, R.M.; McClure, J.W. 1973. ACTION SPECTRA FOR C-GLUCOSYLFLAVONE
ACCUMULATION IN *HORDEUM VULGARE* PLUMULES. Phytochemistry 12: 1009-
1015.

0357. Carpenter, B.H. 1962. THE EFFECT OF FLOWERING OF BILOXI SOYBEAN OF
MULTIPLE LIGHT PERTURBATIONS WITH DIFFERENT QUALITIES OF RADIATION
GIVEN DURING LONG DARK PERIODS. Ph.D. Thesis, Univ. California,
Los Angeles.

0358. Carpenter, B.H.; Hamner, K.C. 1963. EFFECT OF LIGHT QUALITY ON RHYTH-
MIC FLOWERING RESPONSE OF BILOXI SOYBEAN. Plant Physiol. 38: 698-
703.

0359. Carpenter, B.H. 1965. RED, FAR-RED REVERSIBILITY IN A 72-HOUR CYCLE.
Naturwissenschaften 18: 521.

0360. Carr, D.J.; Reid, D.M. 1966. ACTINOMYCIN-D INHIBITION OF PHYTOCHROME-
MEDIATED RESPONSES. Planta 69: 70-78.

0360.5 Carr, D.J.; Clements, J.B.; Menhenett, R. 1972. STUDIES ON LEAF UNROLL-
ING IN BARLEY. *Plant Growth Substances 1970*. Proc. VII Int. Conf.
Plant Growth Substances, Ed. D.J. Carr, Springer-Verlag, Berlin,
Heidelberg, New York, pp. 633-645 (R).

0361. Carroll, J.W. 1970. THE EFFECTS OF MONOCHROMATIC LIGHT ON THE CELLULAR
DEVELOPMENT AND METABOLISM OF *PROTOSIPHON BOTRYOIDES* KLEBS. Ph.D.
Thesis, Univ. Alabama, University (not obtained, except Diss.
Abstr. Int. B (1971) 31: 5807) (A).

0362. Carroll, J.W.; Thomas, J.; Dunaway, C.; O'Kelley, J.C. 1970. LIGHT
INDUCED SYNCHRONIZATION OF ALGAL SPECIES THAT DIVIDE PREFERENTIALLY
IN DARKNESS. Photochem. Photobiol. 12: 91-98.

0363. Casper, R.; Pirson, A. 1965. GRUND-UND SÄURESTOFFWECHSEL IN BLÄTTERN
VON *KALANCHOË ROTUNDIFOLIA* HAW. BEI FARBLICHTKULTUR. Flora Jena
Abt. A. 156: 177-196 (ENG Summary).

0364. Cathey, H.M.; Borthwick, H.A. 1957. PHOTOREVERSIBILITY OF FLORAL INI-
TIATION IN CHRYSANTHEMUM. Bot. Gaz. (Chicago) 119: 71-76.

0365. Cathey, H.M. 1964. PHYSIOLOGY OF GROWTH RETARDING CHEMICALS. Annu.
Rev. Plant Physiol. 15: 271-302.

0366. Cathey, H.M.; Borthwick, H.A. 1964. SIGNIFICANCE OF DARK REVERSION OF
PHYTOCHROME IN FLOWERING OF *CHRYSANTHEMUM MORIFOLIUM*. Bot. Gaz.
(Chicago) 125: 232-236.

0367. Cathey, H.M.; Hendricks, S.B. 1964. SOME PHYSIOLOGICAL ASPECTS OF
PHYTOCHROME ACTION. Proc. X Int. Bot. Congr., p. 186 (A).

0368. Cathey, H.M. 1969. *CHRYSANTHEMUM MORIFOLIUM* (RAMAT.) HEMSL. *Induction
of Flowering,* Ed. L. Evans, Cornell Univ. Press, Ithaca, pp. 268-290
(R-D).

0369. Cathey, H.M.; Borthwick, H.A. 1970. PHOTOREACTIONS CONTROLLING FLOWER-
ING OF *CHRYSANTHEMUM MORIFOLIUM* (RAMAT. AND HEMSL.) ILLUMINATED WITH
FLUORESCENT LAMPS. Plant Physiol. 45: 235-239.

0370. Cathey, H.M.; Borthwick, H.A. 1971. PHYTOCHROME CONTROL OF FLOWERING
OF *CHRYSANTHEMUM MORIFOLIUM* ON VERY SHORT PHOTOPERIODS. J. Am. Soc.
Hortic. Sci. 96: 544-546.

0371. Cathey, H.M. 1974. PARTICIPATION OF PHYTOCHROME IN REGULATING INTER-
NODE ELONGATION OF *CHRYSANTHEMUM MORIFOLIUM* (RAMAT.) HEMSL. J. Am.
Soc. Hortic. Sci. 99: 17-23.

0372. Cerff, R. 1971. A COMPARATIVE STUDY OF P_{730}-MEDIATED REGULATION OF
NADP-AND NAD-DEPENDENT GLYCERALDEHYDE-3-PHOSPHATE DEHYDROGENASE IN
COTYLEDONS OF *SINAPIS ALBA*. EXPERIMENTAL EVIDENCE FOR THE EXISTENCE
OF TWO INDIVIDUAL PROTEINS WHICH ARE REGULATED DIFFERENTIALLY. Proc.
Eur. Annu. Symp. Plant Photomorphogenesis, (Athens), pp. 13-14 (A).

0373. Cerff, R. 1971. DIE PHYTOCHROMABHÄNGIGE REGULATION DER ENZYME NADP-UND
NAD-SPEZIFISCHE GLYCERINALDEHYD-3-PHOSPHAT DEHYDROGENASE UND
GLYOXYLATREDUKTASE IN DEN KOTYLEDONEN DES SENFKEIMLINGS *(SINAPIS
ALBA* L.). Ph.D. Thesis, Univ. Freiburg, Germany.

0374. Cerff, R. 1972. GLYCERALDEHYDE-3-PHOSPHATE DEHYDROGENASES AND GLYOXY-
LATE REDUCTASE: THEIR REGULATION UNDER CONTINUOUS RED AND FAR-RED
LIGHT IN THE COTYLEDONS OF *SINAPIS ALBA* L. Proc. VI Int. Congr.
Photobiol. Abstr. No. 166 (A).

0375. Cerff, R. 1973. GLYCERALDEHYDE-3-PHOSPHATE DEHYDROGENASES AND GLYOXY-
LATE REDUCTASE. I. THEIR REGULATION UNDER CONTINUOUS RED AND FAR-RED
LIGHT IN THE COTYLEDONS OF *SINAPIS ALBA* L. Plant Physiol. 51: 76-81.

0376. Cerff, R. 1974. INHIBITOR-DEPENDENT, RECIPROCAL CHANGES IN THE ACTIVI-
TIES OF GLYCERALDEHYDE-3-PHOSPHATE DEHYDROGENASES IN *SINAPIS ALBA*
COTYLEDONS. Z. Pflanzenphysiol. 73: 109-118.

0377. Cerff, R.; Quail, P.H. 1974. GLYCERALDEHYDE-3-PHOSPHATE DEHYDROGENASES
AND GLYOXYLATE REDUCTASE II. FAR RED LIGHT-DEPENDENT DEVELOPMENT OF
GLYCERALDEHYDE-3-PHOSPHATE DEHYDROGENASE ISOZYME ACTIVITIES IN
SINAPIS ALBA COTYLEDONS. Plant Physiol. 54: 100-104.

0378. Cerff, R.; Quail, P.H.; Pupillo, P. 1974. LIGHT-DEPENDENT REGULATORY
RELATIONSHIPS BETWEEN GLYCERALDEHYDE-3-PHOSPHATE DEHYDROGENASES
(GPD) IN *SINAPIS ALBA* COTYLEDONS. Proc. Eur. Annu. Symp. Plant
Photomorphogenesis, (Antwerpen), pp. 54-56.

0379. Chailakhyan, M.Kh. 1969. PHOTOPERIODISM IN PLANTS, CHIEF TRENDS IN THE
STUDY OF ITS PHYSIOLOGICAL NATURE. Izv. Akad. Nauk. SSSR Ser. 3,
344-353 (RUS) (ENG Summary) (R).

0380. Charlton, F.B. 1938. FORMATIVE EFFECTS OF RADIATION UPON FERN PROTHAL-
LIA. Am. J. Bot. 25: 431-442.

0381. Chavan, A.R.; Chaudhari, P.I. 1967. INTERACTION OF GIBBERELLIC ACID
AND LIGHT ON THE GERMINATION AND GROWTH OF SEEDLINGS OF *GOSSYPIUM*
HERBACEUM L. VAR. DIGVIJAZ. Indian J. Plant Physiol. 10: 76-83.

0382. Chawan, D.D.; Sharma, K.D.; Sen, D.N. 1971. LIGHT AND GIBBERELLIN-A$_3$
INTERACTION IN THE SEEDLING GROWTH OF *ASTERACANTHA LONGIFOLIA* NEES.
AND *RUELLIA TUBEROSA* L. Oesterr. Bot. Z. 119: 19-24.

0383. Chawan, D.D.; Sen, D.N. 1973. ACTION OF LIGHT IN THE GERMINATION OF
SEEDS AND SEEDLING GROWTH IN TWO DESERT SPECIES OF *SIDA*. Broteria
Ser. Ciênc. Nat. 42: 141-148.

0384. Chen, C.H.; Gordon, S.A. 1972. INHIBITION OF ^{3}H-THYMIDINE INCORPORATION
IN PIG KIDNEY CELLS BY FAR-RED LIGHT. Photochem. Photobiol. 15:
107-109.

0385. Chen, S.S.C.; Thimann, K.V. 1964. STUDIES ON THE GERMINATION OF LIGHT-
INHIBITED SEEDS OF *PHACELIA TANACETIFOLIA*. Isr. J. Bot. 13: 57-73.

0386. Chetram, R.S.; Bendixen, L.E. 1974. PHYTOCHROME CONTROLLED BASAL BULB
FORMATION IN PURPLE NUTSEDGE. Weed Sci. 22: 269-272.

0387. Chon, H.P. 1965. THE EFFECT OF RED LIGHT ON PHOTOTROPIC SENSITIVITY
OF CORN COLEOPTILES. Ph.D. Thesis, Stanford Univ., Stanford.

0388. Chon, H.P.; Briggs, W.R. 1966. EFFECT OF RED LIGHT ON THE PHOTOTROPIC
SENSITIVITY OF CORN COLEOPTILES. Plant Physiol. 41: 1715-1724.

0389. Chorney, W.; Gordon, S.A. 1964. LIGHT-ACTIVATED DISAPPEARANCE OF PHYTO-
CHROME IN SEEDLINGS. Plant Physiol. 39: Suppl.-50 (A).

0390. Chorney, W.; Gordon, S.A. 1966. ACTION SPECTRUM AND CHARACTERISTICS OF
THE LIGHT ACTIVATED DISAPPEARANCE OF PHYTOCHROME IN OAT SEEDLINGS.
Plant Physiol. 41: 891-896.

0391. Chouard, P. 1954. DORMANCES ET INHIBITORS DES GRAINES ET DES BOURGEONS.
C.D.U. Paris, pp. 1-90 (not obtained) (referred to by Rollin, P.
(1963) Thesis, Univ. Paris) (R).

0392. Chouard, P. 1961. REMARQUES SUR LA PORTÉE DES DIFFÉRENCES QUANTITATIVES
ENTRE LES EXIGENCES DES PLANTES DE JOURS LONGS ET CELLES DES PLANTES
DE JOURS COURTS VIS-À-VIS DES ÉCLAIREMENTS RÉDUISANT OU INTERROMPANT
LA DURÉE DE LA NUIT LONGUE. Proc. III Int. Congr. Photobiol. pp.
402-403.

0393. Chua, S.E.; Dickson, M.H. 1964. THE EFFECT OF FLASHING LIGHT SUPPLE-
MENTED BY CONTINUOUS RED AND FAR-RED LIGHT ON THE GROWTH OF *LEMNA
MINOR* L. IN THE PRESENCE OF GROWTH REGULATORS. Can. J. Bot. 42:
57-64.

0394. Chulanovakaya, M.V. 1962. COLLECTION OF TRANSACTIONS ON AGROPHYSICS,
NO. 9. Ed. Selkhozgiz (In Russian) (not obtained) Referred to by
Shulgin, I.A. (1965). Fiziol. Rast. 12: 289-298.

0395. Cieslar, A. 1883. UNTERSUCHUNGEN ÜBER DEN EINFLUSS DES LICHTES AUF DIE
KEIMUNG DER SAMEN. Forsuch. Geb. Agrik. Physik (6), 270-295.

0396. Cihák, A. 1965. CO JSOU FYTOCHROMY. Chem. Listy 59: 1063-1065 [CHEC:
a summary of a review by Siegelman, H.W. and Hendricks, S.B. (1964),
Adv. Enzymol. 26: 1-33] (R).

0397. Claes, H. 1966. MAXIMAL EFFECTIVENESS OF 670 mμ IN THE LIGHT DEPENDENT
CAROTENOID SYNTHESIS IN *CHLORELLA VULGARIS*. Photochem. Photobiol.
5: 515-521.

0398. Clarkson, D.T.; Hillman, W.S. 1966. APPARENT PHYTOCHROME SYNTHESIS IN
PISUM TISSUE. Plant Physiol. 41: Suppl.-14 (A).

0399. Clarkson, D.T.; Hillman, W.S. 1967. STABILITY OF PHYTOCHROME CONCENTRA-
TION IN DICOTYLEDONOUS TISSUES UNDER CONTINUOUS FAR-RED LIGHT.
Planta 75: 286-290.

0400. Clarkson, D.T.; Hillman, W.S. 1967. MODIFICATION OF APPARENT PHYTO-
CHROME SYNTHESIS IN *PISUM* BY INHIBITORS AND GROWTH REGULATORS.
Plant Physiol. 42: 933-940.

0401. Clarkson, D.T.; Hillman, W.S. 1967. APPARENT PHYTOCHROME SYNTHESIS IN
PISUM TISSUE. Nature (London) 213: 468-470.

0402. Clarkson, D.T.; Hillman, W.S. 1968. STABLE CONCENTRATIONS OF PHYTO-
CHROME IN *PISUM* UNDER CONTINUOUS ILLUMINATION WITH RED LIGHT. Plant
Physiol. 43: 88-92.

0403. Clarkson, D.T. 1969. PHYTOCHROME LEVELS OF PLANTS IN RELATION TO
RESPONSE TO LIGHT. British Photobiol. Group Bull. 21, Reading Univ.
(A).

0404. Clauss, H. 1970. EFFECT OF RED AND BLUE LIGHT ON MORPHOGENESIS AND
METABOLISM OF *ACETABULARIA MEDITERRANEA*. *Biology of Acetabularia*.
Ed. J. Brachet and S. Bonotton, Academic Press, New York and London,
pp. 177-191 (R).

0405. Cleland, C.F.; Briggs, W.R. 1968. EFFECT OF LOW-INTENSITY RED AND
FAR-RED LIGHT AND HIGH-INTENSITY WHITE LIGHT ON THE FLOWERING RE-
SPONSE OF THE LONG-DAY PLANT *LEMNA GIBBA* G3. Plant Physiol. 43:
157-162.

0406. Cockshull, K.E.; Hughes, A.P. 1969. EFFECT OF WAVELENGTH OF NIGHT
BREAK LIGHT ON LEAF EXPANSION AND FLOWER INITIATION IN *CALLISTEPHUS*
Chinensis. British Photobiol. Group Bull. 21 Reading Univ. (A).

0407. Cohen, R.Z.; Goodwin, T.W. 1962. THE EFFECT OF RED AND FAR-RED LIGHT
ON CAROTENOID SYNTHESIS BY ETIOLATED MAIZE SEEDLINGS. Phytochemistry
1: 67-72.

0408. Coleman, R.A. 1973. IMMUNOCYTOCHEMICAL DETERMINATION OF PHYTOCHROME
DISTRIBUTION AND LOCALIZATION. Ph.D. Thesis, Vanderbilt Univ.,
Nashville.

0409. Coleman, R.A.; Pratt, L.H. 1974. ELECTRON MICROSCOPIC LOCALIZATION OF
PHYTOCHROME IN PLANTS USING AN INDIRECT ANTIBODY-LABELING METHOD.
J. Histochem. Cytochem. 22: 1039-1047.

0410. Coleman, R.A.; Pratt, L.H. 1974. PHYTOCHROME: IMMUNOCYTOCHEMICAL ASSAY
OF SYNTHESIS AND DESTRUCTION. Planta 119: 221-231.

0411. Coleman, R.A.; Pratt, L.H. 1974. SUBCELLULAR LOCALIZATION OF THE RED-
ABSORBING FORM OF PHYTOCHROME BY IMMUNOCYTOCHEMISTRY. Planta 121:
119-131.

0412. Colla, S. 1931. SULLA FIORITURA ALLA SOLA LUCE DI WOOD. Nuovo G.
Bot. Ital. 38: 509-514.

0413. Collins, W.B. 1966. FLORAL INITIATION IN STRAWBERRY AND SOME EFFECTS
OF RED AND FAR-RED RADIATION AS COMPONENTS OF CONTINUOUS WHITE LIGHT.
Can. J. Bot. 44: 663-668.

0414. Cooke, I.J. 1969. THE INFLUENCE OF FAR-RED LIGHT ON THE DEVELOPMENT
OF TOMATO SEEDLINGS. J. Hortic. Sci. 44: 285-292.

0415. Correll, D.L.; Steers, E., Jr.; Edwards, J.L.; Suriano, J.R.; Shropshire,
W., Jr. 1966. PHYTOCHROME: ISOLATION AND PARTIAL CHARACTERIZATION.
Fed. Proc. Fed. Am. Soc. Exp. Biol. Abstr. 25: 3086 (A).

0416. Correll, D.L.; Steers, E., Jr.; Edwards, J.L.; Suriano, J.R.; Shropshire,
W., Jr. 1966. PHYTOCHROME: ISOLATION FROM RYE AND PARTIAL CHARAC-
TERIZATION. Plant Physiol. 41: Suppl.-16-17 (A).

0417. Correll, D.L. 1968. THE PROPERTIES OF ISOLATED PHYTOCHROME. Proc. V
Int. Congr. Photobiol., p. 91 (A).

0418. Correll, D.L.; Edwards, J.L.; Medina, V.J. 1968. PHYTOCHROME IN ETIO-
       LATED ANNUAL RYE. II. DISTRIBUTION OF PHOTOREVERSIBLE PHYTOCHROME
       IN THE COLEOPTILE AND PRIMARY LEAF. Planta 79: 284-291.

0419. Correll, D.L.; Edwards, J.L.; Shropshire, W., Jr. 1968. MULTIPLE CHRO-
       MOPHORE SPECIES IN PHYTOCHROME. Photochem. Photobiol. 8: 465-475.

0420. Correll, D.L.; Edwards, J.L.; Klein, W.H.; Shropshire, W., Jr. 1968.
       PHYTOCHROME IN ETIOLATED ANNUAL RYE. III. ISOLATION OF PHOTOREVERSI-
       BLE PHYTOCHROME. Biochim. Biophys. Acta 168: 36-45.

0421. Correll, D.L.; Shropshire, W. Jr., 1968. PHYTOCHROME IN ETIOLATED ANNUAL
       RYE. I. CHANGES DURING GROWTH IN THE AMOUNT OF PHOTOREVERSIBLE PHYTO-
       CHROME IN THE COLEOPTILE AND PRIMARY LEAF. Planta 79: 275-283.

0422. Correll, D.L.; Steers, E. Jr.; Towe, K.M.; Shropshire, W. Jr., 1968.
       PHYTOCHROME IN ETIOLATED ANNUAL RYE. IV. PHYSICAL AND CHEMICAL
       CHARACTERIZATION OF PHYTOCHROME. Biochim. Biophys. Acta 168: 46-57.

0423. Correll, D.L.; Edwards, J.L. 1970. THE AGGREGATION STATES OF PHYTO-
       CHROME FROM ETIOLATED RYE AND OAT SEEDLINGS. Plant Physiol. 45: 81-
       85.

0424. Craker, L.E.; Abeles, F.B.; Shropshire, W. Jr., 1973. LIGHT-INDUCED
       ETHYLENE PRODUCTION IN SORGHUM. Plant Physiol. 51: 1082-1083.

0425. Creasy, L.L.; Swain, T. 1966. FLAVAN PRODUCTION IN STRAWBERRY LEAVES.
       Phytochemistry 5: 501-509.

0430. Crespi, H.L.; Smith, U.; Katz, J.J. 1968. PHYCOCYANOBILIN STRUCTURE
       AND EXCHANGE STUDIES BY NUCLEAR MAGNETIC RESONANCE AND ITS MODE OF
       ATTACHMENT IN PHYCOCYANIN. A MODEL FOR PHYTOCHROME. Biochemistry 7:
       2232-2242.

0431. Creutz, C. 1972. PHOTOSTATIONARY STATE STUDIES OF IN VITRO PHYTOCHROME.
       Ph.D. Thesis, Univ. Pennsylvania, Philadelphia.

0432. Crocker, W. 1936. EFFECT OF THE VISIBLE SPECTRUM UPON THE GERMINATION
       OF SEEDS AND FRUITS. Biological Effects of Radiation. Ed. B.M.
       Duggar, McGraw-Hill, New York and London II: 791-827 (R).

0433. Cross, D.R.; Linschitz, H.; Kasche, V.; Tenenbaum, J. 1968. LOW-TEM-
       PERATURE STUDIES ON PHYTOCHROME: LIGHT AND DARK REACTIONS IN THE RED
       TO FAR-RED TRANSFORMATION AND NEW INTERMEDIATE FORMS OF PHYTOCHROME.
       Proc. Nat. Acad. Sci. USA 61: 1095-1101.

0434. Cumming, B.G.; Hay, J.R. 1958. LIGHT AND DORMANCY IN WILD OATS (AVENA
       FATUA L.). Nature (London) 182: 609-610.

0435. Cumming, B.G. 1959. LIGHT AND TEMPERATURE SENSITIVITY IN GERMINATION AND VERY EARLY FLORAL INITIATION OF SOME *CHENOPODIUM* SPECIES. Proc. IX Int. Bot. Congr. p. 83 (A).

0436. Cumming, B.G. 1959. EXTREME SENSITIVITY OF GERMINATION AND PHOTOPERIODIC REACTION IN THE GENUS *CHENOPODIUM* (TOURN.) L. Nature (London) 184: 1044-1045.

0437. Cumming, B.G. 1962. EVIDENCE OF AN OPTIMAL RATIO OF THE TWO PHYTOCHROME FORMS FOR FLORAL INITIATION. Plant Physiol. 37: Suppl.-27-28 (A).

0438. Cumming, B.G. 1962. ECOLOGICAL SIGNIFICANCE OF RESPONSE TO DURATION AND QUALITY OF LIGHT IN THE GERMINATION OF *CHENOPODIUM* SPP. Plant Physiol. 37: Suppl.-68 Abstr. No. 917 (A).

0439. Cumming, B.G. 1963. EVIDENCE OF A REQUIREMENT FOR PHYTOCHROME P_{fr} IN THE FLORAL INITIATION OF *CHENOPODIUM RUBRUM*. Can. J. Bot. 41: 901-926.

0440. Cumming, B.G. 1963. THE DEPENDENCE OF GERMINATION ON PHOTOPERIOD, LIGHT QUALITY, AND TEMPERATURE, IN *CHENOPODIUM* SPP. Can. J. Bot. 41: 1211-1233.

0441. Cumming, B.G.; Hendricks, S.B.; Borthwick, H.A. 1965. RHYTHMIC FLOWERING RESPONSES AND PHYTOCHROME CHANGES IN A SELECTION OF *CHENOPODIUM RUBRUM*. Can. J. Bot. 43: 825-853.

0442. Cumming, B.G. 1967. GERMINATION, AS INFLUENCED BY LIGHT AND TEMPERATURE, PARTICULARLY IN *CHENOPODIUM* SPP. Proc. Int. Symp. Physiol., Ecol., Biochem. Germination; 1963, Ed. H. Borriss; Ernest-Moritz-Arndt Univ.; Greifswald, Germany 1: 113-130 (R).

0443. Cumming, B.G. 1967. CIRCADIAN RHYTHMIC FLOWERING RESPONSES IN *CHENOPODIUM RUBRUM*: EFFECTS OF GLUCOSE AND SUCROSE. Can. J. Bot. 45: 2173-2193.

0444. Cumming, B.G.; Wagner, E. 1968. RHYTHMIC PROCESSES IN PLANTS. Annu. Rev. Plant Physiol. 19: 381-416 (R).

0445. Cumming, B.G. 1969. PHOTOPERIODISM AND RHYTHMIC FLOWER INDUCTION: COMPLETE SUBSTITUTION OF INDUCTIVE DARKNESS BY LIGHT. Can. J. Bot. 47: 1241-1250.

0446. Cundiff, S.C.; Pratt, L.H. 1972. IMMUNOCHEMICAL CHARACTERIZATION OF PHYTOCHROME. Proc. VI Int. Congr. Photobiol. Abstr. No. 155 (A).

0447. Cundiff, S.C. 1973. AN IMMUNOCHEMICAL, BIOCHEMICAL, AND SPECTRAL CHARACTERIZATION OF LARGE GARRY OAT PHYTOCHROME. Ph.D. Thesis, Vanderbilt Univ., Nashville.

0448. Cundiff, S.C.; Pratt, L.H. 1973. IMMUNOLOGICAL DETERMINATION OF THE RELATIONSHIP BETWEEN LARGE AND SMALL SIZES OF PHYTOCHROME. Plant Physiol. 51: 210-213.

0449. Curry, G.M.; Wassink, E.C. 1956. PHOTOPERIODIC AND FORMATIVE EFFECTS OF VARIOUS WAVELENGTH REGIONS IN *HYOSCYAMUS NIGER* AS INFLUENCED BY GIBBERELLIC ACID. Meded. Landbouwhogesch. Wageningen 56-14: 1-8.

0450. Curry, G.M. 1957. STUDIES ON THE SPECTRAL SENSITIVITY OF PHOTOTROPISM. Ph.D. Thesis, Harvard Univ., Cambridge.

0451. Curry, G.M. 1969. PHOTOTROPISM. *Physiology of Plant Growth and Development*. Ed. M.B. Wilkins, McGraw-Hill, New York, pp. 245-273.

0452. Czopek, M. 1960. EKOLOGICZNO-FIZJOLOGICZNE BADANIA NAD ZAKWITANIEM GATUNKOWZ RODZINY *LEMNACEAE*. Wiad. Bot. 6: 263-280 (R).

0453. Czopek, M. 1962. THE OLIGODYNAMIC ACTION OF LIGHT ON THE GERMINATION OF TURIONS OF *SPIRODELA POLYRRHIZA* (L.) SCHLEIDEN. Acta Soc. Bot. Pol. 31: 703-722.

0454. Czopek, M. 1963. WPLYW ŚWIATLA CHROMATYCZNEGO NA KIELKOWANIE NASION. Wiad. Bot. 7: 11-23 (R).

0455. Czopek, M. 1964. THE ACTION OF KINETIN, GIBBERELLIC ACID AND RED LIGHT ON THE GERMINATION OF TURIONS OF *SPIRODELA POLYRRHIZA*. Bull. Acad. Pol. Sci. Ser. Sci. Biol. 12: 177-182.

0456. Czopek, M. 1967. THE OLIGODYNAMIC ACTION OF LIGHT ON THE GERMINATION OF TURIONS OF *SPIRODELA POLYRRHIZA*. Proc. Int. Symp. Physiol. Ecol. Biochem. Germination, Ed. H. Borriss, Greifswald; Ernst-Moritz-Arndt-University, 1967 1: 833-841 (R).

0457. Dale, J.E.; Murray, D. 1968. PHOTOMORPHOGENESIS, PHOTOSYNTHESIS, AND EARLY GROWTH OF PRIMARY LEAVES OF *PHASEOLUS VULGARIS*. Ann. Bot. (London) 32: 767-780.

0458. Dale, J.E.; Murray, D. 1969. LIGHT AND CELL DIVISION IN PRIMARY LEAVES OF *PHASEOLUS*. Proc. R. Soc. London Ser. B. 173: 541-555.

0459. Darwin, F. 1898. OBSERVATIONS ON STOMATA. Philos. Trans. R. Soc. London Ser. B: 190: 531-621.

0460. Das, V.S.R.; Raju, P.V. 1965. PHOTOSYNTHETIC $^{14}CO_2$ ASSIMILATION BY
       RICE LEAVES UNDER THE INFLUENCE OF BLUE LIGHT. Indian J. Plant
       Physiol. 8: 1-5.

0461. Datta, S.C.; Biswas, K.K. 1968. INFLUENCE OF TEMPERATURE, LIGHT, AND
       STIMULATORS AND THEIR INTERACTION ON THE GERMINATION AND SEEDLING
       GROWTH OF *ALTERNANTHERA SESSILIS*. Oesterr. Bot. Z. 115: 391-399.

0462. Daubeny, C. 1836. ON THE ACTION OF LIGHT UPON PLANTS, AND OF PLANTS
       UPON THE ATMOSPHERE. Philos. Trans. R. Soc. London Ser. B: 149-175.

0463. Davenport, C.B. 1908. EFFECT OF LIGHT UPON GROWTH. *"Experimental
       Morphology"*, Macmillan Co., New York and London, pp. 416-449 (R).

0464. Davidson, A.W.; Yeoman, M.M. 1974. A PHYTOCHROME-MEDIATED SEQUENCE OF
       REACTIONS REGULATING CELL DIVISION IN DEVELOPING CALLUS CULTURES.
       Ann. Bot. (London) 38: 545-554.

0465. Davis, B.D. 1968. EFFECT OF LIGHT QUALITY ON THE TRANSITION TO TWO
       DIMENSIONAL GROWTH BY GAMETOPHYTES OF *PTERIDIUM AQUILINUM*. Bull.
       Torrey Bot. Club 95: 31-36.

0466. De Candolle, C. 1892. ÉTUDE DE L'ACTION DES RAYONS ULTRAVIOLETS SUR
       LA FORMATION DES FLEURS. Arch. Sci. Phys. Nat. 28: 265-277.

0467. DeGreef, J.A. 1966. ON PHYTOCHROME AND CYTOCHROMES IN PHOTOPERIODIC
       PHENOMENA: A BIOCHEMICAL APPROACH. Photochem. Photobiol. 5: 485-487
       (R).

0468. DeGreef, J.A.; Fredericq, H. 1967. ALTERNATIVE INTERPRETATIONS OF THE
       EXPERIMENTAL RESULTS OBTAINED BY SHORT, TERMINAL IRRADIATIONS AT THE
       END OF WHITE FLUORESCENT PHOTOPERIODS. Proc. Eur. Annu. Symp. Plant
       Photomorphogenesis (Hvar), pp. 21-24. (R).

0469. DeGreef, J.A.; Fredericq, H. 1968. CYTOLOGICAL EFFECTS OF RED/FAR-RED
       TERMINAL IRRADIATIONS ON GROWING AND NONGROWING PARTS OF *MARCHANTIA
       POLYMORPHA* L. Proc. V Int. Congr. Photobiol. p. 63 (A).

0470. DeGreef, J.A.; Fredericq, H. 1969. PHOTOMORPHOGENIC AND CHLOROPHYLL
       STUDIES IN THE BROPHYTE *MARCHANTIA POLYMORPHA*. II. PHOTOBIOLOGICAL
       RESPONSES TO TERMINAL IRRADIATIONS WITH DIFFERENT RED/FAR-RED RATIOS.
       Physiol. Plant. 22: 462-468.

0471. DeGreef, J.A.; Butler, W.L.; Roth, T.F. 1971. GREENING OF ETIOLATED
       BEAN LEAVES IN FAR RED LIGHT. Plant Physiol. 47: 457-464.

0472. DeGreef, J.A.; Butler, W.L.; Roth, T.F.; Fredericq, H. 1971. SENES-
CENCE AND PHYTOCHROME IN THE LIVERWORT *MARCHANTIA*. Proc. Eur. Annu.
Symp. Plant Photomorphogenesis, (Athens), pp. 15-17 (A).

0473. DeGreef, J.A.; Butler, W.L.; Roth, T.F.; Fredericq, H. 1971. CONTROL
OF SENESCENCE IN *MARCHANTIA* BY PHYTOCHROME. Plant Physiol. 48: 407-
412.

0474. DeGreef, J.A.; Caubergs, R. 1971. CHLOROPHYLL FORMATION AND PROTOCHLO-
ROPHYLL REGENERATION DURING THE EARLY GREENING STAGES OF ETIOLATED
SEEDLINGS OF << *PHASEOLUS VULGARIS* CULTIVAR >> LIMBURG. Arch. Int.
Physiol. Biochim. 79: 412-414.

0475. DeGreef, J.A.; Caubergs, R. 1971. FOTO-REVERSIEBELE KONTROLE VAN DE
EMBRYONALE AS OP DE CHLOROFYL-SYNTHESE IN GEËTIOLEERDE BLADEREN.
Arch. Int. Physiol. Biochim. 79: 1017-1019.

0476. DeGreef, J.A.; Caubergs, R.; Verbelen, J.P. 1971. LOKALISATIE VAN EEN
LICHT-REAKTIE IN DE APEX TIJDENS HET GROENINGSPROCES VAN GEËTIOLEERDE
KIEMPLANTEN. Arch. Int. Physiol. Biochim. 79: 826-827.

0477. DeGreef, J.A.; Caubergs, R.; Verbelen, J.P. 1971. CONTROL OF CHLORO-
PHYLL SYNTHESIS AND PLASTID DEVELOPMENT IN LEAVES BY A PHYTOCHROME-
MEDIATED STIMULUS IN THE EMBRYONIC AXIS OF ETIOLATED BEAN SEEDLINGS.
Proc. Eur. Annu. Symp. Plant Photomorphogenesis, (Athens), pp. 18-20
(A).

0478. DeGreef, J.A.; Caubergs, R. 1972. THE DIFFERENTIAL ACTION OF THE
EMBRYONIC AXIS IN PHOTOCHROME-MEDIATED LEAF EXPANSION. Plant
Physiol. 49: Suppl.-62 Abstr. No. 352 (A).

0479. DeGreef, J.A.; Caubergs, R. 1972. MORPHOGENIC CORRELATIONS BETWEEN
PLANT ORGANS BY TRANSFER OF LIGHT-INDUCED STIMULI. Arch. Int.
Physiol. Biochim. 80: 390-391.

0480. DeGreef, J.A.; Caubergs, R. 1972. INTERORGAN CORRELATIONS AND PHYTO-
CHROME: HYPOCOTYL HOOK OPENING. Arch. Int. Physiol. Biochim. 80:
959-960.

0481. DeGreef, J.A.; Caubergs, R. 1972. INTERORGAN CORRELATIONS AND PHYTO-
CHROME: LEAF EXPANSION. Arch. Int. Physiol. Biochim. 80: 961-962.

0482. DeGreef, J.A.; Caubergs, R. 1972. STUDIES ON GREENING OF ETIOLATED
SEEDLINGS I. ELIMINATION OF THE LAG PHASE OF CHLOROPHYLL BIOSYNTHE-
SIS BY A PRE-ILLUMINATION OF THE EMBRYONIC AXIS IN INTACT PLANTS.
Physiol. Plant. 26: 157-165.

0483. DeGreef, J.A.; Caubergs, R.; Verbelen, J.P. 1972. PHOTOMORPHOGENIC EXPRESSIONS IN PLANT DEVELOPMENT BY INTER-ORGAN CORRELATIONS. Proc. VI Int. Congr. Photobiol. Abstr. No. 172 (A) (R).

0484. DeGreef, J.A.; Fredericq, H. 1972. ENHANCEMENT OF SENESCENCE BY FAR-RED LIGHT. Planta 104: 272-274.

0485. DeGreef, J.A.; Verbelen, J.P. 1972. INTER-ORGAN CORRELATIONS AND PHY-TOCHROME: CHANGES IN PLASTID ULTRASTRUCTURE DURING DE-ETIOLATION PROCESSES. Arch. Int. Physiol. Biochim. 80: 962-963.

0486. DeGreef, J.A.; Caubergs, R. 1973. STUDIES ON GREENING OF ETIOLATED SEEDLINGS II. LEAF GREENING BY PHYTOCHROME ACTION IN THE EMBRYONIC AXIS. Physiol. Plant. 28: 71-76.

0487. DeGreef, J.A.; Caubergs, R. 1973. THE BIOCHEMICAL SIGNIFICANCE OF THE INCUBATION PERIOD IN PHOTOMORPHOGENETIC PROCESSES. Arch. Int. Physiol. Biochim. 81: 368.

0488. DeGreef, J.A.; Verbelen, J.P. 1973. DNP-INHIBITION OF PHYTOCHROME-INDUCED GREENING PROCESS. Arch. Int. Physiol. Biochim. 81: 797.

0489. DeGreef, J.; Caubergs, R. 1974. STATISTICAL EVALUATION OF HOOK OPENING REACTION AS A FUNCTION OF INTERORGAN COÖPERATION. Proc. Eur. Annu. Symp. Plant Photomorphogenesis, (Antwerpen) pp. 118-123.

0490. DeGreef, J.A.; Dow, D. 1974. A LONG-TERM EFFECT OF PHYTOCHROME ON THE INDUCTION OF CHLOROPHYLL SYNTHESIS. Arch. Int. Physiol. Biochim. 82: 796.

0491. DeGreef, J.; DeProft, M.; Caubergs, R. 1974. R/FR-CONTROL OF ABSCIS-SION MEASURED BY AN INDUCTIVE FORCE TRANSDUCER. Proc. Eur. Annu. Symp. Plant Photomorphogenesis, (Antwerpen), pp. 91-96.

0492. DeGreef, J.; Moereels, E. 1974. FAST CHANGES OF P_I-LEVELS IN COTYLEDONS OF ETIOLATED BEAN SEEDLINGS AFTER SHORT RED IRRADIATION AND ATP INCUBATION. Proc. Eur. Annu. Symp. Plant Photomorphogenesis, (Antwerpen), pp. 113-116.

0493. Deherain, P.P. 1869. SUR L'ÉVAPORATION DE L'EAU ET LA DÉCOMPOSITION DE L'ACIDE CARBONIQUE PAR LES FEUILLES DES VÉGÉTAUX. Ann. Sci. Nat. Bot. Ser. 5, 12: 1-23.

0493.5 Deimling, A.v. 1966. DIE QUANTITATIVE ZUSAMMENSETZUNG DER PROTEIN-AMINOSÄUREN UND DER FREIEN AMINOSÄUREN IN MORPHOGENETISCH VERSCHIE-DENEN FARNVORKEIMEN (*Dryopteris filix-mas*), Ph.D. Thesis, Univ. Freiburg, Germany.

0494. Deimling, A.v.; Mohr, H. 1967. EINE ANALYSE DER DURCH BLAULICHT BEWIRK-
TEN STEIGERUNG DER PROTEINSYNTHESE BEI FARNVORKEIMEN AUF DER EBENE
DER AMINOSÄUREN. Planta 76: 269-284 (ENG Summary).

0495. Delaveau, P. 1967. LES FLAVONOÏDES DE LA GRANDE CAPUCINE *(TROPAEOLUM
MAJUS* L.). Physiol. Veg. 5: 357-390 (ENG Summary).

0496. DeLint, P.J.A.L. 1957. DOUBLE ACTION OF NEAR INFRARED IN LENGTH GROWTH
OF THE *AVENA* COLEOPTILE. Meded. Landbouwhogesch. Wageningen 57-10:
1-9.

0497. DeLint, P.J.A.L. 1958. STEM FORMATION IN *HYOSCYAMUS NIGER* UNDER SHORT
DAYS INCLUDING SUPPLEMENTARY IRRADIATION WITH NEAR INFRARED. Meded.
Landbouwhogesch. Wageningen 58-10: 1-5.

0498. DeLint, P.J.A.L. 1959. COMPLEX REACTION IN *HYOSCYAMUS NIGER* UPON NIGHT
INTERRUPTION WITH RED LIGHT. Nature (London) 184: 731-732.

0499. DeLint, P.J.A.L. 1960. AN ATTEMPT TO ANALYSIS OF THE EFFECT OF LIGHT
ON STEM ELONGATION AND FLOWERING IN *HYOSCYAMUS NIGER*. L. Meded.
Landbouwhogesch. Wageningen 60-14: 1-59 (DUT Summary).

0500. DeLint, P.J.A.L. 1961. DEPENDENCE OF ELONGATION ON WAVE-LENGTH OF
SUPPLEMENTARY IRRADIATION. Meded. Landbouwhogesch. Wageningen 61-16:
1-14.

0501. DeLint, P.J.A.L.; Edwards, J.L.; Klein, W.H. 1963. THE RED, FAR-RED
SYSTEM AND PHYTOCHROME. Plant Physiol. 38: Suppl.-24 (A).

0502. DeLint, P.J.A.L.; Spruit, C.J.P. 1963. PHYTOCHROME DESTRUCTION FOLLOW-
ING ILLUMINATION OF MESOCOTYLS OF *ZEA MAYS* L. Meded. Landbouwhogesch. Wageningen 63-14: 1-7.

0503. Demkiv, O.T.; Ripetsky, R.T. 1970. MORPHOLOGICAL RESPONSE OF THE
PROTONEMA CELLS TO THE RED LIGHT. Ukr. Bot. Zh. 27: 758-762 (UKR)
(ENG Summary).

0504. Deutch, B. 1974. BULBLET FORMATION IN *ACHIMENES LONGIFLORA*. Physiol.
Plant. 30: 113-118.

0505. Deutch, B.; Deutch, B.I. 1974. CEREAL LEAF UNFOLDING - THE ACTION OF
PHYTOCHROME INTERMEDIATES ON SHORT TERM PHENOMENA. Proc. Eur. Annu.
Symp. Plant Photomorphogenesis, (Antwerpen), pp. 33-36.

0506. Deutch, B.; Deutch, B.I. 1974. A KINETIC THEORY OF FIRST ORDER CYCLI-
CAL PROCESSES - PHYTOCHROME CONTROLLED RED LIGHT INDUCED CEREAL LEAF
UNFOLDING COMPARED WITH THEORY. Physiol. Plant. 32: 273-281

0507. Deutch, B.; Rasmussen, O. 1974. GROWTH CHAMBER ILLUMINATION AND PHOTO-
MORPHOGENETIC EFFICACY I. PHYSIOLOGICAL ACTION OF INFRARED RADIATION
BEYOND 750 nm. Physiol. Plant. 30: 64-71.

0508. Devay, M. 1967. BIOCHEMICAL PROCESSES OF VERNALIZATION VI. THE CHANGE
OF THE PHYTOCHROME CONTENT IN THE COURSE OF VERNALIZATION. Acta
Agron. Acad. Sci. Hung. 16: 289-295.

0509. Diekmann, H.; Kranz, A.R. 1973. INTERACTIONS BETWEEN PHYTOCHROME (P_{fr}),
GIBBERELLIC ACID (GA_3), AND CYCLIC ADENOSINE MONOPHOSPHATE (C-AMP)
IN SEED GERMINATION OF HETEROALLELIC GENOTYPES OF *ARABIDOPSIS
THALIANA* (L.) HEYNH. Arabidopsis Info. Serv. 10: 14-15.

0510. Dierickx, P.J.; Vendrig, J.C. 1973. THE INFLUENCE OF THE SYNTHETIC
GROWTH REGULATOR α-CHLORO-β-(3-CHLORO-O-TOLYL) PROPIONITRILE ON SOME
PHYTOCHROME-MEDIATED PROCESSES. Physiol. Plant. 28: 374-377.

0511. Dimitrova-Rousseva, E. 1970. EFFECT OF LIGHT ON DIFFERENT SPECTRAL
REGIONS ON THE GROWTH AND TERPENE BIOGENESIS IN *MENTHA PIPERITA* L.
C.R. Acad. Bulg. Sci. 3: 5-9.

0512. Dinus, R.J. 1968. EFFECT OF RED AND FAR-RED LIGHT UPON GROWTH OF
DOUGLAS-FIR *(PSEUDOTSUGA MENZIESII* (MIRB.) FRANCO) SEEDLINGS. Ph.D.
Thesis, Oregon State Univ., Corvallis.

0512.5 Dittes, H. 1970. MAK-CHROMATOGRAPHIE DER NUCLEINSÄUREN IM ZUSAMMENHANG
MIT DER PHYTOCHROMGESTEUERTEN PHOTOMORPHOGENESE DES SENFKEIMLINGS
(SINAPIS ALBA L.). Ph.D. Thesis, Univ. Freiburg, Germany.

0513. Dittes, H.; Mohr, H. 1970. MAK-CHROMATOGRAPHIE DER RNS IM ZUSAMMENHANG
MIT DER PHYTOCHROMGESTEUERTEN MORPHOGENESE. Z. Naturforsch. 25:
708-710 (ENG Summary).

0514. Dittes, L.; Rissland, I.; Mohr, H. 1971. ON THE REGULATION OF ENZYME
LEVELS (PHENYLALANINE AMMONIA-LYASE) IN DIFFERENT ORGANS OF A PLANT
(SINAPIS ALBA L.). Z. Naturforsch. 26: 1175-1180.

0515. Dmitrieva, V.I. 1970. ROLE OF THE SPECTRAL COMPOSITION OF LIGHT IN THE
PHOTOPERIODIC REACTION OF PLANTS. Uch. Zap. Chuv. Gos. Pedagog.
Inst. 31: 26-32 (RUS) (not obtained).

0516. Doorenbos, J.; Wellensiek, S.J. 1959. PHOTOPERIODIC CONTROL OF FLORAL
INDUCTION. Annu. Rev. Plant Physiol. 10: 147-184 (R).

0517. Dooskin, R.H. 1967. STUDIES ON *IN VIVO* PHYTOCHROME DARK DECAY AND
COLEOPTILE ELONGATION IN *AVENA* FOLLOWING VARIOUS LIGHT TREATMENTS.
Ph.D. Thesis, Columbia Univ., New York.

0518. Dooskin, R.H.; Mancinelli, A.L. 1968. PHYTOCHROME DECAY AND COLEOPTILE
       ELONGATION IN *AVENA* FOLLOWING VARIOUS LIGHT TREATMENTS. Bull. Torrey
       Bot. Club 95: 474-487.

0519. Dörffling, K. 1973. DIE REGULATION DES INTERNODIENWACHSTUMS VON ERBSEN-
       KEIMLINGEN DURCH LICHT UND ABSCISINSÄURE. Z. Pflanzenphysiol. 70:
       131-137 (ENG Summary).

0520. Dorscheid, T. 1966. UNTERSUCHUNGEN ÜBER DIE SCHWACHLICHTBEWEGUNG DES
       MESOTAENIUM CHLOROPLASTEN. Ph.D. Thesis, Univ. Saarlandes,
       Saarbrücken, Germany.

0521. Dorscheid, T.; Wartenberg, A. 1966. CHLOROPHYLL ALS PHOTORECEPTOR BEI
       DER SCHWACHLICHTBEWEGUNG DES *MESOTAENIUM* CHLOROPLASTEN. Planta 70:
       187-192 (ENG Summary).

0522. Dorscheid, T. 1969. DIE ORIENTIERUNG AKTIVER MOLEKÜLE DES CHLOROPHYLL A
       IM CHLOROPLASTEN VON *MESOTAENIUM CALDARIORUM*. Z. Pflanzenphysiol.
       61: 46-51 (ENG Summary).

0523. Dorschied, T. 1969. DIE TEMPERATURABHÄNGIGKEIT DER POSITIVEN CHLORO-
       PLASTENPHOTOTAXIS BEI *MESOTAENIUM CALDARIORUM*. Z. Pflanzenphysiol.
       61: 52-57 (ENG Summary).

0524. Downs, R.J. 1954. REGULATORY EFFECTS OF LIGHT ON PLANT GROWTH AND
       REPRODUCTION. Ph.D. Thesis, George Washington Univ., Washington,
       D.C.

0525. Downs, R.J. 1955. PHOTOREVERSIBILITY OF LEAF AND HYPOCOTYL ELONGATION
       OF DARK GROWN RED KIDNEY BEAN SEEDLINGS. Plant Physiol. 30: 468-473.

0526. Downs, R.J. 1956. PHOTOREVERSIBILITY OF FLOWER INITIATION. Plant
       Physiol. 31: 279-284.

0527. Downs, R.J.; Hendricks, S.B.; Borthwick, H.A. 1956. PHOTOREVERSIBLE
       CONTROL OF ELONGATION OF BEANS AND OTHER PLANTS UNDER NORMAL CONDI-
       TIONS OF GROWTH. Plant Physiol. 31: Suppl.-12-13 (A).

0528. Downs, R.J.; Hendricks, S.B.; Borthwick, H.A. 1957. PHOTOREVERSIBLE
       CONTROL OF ELONGATION OF PINTO BEANS AND OTHER PLANTS UNDER NORMAL
       CONDITIONS OF GROWTH. Bot Gaz. (Chicago) 118: 199-208.

0529. Downs, R.J.; Borthwick, H.A.; Piringer, A.A. 1958. COMPARISON OF INCAN-
       DESCENT AND FLUORESCENT LAMPS FOR LENGTHENING PHOTOPERIODS. Proc.
       Am. Soc. Hortic. Sci. 71: 568-578.

0530. Downs, R.J. 1959. INFLUENCE OF THE PHOTOMORPHOGENIC REACTION ON ELON-
       GATION. Proc. IX Int. Bot. Congr. 2: 96 (A).

0531. Downs, R.J.   1959.   PHOTOCONTROL OF VEGETATIVE GROWTH. *Photoperiodism and Related Phenomena,* Ed. R.B. Withrow, A.A.A.S., Washington, D.C., pp. 129-135 (R).

0532. Downs, R.J.; Piringer, A.A.; Wiebe, G.A.   1959.   EFFECTS OF PHOTOPERIOD AND KIND OF SUPPLEMENTAL LIGHT ON GROWTH AND REPRODUCTION OF SEVERAL VARIETIES OF WHEAT AND BARLEY. Bot. Gaz. (Chicago) 120: 170-177.

0533. Downs, R.J.; Cathey, H.M.   1960.   EFFECTS OF LIGHT, GIBBERELLIN, AND A QUATERNARY AMMONIUM COMPOUND ON THE GROWTH OF DARK-GROWN RED KIDNEY BEANS. Bot. Gaz. (Chicago) 121: 233-237.

0534. Downs, R.J.   1961.   PHOTOCONTROL OF ANTHOCYANIN SYNTHESIS IN DARK-GROWN MILO SEEDLINGS. Plant Physiol. 36: Suppl.-42 (A).

0535. Downs, R.J.   1961.   THE INFLUENCE OF THE PHOTOMORPHOGENIC REACTION ON ELONGATION. Recent Adv. Bot. 2: 1033-1035.

0536. Downs, R.J.   1962.   EFFECT OF LIGHT WAVELENGTHS ON GROWTH: PLANTS. *"Growth",* Ed. A.L. Altman and D.S. Dittmer. Publ. by Fed. Am. Soc. Exp. Biol., page 506 (A).

0537. Downs, R.J.; Siegelman, H.W.   1963.   PHOTOCONTROL OF ANTHOCYANIN SYNTHESIS IN MILO SEEDLINGS. Plant Physiol. 38: 25-30.

0538. Downs, R.J.   1964.   PHOTOCONTROL OF GERMINATION OF SEEDS OF THE *BROMELIACEAE.* Phyton 21: 1-6.

0539. Downs, R.J.   1964.   PHOTOCONTROL OF ANTHOCYANIN SYNTHESIS. J. Wash. Acad. Sci. 54: 112-120.

0540. Downs, R.J.; Siegelman, H.W.; Butler, W.L.; Hendricks, S.B.   1965. PHOTORECEPTIVE PIGMENTS FOR ANTHOCYANIN SYNTHESIS IN APPLE SKIN. Nature (London) 205: 909-910.

0541. Dring, M.J.   1967.   PHYTOCHROME IN RED ALGA, *PORPHYRA TENERA.* Nature (London) 215: 1411-1412.

0542. Dring, M.J.   1970.   PHOTOPERIODIC EFFECTS IN MICROORGANISMS. *Photobiology of Microorganisms,* Ed. P. Halldal, Wiley-Interscience, New York, pp. 345-368 (R).

0543. Drumm, H.   1966.   DIE REGULATION DER RNS-SYNTHESE IN FARNGAMETOPHYTEN *(DRYOPTERIS FILIX-MAS* (L.) SCHOTT) DURCH LICHT. Ph.D. Thesis, Univ. Freiburg, Germany.

0544. Drumm, H.; Mohr, H.   1967.   DIE REGULATION DER RNS-SYNTHESE IN FARNGAMETOPHYTEN DURCH LICHT. Planta 72: 232-246 (ENG Summary).

0545. Drumm, H.; Mohr, H. 1967. DIE REGULATION DER DNS-SYNTHESE IN FARNGAME-
TOPHYTEN DURCH LICHT. Planta 75: 343-351 (ENG Summary).

0546. Drumm, H.; Falk, H.; Möller, J.; Mohr, H. 1970. THE DEVELOPMENT OF
CATALASE IN THE MUSTARD SEEDLING. Cytobiologie Z. Exp. Zellforsch.
2: 335-340.

0547. Drumm, H.; Elchinger, I.; Möller, J.; Peter, K.; Mohr, H. 1971. INDUC-
TION OF AMYLASE IN MUSTARD SEEDLINGS BY PHYTOCHROME. Planta 99:
265-274.

0548. Drumm, H.; Möller, J.; Mohr, H. 1971. PHYTOCHROME-MEDIATED SYNTHESIS OF
α-AMYLASE (EC 3.2.1.1.) IN MUSTARD SEEDLINGS. Naturwissenschaften
58: 97-98.

0549. Drumm, H.; Mohr, H. 1971. INDUCTION OF AMYLASE IN MUSTARD SEEDLINGS BY
PHYTOCHROME. Proc. Eur. Annu. Symp. Plant Photomorphogenesis,
(Athens), p. 21 (A).

0550. Drumm, H.; Brüning, K.; Mohr, H. 1972. PHYTOCHROME-MEDIATED INDUCTION
OF ASCORBATE OXIDASE IN DIFFERENT ORGANS OF A DICOTYLEDONOUS SEED-
LING (SINAPIS ALBA L.). Planta 106: 259-267 (ENG Summary).

0551. Drumm, H.; Mohr, H. 1972. INDUCTION OF ASCORBATE OXIDASE BY PHYTO-
CHROME. Proc. VI Int. Congr. Photobiol. Abstr. No. 165 (A).

0552. Drumm, H.; Mohr, H. 1973. CONTROL BY PHYTOCHROME OF GLUTATHIONE REDUC-
TASE LEVELS IN THE MUSTARD SEEDLING. Z. Naturforsch. Teil C. 28:
559-563.

0553. Drumm, H.; Mohr, H. 1974. THE DOSE RESPONSE CURVE IN PHYTOCHROME-
MEDIATED ANTHOCYANIN SYNTHESIS IN THE MUSTARD SEEDLING. Photochem.
Photobiol. 20: 151-157.

0554. Drumm, H.; Schopfer, P. 1974. EFFECT OF PHYTOCHROME ON DEVELOPMENT OF
CATALASE ACTIVITY AND ISOENZYME PATTERN IN MUSTARD (SINAPIS ALBA L.)
SEEDLINGS. Planta 120: 13-30.

0555. Dubois, J. 1973. ACTION DE LA LUMIÈRE SUR LA CROISSANCE ET LA TENEUR
EN PIGMENTS PLASTIDAUX DES TISSUS ISOLÉS DE CAROTTE. Bull. Soc.
Bot. Fr. 120: 3-26 (ENG Summary).

0556. DuBuy, H.G.; Nuernbergk, E. 1929. UEBER DAS WACHSTUM DER KOLEOPTILE
UND DES MESOKOTYLS VON AVENA SATIVA UNTER VERSCHIEDENEN AUSSENBEDIN-
GUNGEN (VORLÄUFIGE MITTEILUNG). Proc. K. Ned. Akad. Wet. 32:
614-624.

0557. DuBuy, H.G.; Nuernbergk, E. 1929. WEITERE UNTERSUCHUNGEN ÜBER DEN EIN-
FLUSS DES LICHTES AUF DAS WACHSTUM VON KOLEOPTILE UND MESOKOTYL BEI
AVENA SATIVA. II. (VORLÄUFIGE MITTEILUNG). Proc. K. Ned. Akad. Wet.
32: 808-817.

0558. DuBuy, H.G.; Nuernbergk, E. 1930. UEBER DAS WACHSTUM DER KOLEOPTILE
UND DES MESOKOTYLS VON *AVENA SATIVA* UNTER VERSCHIEDENEN BEDINGUNGEN
(III. MITTEILUNG). Proc. K. Ned. Akad. Wet. 33: 542-556 (R-D).

0559. DuBuy, H.G.; Nuernbergk, E. 1932. PHOTOTROPISMUS UND WACHSTUM DER
PFLANZEN I. Ergeb. Biol. 9: 358-544 (R).

0560. DuBuy, H.G. 1933. UBER WACHSTUM UND PHOTOTROPISMUS VON *AVENA SATIVA*.
Rec. Trav. Bot. Neerl. 30: 798-925.

0561. DuBuy, H.G.; Nuernbergk, E. 1934. PHOTOTROPISMUS UND WACHSTUM DER
PFLANZEN. Ergeb. Biol. 10: 207-322.

0562. DuBuy, H.G.; Nuernbergk, E. 1935. PHOTOTROPISMUS UND WACHSTUM DER
PFLANZEN III. Ergeb. Biol. 12: 325-543 (R).

0563. Duda, M. 1968. EINFLUSS VON ZUSATZLICHT VERSCHIEDENER QUALITÄT AUF DEN
WUCHS UND DIE ENTWICKLUNG EINIGER PFLANZENARTEN. Biologia (Bratislava) 23: 777-792 (CZEC, RUS Summaries).

0564. Duke, S.O.; Wickliff, J.L. 1969. ZEA SHOOT DEVELOPMENT IN RESPONSE TO
RED LIGHT INTERRUPTION OF THE DARK-GROWTH PERIOD. I. INHIBITION OF
FIRST INTERNODE ELONGATION. Plant Physiol. 44: 1027-1030.

0565. Duke, S.O.; Naylor, A.W. 1974. EFFECTS OF LIGHT ON PHENYLALANINE
AMMONIA-LYASE ACTIVITY IN DARK-GROWN *ZEA MAYS* (L.) SEEDLINGS.
Plant Sci. Lett. 2: 289-293.

0566. Dunn, S. 1970. LIGHT QUALITY EFFECTS ON THE LIFE CYCLE OF COMMON PURS-
LANE. Weed Sci. 18: 611-613.

0567. Durandin, A.I. 1972. EFFECT OF THE SPECTRAL COMPOSITION OF LIGHT ON
THE GROWTH AND HORMONAL METABOLISM OF BARLEY SHOOTS. Byull. Gl. Bot.
Sada, Acad. Nauk SSSR (#83), 89-92 (RUS).

0568. Durant, J.P.; Spratling, L.; O'Kelley, J.C. 1968. A STUDY OF LIGHT
INTENSITY, PERIODICITY, AND WAVELENGTH ON ZOOSPORE PRODUCTION BY
PROTOSIPHON BOTRYOIDES KLEBS. J. Phycol. 4: 356-362.

0569. Durst, F.; Mohr, H. 1966. PHYTOCHROME-MEDIATED INDUCTION OF ENZYME
SYNTHESIS IN MUSTARD SEEDLINGS *(SINAPIS ALBA* L.). Naturwissenschaften 53: 531-532.

0570. Durst, F.; Mohr, H. 1966. HALF-LIFE OF PHYTOCHROME-INDUCED PHENYLALA-
NINE DEAMINASE IN MUSTARD SEEDLINGS *(SINAPIS ALBA* L.). Naturwissenschaften 53: 707.

0571. Durst, F. 1970. LUMIÈRE ET ACTIVITÉ ENZYMATIQUE DANS LES TISSUS DU
TOPINAMBOUR CULTIVÉS *IN VITRO.* Physiol. Veg. 8: 531 (A).

0572. Durst, F.; Duranton, H. 1970. PHYTOCHROME ET PHÉNYLALANINE AMMONIA
LYASE DANS LES TISSUS DU TOPINAMBOUR *(HELIANTHUS TUBEROSUS* L.,
VARIÉTÉ BLANC COMMUN) CULTIVÉS *IN VITRO.* C.R. Acad. Sci. Ser. D.
270: 2940-2942.

0573. Durst, F.; Lambert, C.; Elchinger, I.; Duranton, H. 1970 ÉTUDE DE
L'ACTION DE LA LUMIÈRE SUR LES ACTIVITÉS ENZYMATIQUES DE TISSUS DE
TOPINAMBOUR CULTIVÉS *IN VITRO.* Colloq. Int. C.N.R.S. No. 193,
pp. 403-410 (ENG Summary).

0574. Edwards, J.L.; Klein, W.H. 1964. RELATIONSHIP OF PHYTOCHROME CONCEN-
TRATION TO PHYSIOLOGICAL RESPONSES. Plant Physiol. 39: Suppl.-50
(A).

0575. Edwards, J.L.; Correll, D.L. 1967. KINETICS OF THE DARK REVERSION OF
PHYTOCHROME *IN VITRO.* Plant Physiol. 42: Suppl.-10 (A).

0576. Edwards, J.L. 1968. PHYTOCHROME MEASUREMENTS *IN VIVO.* Proc. V Int.
Congr. Photobiol., p. 91 (A).

0577. Egles, D.; Rollin, P. 1968. LA PHOTOSENSIBILITÉ DES GRAINES DE TOMATE
VAR. ST. PIERRE. C.R. Acad. Sci. Ser. D, 266: 1017-1020.

0578. Eisenstadt, F.A. 1973. DIVERSE ASPECTS OF PHYTOCHROME CONTROLLED SEED
GERMINATION. Ph.D. Thesis, Columbia Univ., New York.

0579. Eisenstadt, F.A.; Mancinelli, A.L. 1974. PHYTOCHROME AND SEED GERMINA-
TION VI. PHYTOCHROME AND TEMPERATURE INTERACTION IN THE CONTROL OF
CUCUMBER SEED GERMINATION. Plant Physiol. 53: 114-117.

0580. Eldabh, R.; Fredericq, H.; DeGreef, J. 1972. INTERACTIONS BETWEEN
PHOTOPERIOD AND TERMINAL IRRADIATIONS IN SEED GERMINATION. Proc.
VI Int. Congr. Photobiol. Abstr. No. 171 (A).

0581. Eldabh, R.; Fredericq, H.; Maton, J.; DeGreef, J. 1974. PHOTOPHYSIOLOGY
OF *KALANCHOË* SEED GERMINATION I. INTERRELATIONSHIP BETWEEN PHOTO-
PERIOD AND TERMINAL FAR-RED LIGHT. Physiol. Plant. 30: 185-191.

0582. El Hattab, A.H. 1968. EFFECTS OF LIGHT QUALITY ON FLOWERING AND MORPHO-
GENESIS IN *HYOSCYAMUS NIGER* L. Meded. Landbouwhogesch. Wageningen
68-12, 1-111 (Ph.D. Thesis, Univ. Wageningen, Netherlands).

0583. Eliason, E.J.; Heit, C.E. 1940. THE EFFECT OF LIGHT AND TEMPERATURE ON THE DORMANCY OF SCOTCH PINE SEED. Proc. Assoc. Off. Seed Anal. 32: 92-102.

0584. Elliott, R.F.; French, C.S. 1959. GERMINATION OF LIGHT SENSITIVE SEED IN CROSSED GRADIENTS OF TEMPERATURE AND LIGHT. Plant Physiol. 34: 454-456.

0585. Elliott, W.M.; Miller, J.H. 1969. CHANGES IN PHOTOSENSITIVE STEM GROWTH IN INTACT PEAS FOLLOWING IRRADIATION. Plant Physiol. 44: 623-630.

0586. Elliott, W.M.; Miller, J.H. 1970. PHOTOSENSITIVE STEM GROWTH IN WHITE-LIGHT GROWN AND RED-LIGHT TREATED PEAS (PISUM SATIVUM CV ALASKA). Plant Physiol. 46: Suppl.-1 (A).

0587. Elliott, W.M. 1972. LIGHT CONTROLLED LEAF EXPANSION IN ALASKA PEAS GROWN UNDER VARIED LIGHT CONDITIONS. Plant Physiol. 49: Suppl.-62 Abstr. No. 350 (A).

0588. Elliott, W.M.; Miller, J.H. 1974. LIGHT-CONTROLLED STEM ELONGATION IN PEA SEEDLINGS GROWN UNDER VARIED LIGHT CONDITIONS. Plant Physiol. 53: 279-283.

0589. Eltinge, E.T. 1928. THE EFFECT OF ULTRA-VIOLET RADIATION UPON HIGHER PLANTS. Ann. Mo. Bot. Gard. 15: 169-240.

0590. Engelmann, W. 1960. ENDOGENE RHYTHMIK UND PHOTOPERIODISCHE BLÜHINDUK-TION BEI KALANCHOË. Planta 55: 496-511 (ENG Summary).

0591. Engelsma, G. 1965. PHOTO-INDUCED HYDROXYLATION OF CINNAMIC ACID IN GHERKIN HYPOCOTYLS. Nature (London) 208: 1117-1119.

0592. Engelsma, G.; Meijer, G. 1965. THE INFLUENCE OF LIGHT OF DIFFERENT SPECTRAL REGIONS ON THE SYNTHESIS OF PHENOLIC COMPOUNDS IN GHERKIN SEEDLINGS IN RELATION TO PHOTOMORPHOGENESIS I. BIOSYNTHESIS OF PHENOLIC COMPOUNDS. Acta Bot Neerl. 14: 54-72.

0593. Engelsma, G.; Meijer, G. 1965. THE INFLUENCE OF LIGHT OF DIFFERENT SPECTRAL REGIONS ON THE SYNTHESIS OF PHENOLIC COMPOUNDS IN GHERKIN SEEDLINGS IN RELATION TO PHOTOMORPHOGENESIS II. INDOLEACETIC ACID OXIDASE ACTIVITY AND GROWTH. Acta Bot. Neerl. 14: 73-92.

0594. Engelsma, G. 1966. THE INFLUENCE OF LIGHT OF DIFFERENT SPECTRAL REGIONS ON THE SYNTHESIS OF PHENOLIC COMPOUNDS IN GHERKIN SEEDLINGS IN RELATION TO PHOTOMORPHOGENESIS. III. HYDROXYLATION OF CINNAMIC ACID. Acta Bot. Neerl. 15: 394-405.

0595. Engelsma, G. 1967. PHENOL SYNTHESIS AND PHOTOMORPHOGENESIS. Philips
         Tech. Rev. 28: 101-110 (R).

0596. Engelsma, G. 1967. EFFECT OF CYCLOHEXIMIDE ON THE INACTIVATION OF
         PHENYLALANINE DEAMINASE IN GHERKIN SEEDLINGS. Naturwissenschaften
         54: 319-320.

0597. Engelsma, G. 1967. PHOTOINDUCTION OF PHENYLALANINE DEAMINASE IN GHERKIN
         SEEDLINGS I. EFFECT OF BLUE LIGHT. Planta 75: 207-219.

0598. Engelsma, G. 1967. PHOTOINDUCTION OF PHENYLALANINE DEAMINASE IN GHERKIN
         SEEDLINGS II. EFFECT OF RED AND FAR-RED LIGHT. Planta 77: 49-57.

0599. Engelsma, G. 1968. ZEITMESSUNG IN PFLANZEN. Umsch. Wiss. Tech. 23:
         727-728 (R).

0600. Engelsma, G. 1968. THE INFLUENCE OF LIGHT OF DIFFERENT SPECTRAL REGIONS
         ON THE SYNTHESIS OF PHENOLIC COMPOUNDS IN GHERKIN SEEDLINGS, IN RE-
         LATION TO PHOTOMORPHOGENESIS IV. MECHANISM OF FAR-RED ACTION. Acta
         Bot. Neerl. 17: 85-89.

0601. Engelsma, G. 1968. PHOTOINDUCTION OF PHENYLALANINE DEAMINASE IN GHERKIN
         SEEDLINGS III. EFFECTS OF EXCISION AND IRRADIATION OF ENZYME DEVELOP-
         MENT IN HYPOCOTYL SEGMENTS. Planta 82: 355-368.

0602. Engelsma, G. 1968. THE INFLUENCE OF LIGHT OF DIFFERENT SPECTRAL REGIONS
         ON THE SYNTHESIS OF PHENOLIC COMPOUNDS IN GHERKIN SEEDLINGS, IN
         RELATION TO PHOTOMORPHOGENESIS V. THE TEMPERATURE DEPENDENCE. Acta
         Bot. Neerl. 17: 499-505.

0603. Engelsma, G. 1969. THE INFLUENCE OF LIGHT OF DIFFERENT SPECTRAL REGIONS
         ON THE SYNTHESIS OF PEHNOLIC COMPOUNDS IN GHERKIN SEEDLINGS, IN
         RELATION TO PHOTOMORPHOGENESIS. VI. PHENOL SYNTHESIS AND PHOTO-
         PERIODISM. Acta Bot. Neerl. 18: 347-352.

0604. Engelsma, G. 1970. A COMPARATIVE INVESTIGATION OF THE CONTROL OF
         PHENYLALANINE AMMONIA-LYASE ACTIVITY IN GHERKIN AND RED CABBAGE
         HYPOCOTYLS. Acta Bot. Neerl. 19: 403-414.

0605. Engelsma, G. 1970. PHOTOINDUCTION OF PHENYLALANINE DEAMINASE IN
         GHERKIN SEEDLINGS IV. THE ROLE OF THE TEMPERATURE. Planta 90:
         133-141.

0606. Engelsma, G. 1972. A POSSIBLE ROLE OF MANGANESE IONS IN THE PHOTOIN-
         DUCTION OF PHENYLALANINE AMMONIA-LYASE. Proc. VI Int. Congr.
         Photobiol. Abstr. No. 168 (A).

0607. Engelsma, G. 1972. A POSSIBLE ROLE OF DIVALENT MANGANESE IONS IN THE PHOTOINDUCTION OF PHENYLALANINE AMMONIA-LYASE. Plant Physiol. 50: 599-602.

0608. Engelsma, G. 1974. ON THE MECHANISM OF THE PHOTOINDUCED CHANGES IN THE PHENYLALANINE AMMONIA-LYASE ACTIVITY IN GHERKIN HYPOCOTYLS. Proc. Eur. Annu. Symp. Plant Photomorphogenesis, (Antwerpen), pp. 57-59.

0609. Engelsma, G. 1974. ON THE MECHANISM OF THE CHANGES IN PHENYLALANINE AMMONIA-LYASE ACTIVITY INDUCED BY ULTRAVIOLET AND BLUE LIGHT IN GHERKIN HYPOCOTYLS. Plant Physiol. 54: 702-705.

0610. Enloe, A. 1959. PIGMENT TRANSFORMATION IN SOYBEAN COTYLEDONS. M.S. Thesis, Univ. California, Berkeley.

0611. Erez, A.; Samish, R.M.; Lavee, S. 1966. THE ROLE OF LIGHT IN LEAF AND FLOWER BUD BREAK OF THE PEACH *(PRUNUS PERSICA)*. Physiol. Plant. 19: 650-659.

0612. Erez, A.; Kadman-Zahavi, A. 1972. THE EFFECT OF HIGH ENERGY IRRADIATION ON SOME ENZYME SYSTEMS AND ETHYLENE PRODUCTION IN PEACH APICES. Proc. VI Int. Congr. Photobiol. Abstr. No. 174 (A).

0613. Erez, A.; Kadman-Zahavi, A. 1972. GROWTH OF PEACH PLANTS UNDER DIFFERENT FILTERED SUNLIGHT CONDITIONS. Physiol. Plant. 26: 210-214.

0614. Erner, Y.; Goren, R.; Monselise, S.P. 1972. INFLUENCE OF LIGHT OF DIFFERENT SPECTRAL COMPOSITIONS ON GROWTH AND METABOLISM OF CITRUS SEEDLINGS. Physiol. Plant. 27: 327-330.

0615. Ernst, A. 1906. DAS KEIMEN DER DIMORPHEN FRÜCHTCHEN VON *SYNEDRELLA NODIFLORA* (L.) GRTN. Ber. Dtsch. Bot. Ges. 24: 450-458.

0616. Esashi, Y. 1963. STUDIES ON THE FORMATION AND SPROUTING OF AERIAL TUBERS IN *BEGONIA EVANSIANA* ANDR. VIII. DUAL EFFECT ON TUBERIZATION OF NEAR INFRARED LIGHT GIVEN IN DARK PERIODS. Plant Cell Physiol. 4: 135-143.

0617. Esashi, Y.; Oda, Y. 1964. INHIBITORY EFFECT OF FAR-RED LIGHT ON THE FLOWERING OF *XANTHIUM PENSYLVANICUM*. Plant Cell Physiol. 5: 507-511.

0618. Esashi, Y. 1966. THE RELATION BETWEEN RED AND BLUE OR FAR-RED LIGHTS IN THE NIGHT-INTERRUPTION OF THE PHOTOPERIODIC TUBERIZATION IN *BEGONIA EVANSIANA*. Plant Cell Physiol. 7: 405-414.

0619. Esashi, Y. 1966. EFFECTS OF LIGHT QUALITY AND GAS CONDITION IN THE MAIN LIGHT PERIOD ON THE PHOTOPERIODIC TUBERIZATION OF *BEGONIA EVANSIANA*. Plant Cell Physiol. 7: 465-474.

0620. Esashi, Y.; Oda, Y. 1966. TWO LIGHT REACTIONS IN THE PHOTOPERIODIC CONTROL OF FLOWERING OF *LEMNA PERPUSILLA* AND *L. GIBBA*. Plant Cell Physiol. 7: 59-74.

0621. Esashi, Y. 1969. DIFFERENT ACTIONS OF RED AND BLUE OR FAR-RED LIGHTS IN THE PHOTOPERIODIC TUBERIZATION OF *BEGONIA EVANSIANA*. Plant Cell Physiol. 10: 349-356.

0622. Esashi, Y. 1969. THE RELATION BETWEEN LIGHT AND TEMPERATURE EFFECTS IN THE INDUCTION AND RELEASE OF DORMANCY IN THE AERIAL TUBER OF *BEGONIA EVANSIANA*. Plant Cell Physiol. 10: 583-595.

0623. Etzold, H. 1965. DER POLAROTROPISMUS UND PHOTOTROPISMUS DER CHLORONEMEN VON *DRYOPTERIS FILIX-MAS* (L.) SCHOTT. Planta 64: 254-280 (ENG Summary).

0624. Evans, L.T. 1964. SPECTRAL DEPENDENCE OF FLOWERING IN LONG-DAY PLANTS. Proc. IV Int. Congr. Photobiol., pp. 95-96 (A).

0625. Evans, L.T. 1965. RAPPORTEUR'S REPORT. Proc. IV Int. Congr. Photobiol. pp. 187-212 (R).

0626. Evans, L.T.; Borthwick, H.A.; Hendricks, S.B. 1965. INFLORESCENCE INITIATION IN *LOLIUM TEMULENTUM* L. VII. THE SPECTRAL DEPENDENCE OF INDUCTION. Aust. J. Biol. Sci. 18: 745-762.

0627. Evans, L.T.; Hendricks, S.B.; Borthwick, H.A. 1965. THE ROLE OF LIGHT IN SUPPRESSING HYPOCOTYL ELONGATION IN LETTUCE AND *PETUNIA*. Planta 64: 201-218.

0628. Evans, L.T.; King, R.W. 1969. ROLE OF PHYTOCHROME IN PHOTOPERIODIC INDUCTION OF *PHARBITIS NIL*. Z. Pflanzenphysiol. 60: 277-288 (GER Summary).

0629. Evans, L.T. 1971. FLOWER INDUCTION AND THE FLORIGEN CONCEPT. Annu. Rev. Plant Physiol. 22: 365-394 (R).

0630. Evans, L.T.; Allaway, W.G. 1972. ACTION SPECTRUM FOR THE OPENING OF *ALBIZIA JULIBRISSIN* PINNULES, AND THE ROLE OF PHYTOCHROME IN THE CLOSING MOVEMENTS OF PINNULES AND OF STOMATA OF *VICIA FABA*. Aust. J. Biol. Sci. 25: 885-893.

0631. Evenari, M.; Neumann, G. 1953. THE GERMINATION OF LETTUCE SEEDS. III. THE EFFECT OF LIGHT ON GERMINATION. Bull. Res. Counc. Isr. Sect. D: 3: 136-145.

0632. Evenari, M.; Neumann, G.; Stein, G. 1953. FACTORS MODIFYING THE INFLUENCE OF LIGHT ON GERMINATION. Nature (London) 172: 452-453.

0633. Evenari, M.; Stein, G. 1953. THE INFLUENCE OF LIGHT UPON GERMINATION. Experientia 9: 94-95 (R).

0634. Evenari, M.; Mayer, A.M. 1954. THE EFFECT OF AUXIN ON THE GERMINATION OF LETTUCE SEEDS. Bull. Res. Counc. Isr. Sect. D: 4: 81-82.

0635. Evenari, M.; Stein, G.; Neumann, G. 1954. THE ACTION OF LIGHT IN CONJUNCTION WITH THIOUREA ON GERMINATION. Proc. I Int. Congr. Photobiol. pp. 82-86.

0636. Evenari, M.; Neumann, G.; Klein, S. 1955. THE INFLUENCE OF RED AND INFRARED LIGHT ON THE RESPIRATION OF PHOTOBLASTIC SEEDS. Physiol. Plant. 8: 33-47.

0637. Evenari, M. 1956. SEED GERMINATION. *Radiation Biology: Visible and Near Visible Light.* Ed. A. Hollaender, III: 519-549 (R).

0638. Evenari, M. 1957. LES PROBLEMES PHYSIOLOGIQUES DE LA GERMINATION. Bull. Soc. Fr. Physiol. Veg. 3: 105-124.

0639. Evenari, M. 1957. THE PHYSIOLOGICAL ACTION AND BIOLOGICAL IMPORTANCE OF GERMINATION INHIBITORS. Symp. Soc. Exp. Biol. 11: 21-43 (R).

0640. Evenari, M.; Neumann, G.; Stein, G. 1957. ACTION OF BLUE LIGHT ON THE GERMINATION OF SEEDS. Nature (London) 180: 609-610.

0641. Evenari, M.; Neumann, G.; Blumenthal-Goldschmidt, S.; Mayer, A.M.; Poljakoff-Mayber, A. 1958. THE INFLUENCE OF GIBBERELLIC ACID AND KINETIN ON GERMINATION AND SEEDLING GROWTH OF LETTUCE. Bull. Res. Counc. Isr. Sect. D: 6: 65-72.

0642. Evenari, M. 1961. A SURVEY OF THE WORK DONE IN SEED PHYSIOLOGY BY THE DEPARTMENT OF BOTANY, HEBREW UNIVERSITY, JERUSALEM (ISRAEL). Proc. Int. Seed Test. Assoc. 26: 597-658 (R).

0643. Evenari, M. 1965. INTRODUCTORY LECTURE. *Recent Progress in Photobiology:* Proc. IV Int. Congr. Photobiol., Ed. E.J. Bowen, Academic Press, New York and London, pp. 161-186 (R).

0644. Evenari, M. 1965. LIGHT AND SEED DORMANCY. *Handbuch der Pflanzenphysiologie.* Ed. W. Ruhland, Berlin-Göttingen Heidelberg, Springer XV/2: 804-847 (R-D).

0645. Evenari, M. 1965. PHYSIOLOGY OF SEED DORMANCY, AFTER-RIPENING AND GERMINATION. Proc. Int. Seed Test. Assoc. 30: 49-71 (R).

0646. Everett, M.S.; Briggs, W.R. 1970. SOME SPECTRAL PROPERTIES OF PEA PHYTOCHROME *IN VIVO* AND *IN VITRO*. Plant Physiol. 45: 679-683.

0647. Everett, M.S.; Briggs, W.R.; Purves, W.K. 1970. KINETICS OF PHYTOCHROME PHOTOTRANSFORMATION. A RE-EXAMINATION. Plant Physiol. 45: 805-806.

0648. Everett, M. 1974. DOSE-RESPONSE CURVES FOR RADISH SEEDLING PHOTOTROP-ISM. Plant Physiol. 54: 222-225.

0649. Faivre, E. 1879. LE LATEX PENDANT L'ÉVOLUTION GERMINATIVE DU *TRAGOPOGON PORRIFOLIUS* EFFECTUÉE DANS LES CONDITIONS DIVERSES DE MILIEU EXTÉRIEUR. C.R. Acad. Sci. Ser. D: 88: 369-371.

0650. Falk, H.; Steiner, A.M. 1968. PHYTOCHROME-MEDIATED POLAROTROPISM: AN ELECTRON MICROSCOPICAL STUDY. Naturwissenschaften 55: 500.

0651. Famintzin, A. 1866. DIE WIRKUNG DES LICHTES UND DER DUNKELHEIT AUF DIE VERTHEILUNG DER CHLOROPHYLLKÖRNER IN DEN BLÄTTERN VON MNIUM SP? Bull. Acad. Imp. Sci. St. Petersbourg XI: 130-136 (also identical article in 1867 Jahrb. Wiss. Bot. 6: 49-54).

0652. Feierabend, J.; Pirson, A. 1966. DIE WIRKUNG DES LICHTS AUF DIE BILDUNG VON PHOTOSYNTHESEENZYMEN IN ROGGENKEIMLINGEN. Z. Pflanzenphysiol. 55: 235-245 (ENG Summary).

0653. Feierabend, J. 1967. REGULATIONSVORGÄNGE BEI DER BILDUNG VON PHOTOSYN-THESEENZYMEN. Umschau 15: 494-495 (A).

0654. Feierabend, J. 1969. DER EINFLUSS VON CYTOKININEN AUF DIE BILDUNG VON PHOTOSYNTHESEENZYMEN IN ROGGENKEIMLINGEN. Planta 84: 11-29 (ENG Summary).

0655. Felippe, G.M.; Dale, J.E. 1968. EFFECTS OF A GROWTH RETARDANT, CCC, ON LEAF GROWTH IN *PHASEOLUS VULGARIS*. Planta 80: 328-343.

0656. Felippe, G.M.; Lucas, N.M.C. 1971. ESTUDOS DE GERMINAÇÃO EM *POROPHYL-LUM LANCEOLATUM* DC. II. EFEITO DE LUZ VERMELHA, GA$_3$ E CCC. Hoehnea 1: 11-19.

0657. Feltner, K.C.; Vesecky, J.F. 1968. LIGHT QUALITY AND TEMPERATURE EFFECTS ON WEED SEED GERMINATION IN TWO KANSAS SOILS. Trans. Kans. Acad. Sci. 71: 7-12.

0658. Fernqvist, I.B.; Leopold, A.C. 1959. LIGHT EFFECTS ON ROOTING OF *PHASEOLUS* CUTTING. Plant Physiol. 34: Suppl.-4 (A).

0659. Fetzer, J. 1963. ÜBER DIE BETEILIGUNG ENERGIELIEFERNDER STOFFWECHSEL-PROZESSE AN DEN LICHTINDUZIERTEN CHLOROPLASTENBEWEGUNGEN VON *MOUGEOTIA*. Z. Bot. 51: 468-506 (ENG Summary).

0660. Filner, B.; Klein, A.O. 1968. CHANGES IN ENZYMATIC ACTIVITIES IN
ETIOLATED BEAN SEEDLING LEAVES AFTER A BRIEF ILLUMINATION. Plant
Physiol. 43: 1587-1596.

0660.5 Firn, R.D. 1974. ON THE RED LIGHT INHIBITION OF PEA INTERNODE ELONGA-
TION, WITH AN EMPHASIS ON THE ROLE OF XANTHOXIN. Plant Growth
Substances 1973, Proc. VIII Int. Conf. Growth Subst., Tokyo,
pp. 1225-1230.

0661. Fischer, W. 1963. UNTERSUCHUNGEN ÜBER DIE INVERSION DER SCHWACHLICHT-
BEWEGUNG DES MOUGEOTIA CHLOROPLASTEN. Z. Bot. 51: 348-387 (ENG
Summary).

0662. Fischer-Arnold, G. 1963. UNTERSUCHUNGEN ÜBER DIE CHLOROPLASTENBEWEGUNG
BEI VAUCHERIA SESSILIS. Protoplasma 56: 495-520.

0663. Fisher, R.W.; Miller, J.H. 1974. THE EFFECTS OF LIGHT ON ETHYLENE
INHIBITION OF SPORE GERMINATION IN THE FERN ONOCLEA SENSIBILIS.
Plant Physiol. 53: Suppl.-6 Abstr. No. 27 (A).

0664. Flammarion, C. 1895. ÉTUDE DE L'ACTION DES DIVERSES RADIATIONS DU
SPECTRE SOLAIRE SUR LA VÉGÉTATION. C.R. Acad. Sci. Ser. D. 121:
957-960 (also identical article in 1896 J. Agric. Prat. 1: 235-238).

0665. Flammarion, C. 1897. UEBER DIE WIRKUNG DER VERSCHIEDENEN STRAHLEN DES
SONNENSPEKTRUMS AUF DIE VEGETATION. Biedermann's Zentralkb. 26:
171-173 (A).

0666. Flammarion, C. 1898. PHYSICAL AND METEOROLOGICAL RESEARCHES, PRINCI-
PALLY ON SOLAR RAYS, MADE AT THE STATION OF AGRICULTURAL CLIMATOLOGY
AT THE OBSERVATORY OF JUVISY. Exp. St. Rec. 10: 103-114.

0667. Flammarion, C. 1898. REPORT ON THE WORK OF THE STATION OF AGRICULTURAL
CLIMATOLOGY AT JUVISY DURING 1897. Exp. St. Rec. 10: 613-616 (also
Abstr. Bull. Min. Agric. [Fr], 17: 775-811, 1898).

0668. Flammarion, C. 1901. RAPPORT SUR LES TRAVAUX DE LA STATION DE CLIMATO-
LOGIE AGRICOLE DE JUVISY PENDANT L'ANNÉE 1900. Bull. Min. Agric.
1901 No. 3: 1-3.

0669. Flemion, F. 1959. EFFECT OF TEMPERATURE, LIGHT AND GIBBERELLIC ACID
ON STEM ELONGATION AND LEAF DEVELOPMENT IN PHYSIOLOGICALLY DWARFED
SEEDLINGS OF PEACH AND RHODOTYPOS. Contrib. Boyce Tompson Inst. 20:
57-70.

0670. Fletcher, L.A. 1929. A PRELIMINARY STUDY OF THE FACTORS AFFECTING THE
RED COLOR ON APPLES. Proc. Am. Soc. Hortic. Sci. 26: 191-196.

0671. Fletcher, R.A.; Zalik, S. 1964. EFFECT OF LIGHT QUALITY ON GROWTH AND FREE INDOLEACETIC ACID CONTENT IN *PHASEOLUS VULGARIS*. Plant Physiol. 39: 328-331.

0672. Fletcher, R.A.; Peterson, R.L.; Zalik, S. 1965. EFFECT OF LIGHT QUALITY ON ELONGATION, ADVENTITIOUS ROOT PRODUCTION AND THE RELATION OF CELL NUMBER AND CELL SIZE TO BEAN SEEDLING ELONGATION. Plant Physiol. 40: 541-548.

0673. Fletcher, R.A.; Zalik, S. 1965. EFFECT OF LIGHT OF SEVERAL SPECTRAL BANDS ON THE METABOLISM OF RADIOACTIVE 1AA IN BEAN SEEDLINGS. Plant Physiol. 40: 549-552.

0674. Flint, L.H. 1934. LIGHT IN RELATION TO DORMANCY AND GERMINATION IN LETTUCE SEED. Science 80: 38-40.

0675. Flint, L.H. 1934. LIGHT SENSITIVITY IN RELATION TO DORMANCY IN LETTUCE SEED. C.R. Assoc. Int. Essais. Semences 6: 487-489.

0676. Flint, L.H. 1935. SENSITIVITY OF DORMANT LETTUCE SEED TO LIGHT AND TEMPERATURE. J. Wash. Acad. Sci. 25: 95-96.

0677. Flint, L.H.; McAlister, E.D. 1935. WAVELENGTHS OF RADIATION IN THE VISIBLE SPECTRUM INHIBITING THE GERMINATION OF LIGHT-SENSITIVE LETTUCE SEED. Smithson. Misc. Collect. 94(5): 1-11.

0678. Flint, L.H. 1936. THE ACTION OF RADIATION OF SPECIFIC WAVELENGTHS IN RELATION TO THE GERMINATION OF LIGHT-SENSITIVE LETTUCE SEED. C.R. Assoc. Int. Essais. Semences 8: 1-4.

0679. Flint, L.H.; McAlister, E.D. 1937. WAVE LENGTHS OF RADIATION IN THE VISIBLE SPECTRUM PROMOTING THE GERMINATION OF LIGHT-SENSITIVE LETTUCE SEED. Smithson. Misc. Collect. 96(2): 1-8.

0680. Flint, L.H. 1938. ON THE ORIGIN OF LIGHT-SENSITIVITY IN SEEDS. Proc. Summer Conf. Spectros. Its Appl.: V: 116-117.

0681. Flint, L.H. 1938. IMMEDIATE PROBLEMS IN THE LIGHT-SENSITIVITY OF PLANTS. Proc. Summer Conf. Spectros. Its Appl.: V: 118-122 (R).

0682. Flint, L.H.; Moreland, C.F. 1939. RESPONSE OF LETTUCE SEEDLINGS TO 7600Å RADIATION. Am. J. Bot. 26: 231-233.

0683. Flint, L.H.; Moreland, C.F. 1942. A COMPARISON OF THE EFFECTS OF GREEN LIGHT AND OF RED LIGHT ON THE SIMPLE-LEAF DEVELOPMENT OF INTACT AND DECAPITATED BEAN PLANTS. Plant Physiol. 17: 677-681.

0684. Flint, L.H. 1944. LIGHT AND THE ELONGATION OF THE MESOCOTYL IN CORN. Plant Physiol. 19: 537-543.

0685. Flohrs, H.; Haupt, W.   1971.   TAGESPERIODISCHE EMPFINDLICHKEITSSCHWANKUN-
       GEN DER LICHTINDUZIERTEN CHLOROPLASTENBEWEGUNG VON *MOUGEOTIA*.   Z.
       Pflanzenphysiol. 65: 65-69 (ENG Summary).

0686. Fondeville, J.C.; Borthwick, H.A.; Hendricks, S.B.   1966.   LEAFLET MOVE-
       MENT OF *MIMOSA PUDICA* L. INDICATIVE OF PHYTOCHROME ACTION.   Planta
       69: 357-364.

0687. Fondeville, J.C.; Schneider, M.J.; Borthwick, H.A.; Hendricks, S.B.
       1967.   PHOTOCONTROL OF *MIMOSA PUDICA* L. LEAF MOVEMENT.   Planta 75:
       228-238.

0688. Fondeville, J.C.   1969.   UNE PLANTE COBAYE: LA SENSITIVE.   Nucleus
       (Paris) 10: 180-190 (R).

0689. Förster, K.   1927.   DIE WIRKUNG ÄUSSERER FAKTOREN AUF ENTWICKLUNG UND
       GESTALTBILDUNG BEI *MARCHANTIA POLYMORPHA*.   Planta 3: 325-390.

0690. Fortanier, E.J.   1954.   SOME OBSERVATIONS ON THE INFLUENCE OF SPECTRAL
       REGIONS OF LIGHT ON STEM ELONGATION, FLOWER BUD ELONGATION, FLOWER
       BUD OPENING AND LEAF MOVEMENT IN *ARACHIS HYPOGEA* L.   Meded. Land-
       bouwhogesch. Wageningen 54: 103-114.

0691. Forward, R.; Davenport, D.   1968.   RED AND FAR-RED LIGHT EFFECTS ON A
       SHORT-TERM BEHAVIORAL RESPONSE OF A DINOFLAGELLATE.   Science 161:
       1028-1029.

0692. Forward, R.B. Jr.   1970.   CHANGE IN THE PHOTORESPONSE ACTION SPECTRUM OF
       THE DINOFLAGELLATE *GYRODINIUM DORSUM* KOFOID BY RED AND FAR-RED LIGHT.
       Planta 92: 248-258.

0693. Forward, R.B. Jr.; Davenport, D.   1970.   THE CIRCADIAN RHYTHM OF A
       BEHAVIORAL PHOTORESPONSE IN THE DINOFLAGELLATE *GYRODINIUM DORSUM*.
       Planta 92: 259-266.

0693.5 Forward, R.B. Jr.   1973.   NEUROHUMOR EFFECTS ON DINOFLAGELLATE PHOTO-
       TAXIS.   Proc. I Annu. Meet. Am. Soc. Photobiol., p. 184, Abstr. No.
       ThPM-E8 (A).

0694. Forward, R.B. Jr.   1973.   PHOTOTAXIS IN A DINOFLAGELLATE: ACTION SPECTRA
       AS EVIDENCE FOR A TWO-PIGMENT SYSTEM.   Planta 111: 167-178.

0695. Fosket, E.B.; Briggs, W.R.   1970.   PHOTOSENSITIVE SEED GERMINATION IN
       CATALPA SPECIOSA.   Bot. Gaz. (Chicago) 131: 167-172.

0696. Fox, L.R.; Hillman, W.S.   1968.   PHOTORESPONSE, PHYTOCHROME CONTENT,
       AND DE-ETIOLATION OF PEA STEM TISSUE.   Plant Physiol. 43: Suppl.-14
       (A).

0697. Fox, L.R.; Hillman, W.S. 1968. RESPONSE OF TISSUE WITH DIFFERENT PHYTO-
CHROME CONTENTS TO VARIOUS INITIAL PHOTOSTATIONARY STATES. Plant
Physiol. 43: 823-826.

0698. Fox, L.R.; Hillman, W.S. 1968. DIFFERENCES IN PHOTORESPONSE AND PHYTO-
CHROME SPECTROPHOTOMETRY BETWEEN ETIOLATED AND DE-ETIOLATED PEA STEM
TISSUE. Plant Physiol. 43: 1799-1804.

0699. Fox, L.R.; Hillman, W.S. 1970. THE ISOLATION AND PURIFICATION OF
'P$_{fr}$-KILLER' FROM ETIOLATED PEAS. Plant Physiol. 46: Suppl.-3
Abstr. No. 13 (A).

0700. Fraikin, G.Ya.; Verkhoturov, V.N.; Rubin, L.B. 1973. DISCOVERY OF
PHYTOCHROME SYSTEM IN YEAST *CANDIDA GUILLIERMONDII*. Vestn. Mosk.
Univ. Ser. Biol. Pochvoved. Geol. Geogr. 28: 54-56 (RUS) (ENG
Summary).

0701. Frank, B. 1871. UEBER LICHTWÄRTS SICH BEWEGENDE CHLOROPHYLL-KÖRNER.
Bot. Ztg. 29: 225-232.

0702. Frank, S. 1951. THE RELATION BETWEEN CAROTENOID AND CHLOROPHYLL PIG-
MENTS IN *AVENA* COLEOPTILES. Arch. Biochem. 30: 52-61.

0703. Frankland, B.; Smith, H. 1967. TEMPERATURE AND OTHER FACTORS AFFECTING
CHLORAMPHENICOL STIMULATION OF THE GERMINATION OF LIGHT-SENSITIVE
LETTUCE SEEDS. Planta 77: 354-366.

0704. Frankland, B.; Kendrick, R.E. 1968. ROLE OF PHYTOCHROME IN PHOTOCONTROL
OF SEED GERMINATION IN *AMARANTHUS CAUDATUS*. Proc. V. Int. Congr.
Photobiol., p. 62 (A).

0705. Frankland, B. 1971. VARIATION IN LIGHT SENSITIVITY IN SEED OF *SINAPIS
ARVENSIS*. Proc. Eur. Annu. Symp. Plant Photomorphogenesis, (Athens),
p. 22 (A).

0706. Frankland, B. 1972. KINETICS OF PHYTOCHROME DECAY IN SEEDLING TISSUE.
Proc. VI Int. Congr. Photobiol. Abstr. No. 158 (A).

0707. Frankland, B. 1972. BIOSYNTHESIS AND DARK TRANSFORMATIONS OF PHYTO-
CHROME. *Phytochrome*. Ed. K. Mitrakos and W. Shropshire, Jr.,
Academic Press, New York and London, pp. 195-225 (R).

0708. Fredericq, H. 1963. FACTORS INFLUENCING THE INHIBITION OF FLOWERING OF
SHORT DAY PLANTS BY FAR-RED LIGHT APPLIED AT THE BEGINNING OF THE
NIGHT. Plant. Physiol. 38: Suppl.-48 (A).

0709. Fredericq, H. 1963. FLOWER FORMATION IN *KALANCHOË BLOSSFELDIANA* BY
VERY SHORT PHOTOPERIODS UNDER LIGHT OF DIFFERENT QUALITY. Nature
(London) 198: 101-102.

0710. Fredericq, H. 1964. INFLUENCE FORMATRICE DE LA LUMIÈRE ROUGE-FONCÉ SUR
LE DÉVELOPPEMENT DES THALLES DE *MARCHANTIA POLYMORPHA* L. Bull. Soc.
R. Bot. Belg. 98: 67-76.

0711. Fredericq, H. 1964. CONDITIONS DETERMINING EFFECTS OF FAR-RED AND RED
IRRADIATIONS ON FLOWERING RESPONSE OF *PHARBITIS NIL*. Plant Physiol.
39: 812-816.

0712. Fredericq, H. 1965. ACTION OF RED AND FAR-RED LIGHT AT THE END OF THE
SHORT DAY, AND IN THE MIDDLE OF THE NIGHT, ON FLOWER INDUCTION IN
KALANCHOË BLOSSFELDIANA. Biol. Jaarb. 33: 66-91.

0713. Fredericq, H. 1966. INFLUENCE FORMATRICE DE COURTS ÉCLAIREMENTS A LA
FIN DE LA PHOTOPÉRIODE SUR LA CROISSANCE DE *MARCHANTIA POLYMORPHA*
L., DE *LUNULARIA CRUCIATA* L. ET DE *SELAGINELLA KRAUSSIANA* (KUNZE)
A. BRAU. Bull. Soc. R. Bot. Belg. 99: 91-106 (ENG Summary).

0714. Fredericq, H. 1966. ACTION FORMATRICE DE LA LUMIÈRE ROUGE-FONCÉ ET
PHOTORÉVERSIBILITÉ À LA FIN DE LA PHOTOPÉRIODE, CHEZ *KALANCHOË
BLOSSFELDIANA* ET CHEZ *MARCHANTIA POLYMORPHA*. Congr. Colloq. Univ.
Liege 38: 213-222.

0715. Fredericq, H.; DeGreef, J. 1966. RED (R) FAR-RED (FR) PHOTOREVERSIBLE
CONTROL OF GROWTH AND CHLOROPHYLL CONTENT IN LIGHT-GROWN THALLI OF
MARCHANTIA POLYMORPHA L. Plant Physiol. 41: Suppl.-15 (A).

0716. Fredericq, H.; DeGreef, J. 1966. RED (R), FAR-RED (FR) PHOTOREVERSIBLE
CONTROL OF GROWTH AND CHLOROPHYLL CONTENT IN LIGHT-GROWN THALLI OF
MARCHANTIA POLYMORPHA L. Naturwissenschaften 13: 337.

0717. Fredericq, H.; DeGreef, J.A. 1966. INFLUENCE RÉVERSIBLE PAR LA LUMIÈRE
ROUGE-CLAIR, DE COURTS ÉCLAIREMENTS ROUGE-FONCÉ A LA FIN DE LA
PHOTOPÉRIODE, SUR LA CROISSANCE ET LA TENEUR EN CHLOROPHYLLES DE
MARCHANTIA POLYMORPHA L. Photochem. Photobiol. 5: 431-440 (ENG
Summary).

0718. Fredericq, H.; DeGreef, J. 1967. MORPHOGENESIS AND CHLOROPHYLL METABO-
LISM OF *MARCHANTIA POLYMORPHA* L. IN RESPONSE TO SHORT IRRADIATIONS
OF VARIOUS SPECTRAL COMPOSITION. Proc. Eur. Annu. Symp. Plant
Photomorphogenesis, (Hvar) pp. 137-140.

0719. Fredericq, H.; DeGreef, J.A. 1968. THE ACTION OF TERMINAL IRRADIATIONS
       WITH DIFFERENT RED/FAR-RED RATIOS ON GROWTH AND CHLOROPHYLL CONTENT
       OF THE LIVERWORT *MARCHANTIA POLYMORPHA* L. Proc. V Int. Congr.
       Photobiol. p. 63 (A).

0720. Fredericq, H.; DeGreef, J. 1968. PHOTOMORPHOGENIC AND CHLOROPHYLL
       STUDIES IN THE BRYOPHYTE *MARCHANTIA POLYMORPHA* I. EFFECT OF RED, FAR-
       RED IRRADIATIONS IN SHORT AND LONG-TERM EXPERIMENTS. Physiol. Plant.
       21: 346-359.

0721. Fredericq, H.; DeGreef, J.A. 1971. PHOTOMORPHOGENIC RESPONSES IN
       "MARCHANTIA POLYMORPHA" CONTROLLED BY PHYTOCHROME. Biol. Jaarb. 39:
       338-342.

0722. Fredericq, H.; DeGreef, J.A. 1972. CONTROL OF VEGETATIVE GROWTH BY RED,
       FAR-RED REVERSIBLE PHOTOREACTIONS IN HIGHER AND LOWER PLANT-SYSTEMS.
       Phytochrome. Ed. K. Mitrakos and W. Shropshire, Jr., Academic Press,
       New York and London, pp. 319-346 (R).

0723. Fredericq, H.; DeGreef, J. 1974. PHOTOCONTROL OF ATP-POOLS IN GERMINAT-
       ING *KALANCHOË* SEEDS AND SENESCING *MARCHANTIA* TISSUE. Proc. Eur.
       Annu. Symp. Plant Photomorphenesis, (Antwerpen) pp. 86-89.

0724. French, C.J.; Pecket, R.C.; Smith, H. 1973. EFFECT OF LIGHT AND EXO-
       GENOUSLY APPLIED PRECURSORS ON AMARANTHIN SYNTHESIS IN *AMARANTHUS*
       CAUDATUS. Phytochemistry 12: 2887-2891.

0725. French, C.J. 1974. *IN VITRO* INACTIVATION OF PHENYLALANINE AMMONIA-LYASE
       IN GHERKIN SEEDLINGS IN RELATION TO PHOTOCONTROL. Proc. Eur. Annu.
       Symp. Plant Photomorphogenesis, (Antwerpen) pp. 75-79.

0726. Frey-Wyssling, A.; Bäbler, S. 1957. ZUR BIOCHEMIE DES GEWÄCHSHAUSTA-
       BAKS. Experientia 13: 399-400.

0727. Frick, H.; Mohr, H. 1972. ON THE PHYSIOLOGICAL EQUIVALENCE OF PHYTO-
       CHROME IN GREEN AND ETIOLATED *LEMNA MINOR*. Proc. VI Int. Congr.
       Photobiol. Abstr. No. 164 (A).

0728. Frick, H.; Mohr, H. 1973. PHYTOCHROME-MEDIATED GROWTH RESPONSES IN
       GREEN AND ETIOLATED *LEMNA MINOR*. Planta 109: 281-292.

0729. Friederich, K.-E. 1968. UNTERSUCHUNGEN ZUR ENERGETIK DER PHYTOCHROMIN-
       DUZIERTEN PHOTOMORPHOGENESE DES SENFKEIMLINGS *(SINAPIS ALBA* L.).
       Ph.D. Thesis, Univ. Freiburg, Germany.

0730. Friederich, K.-E. 1969. UNTERSUCHUNGEN ZUR ENERGETIK DER PHYTOCHROMIN-
 DUZIERTEN PHOTOMORPHOGENESE DES SENFKEIMLINGS *(SINAPIS ALBA* L.).
 Planta 84: 81-93 (ENG Summary).

0731. Friend, D.J.C. 1964. PROMOTION OF FLOWERING OF WHEAT BY FAR-RED
 RADIATION. Plant Physiol. 39: Suppl.-49 (A).

0732. Friend, D.J.C. 1964. THE PROMOTION OF FLORAL INITIATION OF WHEAT BY
 FAR-RED RADIATION. Physiol. Plant. 17: 909-920.

0733. Friend, D.J.C. 1965. INTERACTION OF RED AND FAR-RED RADIATIONS WITH
 THE VERNALIZATION PROCESS IN WINTER RYE. Can. J. Bot. 43: 161-170.

0734. Friend, D.J.C. 1968. PHOTOPERIODIC RESPONSES OF *BRASSICA CAMPESTRIS*
 CV CERES, FACULTATIVE LONG-DAY PLANT WITH SEEDLING SENSITIVITY TO A
 SINGLE INDUCTIVE PHOTOPERIOD. Plant Physiol. 43: Suppl.-22 (A).

0735. Friend, D.J.C. 1968. PROMOTION OF FLOWERING IN *BRASSICA CAMPESTRIS* CV
 CERES, BY LONG PERIODS OF HIGH ENERGY IRRADIATION AT 710-729 NM.
 Proc. V Int. Congr. Photobiol. p. 61 (A).

0736. Friend, D.J.C. 1968. PHOTOPERIODIC RESPONSES OF *BRASSICA CAMPESTRIS* L.
 CV CERES. Physiol. Plant. 21: 990-1002.

0737. Friend, D.J.C. 1968. SPECTRAL REQUIREMENTS FOR FLOWER INITIATION IN TWO
 LONG-DAY PLANTS, RAPE *(BRASSICA CAMPESTRIS* CV CERES), AND SPRING
 WHEAT *(TRITICUM* X *AESTIVUM)*. Physiol. Plant. 21: 1185-1195.

0738. Friend, D.J.C. 1974. POTENTIATION OF PHOTOPERIODIC SENSITIVITY IN THE
 SHORT DAY PLANT *PHARBITIS*. Proc. Am. Soc. Photobiol. 2: 108 Abstr.
 No. THAM-D10 (A).

0739. Frosch, S. 1971. ENDOGENOUS RHYTHMICITY AND PHYTOCHROME CONTROL OF
 ENZYMES INVOLVED IN ENERGY METABOLISM IN *CHENOPODIUM RUBRUM* L.
 Proc. Eur. Annu. Symp. Plant Photomorphogenesis (Athens), p. 23 (A).

0740. Frosch, S.; Wagner, E. 1973. ENDOGENOUS RHYTHMICITY AND ENERGY TRANS-
 DUCTION. II. PHYTOCHROME ACTION AND THE CONDITIONING OF RHYTHMICITY
 OF ADENYLATE KINASE, NAD-AND-NADP-LINKED GLYCERALDEHYDE-3-PHOSPHATE
 DEHYDROGENASE IN *CHENOPODIUM RUBRUM* BY TEMPERATURE AND LIGHT INTEN-
 SITY CYCLES DURING GERMINATION. Can. J. Bot. 51: 1521-1528.

0741. Frosch, S.; Wagner, E. 1973. ENDOGENOUS RHYTHMICITY AND ENERGY TRANS-
 DUCTION. III. TIME COURSE OF PHYTOCHROME ACTION IN ADENYLATE KINASE,
 NAD-AND NADP-LINKED GLYCERALDEHYDE-3-PHOSPHATE DEHYDROGENASE IN
 CHENOPODIUM RUBRUM. Can. J. Bot. 51: 1529-1535.

0742. Frosch, S.; Wagner, E.; Mohr, H. 1974. CONTROL BY PHYTOCHROME OF THE
        LEVEL OF NICOTINAMIDE NUCLEOTIDES IN THE COTYLEDONS OF THE MUSTARD
        SEEDLING. Z. Naturforsch. Teil C: 29: 392-398.

0743. Fry, K.T.; Mumford, F.E. 1971. ISOLATION AND PARTIAL CHARACTERIZATION
        OF A CHROMOPHORE-PEPTIDE FRAGMENT FROM PEPSIN DIGESTS OF PHYTOCHROME.
        Biochem. Biophys. Res. Commun. 45: 1466-1473.

0744. Fry, K.T.; Mumford, F.E. 1972. ISOLATION AND CHARACTERIZATION OF A
        CHROMOPHORE-PEPTIDE FRAGMENT FROM PHYTOCHROME. Plant Physiol. 49:
        Suppl.-53, Abstr. No. 295 (A).

0745. Fujii, R. 1957. EFFECT OF LIGHT ON THE GROWTH OF HIGHER PLANTS RED AND
        NEAR INFRA-RED ON THE *VIGNA* SEEDLING. Seiri Seitai 7: 79-86 (JAP)
        (ENG Summary).

0746. Fujii, R. 1962. INFLUENCE OF METAL IONS OF THE ELONGATION OF LIGHT-
        TREATED BEAN HYPOCOTYLS. Bot. Mag. 75: 176-184.

0747. Fujii, T.; Isikawa, S.; Nakagawa, A. 1960. THE EFFECTS OF GIBBERELLIN
        ON THE GERMINATION OF THE SEEDS OF *SEDUM KAMTSCHATICUM* FISCH. Bot.
        Mag. 73: 404-411.

0748. Fujii, T.; Isikawa, S. 1961. THE EFFECTS OF TEMPERATURE AFTER THE
        LIGHT-EXPOSURE ON THE GERMINATION OF *OENOTHERA* SEEDS. Bot. Mag. 74:
        414-418.

0749. Fujii, T. 1962. STUDIES ON PHOTOPERIODIC RESPONSES INVOLVED IN THE
        GERMINATION OF *ERAGROSTIS* SEEDS. Bot. Mag. 75: 56-62.

0750. Fujii, T.; Isikawa, S. 1962. EFFECTS OF AFTER-RIPENING ON PHOTOPERIODIC
        CONTROL OF SEED GERMINATION IN *ERAGROSTIS FERRUGINEA* BEAUV. Bot.
        Mag. 75: 296-301.

0751. Fujii, T. 1963. ON THE ANAEROBIC PROCESS INVOLVED IN THE PHOTOPERIODI-
        CALLY INDUCED GERMINATION OF *ERAGROSTIS* SEED. Plant Cell Physiol.
        4: 357-359.

0752. Fujii, T. 1964. PHYSIOLOGY OF LIGHT GERMINATION. Bot. Mag. 77: 146-
        154 (JAP) (R).

0753. Fujii, T.; Suzuki, S. 1964. EFFECT OF PURINE AND PYRIMIDINE DERIVATIVES
        ON THE PHOTOPERIODICALLY INDUCED GERMINATION OF *ERAGOSTRIS* SEEDS.
        Bot. Mag. 77: 375-380.

0754. Fujii, T.; Kondo, N. 1969. CHANGES IN THE LEVELS OF NICOTINAMIDE
        NUCLEOTIDES AND IN ACTIVITIES OF NADP-DEPENDENT DEHYDROGENASES AFTER
        A BRIEF ILLUMINATION OF RED LIGHT. Dev. Growth Differ. 11: 40-45.

0755. Fukshanskii, L.Ya.; Gammerman, A. Ya. 1970. ANALYTICAL INVESTIGATION OF THE INTERACTIONS OF PHOTORECEPTIVE ENERGETICS AND REGULATORY SYSTEMS IN HIGHER PLANTS. Bioki-beretika. Models of Biosystem. Mater. IV. Ykrainskii Respublikanskii Scientific Conf., Kiev. (RUS) (not obtained).

0756. Funke, G.L. 1931. ON THE INFLUENCE OF LIGHT OF DIFFERENT WAVELENGTHS ON THE GROWTH OF PLANTS. Recl. Trav. Bot. Neerl. 28: 431-585.

0757. Funke, G.L. 1932. OVER DEN INVLOED VAN LICHT VAN VERSCHILLENDE GOLF-LENGTE OP DE ONTWIKKELING VAN PLANTEN. Natuurwet. Tijdschr. (Ghent) 14: 68-69 (A).

0758. Funke, G.L. 1933. OVER DEN GROEI VAN PLANTEN IN VERSCHILLEND GEKLEURD LICHT. Natuurwet. Tijdschr. (Ghent) 15: 209-214.

0759. Funke, G.L. 1936. PROEVEN OVER PHOTOPERIODICITEIT BIJ VERSCHILLEND GEKLEURD LICHT. Biol. Jaarb. 3: 225-261 (ENG Summary).

0760. Funke, G.L. 1936. OVER HET KWEEKEN VAN PLANTEN BIJ NEONLICHT. Meded. Landbouwhogesch. Opzoekingsstn. Staat Gent 4: 67-86 (ENG Summary).

0761. Funke, G.L. 1937. PROEVEN OVER PHOTOPERIODICITEIT BIJ VERSCHILLEND GEKLEURD LICHT II. Biol. Jaarb. 4: 345-359 (ENG Summary).

0762. Funke, G.L.; Hubert, B. 1937. OVER HET KWEEKEN VAN PLANTEN BIJ NEON-LICHT II. Meded. Landbouwhogesch. Opzoekingsstn. Staat Gent 5: 30-44 (ENG Summary).

0763. Funke, G.L. 1938. PROEVEN OVER PHOTOPERIODICITEIT BIJ VERSCHILLEND GEKLEURD LICHT III. Biol. Jaarb. 5: 404-424 (ENG Summary).

0764. Funke, G.L. 1939. LE PHOTOPÉRIODISME. Compt. Rend. Congres A.F.A.S. Liege, pp. 1003-1006 (R).

0765. Funke, G.L. 1939. PROEVEN OVER PHOTOPERIODICITEIT BIJ VERSCHILLEND GEKLEURD LICHT IV. Biol. Jaarb. 6: 351-376 (ENG Summary).

0766. Funke, G.L. 1941. THE PHOTOPERIODIC RESPONSES OF *ANTHEMIS TINCTORIA* IN DIFFERENT RANGES OF WAVELENGTH. Proc. K. Nedn. Akad. Wet. Ser. C: 44: 989-992.

0767. Funke, G.L. 1943. OBSERVATIONS ON THE FLOWERING PHOTOPERIODICITY. Recl. Trav. Bot. Neerl. 40: 393-412.

0768. Funke, G.L. 1944. DE FORMATIEVE INVLOED VAN HET LICHT OP PLANTEN. Publ. by Noorduyn & Zoon, Gorinchem. referred to by Meijer, G. (1959). The Spectral Dependence of Flowering and Elongation, Thesis, State Univ., Utrecht (not obtained).

0769. Funke, G.L.   1946.   THE FLOWERING PHOTOPERIODICITY OF THE *CRUCIFERAE*.
        Biol. Jaarb. 13: 270-276.

0770. Funke, G.L.   1948.   THE PHOTOPERIODICITY OF FLOWERING UNDER SHORT DAY
        WITH SUPPLEMENTAL LIGHT OF DIFFERENT WAVE LENGTHS, *Vernalization and
        Photoperiodism*, a symposium, Lotsya 1: 79-82 Chronica Botanica Co.,
        Waltham, Mass. (R).

0771. Furuya, M.; Galston, A.W.   1959.   EFFECT OF PRE-INCUBATION WITH MANGANOUS
        ION OR WITH 2,4-DICHLOROPHENOL ON THE SUBSEQUENT ACTIVITY OF THE
        3-INDOLEACETIC ACID (IAA) OXIDASE OF PEAS.   Proc. IX Int. Bot.
        Congr., p. 127 (A).

0772. Furuya, M.; Thomas, R.G.   1962.   CONTROL OF BIOSYNTHESIS OF KAEMPFEROL
        COMPLEXES AND OF GROWTH BY RED AND FAR-RED LIGHT IN ETIOLATED PEAS.
        Plant Physiol. 39: Suppl.-28, Abstr. No. 752 (A).

0773. Furuya, M.; Hillman, W.S.   1964.   OBSERVATIONS ON SPECTROPHOTOMETRICALLY
        ASSAYABLE PHYTOCHROME IN ETIOLATED PEAS.   Plant Physiol. 39:
        Suppl.-50 (A).

0774. Furuya, M.; Hillman, W.S.   1964.   OBSERVATIONS ON SPECTROPHOTOMETRICALLY
        ASSAYABLE PHYTOCHROME *IN VIVO* IN ETIOLATED *PISUM* SEEDLINGS.   Planta
        63: 31-42.

0775. Furuya, M.; Thomas, R.G.   1964.   FLAVONOID COMPLEXES IN *PISUM SATIVUM*
        II. EFFECTS OF RED AND FAR-RED LIGHT ON BIOSYNTHESIS OF KAEMPFEROL
        COMPLEXES AND ON GROWTH OF ETIOLATED PLUMULES.   Plant Physiol. 39:
        634-642.

0776. Furuya, M.; Torrey, J.G.   1964.   EFFECT OF RED AND FAR-RED LIGHT ON
        AUXIN-INDUCED LATERAL ROOT INITIATION IN ISOLATED PEA ROOTS.   Proc.
        IV Int. Congr. Photobiol., p. 96 (A).

0777. Furuya, M.; Torrey, J.G.   1964.   THE REVERSIBLE INHIBITION BY RED AND
        FAR-RED LIGHT OF AUXIN-INDUCED LATERAL ROOT INITIATION ON ISOLATED
        PEA ROOTS.   Plant Physiol. 39: 987-991.

0778. Furuya, M.; Hopkins, W.G.; Hillman, W.S.   1965.   EFFECTS OF METAL-
        COMPLEXING AND SULFHYDRYL COMPOUNDS ON NONPHOTOCHEMICAL PHYTOCHROME
        CHANGES *IN VIVO*.   Arch. Biochem. Biophys. 112: 180-186.

0779. Furuya, M.   1966.   LIGHT, PHYTOCHROME, DIFFERENTIATION GROWTH.   Nature
        (Shizen) 21: 17-25 (JAP) (R).

0780. Furuya, M.   1966.   PHYTOCHROME - GROWTH AND DIFFERENTIATION OF PLANTS.
        Chem. Reg. Plants 1: 111-121 (JAP) (R).

0781. Furuya, M. 1966. PHYTOCHROME - EXTRACTION, PURIFICATION AND CHEMICAL STRUCTURE. Nature (Shizen) 21: 24-32 (JAP) (R).

0782. Furuya, M.; Hillman, W.S. 1966. RAPID DESTRUCTION OF THE P_{fr} FORM OF PHYTOCHROME BY A SUBSTANCE IN EXTRACTS OF *PISUM* TISSUE. Plant Physiol. 41: 1242-1244.

0782.5 Furuya, M.; Ito, M.; Sugai, M. 1967. PHOTOMORPHOGENESIS IN *PTERIS VITTATA*. Jikken Keitaigaku Shi 21: 398-408 (JAP) (ENG Summary).

0783. Furuya, M.; Pjon, C.J.; Ohno, Y. 1967. THE SPECTROPHOTOMETRIC VERSUS THE PHYSIOLOGICAL STATUS OF PHYTOCHROME IN RICE SEEDLINGS. Proc. vii Int. Congr. Biochem. (Tokyo) 968, Abstr. No. J-86 (A).

0784. Furuya, M. 1968. BIOCHEMISTRY AND PHYSIOLOGY OF PHYTOCHROME. *Progress in Phytochemistry,* Ed. L. Reinhold and Y. Liwschitz, Wiley-Interscience, New York 1: 347-405.

0785. Furuya, M.; Manabe, K. 1969. *IN VITRO* NONPHOTOCHEMICAL TRANSFORMATION OF PHYTOCHROME IN *PISUM*. Proc. XI Int. Bot. Congr., p. 66 (A).

0786. Furuya, M.; Pjon, C.J.; Fujii, T.; Ito, M. 1969. PHYTOCHROME ACTION IN *ORYZA SATIVA* L. III. THE SEPARATION OF PHOTOPERCEPTIVE SITE AND GROWING ZONE IN COLEOPTILES, AND AUXIN TRANSPORT AS EFFECTOR SYSTEM. Dev., Growth Differ. 11: 62-76.

0787. Furuya, M.; Suzuki, H. 1969. PHYTOCHROME. Seibutsu Butsuri 9: 11-20 (JAP) (R).

0788. Furuya, M.; Masuda, Y.; Yamamoto, R. 1972. EFFECTS OF ENVIRONMENTAL FACTORS ON MECHANICAL PROPERTIES OF THE CELL WALL IN RICE COLEOPTILES. Dev. Growth Differ. 14: 95-105.

0789. Galatis, B.; Mitrakos, K. 1974. LEAF CELL MICROBODIES OF *VIGNA SINENSIS* GROWN IN DARK OR CONTINUOUS FAR-RED ILLUMINATION. Proc. Eur. Annu. Symp. Plant Photomorphogenesis (Antwerpen), pp. 97-102.

0790. Galmiche, J.M. 1967. INCORPORATION DU CARBONE DU GAZ CARBONIQUE DANS L'ACIDE PHOSPHOGLYCÉRIQUE DE FEUILLES DE TOMATOES SOUMISES A DES ÉCLAIREMENTS DE LUMIÈRE MONOCHROMATIQUE. C.R. Acad. Sci. Ser. D: 264: 2093-2096.

0791. Galmiche, J.M. 1971. WAVELENGTH EFFECT ON $^{14}CO_2$ FIXATION IN TOMATO LEAVES. *Progress in Photosynthesis Research,* Proc. Int. Congr. Photosynth. Res. II: 1875-1881.

0792. Galston, A.W. 1950. PHOTOTROPISM II. Bot. Rev. 16: 361-378 (R).

0793. Galston, A.W.; Baker, R.S. 1952. PHOTOINDUCTIVE EFFECTS OF RED LIGHT ON ETIOLATED PEAS. Proc. Annu. Meeting Am. Soc. Plant Physiol., Sept. 7-10, Ithaca, New York, p. 36 (A).

0794. Galston, A.W.; Baker, R.S. 1953. STUDIES ON THE PHYSIOLOGY OF LIGHT ACTION V. PHOTOINDUCTIVE ALTERATION OF AUXIN METABOLISM IN ETIOLATED PEAS. Am. J. Bot. 40: 512-516.

0795. Galston, A.W.; Tuttle, A.A. 1963. INDUCTIVE EFFECTS OF RED LIGHT ON CIRCUMNUTATION IN ETIOLATED PEAS. Plant Physiol. 38: Suppl.-23 (A).

0796. Galston, A.W. 1964. THE BIOCHEMISTRY OF PHOTOMORPHOGENESIS. Proc. X Int. Bot. Congr., pp. 185-186 (A).

0797. Galston, A.W.; Tuttle, A.A.; Penny, P.J. 1964. A KINETIC STUDY OF GROWTH MOVEMENTS AND PHOTOMORPHOGENESIS IN ETIOLATED PEA SEEDLINGS. Am. J. Bot. 51: 853-858.

0798. Galston, A.W. 1967. REGULATORY SYSTEMS IN HIGHER PLANTS. Am. Sci. 55: 144-160 (R).

0799. Galston, A.W. 1968. MICROSPECTROPHOTOMETRIC EVIDENCE FOR PHYTOCHROME IN PLANT NUCLEI. Proc. Nat. Acad. Sci., USA 61: 454-460.

0800. Galston, A.W. 1969. FLAVONOIDS AND PHOTOMORPHOGENESIS IN PEAS. *Perspectives in Phytochemistry,* Ed. J.B. Harborne and T. Swain, Academic Press, New York and London, pp. 193-204 (R).

0801. Galston, A.W.; Davies, P.J. 1969. HORMONAL REGULATION IN HIGHER PLANTS. Science 163:1288-1297 (R).

0802. Galston, A.W.; Satter, R.L.; Sabnis, D.D. 1969. ON THE MECHANISM OF PHYTOCHROME CONTROL OF NYCTINASTIC LEAFLET CLOSURE IN *ALBIZZIA JULIBRISSIN*. Proc. XI Int. Bot. Congr., p. 67 (A).

0803. Galston, A.W. 1970. THE RELATION OF FLAVONOIDS AND PEROXIDASE ACTIVITY TO THE CONTROL OF GROWTH BY PHYTOCHROME AND HORMONES. Am. J. Bot. (Abstr.) 57: 764 (A).

0804. Galston, A.W.; Davies, P.J. 1970. *Control Mechanisms in Plant Development,* Prentice-Hall, Englewood Cliffs, pp. 1-39 (R).

0805. Galston, A.W.; Satter, R.L. 1970. PHYTOCHROME CONTROLLED NYCTINASTY IN *ALBIZZIA JULIBRISSIN* I. KINETIC STUDIES OF LEAFLET CLOSURE. Plant Physiol. 46: Suppl.-2 Abstr. No. 6 (A).

0806. Galston, A.W.; Satter, R.L. 1972. A STUDY OF THE MECHANISM OF PHYTO-
CHROME ACTION. *Structural and Functional Aspects of Phytochemistry,*
Ed. V.C. Runeckles and T.C. Tso, Academic Press, New York and London
5: 51-79 (R).

0807. Galston, A.W.; Satter, R.L.; Keirns, J.J.; Freeman, J.; Bitensky, M.W.;
Applewhite, P.B.; Bau, Y.S. 1973. PHYSIOLOGY OF PINNA MOVEMENT IN
SAMANEA SAMAN. Plant Physiol. 51: Suppl.-16 Abstr. No. 88 (A).

0808. Galston, A.W. 1974. PLANT PHOTOBIOLOGY IN THE LAST HALF-CENTURY. Plant
Physiol. 54: 427-436.

0809. Galston, A.W.; Satter, R.L. 1974. PHYTOCHROME AND PHOTOMORPHOGENESIS.
Experimental Plant Physiology. Ed. Anthony San Pietro, C.V. Mosby
Company, Saint Louis, pp. 82-97 (R).

0810. Galston, A.W.; Satter, R.L.; Geballe, G.T. 1974. PHYTOCHROME CONTROLLED
K^+ FLUX AND LEAF MOVEMENT IN *SAMANEA.* Plant Physiol. 53: Suppl.-45
Abstr. No. 252 (A).

0811. Gambi, O.V. 1966. INFLUENCE OF LIGHT AND TEMPERATURE ON THE GERMINATION
OF SOME *RUMEX* SEEDS. Webbia Racc. Scr. Bot. 21: 461-474.

0812. Gammerman, A. Ya. 1971. CONCERNING THE ANALYTICAL INVESTIGATION OF THE
REGULATORY SYSTEM OF PHOTOMORPHOGENESIS. Proc. 26th Sci. Tech. Conf.
Med. Cybernetics, L., Izd.-Vo, L.G.V., No. 114 (RUS) (not obtained).

0813. Gammerman, A. Ya.; Fukshanskii, L. Ya. 1971. THEORY AND CALCULATION OF
DYNAMICS OF PHYTOCHROME TRANSFORMATIONS IN THE GREEN LEAF. Fiziol.
Rast. 18: 661-667 (RUS) (See Consultants Bur. ENG Transl. Plant
Physiol. pp. 557-562 [1972]).

0814. Gammerman, A. Ya.; Fukshanskii, L. Ya. 1971. ANALYTICAL STUDY OF THE
DYNAMICS OF PHYTOCHROME TRANSFORMATION DURING SELECTIVE SHIELDING.
Sb. Tr. Agron. Fiz. No. 30, pp. 126-130 (RUS).

0815. Gammerman, A. Ya.; Fukshanskii, L. Ya. 1974. A MATHEMATICAL MODEL OF
PHYTOCHROME - THE RECEPTOR OF PHOTOMORPHOGENETIC PROCESSES IN PLANTS.
Ontogenez 5: 122-129 (RUS) (ENG Summary).

0816. Gardner, D.P. 1844. ÜEBER DIE WIRKUNG DES GELBEN LICHTS BEI ERZEUGUNG
DER GRÜNEN FARBE DER PFLANZEN, SOWIE ÜBER DIE WIRKUNG DES INDIGO-
FARBENEN LICHTES IN BETREFF IHRER BEWEGUNG NACH DEN LICHTE. Frorieps
notizen 30 (11): 161-165.

0817. Gardner, G.M. 1971. PROBLEMS OF PROTEOLYSIS IN THE CHARACTERIZATION OF
       PHYTOCHROME. Proc. Eur. Annu. Symp. Plant Photomorphogenesis,
       (Athens), p. 24 (R).

0818. Gardner, G.; Briggs, W.R. 1971. PROTEOLYSIS DURING PHYTOCHROME PURIFI-
       CATION. Plant Physiol. 47: Suppl.-1 Abstr. No. 2 (A).

0819. Gardner, G.; Pike, C.S.; Rice, H.V.; Briggs, W.R. 1971. "DISAGGREGA-
       TION" OF PHYTOCHROME *IN VITRO* - A CONSEQUENCE OF PROTEOLYSIS. Plant
       Physiol. 48: 686-693.

0820. Gardner, G.M. 1972. RYE PHYTOCHROME: PROTEOLYTIC DEGRADATION AND
       PROPERTIES OF PHOTOTRANSFORMATION. Ph.D. Thesis, Harvard Univ.,
       Cambridge.

0821. Gardner, G.; Briggs, W.R. 1974. SOME PROPERTIES OF PHOTOTRANSFORMATION
       OF RYE PHYTOCHROME *IN VITRO*. Photochem. Photobiol. 19: 367-377.

0822. Gardner, G.; Thompson, W.F.; Briggs, W.R. 1974. DIFFERENTIAL REACTIVITY
       OF THE RED AND FAR-RED-ABSORBING FORMS OF PHYTOCHROME TO [^{14}C]
       N-ETHYL MALEIMIDE. Planta 117: 367-372.

0823. Gardner, G.; Shaw, S.; Wilkins, M.B. 1974. IAA TRANSPORT DURING THE
       PHOTOTROPIC RESPONSES OF INTACT *ZEA* AND *AVENA* COLEOPTILES. Planta
       121: 237-251.

0824. Gärtner, R. 1970. DIE BEWEGUNG DES *MESOTAENIUM* CHLOROPLASTEN IM STARK-
       LICHTBEREICH I. ZEIT UND TEMPERATURABHÄNGIGE SEKUNDÄRPROZESSE. Z.
       Pflanzenphysiol. 63: 147-161 (ENG Summary).

0825. Gärtner, R. 1970. DIE BEWEGUNG DES *MESOTAENIUM* - CHLOROPLASTEN IM
       STARKLICHTBEREICH II. AKTIONSDICHROISMUS UND WECHSELWIRKUNGEN DES
       PHOTORECEPTORS MIT PHYTOCHROM. Z. Pflanzenphysiol. 63: 428-443
       (ENG Summary).

0826. Gasanov, R.A.; Abutalybov, M.G. 1970. ACTION SPECTRUM OF THE EMERSON
       EFFECT AND INTERACTION OF PHOTOCHEMICAL PIGMENTS OF THE PHOTOSYNTHE-
       TIC SYSTEM OF HIGHER PLANTS IN THE INDUCTION PHASE. Dokl. Akad.
       Nauk SSSR 192: 911-914 (RUS).

0827. Gaspar, T. 1966. FACTEURS DE CROISSANCE ET FLORAISON. Bull. Soc. R.
       Sci. Liege 35: 115-124 (ENG Summary) (R).

0828. Gassner, R. 1911. UNTERSUCHUNGEN ÜBER DIE WIRKUNG DES LICHTES UND DES
       TEMPERATURWECHSELS AUF DIE KEIMUNG VON *CHLORIS CILIATA*. Jahrb.
       Hamburg Wiss. anstalt. 29: 1-121.

0829. Gaudet, J.J. 1963. *MARSILEA VESTITA:* CONVERSION OF THE WATER FORM
          TO THE LAND FORM BY DARKNESS AND BY FAR-RED LIGHT. Science 140:
          975-976.

0830. Gawroński, E. 1969. THE INFLUENCE OF HUMIC ACID (HA) ON GERMINATION
          OF PHOTOSENSITIVE LETTUCE SEEDS. PART I. THE COURSE OF GERMINATION
          IN DEPENDENCE ON HA CONCENTRATION, TIME OF SOAKING AND IRRADIATION,
          ENVIRONMENT pH, AND THE ACTION OF KINETIN AND GIBBERELLIC ACID
          (GA_3). Ann. Univ. Mariae Curie-Sklodowska Sect. C. 24: 373-394
          (POL) (ENG Summary).

0831. Gawroński, E. 1969. THE INFLUENCE OF HUMIC ACID (HA) ON GERMINATION
          OF PHOTOSENSITIVE LETTUCE SEEDS. PART II. GERMINATION IN ANAEROBIO-
          SIS. Ann. Univ. Mariae Curie-Sklodowska, Sect. C. 24: 395-405
          (POL) (ENG Summary).

0832. Gawroński, E. 1969. THE INFLUENCE OF HUMIC ACID (HA) ON GERMINATION
          OF PHOTOSENSITIVE LETTUCE SEEDS. PART III. GERMINATION AT VARIOUS
          TEMPERATURES. Ann. Univ. Mariae Curie-Sklodowska, Sect. C. 24:
          407-419 (POL) (ENG Summary).

0833. Gawroński, E. 1969. INFLUENCE OF HUMIC ACID (HA) ON GERMINATION OF
          PHOTOSENSITIVE LETTUCE SEEDS. PART IV. COMPARISON OF A PHYSIOLOGICAL
          ACTIVITY OF HA PREPARATIONS OF DIFFERENT ORIGIN WITH THEIR CHEMICAL
          COMPOSITION. Ann. Univ. Mariae Curie-Sklodowska, Sect. C. 24:
          421-436 (POL) (ENG Summary).

0834. Gentile, A.C.; Klein, R.M. 1964. ABSENCE OF EFFECT OF VISIBLE RADIA-
          TION ON ELONGATION OF DECAPITATED *AVENA* COLEOPTILE SECTIONS.
          Physiol. Plant. 17: 299-300.

0835. Giles, K.L.; Maltzahn, K.E. von. 1967. INTERACTION OF RED, FAR-RED AND
          BLUE LIGHT ON CELLULAR REGENERATION OF LEAVES OF *MNIUM AFFINE*.
          Bryologist 70: 312-315.

0836. Giles, K.L.; Maltzahn, K.E. von. 1968. SPECTROPHOTOMETRIC IDENTIFICA-
          TION OF PHYTOCHROME IN TWO SPECIES OF *MNIUM*. Can. J. Bot. 46:
          305-306.

0837. Giles, K.L. 1970. THE PHYTOCHROME SYSTEM, PHENOLIC COMPOUNDS, AND
          APLANOSPORE FORMATION IN A LICHENIZED STRAIN OF *TREBOUXIA*. Can. J.
          Bot. 48: 1343-1346.

0838. Gimesi, N.; Frenyó, V.; Maróti, M.; Pozsár, B. 1952. ÉTUDES SUR LA
PHYSIOLOGIE DE LA GERMINATION DE LA GRAINE DU TABAC. Acta. Biol.
Acad. Sci. Hung. 3: 419-441 (RUS Summary).

0839. Giudici de Nicola, M.; Piattelli, M.; Castrogiovanni, V.; Amico, V.
1972. THE EFFECTS OF LIGHT AND KINETIN ON AMARANTHIN SYNTHESIS IN
RELATION TO PHYTOCHROME. Phytochemistry 11: 1011-1017.

0840. Giudici de Nicola, M.; Piattelli, M.; Castrogiovanni, V.; Molina, C.
1972. THE EFFECT OF SHORT-TERM IRRADIATION ON KINETIN-INDUCED
AMARATHIN SYNTHESIS IN *AMARANTHUS TRICOLOR* SEEDLINGS. Phytochemistry 11: 1005-1010.

0841. Giudici de Nicola, M.; Piattelli, M.; Amico, V. 1973. PHOTOCONTROL OF
BETAXANTHIN SYNTHESIS IN *CELOSIA PLUMOSA* SEEDLINGS. Phytochemistry
12: 353-357.

0842. Giudici de Nicola, M.; Piattelli, M.; Amico, V. 1973. EFFECT OF CONTIN-
UOUS FAR-RED ON BETAXANTHIN AND BETACYANIN SYNTHESIS. Phytochemistry
12: 2163-2166.

0843. Giudici de Nicola, M.; Amico, V.; Piattelli, M. 1974. EFFECT OF WHITE
AND FAR-RED LIGHT ON BETALAIN FORMATION. Phytochemistry 13: 439-442.

0844. Gladun, A.A.; Melnichuk, Yu. P. 1970. ON MORPHOGENETIC EFFECT OF LIGHT
SPECTRAL COMPOSITION ON THE PLANTS. Fiziol. Biokhim. Kul't. Rast.
2: 27-29 (RUS) (ENG Summary).

0845. Glass, B. 1950. THE EFFECTS OF SUPPLEMENTARY TREATMENT WITH INFRA-RED
RADIATION ON X-RAY INDUCED LETHALS AND CHROMOSOME ABERRATIONS IN
FEMALES OF *DROSOPHILA MELANOGASTER*. Genetics 35: 109-110 (A).

0846. Glass, B. 1955. A COMPARATIVE STUDY OF INDUCED MUTATION IN THE OOCYTES
AND SPERMATOZOA OF *DROSOPHILA MELANOGASTER*. Genetics 40: 252-267.

0847. Globerson, D.; Ginzburg, C.; Kadman-Zahavi, A. 1973. COMPARATIVE STUD-
IES OF SEED GERMINATION OF TWO NEWLY ISOLATED LINES OF GRAND RAPIDS
LETTUCE. Ann. Bot (London) 37: 699-704.

0848. Globerson, D.; Kadman-Zahavi, A.; Ginzburg, C. 1974. A GENETIC METHOD
FOR STUDYING THE ROLE OF THE SEED COATS IN THE GERMINATION OF
LETTUCE. Ann. Bot. (London) 38: 201-203.

0849. Godnev, T.N.; Akulovich, N.K.; Orlovskaa, K.I.; Domash, V.I. 1966.
EFFECT OF THE PHYTOCHROME SYSTEM ON FORMATION OF PIGMENTS IN THE
TISSUE CULTURE OF CARROT. Dokl. Akad. Nauk SSSR 169: 692-694 (RUS).

0850. Godnev, T.N.; Domash, V.I.; Akulovich, N.K. 1969. EFFECT OF THE PHYTOCHROME SYSTEM OF BIOSYNTHESIS OF PHOTOSYNTHESIS PIGMENTS IN SOME PLANTS. Fotosint. Pitan. Rast., pp. 3-8 (RUS).

0851. Goeschl, J.D.; Pratt, H.K.; Bonner, B.A. 1967. AN EFFECT OF LIGHT ON THE PRODUCTION OF ETHYLENE AND THE GROWTH OF THE PLUMULAR PORTION OF ETIOLATED PEA SEEDLINGS. Plant Physiol. 42: 1077-1080.

0852. Goeschl, J.D.; Pratt, H.K. 1968. REGULATORY ROLES OF ETHYLENE IN THE ETIOLATED GROWTH HABIT OF *PISUM SATIVUM*. *Biochemistry and Physiology of Plant Growth Substances*, Ed. Wightman, F. and Setterfield, G., Runge Press, Ottawa, pp. 1229-1242.

0853. Goeschl, J.D. 1969. INTERPRETING THE EFFECTS OF RED LIGHT ON PEA STEM ELONGATION. Proc. XI Int. Bot. Congr., p. 72 (A).

0854. Goethe, J.W. von. 1892. VERSUCHE ÜBER DIE EINWIRKUNG DES LICHTES AUF DAS WACHSTUM DER PFLANZEN. Ausgabe Böhlau, Weimar Abt II, Nat. Wiss. Schr., Bd. 7, II Theil, pp. 310-341.

0855. Goldacre, P.L.; Galston, A.W.; Weintraub, R.L. 1953. THE EFFECT OF SUBSTITUTED PHENOLS ON THE ACTIVITY OF THE INDOLEACETIC ACID OXIDASE OF PEAS. Arch. Biochem. Biophys. 43: 358-373.

0856. Goodwin, R.H. 1941. ON THE INHIBITION OF THE FIRST INTERNODE OF *AVENA* BY LIGHT. Am. J. Bot. 28: 325-332.

0857. Goodwin, R.H.; Owens, O. 1946. THE EFFECT OF MONOCHROMATIC LIGHT ON CHLOROPHYLL FORMATION AND INTERNODE INHIBITION IN *AVENA*. Am. J. Bot. 33: 229 (A).

0858. Goodwin, R.H.; Owens, O.v.H. 1948. AN ACTION SPECTRUM FOR INHIBITION OF THE FIRST INTERNODE OF *AVENA* BY LIGHT. Bull. Torrey Bot. Club 75: 18-21.

0859. Goodwin, R.H.; Owens, O.v.H. 1951. THE EFFECTIVENESS OF THE SPECTRUM IN *AVENA* INTERNODE INHIBITION. Bull. Torrey Bot. Club 78: 11-21.

0860. Gordon, S.A.; Surrey, K. 1958. A BIOCHEMICAL BASIS FOR THE FAR-RED POTENTIATION OF X-RAY INDUCED CHROMOSOMAL BREAKS. Radiat. Res. 9: 121, Abstr. No. 94 (A).

0861. Gordon, S.A.; Surrey, K. 1959. RED, FAR-RED INTERACTION IN OXIDATIVE PHOSPHORYLATION. Plant Physiol. 33: Suppl.-24 (A).

0862. Gordon, S.A. 1959. SPECTRAL POTENTIATION OF X-RAY INDUCED CHROMOSOMAL
ABERRATIONS. U.S. Atomic Energy Comm. T.I.D. 7578, pp. 163-171,
(not obtained) referred to by Gordon, S.A. and Surrey, K. (1961).
Effects of Ionizing Radiations on Seeds, Symp. Int. Atomic Energy
Agency: Vienna, Austria, pp. 189-196 (Held in 1960).

0863. Gordon, S.A.; Surrey, K. 1960. RED AND FAR-RED ACTION ON OXIDATIVE
PHOSPHORYLATION. Radiat. Res. 12: 325-339.

0864. Gordon, S.A. 1961. THE INTRACELLULAR DISTRIBUTION OF PHYTOCHROME IN
CORN SEEDLINGS. U.S. Atomic Energy Comm. Res. and Development
Report ANL-6368, pp. 149-151 and also identical article in Proc. III
Int. Congr. Photobiol., pp. 441-443.

0865. Gordon, S.A.; Surrey, K. 1961. PHOSPHORYLATION AND RED-SPECTRUM PHOTO-
MORPHOGENESIS. *Effects of Ionizing Radiations on Seeds.* 1960.
Symp. Int. Atomic Energy Agency, Vienna, Austria, pp. 189-196 (FR,
RUS, SP Summaries).

0866. Gordon, S.A. 1964. SYMPOSIUM ON PHOTOMORPHOGENESIS. IV. OXIDATIVE
PHOSPHORYLATION AS A PHOTOMORPHOGENIC CONTROL. Q. Rev. Biol. 39:
19-34 (R-D).

0867. Gordon, S.A.; Stroud, A.N.; Chen, C.H. 1971. THE INDUCTION OF CHROMO-
SOMAL ABERRATIONS IN PIG KIDNEY CELLS BY FAR-RED LIGHT. Radiat. Res.
45: 274-287.

0868. Gordon, W.R.; Koukkari, W.L. 1972. THE EFFECT OF CYTOKININS AND AUXINS
ON PHYTOCHROME MEDIATED NYCTINASTY IN *ALBIZZIA JULIBRISSIN*. Plant
Physiol. 49: Suppl.-53, Abstr. No. 299 (A).

0869. Goren, R.; Galston, A.W. 1966. CONTROL OF PHYTOCHROME OF ^{14}C-SUCROSE
INCORPORATION INTO BUDS OF ETIOLATED PEA SEEDLINGS. Plant Physiol.
41: Suppl.-17 (A).

0870. Goren, R.; Galston, A.W. 1966. CONTROL BY PHYTOCHROME OF ^{14}C-SUCROSE
INCORPORATION INTO BUDS OF ETIOLATED PEA SEEDLINGS. Plant Physiol.
41: 1055-1064.

0871. Goren, R.; Galston, A.W. 1967. PHYTOCHROME CONTROLLED ^{14}C-SUCROSE UP-
TAKE INTO ETIOLATED PEA BUDS: EFFECTS OF GIBBERELLIC ACID AND OTHER
SUBSTANCES. Plant Physiol. 42: 1087-1090.

0872. Gorter, C.J. 1964. SPECTRAL SENSITIVITY OF DWARFISM IN PEAS. Acta
Bot. Neerl. 13: 553-558.

0873. Gortikova, N. 1938. THE EFFECT OF PRELIMINARY TREATMENT WITH COLOURED LIGHT ON THE DEVELOPMENT OF PEANUT *(ARACHIS HYPOGAEA* L.) Dokl. Acad. Sci. URSS 19: 417-419.

0874. Gotô, N.; Esashi, Y. 1974. REGULATION OF HYPOCOTYL GROWTH BY ETHYLENE. *Plant Growth Substances, 1973* (Hirokowa Publishing Co., Tokyo, 1974) Proc. 8 Int. Conf. Plant Growth Substances, Tokyo, pp. 853-863.

0875. Gotô, N.; Esashi, Y. 1974. STIMULATION BY ETHYLENE OF AXIS AND HYPOCO-TYL GROWTH IN BEAN AND COCKLEBUR SEEDLINGS. Physiol. Plant 31: 204-210.

0876. Gotô, N.; Esashi, Y. 1974. DIFFERENTIAL HORMONE RESPONSES IN DIFFERENT GROWING ZONES OF THE BEAN HYPOCOTYL. Planta 116: 225-241.

0877. Graham, D.; Grieve, A.M.; Hatch, M.D.; Slack, C.R.; Smillie, R.M. 1968. PHYTOCHROME AS A PRIMARY PHOTOREGULATOR IN THE SYNTHESIS OF ENZYMES OF PHOTOSYNTHETIC CARBON DIOXIDE FIXATION IN HIGHER PLANTS. Proc. V Int. Congr. Photobiol., p. 157 (A).

0878. Graham, D.; Grieve, A.M.; Smillie, R.M. 1968. PHYTOCHROME AS THE PRI-MARY PHOTOREGULATOR OF THE SYNTHESIS OF CALVIN CYCLE ENZYMES IN ETIOLATED PEA SEEDLINGS. Nature (London) 218: 89-90.

0879. Graham, D.; Hatch, M.D.; Slack, C.R.; Smillie, R.M. 1970. LIGHT-INDUCED FORMATION OF ENZYMES OF THE C_4-DICARBOXYLIC ACID PATHWAY OF PHOTO-SYNTHESIS IN DETACHED LEAVES. Phytochemistry 9: 521-532.

0880. Graham, D.; Grieve, A.M.; Smillie, R.M. 1971. PHYTOCHROME-MEDIATED PLASTID DEVELOPMENT IN ETIOLATED PEA STEM APICES. Phytochemistry 10: 2905-2914.

0881. Grahl, A.; Thielebein, M. 1960. WIRKUNG VON LICHT UND DUNKELHEIT AUF DIE KEIMUNG VON SAATGUT. Landbauforsch. Völkenrode 10: 100-103 (R).

0882. Grant Lipp, A.E.; Ballard, L.A.T. 1963. GERMINATION PATTERNS SHOWN BY THE LIGHT-SENSITIVE SEED OF *ANAGALLIS ARVENSIS*. Aust. J. Biol. Sci. 16: 572-584.

0883. Green, J.R. 1897. IV. ON THE ACTION OF LIGHT ON DIASTASE, AND ITS BIOLOGICAL SIGNIFICANCE. Philos. Trans. R. Soc. London, Ser. B. 188: 167-190.

0884. Gregor, H.-D.; Reinert, J. 1972. INDUKTION DER PHENYLALANIN-AMMONIUM-LYASE IN GEWEBEKULTUREN VON *HAPLOPAPPUS GRACILIS*. Protoplasma 74: 307-319 (ENG Summary).

0885. Gregory-Southworth, A.; Klein, A.O. 1974. LIGHT INDUCED SENSITIVITY
OF BEAN SEEDLINGS TO MECHANICAL STIMULATION. Plant Physiol. 53:
Suppl.-46. Abstr. No. 256 (A).

0886. Greppin, H.; Horwitz, B.A.; Horwitz, L.P. 1973. LIGHT-STIMULATED BIO-
ELECTRIC RESPONSE OF SPINACH LEAVES AND PHOTOPERIODIC INDUCTION. Z.
Pflanzenphysiol. 68: 336-345.

0887. Griffith, M.M.; Powell, R.D. 1961. THE TIME COURSE OF CELL ENLARGEMENT
AND LEAF GROWTH AS AFFECTED BY KINETIN AND RED LIGHT. ASB Bull. 8:
24 (A).

0888. Grill, R.; Vince, D. 1964. ANTHOCYANIN FORMATION IN TURNIP SEEDLINGS
(*BRASSICA RAPA* L.): EVIDENCE FOR TWO LIGHT STEPS IN THE BIOSYNTHETIC
PATHWAY. Planta 63: 1-12.

0889. Grill, R. 1965. PHOTOCONTROL OF ANTHOCYANIN FORMATION IN TURNIP SEED-
LINGS. I. DEMONSTRATION OF PHYTOCHROME ACTION. Planta 66: 293-300.

0890. Grill, R.; Vince, D. 1965. PHOTOCONTROL OF ANTHOCYANIN FORMATION IN
TURNIP SEEDLINGS. II. THE POSSIBLE ROLE OF PHYTOCHROME IN THE RE-
SPONSE TO PROLONGED IRRADIATION WITH FAR-RED OR BLUE LIGHT. Planta
67: 122-135.

0891. Grill, R.; Vince, D. 1966. PHOTOCONTROL OF ANTHOCYANIN FORMATION IN
TURNIP SEEDLINGS. III. THE PHOTORECEPTORS INVOLVED IN THE RESPONSES
TO PROLONGED IRRADIATION. Planta 70: 1-12.

0892. Grill, R. 1967. PHOTOCONTROL OF ANTHOCYANIN SYNTHESIS IN TURNIP SEED-
LINGS. IV. THE EFFECT OF FEEDING PRECURSORS. Planta 76: 11-24.

0893. Grill, R.E.M. 1967. THE PROBLEM OF THE FAR-RED HIGH ENERGY REACTION IN
RELATION TO ANTHOCYANIN SYNTHESIS IN THE TURNIP SEEDLING SYSTEM.
Proc. Annu. Eur. Symp. Plant Photomorphogenesis, (Hvar), pp. 25-27.

0894. Grill, R. 1968. PHYTOCHROME CHANGES IN TURNIP SEEDLINGS IN DARKNESS,
FAR-RED LIGHT OR FOLLOWING EXPOSURES TO RED IRRADIATION. Proc. V
Int. Congr. Photobiol., p. 64 (A).

0895. Grill, R.E.M. 1969. PHOTOMORPHOGENESIS IN THE TURNIP SEEDLING. Proc.
British Photobiol. Group Bull., No. 21, pp. 3-4, Reading Univ. (A).

0896. Grill, R. 1969. PHOTOCONTROL OF ANTHOCYANIN FORMATION IN TURNIP SEED-
LINGS. V. DIFFERENTIAL RESPONSE PATTERNS OF HYPOCOTYLS AND COTYLE-
DONS. Planta 85: 42-56.

0897. Grill, R.; Vince, D. 1969. PHOTOCONTROL OF ANTHOCYANIN FORMATION IN
TURNIP SEEDLINGS. VI. LOG PHASES. Planta 86: 116-123.

0898. Grill, R.; Vince, D. 1969. PHOTOCONTROL OF ANTHOCYANIN FORMATION IN
TURNIP SEEDLINGS. VII. PHYTOCHROME CHANGES IN DARKNESS AND ON EX-
POSURE TO RED AND FAR-RED LIGHT. Planta 89: 9-22.

0899. Grill, R.; Vince, D. 1970. PHOTOCONTROL OF ANTHOCYANIN FORMATION IN
TURNIP SEEDLINGS. VIII. WAVE-LENGTH DEPENDENCE. Planta 95: 264-271.

0900. Grill, R. 1972. THE INFLUENCE OF CHLOROPHYLL ON *IN VIVO* DIFFERENCE
SPECTRA OF PHYTOCHROME. Planta 108: 185-202.

0901. Grill, R.; Spruit, C.J.P. 1972. PROPERTIES OF PHYTOCHROME IN GYMNO-
SPERMS. Planta 108: 203-213.

0902. Grodzinskii, D.M. 1972. THE PHYTOCHROME SYSTEM OF PLANTS. In: Bio-
physics of Plants, Kiev, "Science Doomka", pp. 75-110 (RUS) (R).

0903. Gugliada, M.L.; Soriano, A.; Burkart, S. 1967. THE SEED COAT EFFECT IN
RELATION TO THE PHOTOINDUCTION OF GERMINATION IN *DATURA FEROX* L.
Can. J. Bot. 45: 377-381.

0904. Gupta, S.; Maheshwari, S.C. 1970. GROWTH AND FLOWERING OF *LEMNA PAUCI-
COSTATA* I. GENERAL ASPECTS AND ROLE OF CHELATING AGENTS IN FLOWERING.
Plant Cell Physiol. 11: 83-95.

0905. Gutterman, Y.; Evenari, M.; Heydecker, W. 1972. PHYTOCHROME AND TEMPER-
ATURE RELATIONS IN *LACTUCA SATIVA* L. GRAND RAPIDS SEED GERMINATION
AFTER THERMO-DORMANCY. Nature (London) New Biol. 235: 144-145.

0906. Gutterman, Y. 1973. DIFFERENCES IN THE PROGENCY DUE TO DAYLENGTH AND
HORMONE TREATMENT OF THE MOTHER PLANT. Proc. Easter Sch. Agric. Sci.
Univ. Nottingham 19: 59-80 (R).

0907. Gutterman, Y.; Porath, D. 1973. PHYTOCHROME AND GERMINATION OF *CUCUMIS
PROPHETARUM* L. AND *CUCUMIS SATIVUM* L. SEEDS INFLUENCED BY FRUIT
STORAGE UNDER DIFFERENT LIGHT CONDITIONS. Isr. J. Bot. 22: 200 (A).

0908. Gutterman, Y. 1974. THE INFLUENCE OF THE PHOTOPERIODIC REGIME AND RED-
FAR-RED LIGHT TREATMENTS OF *PORTULACA OLERACEA* L. PLANTS ON THE
GERMINABILITY OF THEIR SEEDS. Oecologia (Berlin) 17: 27-38.

0909. Gwynn, D.; Scheibe, J. 1972. AN ACTION SPECTRUM IN THE BLUE FOR INHIBI-
TION OF GERMINATION OF LETTUCE SEED. Planta 106: 247-257.

0910. Haack. 1906. ÜBER DIE KEIMUNG UND BEWERTUNG DES KEIFERNSAMENS NACH
KEIMPROBEN. Z. Forst. Jagdwes. 38: 441-475.

0911. Haack. 1912. DIE PRÜFUNG DES KIEFERNSAMENS. Z. Forst. Jagdwes. 44:
193-307.

0912. Haber, A.H. 1958. RENDERING LIGHT-INSENSITIVE LETTUCE SEED SENSITIVE TO LIGHT. Plant Physiol. 33: Suppl.-23 (A).

0913. Haber, A.H.; Tolbert, N.E. 1958. METABOLISM OF C^{14}-BICARBONATE, P^{32}-PHOSPHATE, OR S^{35}-SULFATE BY LETTUCE SEED DURING GERMINATION. Plant Physiol. 33: Suppl.-24 (A).

0914. Haber, A.H. 1959. RENDERING THE GERMINATION OF LIGHT-INSENSITIVE LETTUCE SEEDS SENSITIVE TO LIGHT. Physiol. Plant. 12: 456-464.

0915. Haber, A.H.; Tolbert, N.E. 1959. METABOLISM OF C^{14}-BICARBONATE, P^{32}-PHOSPHATE, OR S^{35}-SULFATE BY LETTUCE SEED DURING GERMINATION. Plant Physiol. 34: 376-380.

0916. Haber, A.H.; Tolbert, N.E. 1959. EFFECTS OF GIBBERELLIC ACID, KINETIN, AND LIGHT ON THE GERMINATION OF LETTUCE SEED. *Photoperiodism and Related Phenomena in Plants and Animals* Ed. R.B. Withrow, A.A.A.S. Washington, D.C., pp. 197-206.

0917. Haber, A.H.; Luippold, H.J. 1960. EFFECTS OF GIBBERELLIN, KINETIN, THIOUREA, AND PHOTOMORPHOGENIC RADIATION ON MITOTIC ACTIVITY IN DORMANT LETTUCE SEED. Plant Physiol. 35: 486-494.

0918. Haber, A. 1967. AN EXAMINATION OF THE CONCEPTS OF "DORMANCY" AND "GERMINATION" FROM STUDIES WITH LETTUCE SEEDS. Proc. Int. Symp. Physiol. Ecol. Biochem. Germination, Ed. H. Borriss, Greifswald; Ernst-Moritz-Arndt-University 1967 1: 47-53 (R).

0919. Haber, A.H.; Thompson, P.J.; Walne, P.L.; Triplett, L.L. 1969. NON-PHOTOSYNTHETIC RETARDATION OF CHLOROPLAST SENESCENCE BY LIGHT. Plant Physiol. 44: 1619-1628.

0920. Habermann, H.M. 1972. EVIDENCE FOR TWO PHOTOREACTIONS IN LIGHT-DEPENDENT STOMATAL OPENING. Proc. VI Int. Congr Photobiol. Abstr. No. 191 (A).

0921. Habermann, H.M. 1973. EVIDENCE FOR TWO PHOTOREACTIONS AND POSSIBLE INVOLVEMENT OF PHYTOCHROME IN LIGHT-DEPENDENT STOMATAL OPENING. Plant Physiol. 51: 543-548.

0921.2 Habermann, H.M.; Shoemaker, E.W. 1974. LIGHT-DEPENDENT CHANGE IN POTASSIUM CONTENT OF GUARD CELLS DURING STOMATAL OPENING IN MUTANT AND WILD TYPE *HELIANTHUS ANNUS*. Proc. II Annu. Meet. Am. Soc. Photobiol. p. 147, Abstr. No. FPM-C7 (A).

0921.5 Habermann, H.M. 1974. LIGHT REACTIONS OF STOMATAL OPENING: POSSIBLE INVOLVEMENT OF PHYTOCHROME. *Mechanisms of Regulation of Plant Growth,* Ed. R.L. Bieleski; A.R. Ferguson; M.M. Cresswell, R. Soc. N.Z. Bull. 12: 445-453.

0922. Hachtel, W. 1972. DER EINFLUSS DES PLASMOTYPUS AUF DIE REGULATION DER AKTIVITÄT DER L-PHENYLALANIN-AMMONIUM-LYASE (UNTERSUCHUNGEN AN *RAIMANNIA-OENOTHEREN).* Planta 102: 247-260 (ENG Summary).

0923. Häcker, M.; Hartmann, K.M.; Mohr, H. 1964. ZELLTEILUNG UND ZELLWACHSTUM IM HYPOKOTYL VON *LACTUCA SATIVA* L. UNTER DEM EINFLUSS DES LICHTES. Planta 63: 253-268 (ENG Summary).

0924. Häcker, M.; Stöhr, H. 1966. DER ABBAU VON SPEICHERFETT IN DEN KOTYLEDONEN VON *SINAPIS ALBA* L. UNTER DEM EINFLUSS DES PHYTOCHROMS. Planta 68: 215-224 (ENG Summary).

0925. Häcker, M. 1967. DER ABBAU VON SPEICHERPROTEIN UND DIE BILDUNG VON PLASTIDEN IN DEN KOTYLEDONEN DES SENFKEIMLINGS (*SINAPIS ALBA* L.). UNTER DEM EINFLUSS DES PHYTOCHROMS. Planta 76: 309-325 (ENG Summary).

0926. Hadwiger, L.A.; Schwochau, M.E. 1971. ULTRAVIOLET LIGHT-INDUCED FORMATION OF PISATIN AND PHENYLALANINE AMMONIA LYASE. Plant Physiol. 47: 588-590.

0927. Hagen, C.E.; Borthwick, H.A.; Hendricks, S.B. 1954. OXYGEN CONSUMPTION OF LETTUCE SEED IN RELATION TO PHOTOCONTROL OF GERMINATION. Bot. Gaz. (Chicago) 115: 360-364.

0928. Hahn, L.W.; Miller, J.H. 1966. LIGHT DEPENDENCE OF CHLOROPLAST REPLICATION AND STARCH METABOLISM IN THE MOSS *POLYTRICHUM COMMUNE.* Physiol. Plant. 19: 134-141.

0929. Haight, T.H.; Kuehnert, C.C. 1970. THE EFFECT OF COLORED LIGHT ON PIGMENT SYNTHESIS IN CULTURED FERN LEAF PRIMORDIA. Physiol. Plant 23: 704-714.

0930. Halaban, R. 1969. EFFECTS OF LIGHT QUALITY ON THE CIRCADIAN RHYTHM OF LEAF MOVEMENT OF A SHORT-DAY PLANT. Plant Physiol. 44: 973-977.

0931. Halaban, R.; Hillman, W.S. 1970. RESPONSE OF *LEMNA PERPUSILLA* TO PERIODIC TRANSFER TO DISTILLED WATER. Plant Physiol. 46: 641-644.

0932. Halaban, R.; Hillman, W.S. 1970. PHYTOCHROME AND THE INDUCTIVE DARK PERIOD IN *COLEUS*. Plant Physiol. 46: 757-758.

0933. Halaban, R.; Hillman, W.S. 1971. FACTORS AFFECTING THE WATER-SENSITIVE PHASE OF FLOWERING IN THE SHORT DAY PLANT *LEMNA PERPUSILLA*. Plant Physiol. 48: 760-764.

0933.5 Halaban, R. 1973. SPECTRAL SENSITIVITY OF CIRCADIAN RHYTHMS. Proc. I Annu. Meet. Am. Soc. Photobiol. pp. 59-60, Abstr. No. MAM-A2 (A) (R).

0934. Halaban, R.; Hillman, W.S. 1974. PHOTOPERIODIC TIME MEASUREMENT OF FLOWERING IN A SHORT-DAY-PLANT: EFFECTS OF THE EXTERNAL MEDIUM. *Chronobiology*. Ed. L.E. Scheving, F. Halberg and J.E. Pauly. Igaku Shoin LTD, Tokyo, pp. 666-670.

0935. Hall, W.C. 1955. THE EFFECT OF LIGHT AND CHEMICALS ON COTYLEDON AB- SCISSION AND AXILLARY BUD GROWTH IN YOUNG COTTON. Plant Physiol. 30: Suppl.-6 (A).

0936. Hall, W.C.; Liverman, J.L. 1956. EFFECT OF RADIATION AND GROWTH REGU- LATORS ON LEAF ABSCISSION IN SEEDLING COTTON AND BEAN. Plant Physiol. 31: 471-476.

0937. Hamner, K.C. 1958. THE MECHANISM OF PHOTOPERIODISM IN PLANTS. Proc. Annu. Biol. Collog. Oreg. State Univ. 19: 7-16 (R).

0938. Hamner, K.C. 1960. PHOTOPERIODISM AND CIRCADIAN RHYTHMS. Cold Spring Harbor Symp. Quant. Biol. 25: 269-277 (R).

0939. Hamner, K. 1963. ENDOGENOUS RHYTHMS IN CONTROLLED ENVIRONMENTS. *Environmental Control of Plant Growth*, Ed. L.T. Evans, Academic Press, New York and London, pp. 215-232 (R-D).

0940. Hamner, K.C.; Takimoto, A. 1964. CIRCADIAN RHYTHMS AND PLANT PHOTO- PERIODISM. Am. Nat. 98: 295-322 (R).

0941. Hanebuth, W.F. 1972. THE EFFECT OF LIGHT QUALITY UPON PHENYLALANINE AMMONIA-LYASE (PAL) ACTIVITY IN POTATO TUBER TISSUE SLICES. Trans. Ill. State Acad. Sci. 65: 10-13.

0942. Hanebuth, W.F.; Chasson, R.M. 1972. THE EFFECT OF LIGHT UPON DEVELOP- MENT IN POTATO TISSUE SLICES. Plant Physiol. 49: 857-859.

0943. Hanke, J. 1969. DIE WIRKUNG VON "STÖRLICHT" AUF DIE BLÜTENBILDUNG VON *SINAPIS ALBA* L. Ph.D. Thesis, Univ. Freiburg, Germany.

0944. Hanke, J.; Hartmann, K.M.; Mohr, H. 1969. DIE WIRKUNG VON "STÖRLICHT" AUF DIE BLÜTENBILDUNG VON *SINAPIS ALBA* L. Planta 86: 235-249 (ENG Summary).

0945. Hannay, J.W. 1967. LIGHT AND SEED GERMINATION - AN EXPERIMENTAL AP- PROACH TO PHOTOBIOLOGY. J. Biol. Educ. 1: 65-73 (R).

0946. Hansen, D.J.; Bendixen, L.E. 1969. TROPISMS OF *TRIFOLIUM FRAGIFERUM* L. STOLONS CAUSED BY LIGHT, ETHYLENE, AND GIBBERELLIC ACID. Plant Physiol. 44: Suppl.-32 Abstr. No. 151 (A).

0947. Harder, R.; Wallrabe, E.; Quantz, L. 1944. ÜBER DIE ROLLE DER TEMPERATUR BEI DER ZERSTÖRUNG DES BLÜHIMPULSES DURCH ZWISCHENBELICHTUNG BEI DER KURZTAGPFLANZE *KALANCHOË BLOSSFELDIANA*. Planta 34: 41-48.

0948. Harms, H. 1936. BEZIEHUNGEN ZWISCHEN STOMATAWEITE, LICHTSTÄRKE UND LICHTFARBE. Planta 25: 155193.

0949. Harnischfeger, G.; Treharne, K.; Feierabend, J. 1974. STUDIES ON THE PRIMARY PHOTOSYNTHETIC PROCESSES OF PLASTIDS FROM WHEAT GROWN UNDER LIGHT OF DIFFERENT SPECTRAL QUALITY. Plant Sci. Lett. 3: 61-66.

0950. Harper, D.B.; Smith, H. 1969. PRECURSOR-INCORPORATION EVIDENCE ON THE LOCUS OF PHYTOCHROME CONTROL IN THE BIOSYNTHETIC PATHWAY OF FLAVONOIDS IN *PISUM SATIVUM*. Biochim. Biophys. Acta 184: 230-232.

0951. Harper, D.B.; Austin, D.J.; Smith, H. 1970. THE PHOTOCONTROL OF PRECURSOR INCORPORATION INTO THE *PISUM SATIVUM* FLAVONOIDS. Phytochemistry 9: 497-505.

0952. Harraschain, H.; Mohr, H. 1963. DER EINFLUSS SICHTBARER STRAHLUNG AUF DIE FLAVONOLSYNTHESE UND MORPHOGENESE DER BUCHWEIZENKEIMLINGE *(FAGOPYRUM ESCULENTUM* MÖENCH.) II. FLAVONOL SYNTHESE UND HYPOKOTYLWACHSTUM. Z. Bot. 51: 277-299 (ENG Summary).

0953. Hartmann, E. 1970. ÜBER DEN STOFFWECHSEL UND DAS DIFFERENZIERUNGSVERHALTEN DES LAUBMOOSKALLUS IN ABHÄNGIGKEIT VOM LICHT. Ph.D. Thesis, Univ. Mainz, Germany.

0954. Hartmann, E. 1971. ÜBER DEN NACHWEIS EINES NEUROHORMONES BEIM LAUBMOOSCALLUS UND SEINE BEEINFLUSSUNG DURCH DAS PHYTOCHROM. Planta 101: 159-165 (ENG Summary).

0955. Hartmann, E. 1973. ÜBER DIE WIRKUNG DES PHYTOCHROMS BEIM LAUBMOOSKALLUS I. PHOTOMORPHOGENESE UND STOFFWECHSEL. Beitr. Biol. Pflanz. 49: 1-34 (ENG Summary).

0956. Hartmann, E. 1974. ÜBER DIE WIRKUNG DES PHYTOCHROMS BEIM LAUBMOOSKALLUS II. SAUERSTOFFMETABOLISMUS UND ACETYLCHOLINWIRKUNG. Z. Pflanzenphysiol. 71: 349-365 (ENG Summary).

0957. Hartmann, E. 1974. INFLUENCE OF LIGHT AND ACETYCHOLINE ON THE MEMBRANE POTENTIAL OF THE MUNG BEAN HOOK. Proc. Eur. Annu. Symp. Plant Photomorphogenesis, (Antwerpen), pp. 8-14.

0958. Hartmann, K.M.   1962.   DIE REGULATION DER GAMETOGENESE VON *CHLAMYDOMONAS EUGANETOS* UND *CHLAMYDOMONAS MOEWUSII* DURCH EXOGENE UND ENDOGENE FAKTOREN VERGLEICHEND MORPHOLOGISCHE, PHYSIOLOGISCHE UND BIOPHYSI-KALISCHE UNTERSUCHUNGEN.   Ph.D. Thesis, Univ. Tübingen, Germany.

0959. Hartmann, K.M.; Menzel, H.; Mohr, H.   1965.   EIN BEITRAG ZUR THEORIE DER POLAROTROPISCHEN UND PHOTOTROPISCHEN KRÜMMUNG.   Planta 64: 363-375 (ENG Summary).

0960. Hartmann, K.M.   1966.   A GENERAL HYPOTHESIS TO INTERPRET 'HIGH ENERGY PHENOMENA' OF PHOTOMORPHOGENESIS ON THE BASIS OF PHYTOCHROME.   Photochem. Photobiol. 5: 349-366.

0961. Hartmann, K.M.   1967.   PHOTORECEPTOR PROBLEMS IN PHOTOMORPHOGENIC RESPONSES UNDER HIGH-ENERGY-CONDITIONS (UV-BLUE-FAR-RED).   Proc. Eur. Annu. Symp. Plant Photomorphogenesis, (Hvar), pp. 29-32.

0962. Hartmann, K.M.   1967.   PHYTOCHROME 730 (P_{fr}), THE EFFECTOR OF THE 'HIGH ENERGY PHOTOMORPHOGENIC REACTION' IN THE FAR-RED REGION.   Naturwissenschaften 54: 544.

0963. Hartmann, K.M.   1967.   EIN WIRKUNGSSPEKTRUM DER PHOTOMORPHOGENESE UNTER HOCHENERGIEBEDINGUNGEN UND SEINE INTERPRETATION AUF DER BASIS DES PHYTOCHROMS (HYPOKOTYLWACHSTUMSHEMMUNG BEI *LACTUCA SATIVA* L.).   Z. Naturforsch. Teil B: 22: 1172-1175.

0964. Hartmann, K.M.   1968.   IDENTIFICATION OF THE PHOTORECEPTOR OF THE 'HIGH ENERGY PHOTOMORPHOGENIC REACTION' FOR THE FAR-RED REGION.   Proc. V Int. Congr. Photobiol. p. 10 (A).

0965. Hartmann, K.M.   1968.   L'IDENTIFICATION DE QUELQUES PHOTORECEPTEURS, CONTRÔLANT LA PHOTOMORPHOGENÈSE SOUS CONDITIONS NATURELLES.   Somm. I Conf. 23.4, Fac. Sci. Rouen, Mont-Saint-Aignan; Seine-Maritime (2 pp).

0966. Hartmann, K.M.   1968.   QUELQUES CONSIDÉRATIONS CONCERNANT LE PHYTOCHROME COMME RÉGULATEUR DE LA PHOTOMORPHOGENÈSE DANS LES CONDITIONS NATURELLES.   Somm. II Conf. 23.4, Fac. Sci. Rouen, Mont-Saint-Aignan; Seine-Maritime (3 pp).

0967. Hartmann, K.M.; Spruit, C.J.P.   1968.   DIFFERENCE SPECTRA AND PHOTOSTATIONARY STATES FOR PHYTOCHROME *IN VIVO*.   Plant Physiol. 43: Suppl.-15 (A).

0968. Hartmann, K.M. 1969. DESKRIPTIVE UND KINETISCHE STEADY-STATE-ANALYSE DER LICHT-WACHSTRUMSREAKTION VON *LACTUCA SATIVA* L. AUF DER BASIS DES ALLOSTERISCHEN MEMBRAN-EFFEKTORS PHYTOCHROM. Jahresbericht des SFB Molgrudent, Freiburg/Br., pp. 158-163 (R).

0969. Hartmann, K.M. 1969. DIE METHODE ZUM NACHWEIS DES PHYTOCHROMS ALS PHOTOREZEPTOR DER PHOTOMORPHOGENESE UNTER QUASI-NATÜRLICHEN BEDINGUN-GEN. Mimeographed. Zusammenfassung Zum Vortrag vom 13.2 1969 Bot. Institut Univ. Marburg Lahn, 5 pp. (R-D).

0970. Hartmann, K.M.; Menzel, H. 1969. PHYTOCHROME, A PHOTORECEPTOR FOR BLUE-UV MEDIATED RESPONSES? Proc. XI Int. Bot. Congr. p. 85 (A).

0971. Hartmann, K.M.; Unser, I.C. 1972. ANALYTICAL ACTION SPECTROSCOPY WITH LIVING SYSTEMS: PHOTOCHEMICAL ASPECTS AND ATTENUANCE. Ber. Dtsch. Bot. Ges. 85: 481-551.

0972. Hartmann, K.M.; Unser, I.C. 1973. CAROTENOIDS AND FLAVINS VERSUS PHYTO-CHROME AS THE CONTROLLING PIGMENT FOR BLUE-UV-MEDIATED PHOTORESPON-SES. Z. Pflanzenphysiol. 69: 109-124 (ENG Summary).

0973. Hartt, C.E. 1966. TRANSLOCATION IN COLORED LIGHT. Plant Physiol. 41: 369-372.

0974. Hashimoto, N.; Shihira, I.; Ishikawa, S. 1954. EFFECT OF COLORED LIGHT ON THE GERMINATION OF FOREST TREE SEEDS. Nippon Rin Gakkai-shi 36: 63-65 (JAP) (ENG Summary).

0975. Haslett, B.G.; Cammack, R. 1974. THE DEVELOPMENT OF PLASTOCYANIN IN GREENING BEAN LEAVES. Biochem. J. 144: 567-572.

0976. Haupt, W. 1958. HELLROT-DUNKELROT-ANTAGONISMUS BEI DER AUSLÖSUNG DER CHLOROPLASTENBEWEGUNG. Naturwissenschaften 45: 273-274.

0977. Haupt, W.; Mugele, F.; Müller, D. 1959. AUSLÖSUNG DER CHLOROPLASTENDRE-HUNG BEI *MOUGEOTIA* DURCH UV-STRAHLUNG. Naturwissenschaften 46: 409.

0978. Haupt, W. 1959. DIE CHLOROPLASTENDREHUNG BEI *MOUGEOTIA* I. ÜBER DEN QUANTITATIVEN UND QUALITATIVEN LICHTBEDARF DER SCHWACHLICHTBEWEGUNG. Planta 53: 484-501 (ENG Summary).

0979. Haupt, W. 1959. CHLOROPLASTENBEWEGUNG. *Handbuch der Pflanzenphysio-logie*, Ed. E. Bunning, Berlin, Gottingen and Heidelberg; Springer-Verlag 17: 278-317 (R).

0980. Haupt, W.; Köhler, G.; Müller, D. 1960. CHLOROPLASTENBEWEGUNG IN POLARISIERTEN LICHT. Naturwissenschaften 47: 113.

0981. Haupt, W. 1960. DIE CHLOROPLASTENDREHUNG BEI *MOUGEOTIA* II. DIE INDUK-
TION DER SCHWACHLICHTBEWEGUNG DURCH LINEAR POLARISIERTES LICHT.
Planta 55: 465-479 (ENG Summary).

0982. Haupt, W. 1961. CHLOROPLASTENBEWEGUNG IN POLARISIERTEM LICHT. Proc.
III Int. Congr. Photobiol., pp. 363-365 (R).

0983. Haupt, W.; Thiele, R. 1961. CHLOROPLASTENBEWEGUNG BEI *MESOTAENIUM*.
Planta 56: 388-401 (ENG Summary).

0984. Haupt, W. 1962. DIE ORIENTIERUNG DER PHYTOCHROM-MOLEKÜLE IN DER
Mougeotia-ZELLE. Ber. Dtsch. Bot. Ges. 75: 456 (A).

0985. Haupt, W. 1962. INTRACELLULAR MOVEMENTS. *Physiology and Biochemistry
of Algae*, Ed. R.A. Levin, Academic Press, New York and London, pp.
567-572 (R).

0986. Haupt, W. 1962. ÜBER DIE LOKALISIERUNG DES PHYTOCHROMS IN DER *MOUGEOTIA*
ZELLE. *Beiträge zur Physiologie und Morphologie der Algen*, G.
Fischer Stuttgart: pp. 116-122 (R).

0987. Haupt, W.; Bock, G. 1962. DIE CHLOROPLASTENDREHUNG BEI *MOUGEOTIA* IV.
DIE ORIENTIERUNG DER PHYTOCHROM-MOLEKÜLE IM CYTOPLASMA. Planta 59:
38-48 (ENG Summary).

0988. Haupt, W.; Schönbohm, E. 1962. DAS WIRKUNGSSPEKTRUM DER "NEGATIVEN
PHOTOTAXIS" DES *MOUGEOTIA*-CHLOROPLASTEN. Naturwissenschaften 49: 42.

0989. Haupt, W.; Schönfeld, I. 1962. ÜBER DAS WIRKUNGSSPEKTRUM DER "NEGATIVEN
PHOTOTAXIS" DER *VAUCHERIA*-CHLOROPLASTEN. Ber. Dtsch. Bot. Ges. 75:
14-23.

0990. Haupt, W. 1963. PHOTORECEPTORPROBLEME DER CHLOROPLASTENBEWEGUNG. Ber.
Dtsch. Bot. Ges. 76: 313-322 (R).

0991. Haupt, W.; Schönfeld, I. 1963. DIE WIRKUNG VON KURZWELLIGER STRAHLUNG
AUF DIE SCHWACHLICHTBEWEGUNG DES *MOUGEOTIA*-CHLOROPLASTEN. Z. Bot.
51: 17-31 (ENG Summary).

0992. Haupt, W.; Fetzer, J. 1964. ENERGETICS OF THE CHLOROPLAST MOVEMENT IN
MOUGEOTIA. Nature (London) 201: 1048-1049.

0993. Haupt, W. 1964. BEWEGUNGEN. Fortschr. Bot. 26: 267-288 (R).

0994. Haupt, W.; Mugele, F.; Schönbohm, E. 1964. DIE BEEINFLUSSUNG DES PHYTO-
CHROMSYSTEMS DURCH KURZWELLIGE STRAHLUNG. Naturwissenschaften 51:
467-468.

0995. Haupt, W. 1965. DIE ORIENTIERUNG DER PFLANZEN ZUM LICHT. Naturwiss.
Rundsch. 18: 261-267 (R).

0996. Haupt, W. 1965. PERCEPTION OF ENVIRONMENTAL STIMULI ORIENTING GROWTH
       AND MOVEMENT IN LOWER PLANTS. Annu. Rev. Plant Physiol. 16: 267-290
       (R).

0997. Haupt, W. 1966. BEWEGUNGEN. Fortschr. Bot. 28: 135-141 (R).

0998. Haupt, W. 1966. PHOTOTAXIS IN PLANTS. Int. Rev. Cytol. 19: 267-299
       (R).

0999. Haupt, W. 1966. DIE INVERSION DER SCHWACHLICHTBEWEGUNG DES *MOUGEOTIA*-
       CHLOROPLASTEN: VERSUCHE ZUR KINETIK DER PHYTOCHROM-UMWANDLUNG. Z.
       Pflanzenphysiol. 54: 151-160 (ENG Summary).

1000. Haupt, W.; Gärtner, R. 1966. DIE CHLOROPLASTEN-ORIENTIERUNG VON
       MESOTAENIUM IN STARKEM LICHT. Naturwissenschaften 53: 411.

1001. Haupt, W.; Kraml, M. 1966. WECHSELWIRKUNG KURZWELLIGER UND LANGWELLIGER
       STRAHLUNG BEI DER PHOTOMORPHOGENESE VON *PISUM* UND *SINAPIS*. Natur-
       wissenschaften 53: 616.

1002. Haupt, W.; Weisenseel, M. 1966. DIE TEMPERATURABHÄNGIGKEIT DER CHLORO-
       PLASTENBEWEGUNGEN BEI *LEMNA TRISULCA*. Naturwissenschaften 53:
       411-412.

1003. Haupt, W. 1967. SOME NEW ASPECTS OF PHOTOMORPHOGENESIS IN PLANTS.
       Proc. Eur. Annu. Symp. Plant Photomorphogenesis, (Hvar), pp. 3-6 (R).

1004. Haupt, W.; Seitz, K. 1967. FÖRDERNDE UND HEMMENDE DUNKELROT-WIRKUNGEN
       BEI DER PHYTOCHROMINDUZIERTEN CHLOROPLASTENBEWEGUNG VON *MOUGEOTIA*.
       Z. Pflanzenphysiol. 56: 102-103 (ENG Summary).

1005. Haupt, W.; Wirth, H. 1967. NACHWEIS EINER SCHRAUBENSTRUKTUR IN DER
       MOUGEOTIA ZELLE. Plant Cell. Physiol. 8: 541-543 (R).

1006. Haupt, W. 1968. LOCALIZATION AND ORIENTATION OF PHYTOCHROME IN
       MOUGEOTIA. Proc. V. Int. Congr. Photobiol. p. 158 (A).

1007. Haupt, W. 1968. DAS PHYTOCHROMSYSTEM DER MOUGEOTIAZELLE: WEITERE UNTER-
       SUCHUNGEN ÜBER DEN P_{730}-GRADIENTEN. Z. Pflanzenphysiol. 59: 45-55
       (ENG Summary).

1008. Haupt, W. 1968. DIE ORIENTIERUNG DER PHYTOCHROM-MOLEKÜLE IN DER MOU-
       GEOTIAZELLE: EIN NEUES MODELL ZUR DEUTUNG DER EXPERIMENTELLEN BE-
       FUNDE. Z. Pflanzenphysiol. 58: 331-346 (ENG Summary).

1009. Haupt, W. 1968. DIE ORIENTIERUNGSBEWEGUNGEN DER CHLOROPLASTEN. Biol.
       Rundsch. 6: 121-136.

1010. Haupt, W.; Lindner, H. 1968. MORPHOGENESE BEI *PISUM SATIVUM* ALS REAK-
TION AUF MINIMALE P_{730}-KONZENTRATION. Planta 80: 110-112 (ENG
Summary).

1011. Haupt, W. 1969. LOCALIZATION AND DICHROIC ORIENTATION OF PHYTOCHROME.
Proc. XI Int. Bot. Congr. p. 86 (A).

1012. Haupt, W. 1969. BEWEGUNGEN. Fortschr. Bot. 31: 164-171 (R).

1013. Haupt, W. 1969. VERGLEICH DER PHYTOCHROMREAKTIONEN DES INTERNODIUMS
UND DES BLATTSTIELS INTAKTER *PISUM*-KEIMLINGE. Z. Pflanzenphysiol.
61: 401-421 (ENG Summary).

1014. Haupt, W.; Kröger, B.; Laux, A. 1969. AKTIONSDICHROISMUS DER CHLORO-
PLASTENBEWEGUNG VON *MOUGEOTIA* IM BLAULICHT. Naturwissenschaften 56:
642.

1015. Haupt, W.; Mörtel, G.; Winkelnkemper, I. 1969. DEMONSTRATION OF
DIFFERENT DICHROIC ORIENTATION OF PHYTOCHROME P_r AND P_{fr}. Planta 88:
183-186 (ENG Summary).

1016. Haupt, W. 1970. HELLROT-UND DUNKELROT-WECHSELWIRKUNGEN BEI DER CHLORO-
PLASTENDREHUNG VON *MOUGEOTIA*. Wiss. Z. Ernst-Moritz-Arndt-Univ.
Greifsw. Math. Naturwiss. Reihe 19: 47-54 (ENG Summary).

1017. Haupt, W. 1970. ÜBER DEN DICHROISMUS VON PHYTOCHROM$_{660}$ UND PHYTO-
CHROM$_{730}$ BEI *MOUGEOTIA*. Z. Pflanzenphysiol. 62: 287-298 (ENG
Summary).

1018. Haupt, W. 1970. LOCALIZATION OF PHYTOCHROME IN THE CELL. Physiol.
Veg. 8: 551-563 (R).

1019. Haupt, W. 1970. CHLOROPLASTENBEWEGUNG BEI *MOUGEOTIA*: VERGLEICH DER
INDUKTIONSWIRKUNG VON BLAULICHT UND ROTLICHT. Ber. Dtsch. Bot.
Ges. 83: 201 (A).

1020. Haupt, W.; Kröger, B.; Lindner, H. 1970. SCHNELLE PHYTOCHROMREAKTIONEN
BEI *PISUM SATIVUM?* Z. Pflanzenphysiol. 63: 19-24 (ENG Summary).

1021. Haupt, W.; Schönbohm, E. 1970. LIGHT-ORIENTED CHLOROPLAST MOVEMENTS.
Photobiology of Microorganisms, Ed. P. Halldal, Wiley-Interscience,
New York, pp. 283-307 (R).

1022. Haupt, W. 1971. BLUE LIGHT EFFECTS ON PHYTOCHROME RESPONSE IN THE
ALGA *MOUGEOTIA*. Proc. Eur. Annu. Symp. Plant Photomorphogenesis,
(Athens), p. 25 (A).

1023. Haupt, W. 1971. CHLOROPLAST MOVEMENT AS AN EXAMPLE OF ORIENTED
PHYTOCHROME RESPONSE. Adv. Sci. 27: 341-346 (R).

1024. Haupt, W. 1971. SCHWACHLICHTBEWEGUNG DES *MOUGEOTIA*-CHLOROPLASTEN IM
      BLAULICHT. Z. Pflanzenphysiol. 65: 248-265 (ENG Summary).

1025. Haupt, W. 1972. SHORT-TERM PHENOMENA CONTROLLED BY PHYTOCHROME.
      Phytochrome, Ed. K. Mitrakos and W. Shropshire, Jr., Academic
      Press: London and New York, pp. 349-368 (R).

1026. Haupt, W. 1972. LOCALIZATION OF PHYTOCHROME WITHIN THE CELL. *Phyto-
      chrome,* Ed. K. Mitrakos and W. Shropshire, Jr., Academic Press:
      London and New York, pp. 553-569 (R).

1026.5 Haupt, W. 1972. PERCEPTION OF LIGHT DIRECTION IN ORIENTED DISPLACEMENTS
      OF CELL ORGANELLES. Acta Protozool. 11: 179-188 (R).

1027. Haupt, W. 1973. ROLE OF LIGHT IN CHLOROPLAST MOVEMENT. BioScience 23:
      289-296 (R).

1028. Hauschild, A.H.W.; Nelson, C.D.; Krotkov, G. 1961. THE EFFECT OF LIGHT
      QUALITY ON THE PRODUCTS OF PHOTOSYNTHESIS IN *CHLORELLA VULGARIS*.
      Plant Physiol. 36: Suppl.-26 (A).

1029. Hauschild, A.H.W.; Nelson, C.D.; Krotkov, G. 1962. THE EFFECT OF LIGHT
      QUALITY ON THE PRODUCTS OF PHOTOSYNTHESIS IN *CHLORELLA VULGARIS*.
      Can. J. Bot. 40: 179-189.

1030. Hauschild, A.H.W.; Nelson, C.D.; Krotkov, G. 1962. THE EFFECT OF LIGHT
      QUALITY ON THE PRODUCTS OF PHOTOSYNTHESIS IN GREEN AND BLUE-GREEN
      ALGAE, AND IN PHOTOSYNTHETIC BACTERIA. Can. J. Bot. 40: 1619-1630.

1031. Hauschild, A.H.W. 1963. THE EFFECT OF LIGHT QUALITY ON THE SOLUBLE
      PRODUCTS OF PHOTOSYNTHESIS. Ph.D. Thesis, Queen's Univ., Kingston,
      Ontario (not obtained).

1032. Hauschild, A.H.W.; Nelson, C.D.; Krotkov, G. 1964. CONCURRENT CHANGES
      IN THE PRODUCTS AND THE RATE OF PHOTOSYNTHESIS IN *CHLORELLA VULGARIS*
      IN THE PRESENCE OF BLUE LIGHT. Naturwissenschaften 51: 274.

1033. Hauschild, A.H.W.; Nelson, C.D.; Krotkov, G. 1965. ON THE MODE OF
      ACTION OF BLUE LIGHT ON THE PRODUCTS OF PHOTOSYNTHESIS IN *CHLORELLA
      VULGARIS*. Naturwissenschaften 52: 435.

1034. Hayes, R.G.; Klein, W.H. 1974. SPECTRAL QUALITY INFLUENCE OF LIGHT
      DURING DEVELOPMENT OF *ARABIDOPSIS THALIANA* PLANTS IN REGULATING
      SEED GERMINATION. Plant Cell Physiol. 15: 643-653.

1035. Heald, F. De F. 1898. CONDITIONS FOR THE GERMINATION OF THE SPORES OF
      BRYOPHYTES AND PTERIDOPHYTES. Bot. Gaz. (Chicago) 26: 25-45.

1036. Heath, O.V.S. 1959. LIGHT AND CARBON DIOXIDE IN STOMATAL MOVEMENTS. Handb. Pflanzenphysiol. 17/1: 415-464 (R).

1037. Heath, O.V.S.; Vince, D. 1962. SOME NON-PHOTOSYNTHETIC EFFECTS OF LIGHT ON HIGHER PLANTS WITH SPECIAL REFERENCE TO WAVELENGTH. Symp. Soc. Exp. Biol. 16: 110-137 (R).

1038. Hehl, M.; Kranz, A.R. 1971. QUANTITATIVE MODIFICATIONS OF THE PHYTO-CHROME TRIGGER MECHANISM IN SEED DORMANCY OF HOMOALLELIC GENOTYPES. Arabidopsis Inf. Serv. No. 8, pp. 16-17.

1039. Hehl, M.; Kranz, A.R. 1974. PHYTOCHROME-MEDIATED PHOTOPERIODIC REAC-TIONS IN TWO GENOTYPES OF *ARABIDOPSIS THALIANA* (L.) HEYNH. Arabidopsis Inf. Serv. No. 11, pp. 18-19.

1040. Heim, C. 1896. UNTERSUCHUNGEN ÜBER FARNPROTHALLIEN. Flora 82: 329-373.

1041. Heinricher, E. 1899. EIN FALL BESCHLEUNIGENDER WIRKUNG DES LICHTES AUF DIE SAMENKEIMUNG. Ber. Dtsch. Bot. Ges. 17: 308-311.

1042. Heinricher, E. 1908. DIE SAMENKEIMUNG UND DAS LICHT. Ber. Dtsch. Bot. Ges. 26: 298-301.

1043. Heinricher, E. 1909. DIE KEIMUNG VON *PHACELIA TANACETIFOLIA* BENTH. UND DAS LICHT. Bot. Ztg. 67: 45-66.

1044. Heinricher, E. 1912. SAMENREIFE UND SAMENRUHE DER MISTEL *(VISCUM ALBUM* L.) UND DIE UMSTÄNDE, WELCHE DIE KEIMUNG BEEINFLUSSEN. Sitzungsber. Akad. Wiss. Wien Math. Naturwiss. Kl. Abt. 1, 121: 573-613.

1045. Helms, K.; David, D.J. 1973. FAR RED AND WHITE LIGHT-PROMOTED UTILIZA-TION OF CALCIUM BY SEEDLINGS OF *PHASEOLUS VULGARIS* L. Plant Physiol. 51: 37-42.

1046. Hendricks, S.B.; Borthwick, H.A.; Parker, M.W. 1953. ACTION SPECTRA AND PIGMENT TYPE FOR PHOTOPERIODIC CONTROL OF PLANTS. Proc. VII Int. Bot. Congr., p. 785 (A) (R).

1047. Hendricks, S.B.; Borthwick, H.A. 1954. TIME DEPENDENCIES IN PHOTO-PERIODISM. Proc. VIII Int. Bot. Congr., pp. 323-324 (A) (R).

1048. Hendricks, S.B.; Borthwick, H.A. 1954. PHOTOPERIODISM IN PLANTS. Proc. I Int. Congr. Photobiol., pp. 23-35 (R).

1049. Hendricks, S.B.; Borthwick, H.A. 1955. PHOTORESPONSIVE GROWTH. *Aspects of Synthesis and Order in Growth,* Ed. D. Rudnick, pp. 149-169 (R-D).

1050. Hendricks, S.B. 1956. CONTROL OF GROWTH AND REPRODUCTION BY LIGHT AND DARKNESS. Am. Sci. 44: 229-247 (R).

1051. Hendricks, S.B.; Borthwick, H.A.; Downs, R.J. 1956. PIGMENT CONVERSION IN THE FORMATIVE RESPONSES OF PLANTS TO RADIATION. Proc. Nat. Acad. Sci. USA 42: 19-26.

1052. Hendricks, S.B.; Siegelman, H.W. 1956. CONTROL OF ANTHOCYANIN FORMATION IN PLANTS. Science 124: 938 (A).

1053. Hendricks, S.B. 1958. PHOTOPERIODISM. Agron. J. 50: 724-729 (R).

1054. Hendricks, S.B. 1959. SOME PHOTO-REACTIONS CONTROLLING PLANT DEVELOPMENT. Proc. IX Int. Bot. Congr. 2: 161 (A) (R).

1055. Hendricks, S.B. 1959. THE PHOTOREACTION AND ASSOCIATED CHANGES OF PLANT PHOTOMORPHOGENESIS. *Photoperiodism and Related Phenomena,* Ed. R.B. Withrow, A.A.A.S., Washington, D.C., pp. 423-438 (R).

1056. Hendricks, S.B.; Borthwick, H.A. 1959. PHOTOCONTROL OF PLANT DEVELOPMENT BY THE STIMULTANEOUS EXCITATION OF TWO INTERCONVERTIBLE PIGMENTS. II. THEORY AND CONTROL OF ANTHOCYANIN SYNTHESIS. Bot. Gaz. (Chicago) 120: 187-193 (R-D).

1057. Hendricks, S.B.; Borthwick, H.A. 1959. PHOTOCONTROL OF PLANT DEVELOPMENT BY THE SIMULTANEOUS EXCITATIONS OF TWO INTERCONVERTIBLE PIGMENTS. Proc. Nat. Acad. Sci. USA 45: 344-349 (R-D).

1058. Hendricks, S.B.; Toole, E.H.; Toole, V.K.; Borthwick, H.A. 1959. PHOTOCONTROL OF PLANT DEVELOPMENT BY THE SIMULTANEOUS EXCITATIONS OF TWO INTERCONVERTIBLE PIGMENTS. III. CONTROL OF SEED GERMINATION AND AXIS ELONGATION. Bot. Gaz. (Chicago) 121: 1-8.

1059. Hendricks, S.B. 1960. RATES OF CHANGE OF PHYTOCHROME AS AN ESSENTIAL FACTOR DETERMINING PHOTOPERIODISM IN PLANTS. Cold Spring Harbor Symp. Quant. Biol. 25: 245-248.

1060. Hendricks, S.B. 1960. CONTROL OF PLANT GROWTH BY PHYTOCHROME. *Comparative Effects of Radiation,* M. Burton, Krieger, Huntington, New York, pp. 22-43 (R).

1061. Hendricks, S.B. 1960. THE PHOTOREACTIONS CONTROLLING PHOTOPERIODISM AND RELATED RESPONSES. *Symposium on Comparative Biology.* I. Comparative biochemistry of photoreactive systems. Ed. M.B. Allen, Academic Press, New York, pp. 303-319 (R).

1062. Hendricks, S.B.; Butler, W.L. 1961. SOME PHOTOREACTIONS CONTROLLING PLANT DEVELOPMENT. Recent Adv. Bot. 2: 1035-1038 (R-D).

1063. Hendricks, S.B.; Butler, W.L.; Siegelman, H.W. 1962. A REVERSIBLE
      PHOTOREACTION REGULATING PLANT GROWTH. *Symposium on Reversible*
      Photochemical Processes. U.S. Army Research Office (Durham), Duke
      University, pp. 651-662 (R).

1064. Hendricks, S.B.; Butler, W.L.; Siegelman, H.W. 1962. A REVERSIBLE
      PHOTOREACTION REGULATING PLANT GROWTH. J. Phys. Chem. 66: 2550-2555.

1065. Hendricks, S.B. 1963. METABOLIC CONTROL OF TIMING. Science 141: 21-27
      (R).

1066. Hendricks, S.B.; Borthwick, H.A. 1963. CONTROL OF PLANT GROWTH BY
      LIGHT. *Environment Control of Plant Growth,* Ed. L.T. Evans, Academic
      Press, New York and London, pp. 233-263 (R).

1067. Hendricks, S.B. 1964. PHOTOCHEMICAL ASPECTS OF PLANT PHOTOPERIODICITY.
      "Photophysiology" Ed. A.C. Geise, Academic Press: New York and
      London, pp. 305-331 (R).

1068. Hendricks, S.B.; Borthwick, H.A. 1965. THE PHYSIOLOGICAL FUNCTIONS OF
      PHYTOCHROME. *Chemistry and Biochemistry of Plant Pigments.* Ed.
      T.W. Goodwin, Academic Press, New York and London, pp. 405-436 (R).

1069. Hendricks, S.B. 1967. LIGHT IN PLANT LIFE. *Harvesting the Sun;*
      Photosynthesis in Plant Life, Ed. A. San Pietro, Academic Press, New
      York, pp. 1-14 (R).

1070. Hendricks, S.B.; Borthwick, H.A. 1967. THE FUNCTION OF PHYTOCHROME IN
      REGULATION OF PLANT GROWTH. Proc. Nat. Acad. Sci. USA 58: 2125-
      2130 (R).

1071. Hendricks, S.B.; Siegelman, H.W. 1967. PHYTOCHROME AND PHOTOPERIODISM
      IN PLANTS. Comp. Biochem. 27: 211-235 (R).

1072. Hendricks, S.B. 1968. HOW LIGHT INTERACTS WITH LIVING MATTER. Sci.
      Am. 219: 174-186 (R).

1073. Hendricks, S.B.; Toole, V.K.; Borthwick, H.A. 1968. OPPOSING ACTIONS
      OF LIGHT IN SEED GERMINATION OF *POA PRATENSIS* AND *AMARANTHUS ARENI-*
      COLA. Plant Physiol. 43: 2023-2028.

1074. Hendricks, S.B. 1969. LIGHT IN PLANT AND ANIMAL DEVELOPMENT. Dev.
      Biol. Suppl. 3: 227-243 (R).

1075. Hendricks, S.B. 1970. THE PASSING SCENE. Annu. Rev. Plant Physiol. 21:
      1-10 (R).

1076. Henshall, J.D.; Goodwin, T.W. 1964. THE EFFECT OF RED AND FAR-RED
       LIGHT ON CAROTENOID AND CHLOROPHYLL FORMATION IN PEA SEEDLINGS.
       Photochem. Photobiol. 3: 243-247.

1077. Henshall, J.D.; Goodwin, T.W. 1964. AMINO ACID-ACTIVATING ENZYMES IN
       GERMINATING PEA SEEDLINGS. Phytochemistry 3: 677-691.

1078. Henslow, G. 1886. A CONTRIBUTION TO THE STUDY OF THE RELATIVE EFFECTS
       OF DIFFERENT PARTS OF THE SOLAR SPECTRUM ON THE TRANSPIRATION OF
       PLANTS. J. Linn. Soc. London Bot. 22: 81-98.

1079. Herm, K.; Tevini, M. 1974. DIE WIRKUNG VON ROTLICHT AUF DIE SYNTHESE
       DER GLYKO- UND PHOSPHOLIPIDE BEI DER KEIMUNG VON *HORDEUM VULGARE*.
       Z. Pflanzenphysiol. 73: 349-359.

1080. Hewett, E.W.; Wareing, P.F. 1973. CYTOKININS IN *POPULUS* X *ROBUSTA*
       (SCHNEID): LIGHT EFFECTS ON ENDOGENOUS LEVELS. Planta 114: 119-129.

1081. Hibben, S.G. 1924. INFLUENCE OF COLORED LIGHT ON PLANT GROWTH. Trans.
       Illum. Eng. Soc. 19: 1000-1010.

1082. Higgins, G.M.; Sheard, C. 1927. GERMINATION AND GROWTH OF SEEDS AS
       DEPENDENT UPON SELECTIVE IRRADIATION. Plant Physiol. 2: 325-335.

1083. Hillman, W.S.; Galston, A.W. 1956. A PHOTOINDUCED INCREASE OF AN IAA
       OXIDASE INHIBITOR IN ETIOLATED PEAS. Plant Physiol. 31: Suppl.-13
       (A).

1084. Hillman, W.S. 1957. CONTROL OF PEA INTERNODE SECTION GROWTH BY PHOTO-
       PERIODICALLY ACTIVE RADIATIONS, GROWTH SUBSTANCES, AND SUCROSE.
       Plant Physiol. 32: Suppl.-48 (A).

1085. Hillman, W.S. 1957. THE EFFECT OF LIGHT AND KINETIN ON NON-PHOTOSYNTHE-
       TIC GROWTH IN THE *LEMNACEAE*. Plant Physiol. 32: Suppl.-48 (A).

1086. Hillman, W.S.; Galston, A.W. 1957. INDUCTIVE CONTROL OF INDOLEACETIC
       ACID OXIDASE ACTIVITY BY RED AND NEAR INFRARED LIGHT. Plant Physiol.
       32: 129-135.

1087. Hillman, W.S. 1957. NONPHOTOSYNTHETIC LIGHT REQUIREMENT IN *LEMNA MINOR*
       AND ITS PARTIAL SATISFACTION BY KINETIN. Science 126: 165-166.

1088. Hillman, W.S. 1958. PHOTOPERIODIC CONTROL OF FLOWERING IN *LEMNA*
       PERPUSILLA. Nature (London) 181: 1275.

1089. Hillman, W.S. 1959. EXPERIMENTAL CONTROL OF FLOWERING IN *LEMNA* I.
       GENERAL METHODS. PHOTOPERIODISM IN *L. PERPUSILLA* 6746. Am. J. Bot.
       46: 466-473.

1090. Hillman, W.S. 1959. INTERACTION OF GROWTH SUBSTANCES AND PHOTOPERIODI-
CALLY ACTIVE RADIATIONS ON THE GROWTH OF PEA INTERNODE SECTIONS.
Photoperiodism and Related Phenomena in Plants and Animals, Ed.
R.B. Withrow, A.A.A.S., Washington, D.C., pp. 181-196.

1091. Hillman, W.S. 1960. CONTROL BY LIGHT. *Control Mechanisms in Cellular
Processes,* Ed. D.M. Bonner, Ronald Press, New York, pp. 213-226 (R).

1092. Hillman, W.S. 1962. EXPERIMENTAL CONTROL OF FLOWERING IN *LEMNA*. IV.
INHIBITION OF PHOTOPERIODIC SENSITIVITY BY COPPER. Am. J. Bot. 49:
892-897.

1093. Hillman, W.S. 1962. PHOTOPERIODISM: ATTEMPTS AT ANALYSIS. *The
Physiology of Flowering,* Holt, Rinehart and Winston, New York,
pp. 30-53 (R).

1094. Hillman, W.S. 1963. PHOTOPERIODISM: AN EFFECT OF DARKNESS DURING THE
LIGHT PERIOD ON CRITICAL NIGHT LENGTH. Science 140: 1397-1398.

1095. Hillman, W.S. 1964. ENDOGENOUS CIRCADIAN RHYTHMS AND THE RESPONSE OF
LEMNA PERPUSILLA TO SKELETON PHOTOPERIODS. Am. Nat. 98: 323-328.

1096. Hillman, W.S. 1964. PHYTOCHROME LEVELS DETECTABLE BY *IN VIVO* SPECTRO-
PHOTOMETRY IN PLANT PARTS GROWN OR STORED IN THE LIGHT. Am. J.
Bot. 51: 1102-1107.

1097. Hillman, W.S. 1965. PHYTOCHROME CONVERSION BY BRIEF ILLUMINATION AND
THE SUBSEQUENT ELONGATION OF ETIOLATED *PISUM* STEM SEGMENTS. Physiol.
Plant. 18: 346-358.

1098. Hillman, W.S. 1965. RED LIGHT, BLUE LIGHT, AND COPPER ION IN THE PHOTO-
PERIODIC CONTROL OF FLOWERING IN *LEMNA PERPUSILLA* 6746. Plant Cell
Physiol. 6: 499-506.

1099. Hillman, W.S. 1966. RESPONSES OF *AVENA* AND *PISUM* TISSUES TO PHYTOCHROME
CONVERSION BY RED LIGHT. Plant Physiol. 41: 907-908.

1100. Hillman, W.S. 1966. PHOTOPERIODISM IN *LEMNA:* REVERSAL OF NIGHT-
INTERRUPTION DEPENDS ON COLOR OF THE MAIN PHOTOPERIOD. Science 154:
1360-1362.

1101. Hillman, W.S.; Purves, W.K. 1966. LIGHT RESPONSES, GROWTH FACTORS AND
PHYTOCHROME TRANSFORMATIONS OF *CUCUMIS* SEEDLING TISSUES. Planta 70:
275-284.

1102. Hillman, W.S. 1967. BLUE LIGHT, PHYTOCHROME AND THE FLOWERING OF *LEMNA
PERPUSILLA* 6746. Plant Cell Physiol. 8: 467-473.

1103. Hillman, W.S. 1967. THE PHYSIOLOGY OF PHYTOCHROME. Annu. Rev. Plant Physiol. 18: 301-324 (R).

1104. Hillman, W.S.; Koukkari, W.L. 1967. PHYTOCHROME EFFECTS IN THE NYCTI-NASTIC LEAF MOVEMENTS OF *ALBIZZIA JULIBRISSIN* AND SOME OTHER LEGUMES. Plant Physiol. 42: 1413-1418.

1105. Hillman, W.S. 1968. SPECTROPHOTOMETRIC PHYTOCHROME AND PHYSIOLOGICAL PHYTOCHROME. Proc. V Int. Congr. Photobiol., p. 100 (A).

1106. Hillman, W.S. 1968. PHYTOCHROME SPECTRUM OF *PISUM* LEAVES AND STEMS. Biochim. Biophys. Acta 162: 464-466.

1107. Hillman, W.S. 1969. PHOTOPERIODISM AND VERNALIZATION. *Physiology of Plant Growth and Development,* Ed. M.B. Wilkins, McGraw-Hill, New York, pp. 558-601 (R).

1108. Hillman, W.S. 1970. CARBON DIOXIDE OUTPUT AS AN INDEX OF CIRCADIAN TIMING IN *LEMNA* PHOTOPERIODISM. Plant Physiol. 45: 273-279.

1109. Hillman, W.S. 1971. ENTRAINMENT OF *LEMNA* CO_2 OUTPUT THROUGH PHYTO-CHROME. Proc. Eur. Annu. Symp. Plant Photomorphogenesis, (Athens), p. 26 (A).

1110. Hillman, W.S. 1971. ENTRAINMENT OF *LEMNA* CO_2 OUTPUT THROUGH PHYTO-CHROME. Plant Physiol. 47: Suppl.-13, Abstr. No. 77 (A).

1111. Hillman, W.S. 1971. NITRATE AND THE COURSE OF *LEMNA PERPUSILLA* CARBON DIOXIDE OUTPUT UNDER DAILY PHOTOPERIODIC CYCLES. Plant Physiol. 47: 431-434.

1112. Hillman, W.S. 1971. ENTRAINMENT OF *LEMNA* CO_2 OUTPUT THROUGH PHYTO-CHROME. Plant Physiol. 48: 770-774.

1113. Hillman, W.S.; Posner, H.B. 1971. AMMONIUM ION AND THE FLOWERING OF *LEMNA PERPUSILLA*. Plant Physiol. 47: 586-587.

1114. Hillman, W.S. 1972. INTERACTION OF LIGHT AND RHYTHMS. Proc. VI Int. Congr. Photobiol., Abstr. No. 027 (A) (R).

1115. Hillman, W.S. 1972. PHOTOPERIODIC ENTRAINMENT PATTERNS IN THE CO_2 OUT-PUT OF *LEMNA PERPUSILLA* 6746 AND OF SEVERAL OTHER LEMNACEAE. Plant Physiol. 49: 907-911.

1116. Hillman, W.S. 1972. ON THE PHYSIOLOGICAL SIGNIFICANCE OF *IN VIVO* PHYTOCHROME ASSAYS. *Phytochrome,* Ed. K. Mitrakos and W. Shropshire, Jr., Academic Press, New York and London, pp. 573-584 (R).

1117. Hillman, W.S. 1973. LIGHT, TIME, AND THE SIGNALS OF THE YEAR. BioScience 23: 81-86 (R).

1118. Hillman, W.S. 1974. TOWARDS A REAL-TIME ANALYSIS OF PHOTOPERIODISM: EFFECTS OF NITROGEN SOURCE ON TIMING AND PHYTOCHROME RESPONSE IN *LEMNA* CARBON DIOXIDE OUTPUT. Am. J. Bot. 61: 28 (A).

1119. Hobson, D.J. 1974. THE PHOTOCONTROL OF THE RATE OF AMINO ACID INCORPORATION INTO BEAN LEAF PROTEINS. Proc. Eur. Annu. Symp. Plant Photomorphogenesis, (Antwerpen), pp. 46-52.

1120. Hock, B.; Mohr, H. 1964. DIE REGULATION DER O_2-AUFNAHME VON SENFKEIMLINGEN *(SINAPIS ALBA* L.) DURCH LICHT. Planta 61: 209-228 (ENG Summary).

1120.5 Hock, B. 1965. DIE REGULATION DER SAUERSTOFFAUFNAHME UND EINIGER WACHSTUMSVORGÄNGE BEI SENFKEIMLINGEN *(SINAPIS ALBA* L.) DURCH LICHT. Ph.D. Thesis Univ., Freiburg, Germany.

1121. Hock, B.; Mohr, H. 1965. EINE QUANTITATIVE ANALYSE VON WACHSTUMSVORGÄNGEN IM ZUSAMMENHANG MIT DER PHOTOMORPHOGENESE VON SENFKEIMLINGEN *(SINAPIS ALBA* L.). Planta 65: 1-16 (ENG Summary).

1122. Hock, B.; Kühnert, E.; Mohr, H. 1965. DIE REGULATION VON FETTABBAU UND ATMUNG BEI SENFKEIMLINGEN DURCH LICHT *(SINAPIS ALBA* L.). Planta 65: 129-138 (ENG Summary).

1123. Hodson, H.K. 1965. THE EFFECT OF RED AND FAR-RED LIGHT ON THE DIURNAL LEAF MOVEMENTS IN *MARSILEA QUADRIFOLIA* L. Plant Physiol. 40: Suppl.-54 (A).

1124. Holdgate, D.P.; Goodwin, T.W. 1964. THE EFFECT OF RED AND FAR-RED LIGHT ON NUCLEIC ACID METABOLISM IN RYE SEEDLINGS. Proc. IV Int. Congr. Photobiol., pp. 98-99 (A).

1125. Holdgate, D.P.; Goodwin, T.W. 1965. THE EFFECT OF RED AND FAR-RED LIGHT ON NUCLEIC ACID METABOLISM IN RYE SEEDLING SHOOTS. Photochem. Photobiol. 4: 1-6.

1126. Holdsworth, M. 1960. THE SPECTRAL SENSITIVITY OF LIGHT-INDUCED LEAF MOVEMENTS. J. Exp. Bot. 11: 40-44.

1127. Holdsworth, M. 1972. PHYTOCHROME AND SEED GERMINATION. New Phytol. 71: 105-110.

1128. Holland, R.W.K.; Vince, D. 1968. PHOTOPERIODIC CONTROL OF FLOWERING AND ANTHOCYANIN FORMATION IN *FUCHSIA*. Nature (London) 219: 511-513.

1129. Holland, R.W.K. 1969. THE EFFECT OF RED AND FAR-RED LIGHT ON FLORAL INITIATION IN *LOLIUM TEMULENTUM* AND OTHER LONG-DAY PLANTS. Ph.D. Thesis, Univ. Reading, England.

1130. Holland, R.W.K.; Vince, D. 1971. FLORAL INITIATION IN *LOLIUM TEMULENTUM* L.: THE ROLE OF PHYTOCHROME IN THE RESPONSES TO RED AND FAR-RED LIGHT. Planta 98: 232-243.

1131. Holmes, M.G. 1974. PRELIMINARY STUDIES ON THE ROLE OF PHYTOCHROME IN THE NATURAL ENVIRONMENT. Proc. Eur. Annu. Symp. Plant Photomorphogenesis, (Antwerpen), pp. 37-43.

1132. Holowinsky, A.W.; Moore, P.B.; Torrey, J.G. 1965. REGULATORY ASPECTS OF CHLOROPLAST GROWTH IN LEAVES OF *XANTHIUM PENSYLVANICUM* AND ETIOLATED RED KIDNEY BEAN SEEDLING LEAVES. Protoplasma 60: 94-110.

1133. Holowinsky, A.W.; Schiff, J.A. 1970. EVENTS SURROUNDING THE EARLY DEVELOPMENT OF *EUGLENA* CHLOROPLASTS. Plant Physiol. 45: 339-347.

1134. Holowinsky, A.W.; O'Brien, T.P. 1972. BIOGENESIS OF CHLOROPLAST LAMELLAE IN ETIOLATED BEAN LEAVES; PHYTOCHROME CONTROL OF PROTEIN SYNTHESIS. Proc. VI Int. Congr. Photobiol. Abstr. No. 183 (A).

1135. Hopkins, D.W.; Butler, W.L. 1968. CIRCULAR DICHROISM OF PHYTOCHROME. Proc. V Int. Congr. Photobiol., p. 93 (A).

1136. Hopkins, D.W.; Butler, W.L. 1970. IMMUNOCHEMICAL AND SPECTROSCOPIC EVIDENCE FOR PROTEIN CONFORMATIONAL CHANGES IN PHYTOCHROME TRANSFORMATIONS. Plant Physiol. 45: 567-570.

1137. Hopkins, D.W. 1971. PROTEIN CONFORMATIONAL CHANGES OF PHYTOCHROME. Ph.D. Thesis, Univ. California, San Diego.

1138. Hopkins, D.W.; Briggs, W.R. 1973. PHYTOCHROME AND NAD KINASE: A REEXAMINATION. Plant Physiol. 51: Suppl.-52, Abstr. No. 284 (A).

1139. Hopkins, T.R. 1970. *IN VIVO* DENATURATION OF PHYTOCHROME. Proc. Univ. Otago Med. Sch. 48: 39-40.

1140. Hopkins, W.G.; Hillman, W.S. 1963. TIME-COURSE STUDIES OF NONPHOTOCHEMICAL TRANSFORMATIONS OF PHYTOCHROME IN ETIOLATED TISSUE SEGMENTS. Plant Physiol. 39: Suppl.-50 (A).

1141. Hopkins, W.G. 1964. CHEMICAL CHANGES ASSOCIATED WITH LIGHT-INDUCED LEAF EXPANSION. Ph.D. Thesis, Indiana Univ., Bloomington.

1142. Hopkins, W.G.; Hillman, W.S. 1965. RELATIONSHIPS BETWEEN PHYTOCHROME STATE AND PHOTOSENSITIVE GROWTH OF *AVENA* COLEOPTILE SEGMENTS. Plant Physiol. 40: Suppl.-54 (A).

1143. Hopkins, W.G.; Hillman, W.S. 1965. PHYTOCHROME CHANGES IN TISSUES OF DARK-GROWN SEEDLINGS REPRESENTING VARIOUS PHOTOPERIODIC CLASSES. Am. J. Bot. 52: 427-432.

1144. Hopkins, W.G.; Hillman, W.S. 1965. RESPONSE OF EXCISED *AVENA* COLEOPTILE SEGMENTS TO RED AND FAR-RED LIGHT. Planta 65: 157-166.

1145. Hopkins, W.G.; Hillman, W.S. 1966. RELATIONSHIPS BETWEEN PHYTOCHROME STATE AND PHOTOSENSITIVE GROWTH OF *AVENA* COLEOPTILE SEGMENTS. Plant Physiol. 41: 593-598.

1146. Hopkins, W.G. 1968. *AVENA* COLEOPTILE ELONGATION: STIMULATION BY RED LIGHT AND FLUOROPHENYLALANINE. Plant Physiol. 43: Suppl.-14 (A).

1147. Hopkins, W.G.; Bonnell, K.F. 1969. *AVENA* COLEOPTILE ELONGATION: STIMU-LATION BY FLUOROPHENYLALANINE. Plant Physiol. 44: 281-286.

1148. Hopkins, W.G. 1971. CORRELATION OF PHYTOCHROME TRANSFORMATIONS WITH PHOTOCONTROL OF *AVENA* COLEOPTILE SEGMENT ELONGATION. Can. J. Bot. 49: 467-470.

1149. Hopkins, W.G. 1972. INDEPENDENCE OF PHYTOCHROME DESTRUCTION AND PHYSIO-LOGICAL RESPONSE IN *AVENA* AND *PISUM* SEGMENT ELONGATION. Can. J. Bot. 50: 1-7.

1150. Horváth, I.; Szász, K. 1969. EFFECT OF SPECTRAL COMPOSITION OF LIGHT ON THE ACCUMULATION OF CARBOHYDRATES AND NITROGEN COMPOUNDS. A PROBABLE INTERPRETATION. Prog. Photosynthesis Res. 3: 1675-1677.

1151. Hoshizaki, T.; Hamner, K.C. 1969. INTERACTIONS BETWEEN LIGHT AND CIRCA-DIAN RHYTHMS IN PLANT PHOTOPERIODISM. Photochem. Photobiol. 10: 87-96 (R-D).

1152. Howland, G.P. 1971. STRUCTURAL, BIOCHEMICAL, AND PHYSIOLOGICAL ASPECTS OF PHOTOMORPHOGENESIS IN FERN GAMETOPHYTES. Ph.D. Thesis, Yale Univ. New Haven.

1153. Hsiao, A.I.; Vidaver, W. 1969. FACTORS INFLUENCING THE EFFECT OF LIGHT ON GERMINATION OF LETTUCE SEED (*LACTUCA SATIVA* L. VAR GRAND RAPIDS). Proc. 50th Annu. Meet. West. Soc. Nat. Los Angeles, Calif., p. 31 (A) (not obtained).

1154. Hsiao, A.I.; Vidaver, W. 1971. WATER CONTENT AND PHYTOCHROME-INDUCED POTENTIAL GERMINATION RESPONSES IN LETTUCE SEEDS. Plant Physiol. 47: 186-188.

1155. Hsiao, A.I.; Vidaver, W. 1971. SEED WATER CONTENT IN RELATION TO PHYTO-CHROME-MEDIATED GERMINATION OF LETTUCE SEEDS (*LACTUCA SATIVA* L. VAR. GRAND RAPIDS). Can. J. Bot. 49: 111-115.

1156. Hsiao, A.I.; Vidaver, W. 1973. DARK REVERSION OF PHYTOCHROME IN LETTUCE SEEDS STORED IN A WATER-SATURATED ATMOSPHERE. Plant Physiol. 51: 459-463.

1157. Hsiao, A.I.; Vidaver, W. 1973. INDUCED REQUIREMENTS FOR GIBBERELLIC ACID AND RED LIGHT IN GRAND RAPIDS LETTUCE SEEDS. Plant Physiol. 51: Suppl.-36, Abstr. No. 196 (A).

1158. Hsiao, A.I.; Vidaver, W. 1974. PHYTOCHROME-MEDIATED GERMINATION RESPONSES IN γ-IRRADIATED LETTUCE SEEDS. Plant Physiol. 54: 72-75.

1159. Hsiao, T.C.; Allaway, W.G.; Evans, L.T. 1973. ACTION SPECTRA FOR GUARD CELL Rb^+ UPTAKE AND STOMATAL OPENING IN *VICIA FABA*. Plant Physiol. 51: 82-88.

1160. Huault, C. 1969. L'ACTION DU PHYTOCHROME SUR LA RÉGULATION DE LA SYNTHÉSE DE LA PHENYLALANINE AMMONIA-LYASE CHEZ LA PLANTULE DE MOUTARDE (*SINAPIS ALBA* L.): UN PROBLÉME DE BIOLOGIE MOLÉCULAIRE. Ph.D. Thesis, Univ. Rouen, France (not obtained).

1161. Huault, C. 1970. CONTRÔLE DE L'ACTIVITÉ DE LA PHÉNYLALANINE AMMONIA-LYASE (PAL) PAR LE PHYTOCHROME DANS LES PLANTULES DE RADIS ET DE MOUTARDE. Physiol. Veg. 8: 532 (A).

1162. Huault, C. 1971. PHYTOCHROME AND ENZYME ACTIVITY. Proc. Eur. Annu. Symp. Plant Photomorphogenesis, (Athens), pp. 27-28 (A).

1163. Huault, C.; Klein-Eude, D.; Rollin, P.; Blondel, J.D. 1971. INFLUENCE DE LA LUMIÈRE SUR L'ACTIVITÉ PAL (=PHÉNYLALANINE AMMONIAC-LYASE, EC. 4.3.1.5) DES COTYLÉDONS DE RADIS. RÔLE DU PHYTOCHROME ET DE L'ÂGE DES TISSUS. C.R. Acad. Sci. Ser. D. 273: 745-748.

1164. Huault, C.; Larcher, G.; Malcoste, R. 1971. ANALYSE DES CINÉTIQUES DE VARIATIONS D'ACTIVITÉ-PAL (= PHÉNYLALANINE AMMONIAC-LYASE, EC. 4.3.1.5) DANS LES COTYLÉDONS DE *RAPHANUS SATIVUS* L. C.R. Acad. Sci. Ser. D: 273: 1371-1374.

1165. Huault, C. 1974. PHYTOCHROME REGULATION OF PHENYLALANINE AMMONIA-LYASE (PAL) ACTIVITY IN RADISH COTYLEDONS: A THRESHOLD MECHANISM. Plant Sci. Lett. 3: 149-155.

1166. Hughes, A.P.; Cockshull, K.E. 1964. EFFECTS OF A NIGHT BREAK OF RED FLUORESCENT LIGHT ON LEAF GROWTH OF *CALLISTEPHUS CHINENSIS* (VAR. QUEEN OF THE MARKET). Nature (London) 201: 413.

1167. Hughes, A.P.; Cockshull, K.E. 1964. THE EFFECTS OF A NIGHT BREAK OF RED
FLUORESCENT LIGHT ON LEAF GROWTH OF *CALLISTEPHUS CHINENSIS*. Proc. IV
Int. Congr. Photobiol., p. 100 (A).

1168. Hughes, A.P. 1965. DISCUSSION SECRETARY'S REPORT. *Recent Progress in
Photobiol.*, Proc. IV Int. Congr. Photobiol., Ed. E.J. Bowen, Blackwell Scientific Publications, Oxford, 1965, pp. 213-218 (R).

1169. Hughes, A.P. 1965. PHYTOCHROME DISCUSSION. *Recent Progress in Photobiol.*, Proc. IV Int. Congr. Photobiol., Ed. E.J. Bowen, Blackwell
Scientific Publications, Oxford, 1965, pp. 219-222 (R).

1170. Huisinga, B. 1964. INFLUENCE OF LIGHT ON GROWTH, GEOTROPISM AND GUTTA-
TION OF *AVENA* SEEDLINGS GROWN IN TOTAL DARKNESS. Acta Bot. Neerl.
13: 445-487.

1171. Huisinga, B. 1967. INFLUENCE OF IRRADIATION ON THE DISTRIBUTION OF
GROWTH IN DARK-GROWN *AVENA* SEEDLINGS. Acta Bot. Neerl. 16: 197-201.

1172. Huisinga, B. 1968. INFLUENCE OF RED LIGHT ON TRANSPORT OF FLUORESCEIN
IN THE MESOCOTYLS OF DARK-GROWN *AVENA* SEEDLINGS. Acta Bot. Neerl.
17: 390-392.

1173. Humphries, E.C.; Wheeler, A.W. 1963. THE PHYSIOLOGY OF LEAF GROWTH.
Annu. Rev. Plant Physiol. 14: 385-410 (R).

1174. Hunt, R. 1848. RESEARCHES ON THE INFLUENCE OF THE SOLAR RAYS ON THE
GROWTH OF PLANTS. Rep. 17th Meet. British Assoc. Adv. Sci., Oxford,
June, 1847, Published in London (1848) (8), pp. 17-30.

1175. Hunter, N.W.; Hunter, R. Jr.; King, J.W.; Pinkney, A.V. Jr. 1956.
EFFECTS OF LIGHT ON THE RATE OF RESPIRATION IN THE STEM OF *PISUM
SATIVUM* L. Plant Physiol. 31: 167-169.

1176. Hüsemann, W. 1970. DER EINFLUSS VERSCHIEDENER LICHTQUALITÄTEN AUF
CHLOROPHYLLGEHALT UND WACHSTUM VON GEWEBEKULTUREN AUS *CREPIS CAPILL-
ARIS* (L.) WALLR. Plant Cell Physiol. 11: 315-322 (ENG Summary).

1177. Ikeda, K.; Kimura, K. 1967. THE TEMPERATURE DEPENDENCE OF FLORAL INI-
TIATION. *Physiology of Flowering in Pharbitis nil*. Ed. S. Imamura,
Japanese Society of Plant Physiologist, Tokyo, pp. 95-105 (R).

1178. Ikuma, H.; Thimann, K.V. 1959. PHOTOSENSITIVE SITE IN LETTUCE SEEDS.
Science 130: 568-569.

1179. Ikuma, H.; Thimann, K.V. 1960. ACTION OF GIBBERELLIC ACID ON LETTUCE
SEED GERMINATION. Plant Physiol. 35: 557-566.

1180. Ikuma, H.; Thimann, K.V. 1961. EFFECTS OF NITROGEN ATMOSPHERE ON THE
GERMINATION OF PHOTOSENSITIVE LETTUCE SEEDS. Plant Physiol. 36:
Suppl.-42 (A).

1181. Ikuma, H.; Thimann, K.V. 1963. ACTION OF KINETIN ON PHOTOSENSITIVE GER-
MINATION OF LETTUCE SEED AS COMPARED WITH THAT OF GIBBERELLIC ACID.
Plant Cell Physiol. 4: 113-128.

1182. Ikuma, H.; Thimann, K.V. 1963. THE ROLE OF THE SEED-COATS IN GERMINA-
TION OF PHOTOSENSITIVE LETTUCE SEEDS. Plant Cell Physiol. 4: 169-
185.

1183. Ikuma, H.; Thimann, K.V. 1963. ACTIVITY OF GIBBERELLIN "D" ON THE GER-
MINATION OF PHOTOSENSITIVE LETTUCE SEEDS. Nature (London) 197:
1313-1314.

1184. Ikuma, H. 1964. THE EFFECTS OF TEMPERATURE ON THE GERMINATION AND RADI-
CLE GROWTH OF PHOTOSENSITIVE LETTUCE SEED. Plant Cell Physiol. 5:
429-439.

1185. Ikuma, H.; Bonner, W.D. Jr. 1964. EFFECT OF RED AND FAR-RED LIGHT ON
OXIDATIVE PHOSPHORYLATION BY ANIMAL AND PLANT MITOCHONDRIA. Proc. VI
Int. Congr. Biochem. New York, p. 780, Abstr. No. 31 (A).

1186. Ikuma, H.; Thimann, K.V. 1964. ANALYSIS OF GERMINATION PROCESSES OF
LETTUCE SEED BY MEANS OF TEMPERATURE AND ANAEROBIOSIS. Plant
Physiol. 39: 756-767.

1187. Imaseki, H.; Pjon, C.J.; Furuya, M. 1971. PHYTOCHROME ACTION IN *ORYZA
SATIVA* L. IV. RED AND FAR-RED REVERSIBLE EFFECT ON THE PRODUCTION
OF ETHYLENE IN EXCISED COLEOPTILES. Plant Physiol. 48: 241-244.

1188. Imhoff, C.; Brulfert, J.; Jacques, R. 1971. MISE À FLEURS, EN ÉCLAIRE-
MENT MONOCHROMATIQUE, DE L'*ANAGALLIS ARVENSIS* L. PLANTE DE JOURS
LONGS ABSOLUE: SPECTRE D'ACTION ET RÔLE DU PHYTOCHROME. C.R. Acad.
Sci. Ser. D: 273: 737-740.

1189. Inada, K. 1969. EFFECT OF BLUE LIGHT ON THE PHOTONASTIC REACTION OF
RICE LEAVES. Plant Cell Physiol. 10: 845-854.

1190. Inada, K. 1973. SPECTRAL DEPENDENCE OF GROWTH AND DEVELOPMENT OF RICE
PLANT. I. EFFECTS OF THE SELECTIVE REMOVAL OF SPECTRAL COMPONENTS
FROM WHITE LIGHT ON THE GROWTH OF SEEDLINGS. Nippon Sakumotsu Gakkai
Kiji 42: 63-71.

1191. Inoue, H. 1960. STUDIES IN SPORE GERMINATION AND THE EARLIER STAGES OF GAMETOPHYTE DEVELOPMENT IN THE *MARCHANTIALES*. J. Hattori. Bot. Lab. 23: 148-191.

1192. Irvine, J.E.; Freyre, R.H. 1961. DIAGEOTROPISM IN VANILLA ROOTS. Science 124: 56-57.

1193. Isaia, A.; Bulard, C. 1970. COMPLEXITÉ DU MODE D'ACTION DE DIVERS RÉGULATEURS DE CROISSANCE SUR LA PREMIÈRE FEUILLE DE BLÉ. C.R. Acad. Sci. Ser D.: 270: 78-81.

1194. Ishiguri, Y.; Oda, Y. 1972. THE RELATIONSHIP BETWEEN RED AND FAR-RED LIGHT ON FLOWERING OF THE LONG-DAY PLANT, *LEMNA GIBBA*. Plant Cell Physiol. 13: 131-138.

1195. Ishiguri, Y.; Oda, Y. 1974. FLOWERING OF THE LONG-DAY PLANT, *LEMNA GIBBA*, UNDER SHORT-DAY SCHEDULES COMPOSED OF RED AND FAR-RED LIGHT. Plant Cell Physiol. 15: 287-293.

1196. Isikawa, S. 1957. INTERACTION OF TEMPERATURE AND LIGHT IN THE GERMINA-TION OF *NIGELLA* SEEDS II. Bot. Mag. 70: 271-275.

1197. Isikawa, S.; Ishikawa, T. 1960. REQUIREMENT OF LOW TEMPERATURE TREAT-MENT FOLLOWING ILLUMINATION IN THE GERMINATION OF SEED OF *ELSHOLTZIA*. Plant Cell Physiol. 1: 143-149.

1198. Isikawa, S.; Fujii, T. 1961. PHOTOCONTROL AND TEMPERATURE DEPENDENCE OF GERMINATION OF *RUMEX* SEEDS. Plant Cell Physiol. 2: 51-62.

1199. Isikawa, S.; Fujii, T.; Yokohama, Y. 1961. PHOTOPERIODIC CONTROL OF THE GERMINATION OF *ERAGROSTIS* SEEDS. Bot. Mag. 74: 14-18.

1200. Isikawa, S. 1962. LIGHT SENSITIVITY AGAINST THE GERMINATION III. STUDIES ON VARIOUS PARTIAL PROCESSES IN LIGHT SENSITIVE SEEDS. Jpn. J. Bot. 18: 105-132.

1201. Ito, M. 1967. INDUCTION OF SYNCHRONOUS CELL DIVISION OF *PTERIS* BY LIGHT Proc. 32nd Annu. Meet. Bot. Soc. Japan (not obtained) [referred to by Maeda, M.; Imahori, K. (1968)], Sci. Reports, Osaka Univ. 17: 23-31.

1202. Ito, M. 1970. LIGHT-INDUCED SYNCHRONY OF CELL DIVISION IN THE PROTONEMA OF THE FERN, *PTERIS VITTATA*. Planta 90: 22-31.

1203. Iwakawa, M.; Kotani, S. 1954. EFFECT OF COLORED LIGHT ON THE GERMINA-TION OF AKAMATSU (*PINUS DENSIFLORA*) AND KUROMATSU (*PINUS THUNBERGII*) SEEDS. Nippon Rin Gakkai shi 36: 249-252 (JAP) (ENG Summary).

1204. Iwanoff, L.A.; Thielmann, M. 1923. ÜBER DEN EINFLUSS DES LICHTES VERSCHIEDENER WELLENLÄNGE AUF DIE TRANSPIRATION DER PFLANZEN. Flora 116: 296-311.

1205. Jabben, M. 1974. UNTERSUCHUNGEN ZUR PHYTOCHROM-REGULIERTEN PROTOCHLORO-PHYLL BILDUNG BEI *SINAPIS ALBA* L. Ph.D. Thesis Univ. Freiburg, Germany.

1206. Jabben, M.; Kasemir, H. 1974. PHYTOCHROME STIMULATED REGENERATION OF PROTOCHLOROPHYLL IN THE COTYLEDONS OF THE MUSTARD SEEDLING. Proc. Eur. Annu. Symp. Plant Photomorphogenesis, (Antwerpen), pp. 81-82.

1207. Jabben, M.; Masoner, M.; Kasemir, H.; Mohr, H. 1974. PHYTOCHROME-STIMULATED REGENERATION OF PROTOCHLOROPHYLL IN COTYLEDONS OF THE MUS-TARD SEEDLING. Photochem. Photobiol. 20: 233-239.

1208. Jacobi, A.; Kandeler, R. 1965. DIE WIRKUNG DER TEMPERATUR AUF DIE LICHTSTEUERUNG DER KEIMUNG VON *LACTUCA SATIVA*. SORTE ATTRAKTION. Z. Pflanzenphysiol. 53: 262-270 (ENG Summary).

1209. Jacobi, G. 1928. UNTERSUCHENGEN ÜBER DIE WIRKUNG DES ULTRAVIOLETTEN LICHTES AUF KEIMUNG UND WACHSTUM. Beitr. Biol. Pflanz. 16: 405-464.

1210. Jacobi, H. 1914. WACHSTUMSREAKTIONEN VON KEIMLINGEN, HERVORGERUFEN DURCH MONOCHROMATISCHES LICHT. I. ROT. Sitzungsber. Akad. Wiss. Wien., Math.-Naturwiss. Kl. Abt. 1, 123: 617-631.

1211. Jacobi, H. 1918. WACHSTUMSREAKTIONEN VON KEIMLINGEN, HERVORGERUFEN DURCH MONOCHROMATISCHES LICHT. II. BLAU UND GRÜN. Denkschr. Akad. Wiss. Wien, Math.-Naturwiss. Kl. Bd. 94: 113-125 und fünf Tafeln.

1212. Jacques, M.; Jacques, R. 1969. SPECTRE D'ACTION DE 1'INDUCTION FLORALE DE DEUX CHÉNOPODIACÉES DE JOURS LONGS. C.R. Acad. Sci. Ser D: 269: 2107-2109.

1213. Jacques, R.; Jacques, M. 1961. QUELQUES EFFECTS D'ÉCLAIREMENTS COLORIÉS SUR *CHENOPODIUM POLYSPERMUM*. Prog. Photobiol. Proc. Int. Congr. 3rd Copenhagen, 1960, pp. 403-406.

1214. Jacques, R. 1967. STIMULATION PAR LA LUMIÈRE DE LA GERMINATION DE SEMENCES DE *CHENOPODIUM POLYSPERMUM* L.: SPECTRE D'ACTION ET RÔLE DU PHYTOCHROME. C.R. Acad. Sci. Ser. D 264: 1782-1784.

1215. Jacques, R. 1967. BLUE LIGHT STIMULATION OF GERMINATION - ROLE OF PHYTOCHROME. Proc. Eur. Annu. Symp. Plant Photomorphogenesis, (Hvar) pp. 41-44.

1216. Jacques, R. 1968. ÉTUDE PAR SPECTROPHOTOMÉTRIE *IN VIVO* DE QUELQUES PROPRIÉTÉS NOUVELLES DU PHYTOCHROME. Physiol. Veg. 6: 93-116 (ENG Summary).

1217. Jacques, R. 1968. ACTION DE LA LUMIÈRE PAR l'INTERMÉDIAIRE DU PHYTO-CHROME SUR LA GERMINATION, LA CROISSANCE ET LE DÉVELOPPEMENT DE *CHENOPODIUM POLYSPERMUM* L. Physiol. Veg. 6: 137-164 (ENG Summary).

1218. Jacques, R. 1968. ACTION DE LA LUMIÈRE BLEUE SUR LA GERMINATION. Bull. Soc. Fr. Physiol. Veg. 14: 65-71 (ENG Summary).

1219. Jacques, R. 1969. ACTION DE LA LUMIÈRE ROUGE SUR LA CROISSANCE: SPECTRE D'ACTION ET RÔLE DU PHYTOCHROME. C.R. Acad. Sci. Ser. D: 269: 1260-1263.

1220. Jacques, R. 1970. ACTION D'UN ÉCLAIREMENT ROUGE SOMBRE DE LONGUE DURÉE SUR LA CROISSANCE ET LA FLORAISON. Physiol. Veg. 8: 530-531.

1221. Jaffe, L. 1962. EVIDENCE THAT THE ELECTRIC VECTOR GOVERNS LIGHT ABSORP-TION IN VISION, PHOTOTROPISM AND PHOTOTAXIS. Photochem. Photobiol. 1: 211-216 (R-D).

1222. Jaffe, L.; Etzold, H. 1964. PHOTOTROPIC RESPONSES OF *FUNARIA* SPORES TO RED LIGHT. Proc. IV Int. Congr. Photobiol. p. 77 (A).

1223. Jaffe, L.; Etzold, H. 1965. TROPIC RESPONSES OF *FUNARIA* SPORES TO RED LIGHT. Biophys. J. 5: 715-742.

1224. Jaffe, M.J.; Galston, A.W. 1966. ENERGETICS OF CONTRACTION AND COILING IN PEA TENDRILS. Plant Physiol. 41: Suppl.-43 (A).

1225. Jaffe, M.J.; Galston, A.W. 1966. PHYSIOLOGICAL STUDIES ON PEA TENDRILS. II. THE ROLE OF LIGHT AND ATP IN CONTACT COILING. Plant Physiol. 41: 1152-1158.

1226. Jaffe, M.J.; Galston, A.W. 1967. PHYTOCHROME CONTROL OF RAPID NYCTINAS-TIC MOVEMENTS AND MEMBRANE PERMEABILITY IN *ALBIZZIA JULIBRISSIN*. Planta 77: 135-141.

1227. Jaffe, M.J. 1968. CHANGES IN ENDOGENOUS RNA DURING PHYTOCHROME CON-TROLLED DE-ETIOLATION OF TERMINAL BUDS OF *PISUM SATIVUM* VAR. ALASKA. Proc. V Int. Congr. Photobiol., p. 156 (A).

1228. Jaffe, M.J. 1968. PHYTOCHROME-MEDIATED BIOELECTRIC POTENTIALS IN MUNG BEAN SEEDLINGS. Science 162: 1016-1017.

1229. Jaffe, M.J. 1969. PHYTOCHROME CONTROLLED RNA CHANGES IN TERMINAL BUDS OF DARK GROWN PEAS (*PISUM SATIVUM* CV. ALASKA). Physiol. Plant. 22: 1033-1037.

1230. Jaffe, M.J. 1969. RAPID PHYTOCHROME RESPONSES. Proc. XI Int. Bot. Congr. p. 100 (A) (R).

1231. Jaffe, M.J. 1969. COMPARATIVE STUDIES OF RAPIDLY RESPONDING MECHANO- AND PHOTO-SENSITIVE SYSTEMS. Plant Physiol. 44: Suppl.-18 (A) (R).

1232. Jaffe, M.J. 1970. ACETYLCHOLINE: A NEW PLANT HORMONE REGULATING PHYTO- CHROME-MEDIATED RESPONSES IN MUNG BEAN ROOTS. Plant Physiol. 46: Suppl.-2, Abstr. No. 9 (A).

1233. Jaffe, M.J. 1970. ON HELIOTROPISM IN TENDRILS OF *PISUM SATIVUM*: A RESPONSE TO INFRARED IRRADIATION. Planta 92: 146-151.

1234. Jaffe, M.J. 1970. EVIDENCE FOR THE REGULATION OF PHYTOCHROME-MEDIATED PROCESSES IN BEAN ROOTS BY THE NEUROHUMOR, ACETYLCHOLINE. Plant Physiol. 46: 768-777.

1235. Jaffe, M.J.; Thoma, L. 1971. RAPID PHYTOCHROME MEDIATED RESPONSES IN- VOLVING UPTAKE AND TRANSLOCATION IN BEAN ROOTS. Plant Physiol. 47: Suppl.-2, Abstr. No. 8 (A).

1236. Jaffe, M.J. 1972. ACETYLCHOLINE AS A NATIVE METABOLIC REGULATOR OF PHYTOCHROME-MEDIATED PROCESSES IN BEAN ROOTS. *Structural and Functional Aspects of Phytochemistry. Recent Advances in Phytochemistry*, Ed. V. C. Runeckles and T.C. Tso, Academic Press, New York and London, 5: 81-104.

1237. Jaffe, M.J.; Fluck, R. 1972. THE MEDIATION OF BEAN ROOT ACETYLCHOLINE- STERASE ACTIVITY BY PHYTOCHROME AND OTHER PHOTOCHROMIC PIGMENTS. Plant Physiol. 49: Suppl.-53, Abstr. No. 300 (A).

1238. Jaffe, M.J.; Thoma, L. 1973. RAPID PHYTOCHROME-MEDIATED CHANGES IN THE UPTAKE BY BEAN ROOTS OF SODIUM ACETATE $[1-^{14}C]$ AND THEIR MODIFICATION BY CHOLINERGIC DRUGS. Planta 113: 283-291.

1239. Jakobs, M. 1966. DER EINFLUSS VON PHYTOCHROM AUF DEN PROTEINSTOFFWECH- SEL UND AUF DIE TRANSLOKATION STICKSTOFFHALTIGER VERBINDUNGEN IM SENFKEIMLING (*SINAPIS ALBA* L.). Ph.D. Thesis, Univ. Freiburg, Germany.

1240. Jakobs, M.; Mohr, H. 1966. KINETISCHE STUDIEN ZUR PHYTOCHROMINDUZIERTEN PROTEINSYNTHESE. Planta 69: 187-197 (ENG Summary).

1241. Janistyn, B.; Drumm, H. 1972. LIGHT-MEDIATED CHANGES OF CONCENTRATION OF C-AMP IN MUSTARD SEEDLINGS. Naturwissenschaften 59: 218.

1242. Jarvis, S.J.; Wilkins, M.B. 1973. PHOTORESPONSES OF *MATTEUCCIA STRUTHIOPTERIS* L. TODARO. J. Exp. Bot. 24: 1149-1157.

1243. Jen, J.J. 1974. INFLUENCE OF SPECTRAL QUALITY OF LIGHT ON PIGMENT SYSTEMS OF RIPENING TOMATOES. J. Food Sci. 39: 907-910.

1244. Jenner, E.L.; Mumford, F.E. 1967. PURIFICATION AND CHARACTERIZATION OF PHYTOCHROME FROM OAT SEEDLINGS. Plant Physiol. 42: Suppl.-10-11 (A).

1245. Johnnykutty, A.T.; Khudairi, A.K. 1972. ROLE OF ASCORBIC ACID IN BUD DEVELOPMENT. Physiol. Plant. 26: 285-288.

1246. Johnson, C.B. 1974. *IN VIVO* REGULATION OF PHENYLALANINE AMMONIA-LYASE ACTIVITY IN GHERKIN SEEDLINGS. Proc. Eur. Annu. Symp. Plant Photomorphogenesis, (Antwerpen), pp. 70-74.

1246.5 Johnson, M.I.; Wickliff, J.L. 1974. SEED GERMINATION IN *GINKGO BILOBA* L. I. INFLUENCES OF COLD TREATMENT, GIBBERELLIC ACID AND RED LIGHT. Proc. Arkansas Acad. Sci. 28: 34-36.

1247. Johnson, S.P.; Hall, W.C.; Liverman, J.L. 1956. GROWTH AND FRUITING RESPONSES OF INTACT TOMATO PLANTS TO FAR-RED RADIATION. Physiol. Plant. 9: 389-395.

1248. Johnson, S.P.; Liverman, J.L. 1957. THE CONTROL OF SUMMER DORMANCY IN TOMATO BY GIBBERELLIC ACID. Plant Physiol. 32: Suppl.-48 (A).

1249. Johnston, E.S. 1932. THE FUNCTIONS OF RADIATION IN THE PHYSIOLOGY OF PLANTS II. SOME EFFECTS OF NEAR INFRA-RED RADIATION ON PLANTS. Smithson. Misc. Collect. 87, No. 14: 1-15.

1250. Johnston, E.S. 1937. SUN RAYS AND PLANT LIFE. Smithson. Year Annu. Rep. Smithson. Inst. (1936), pp. 353-371 (R).

1251. Johnston, E.S. 1937. GROWTH OF *AVENA* COLEOPTILE AND FIRST INTERNODE IN DIFFERENT WAVE-LENGTH BANDS OF THE VISIBLE SPECTRUM. Smithson. Misc. Collect. 96, No. 1-19.

1252. Johnston, E.S. 1938. PLANT GROWTH IN RELATION TO WAVE-LENGTH BALANCE. Smithson. Misc. Collect. 97, No. 2: 1-18.

1253. Jones, M.B.; Bailey, L.F. 1956. LIGHT EFFECTS ON THE GERMINATION OF SEEDS OF HENBIT (*LAMIUM AMPLEXICAULE* L.). Plant Physiol. 31: 347-349.

1254. Jones, R.W.; Sheard, R.W. 1972. NITRATE REDUCTASE ACTIVITY: PHYTOCHROME MEDIATION OF INDUCTION IN ETIOLATED PEAS. Nature (London) 238: 221-222.

1255. Jones, R.W.; Sheard, R.W. 1974. BLUE-LIGHT-ENHANCED NITRATE REDUCTASE ACTIVITY IN ETIOLATED PEA TERMINAL BUDS. Can. J. Bot. 52: 1433-1435.

1256. Jönsson, B. 1893. IAKTTAGELSER ÖFVER LJUSETS BETYDELSE FÖR FRÖNS GRON-ING. Lunds Univ., Arsskr. Avd. 29: 40-47.

1257. Joustra, M.K. 1970. FLOWER INITIATION IN *HYOSCYAMUS NIGER* L. AS INFLU-ENCED BY WIDELY DIVERGENT DAYLENGTHS IN DIFFERENT LIGHT QUALITIES. Meded. Landbouwhogesch. Wageningen 70-19: 1-78.

1258. Kadman-Zahavi, A. 1955. THE EFFECT OF LIGHT AND TEMPERATURE ON THE GER-MINATION OF *AMARANTHUS BLITOIDES* SEEDS. Bu.. Res. Counc. Isr. Sect. D. 4: 370-374.

1259. Kadman-Zahavi, A. 1957. EFFECTS OF RED AND FAR-RED RADIATION ON SEED GERMINATION. Nature (London) 180: 996-997.

1260. Kadman-Zahavi, A. 1960. EFFECTS OF SHORT AND CONTINUOUS ILLUMINATIONS ON THE GERMINATION OF *AMARANTHUS RETROFLEXUS* SEEDS. Bull. Res. Counc. Isr. Sect. D 9: 1-20.

1261. Kadman-Zahavi, A. 1963. EFFECTS OF LIGHT, KINETIN, AND GIBBERELLIC ACID ON FLOWER INITIATION IN *PHARBITIS NIL* CHOIS. Bull. Res. Counc. Isr. Sect. D 11: 191-197.

1262. Kadman-Zahavi, A. 1964. THE EFFECT OF THE DURATION OF LIGHT AND DARK-NESS ON THE FLOWERING OF *PHARBITIS NIL* USING A SINGLE LIGHT-DARKNESS CYCLE. Proc. IV Int. Congr. Photobiol. p. 101 (A).

1263. Kadman-Zahavi, A.; Vega, E.A. 1964. THE USE OF COLOURED LIGHT FOR AGRICULTURAL PURPOSES. Proc. IV Int. Congr. Photobiol. p. 102 (A).

1264. Kadman-Zahavi, A. 1965. A HYPOTHESIS REGARDING THE PARTICIPATION OF TWO TYPES OF PHYTOCHROME IN THE FLOWERING OF SHORT-DAY PLANTS. Volcani Inst. Agric. Res. Rehovot Div. Sci. Publ. Pam. No. 95: 1-15 (HEB Summary).

1265. Kadman-Zahavi, A.; Alvares-Vega, E.; Neeman, M. 1966. THE GROWTH OF *GERBERA* UNDER COLORED LIGHT. Volcani Inst. Agric. Res. Rehovot Prel. Rep. No. 536: 1-16 (HEB) (ENG Summary).

1266. Kadman-Zahavi, A. 1968. EFFECTS OF HIGH INTENSITY BLUE LIGHT ON THE DEVELOPMENT OF *SINAPIS ALBA*. Plant Physiol. 43: Suppl.-49 (A).

1267. Kadman-Zahavi, A. 1968. A SUGGESTION ON THE PARTICIPATION OF TWO FORMS OF PHYTOCHROME IN THE FLOWERING OF SHORT DAY PLANTS. Proc. V Int. Congr. Photobiol. p. 156(A).

1268. Kadman-Zahavi, A. 1968. LIGHT AS A GROWTH FACTOR. Hassadeh 49: 1353-1358 (HEB).

1269. Kadman-Zahavi, A.; Alvarez-Vega, E. 1968. THE USE OF COLORED LIGHT FOR AGRICULTURE. Final Report to the Ford Foundation, Volcani Inst. Agric. Res. Div. Sci. Publ, pp. 226-284.

1270. Kadman-Zahavi, A. 1970. THE EFFECT OF DAY LENGTH, LIGHT COMPOSITION, AND LIGHT INTENSITY ON RUNNER PRODUCTION, FLOWER INITIATION AND FLOWERING IN STRAWBERRY. Volcani Inst. Agric. Res. Div. Sci. Publ. Prel. Rep. No. 676: 1-42 (HEB) (ENG Summary).

1271. Kadman-Zahavi, A. 1970. THE EFFECTS OF AMITROLE ON FLOWER INDUCTION AND ON VEGETATIVE DEVELOPMENT IN *PHARBITIS NIL*. Isr. J. Bot. 19: 558-560.

1272. Kadman-Zahavi, A.; Yahel, H. 1970. THE EFFICIENCY OF DIFFERENT LIGHT SOURCES AND OF DIFFERENT ILLUMINATION REGIMES IN PREVENTING FLOWERING IN *CHRYSANTHEMUM MORIFOLIUM*. Hassadeh 51: 286-289 (HEB).

1273. Kadman-Zahavi, A. 1971. PERSISTENCE OF P_{fr} AND OTHER MANIFESTATIONS OF PHYTOCHROME IN THE NYCTINASTIC LEAFLET MOVEMENTS OF PEANUT *(ARACHIS HYPOGAEA* L.). Proc. Eur. Annu. Symp. Plant Photomorphogenesis, (Athens), p. 29 (A).

1274. Kadman-Zahavi, A. 1971. THE PHYTOCHROME SYSTEM AND ITS EFFECTS ON PLANT DEVELOPMENT. Mada 16: 41-48 (HEB).

1275. Kadman-Zahavi, A.; Yahel, H. 1971. PHYTOCHROME EFFECTS IN NIGHT-BREAK ILLUMINATIONS ON FLOWERING OF *CHRYSANTHEMUM*. Physiol. Plant. 25: 90-93.

1276. Kadman-Zahavi, A. 1972. PERSISTENCE OF P_{fr} AND OTHER MANIFESTATIONS OF PHYTOCHROME IN THE NYCTINASTIC LEAFLET MOVEMENTS OF PEANUT (*ARACHIS HYPOGAEA* L.). Isr. J. Bot. 21: 142-149.

1277. Kadman-Zahavi, A.; Ephrat, E. 1973. THE RELATIONSHIP BETWEEN PHYTOCHROME AND THE HIGH ENERGY REACTION SYSTEM: COMPARISONS OF THE EFFECTS OF THE SPECTRAL COMPOSITION OF COLOURED GREENHOUSES AND THE EFFECTS OF END-OF-DAY RED OR FAR-RED IRRADIATIONS ON PLANT DEVELOPMENT. Proc. Sect. Sci. Isr. Acad. Sci. Humanit., 1-22 (HEB).

1278. Kadman-Zahavi, A.: Ephrat, E. 1973. EFFECT OF RED AND FAR-RED ILLUMINATIONS AT THE END OF SHORT DAYS AND THEIR INTERACTION WITH NIGHT-BREAK ILLUMINATIONS, ON FLOWERING OF *CHRYSANTHEMUM MORIFOLIUM* PLANTS. Plant Cell Physiol. 14: 409-411.

1279. Kadman-Zahavi, A.; Ephrat, E. 1974. HIGH-FR AND LOW-FR RESPONSE GROUPS IN SHORT-DAY PLANTS. Plant Physiol. 53: Suppl.-3, Abstr. No. 12 (A).

1280. Kadman-Zahavi, A.; Ephrat, E. 1974. OPPOSITE RESPONSE GROUPS OF SHORT-DAY PLANTS TO THE SPECTRAL COMPOSITION OF THE MAIN LIGHT PERIOD AND TO END-OF-DAY RED OR FAR-RED IRRADIATIONS. Plant Cell Physiol. 15: 693-699.

1281. Kahn, A.; Goss, J.A.; Smith, D.E. 1956. LIGHT AND CHEMICAL EFFECTS ON LETTUCE SEED GERMINATION. Plant Physiol. 31: Suppl.-37 (A).

1282. Kahn, A.; Goss, J.A.; Smith, D.E. 1957. EFFECT OF GIBBERELLIN ON GERMINATION OF LETTUCE SEED. Science 125: 645-646.

1283. Kahn, A. 1960. AN ANALYSIS OF "DARK-OSMOTIC INHIBITION" OF GERMINATION OF LETTUCE SEEDS. Plant Physiol. 35: 1-7.

1284. Kahn, A. 1960. PROMOTION OF LETTUCE SEED GERMINATION BY GIBBERELLIN. Plant Physiol. 35: 333-339.

1285. Kalinin, F.L.; Gladun, A.A.; Melnichuk, Yu.P. 1970. NUCLEAR AND CYTOPLASMIC PROTEINS OF WHEAT SPROUTS DURING THE ACTIVATION OF PHYTOCHROME WITH RED LIGHT. Fiziol. Biokhim. Kul't. Rast. 2: 487-490 (RUS) (ENG Summary).

1286. Kandeler, R. 1956. ÜBER DIE BLÜTENBILDUNG BEI *LEMNA GIBBA* L. II. DAS WIRKUNGSSPEKTRUM VON BLÜHFÖRDERNDEM SCHWACHLICHT. Z. Bot. 44: 153-174.

1287. Kandeler, R. ÜBER DIE LICHTABHÄNGIGKEIT DER ANTHOCYANBILDUNG. Ber. Dtsch. Bot. Ges. 71: (24)-(25) (A).

1288. Kandeler, R. 1958. DIE WIRKUNG VON FARBIGEM UND WEISSEM LICHT AUF DIE ANTHOCYANBILDUNG BEI CRUCIFEREN-KEIMLINGEN. Ber. Dtsch. Bot. Ges. 71: 34-44.

1289. Kandeler, R. 1959. ÜBER DIE WIRKUNG VON DUNKELROT UND WEISSLICHT AUF DIE ANTHOCYANBILDUNG NACH AUSSCHALTUNG DER CHLOROPHYLLBILDUNG DURCH ANTIBIOTIKA. Naturwissenschaften 46: 452-453.

1290. Kandeler, R. 1960. ÜBER DIE LICHTABHÄNGIGKEIT DER ANTHOCYANBILDUNG. Flora 149: 487-519.

1291. Kandeler, R. 1960. PHYSIKALISCHE UND CHEMISCHE GRUNDLAGEN DER LEBENSPROZESSE (STRAHLENBIOLOGIE). Fortschr. Bot. 22: 142-148 (R).

1292. Kandeler, R. 1962. DIE AUFHEBUNG DER PHOTOPERIODISCHEN STEUERUNG BEI *LEMNA GIBBA*. Ber. Dtsch. Bot. Ges. 75: 431-442.

1293. Kandeler, R. 1963. PHYSIKALISCHE UND CHEMISCHE GRUNDLAGEN DER LEBENSPROZESSE (STRAHLENBIOLOGIE). III. LICHTWIRKUNGEN. Fortschr. Bot. 25: 201-211 (R).

1294. Kandeler, R. 1963. PHYTOCHROM-WIRKUNG AUF DIE VEGETATIVE ENTWICKLUNG VON *LEMNA GIBBA*. Naturwissenschaften 50: 551-552.

1295. Kandeler, R. 1966. VI. STRAHLENWIRKUNGEN SICHTBARE STRAHLUNG UND INFRA-ROT. Fortsch. Bot. 28: 125-134 (R).

1296. Kandeler, R. 1966. TRENNUNG ZWEIER DUNKELROTWIRKUNGEN BEI DER LICHT-STEUERUNG DER SPROSSVERMEHRUNG VON *LEMNA GIBBA*. Z. Pflanzenphysiol. 54: 161-173 (ENG Summary).

1297. Kandeler, R. 1970. DIE WIRKUNG VON LITHIUM UND ADP AUF DIE PHYTOCHROM-STEUERUNG DER BLÜTENBILDUNG. Planta 90: 203-207 (ENG Summary).

1298. Kandeler, R. 1974. PHOTOMORPHOGENESE: DIE ROLLE DER HORMONE. Ber. Dtsch. Bot. Ges. 87: 71-81 (ENG Summary).

1299. Kang, B.G.; Yocum, C.S.; Burg, S.P.; Ray, P.M. 1967. ETHYLENE AND CAR-BON DIOXIDE: MEDIATION OF HYPOCOTYL HOOK-OPENING RESPONSE. Science 156: 958-959.

1300. Kang, B.G.; Ray, P.M. 1969. ROLE OF GROWTH REGULATORS IN THE BEAN HYPOCOTYL HOOK OPENING RESPONSE. Planta 87: 193-205.

1301. Kang, B.G.; Ray, P.M. 1969. ETHYLENE AND CARBON DIOXIDE AS MEDIATORS IN THE RESPONSE OF THE BEAN HYPOCOTYL HOOK TO LIGHT AND AUXINS. Planta 87: 206-216.

1302. Kang, B.G.; Ray, P.M. 1969. EFFECTS OF INHIBITORS OF RNA AND PROTEIN SYNTHESIS ON BEAN HYPOCOTYL HOOK OPENING AND THEIR IMPLICATIONS RE-GARDING PHYTOCHROME ACTION. Planta 87: 217-226.

1303. Kang, B.G. 1971. PHYTOCHROME-CONTROLLED LEAF UNROLLING AND PROTEIN SYNTHESIS. Plant Physiol. 47: 352-356.

1304. Kang, B.G.; Burg, S.P. 1972. PHYTOCHROME CONTROL OF CELL DIVISION AND EXPANSION IN ETIOLATED PEA SEEDLINGS. Plant Physiol. 49: Suppl.-54, Abstr. No. 306 (A).

1305. Kang, B.G.; Burg, S.P. 1972. ETHYLENE INVOLVEMENT IN PHYTOCHROME-MEDIATED PHOTORESPONSES; ITS RELATIONSHIP TO ANTHOCYANIN SYNTHESIS. Proc. VI Int. Congr. Photobiol. Abstr. No. 197 (A).

1306. Kang, B.G.; Burg, S.P. 1972. INVOLVEMENT OF ETHYLENE IN PHYTOCHROME-MEDIATED CAROTENOID SYNTHESIS. Plant Physiol. 49: 631-633.

1307. Kang, B.G.; Burg, S.P. 1972. RELATION OF PHYTOCHROME-ENHANCED GEOTROPIC SENSITIVITY TO ETHYLENE PRODUCTION. Plant Physiol. 50: 132-135.

1307.5 Kang, B.G.; Burg, S.P.   1973.   PHYTOCHROME-ENHANCED PHOTOTROPIC RESPONSE
IN PEA STEM.   Proc. I Annu. Meet. Am. Soc. Photobiol. p. 181, Abstr.
No. Th PM-EI (A).

1308.   Kang, B.G.; Burg, S.P.   1973.   ROLE OF ETHYLENE IN PHYTOCHROME-INDUCED
ANTHOCYANIN SYNTHESIS.   Planta 110: 227-235.

1309.   Kang, B.G.; Burg, S.P.   1974.   RED LIGHT ENHANCEMENT OF THE PHOTOTROPIC
RESPONSE OF ETIOLATED PEA STEMS.   Plant Physiol. 53: 445-448.

1310.   Karow, H.; Mohr, H.   1967.   AKTIVITÄTSÄNDERUNGEN DER ISOCITRITASE (EC.
4.1.3.1.) WÄHREND DER PHOTOMORPHOGENESE BEIM SENFKEIMLING *(SINAPIS
ALBA* L.).   Planta 72: 170-186 (ENG Summary).

1311.   Karow, H.; Mohr, H.   1969.   PHYTOCHROME-MEDIATED REPRESSION OF ENZYME
INCREASE IN MUSTARD SEEDLINGS.   Naturwissenschaften 56: 94-95.

1312.   Karssen, C.M.   1967.   THE LIGHT PROMOTED GERMINATION OF THE SEEDS OF
CHENOPODIUM ALBUM L. I. THE INFLUENCE OF THE INCUBATION TIME ON
QUANTITY AND RATE OF THE RESPONSE TO RED LIGHT.   Acta Bot. Neerl. 16:
156-160.

1313.   Karssen, C.M.   1970.   THE LIGHT PROMOTED GERMINATION OF THE SEEDS OF
CHENOPODIUM ALBUM L. III. EFFECT OF THE PHOTOPERIOD DURING GROWTH
AND DEVELOPMENT OF THE PLANTS ON THE DORMANCY OF THE PRODUCED SEEDS.
Acta Bot. Neerl. 19: 81-94.

1314.   Karssen, C.M.   1970.   THE LIGHT PROMOTED GERMINATION OF THE SEEDS OF
CHENOPODIUM ALBUM L. IV. EFFECTS OF RED, FAR-RED AND WHITE LIGHT ON
NON-PHOTOBLASTIC SEEDS INCUBATED IN MANNITOL.   Acta Bot. Neerl. 19:
95-108.

1315.   Karssen, C.M.   1970.   THE LIGHT PROMOTED GERMINATION OF THE SEEDS OF
CHENOPODIUM ALBUM L. V. DARK REACTIONS REGULATING QUANTITY AND RATE
OF THE RESPONSE TO RED LIGHT.   Acta Bot. Neerl. 19: 187-196.

1316.   Karssen, C.M.   1970.   THE LIGHT PROMOTED GERMINATION OF THE SEEDS OF
CHENOPODIUM ALBUM L. VI. P_{fr} REQUIREMENT DURING DIFFERENT STAGES
OF THE GERMINATION PROCESS.   Acta Bot. Neerl. 19: 297-312.

1317.   Karvé, A.   1961.   DIE WIRKUNG VERSCHIEDENER LICHTQUALITÄTEN AUF DIE
ÖFFNUNGSBEWEGUNG DER STOMATA.   Z. Bot. 49: 47-72.

1318.   Karvé, A.; Engelmann, W.; Schoser, G.   1961.   INITIATION OF RHYTHMICAL
PETAL MOVEMENTS IN *KALANCHOË BLOSSFELDIANA* BY TRANSFER FROM CONTINU-
OUS DARKNESS TO CONTINUOUS LIGHT OR VICE VERSA.   Planta 56: 700-711.

1319. Karvé, A.D. 1964. UPON THE FORMATION AND OPENING OF PLUMULAR HOOKS IN SEEDLINGS OF *CARTHAMUS TINCTORIUS* L. Naturwissenschaften 51: 441-442.

1320. Karvé, A.D.; Jigajinni, S.G. 1966. PIGMENT SYSTEM INVOLVED IN THE PHOTOPERIODIC ENTRAINMENT OF CIRCADIAN LEAF MOVEMENTS. Naturwissenschaften 53: 181.

1321. Kasemir, H. 1963. DER EINFLUSS SICHTBARER STRAHLUNG AUF DIE FLAVONOL-SYNTHESE UND AUF DAS HYPOKOTYLWACHSTUM DER BUCHWEIZEN-KEIMLINGE (*FAGOPYRUM ESCULENTUM* MOENCH). Ph.D. Thesis, Univ. Freiburg, Germany.

1322. Kasemir, H.; Mohr, H. 1965. DIE REGULATION VON CHLOROPHYLL UND PROTEIN-GEHALT IN FARNVORKEIMEN DURCH SICHTBARE STRAHLUNG. Planta 67: 33-43 (ENG Summary).

1323. Kasemir, H.; Mohr, H. 1967. DIE WIRKUNG VON PHYTOCHROM UND ACTINOMYCIN D AUF DIE CHLOROPHYLL A-SYNTHESE VON SENFKEIMLINGEN (*SINAPIS ALBA* L.). Planta 72: 187-197 (ENG Summary).

1324. Kasemir, H.; Mohr, H. 1972. INVOLVEMENT OF ACETYLCHOLINE IN PHYTOCHROME-MEDIATED PROCESSES. Plant Physiol. 49: 453-454.

1325. Kasemir, H.; Oberdorfer, U.; Mohr, H. 1973. A TWOFOLD ACTION OF PHYTO-CHROME IN CONTROLLING CHLOROPHYLL A ACCUMULATION. Photochem. Photobiol. 18: 481-486.

1326. Kasperbauer, M.J.; Borthwick, H.A.; Hendricks, S.B. 1962. INHIBITION OF FLOWERING OF *CHENOPODIUM RUBRUM* BY PROLONGED IRRADIATION WITH FAR-RED. Plant Physiol. 37: Suppl.-28, Abstr. No. 754 (A).

1327. Kasperbauer, M.J.; Borthwick, H.A.; Hendricks, S.B. 1963. INHIBITION OF FLOWERING OF *CHENOPODIUM RUBRUM* BY PROLONGED FAR-RED RADIATION. Bot. Gaz. (Chicago) 124: 444-451.

1328. Kasperbauer, M.J.; Lane, H.C. 1963. PHYTOCHROME-CONTROLLED RESPONSES IN SEEDLINGS OF *CUSCUTA INDECORA* CHOIS. Plant Physiol. 38: Suppl.-24 (A).

1329. Kasperbauer, M.J.; Borthwick, H.A. 1964. PHOTOREVERSIBILITY OF STEM ELONGATION IN *MELILOTUS ALBA* DESR. Crop Sci. 4: 42-44.

1330. Kasperbauer, M.J.; Borthwick, H.A.; Hendricks, S.B. 1964. REVERSION OF PHYTOCHROME 730 (P_{fr}) TO P660 (P_r) ASSAYED BY FLOWERING IN *CHENOPODIUM RUBRUM*. Bot. Gaz. (Chicago) 125: 75-80.

1331. Kasperbauer, M.J.; Hiatt, A.J. 1966. PHOTOREVERSIBLE CONTROL OF LEAF SHAPE AND CHLOROPHYLL CONTENT IN *NICOTIANA TABACUM* L. Tob. Sci. 10: 29-32.

1332. Kasperbauer, M.J.; Reinert, R.A. 1966. BIOLOGICAL DETECTION OF PHYTO-CHROME IN CALLUS TISSUE OF *NICOTIANA TABACUM* L. Nature (London) 211: 744-745.

1333. Kasperbauer, M.J.; Reinert, R.A. 1967. PHOTOMETRICALLY ASSAYABLE PHY-TOCHROME *IN VIVO* IN CALLUS TISSUE CULTURED FROM *NICOTIANA TABACUM*. Physiol. Plant. 20: 977-981.

1334. Kasperbauer, M.J.; Tso, T.C.; Sorokin, T.P. 1970. EFFECTS OF END-OF-DAY RED AND FAR-RED RADIATION ON FREE SUGARS, ORGANIC ACIDS AND AMINO ACIDS OF TOBACCO. Phytochemistry 9: 2091-2095.

1335. Kasperbauer, M.J. 1971. SPECTRAL DISTRIBUTION OF LIGHT IN A TOBACCO CANOPY AND EFFECTS OF END-OF-DAY LIGHT QUALITY ON GROWTH AND DEVELOP-MENT. Plant Physiol. 47: 775-778.

1336. Kasperbauer, M.J. 1972. INFLUENCE OF END-OF-DAY PHYTOCHROME MANIPULA-TION ON GROWTH AND DEVELOPMENT OF *NICOTIANA TABACUM*. Proc. VI Int. Congr. Photobiol. Abstr. No. 170 (A).

1337. Kasperbauer, M.J.; Peaslee, D.E. 1973. MORPHOLOGY AND PHOTOSYNTHETIC EFFICIENCY OF TOBACCO LEAVES THAT RECEIVED END-OF-DAY RED OR FAR-RED LIGHT DURING DEVELOPMENT. Plant Physiol. 52: 440-442.

1338. Kass, L.B.; Paolillo, D.J. Jr. 1974. ON THE LIGHT REQUIREMENT FOR REPLICATION OF PLASTIDS IN POLYTRICHUM. Plant Sci. Lett. 3: 81-85.

1339. Kato, Y. 1965. PHYSIOLOGICAL AND MORPHOGENETIC STUDIES OF FERN GAMETO-PHYTE AND SPOROPHYTE BY ASEPTIC CULTURE V. FURTHER STUDIES ON ONE- AND TWO-DIMENSIONAL GROWTH IN GAMETOPHYTES OF *PTERIS VITTATA*. Bot. Mag. 78: 149-155.

1340. Katunskij, V.M. 1937. DEPENDENCY OF PHOTOPERIODIC REACTIONS OF PLANTS ON THE SPECTRAL COMPOSITION OF LIGHT. Akad. Nauk SSSR Dokl. 15: 509-512 (1937).

1341. Kaufmann, B.P.; Hollaender, A. 1942. CHROMOSOME BREAKAGE AND RECOMBI-NATION. Carnegie Inst. Washington, Yearb. 41: 192-194.

1342. Kaufmann, B.P.; Gay, H. 1945. CYTOGENETICS OF *DROSOPHILA*. Carnegie Inst. Washington Yearb. 44: 121-127 (A).

1343. Kaufmann, B.P.; Hollaender, A. 1945. ALTERATION OF THE FREQUENCY OF X-RAY-INDUCED CHROMOSOMAL BREAKS BY USE OF ULTRAVIOLET AND NEAR INFRARED RADIATION. Genetics 30: 11-12 (A).

1344. Kaufmann, B.P. 1946. MODIFICATION OF THE FREQUENCY OF CHROMOSOMAL RE-ARRANGEMENTS INDUCED BY X-RAYS IN *DROSOPHILA*. III. EFFECT OF SUPPLE-MENTARY TREATMENT AT THE TIME OF CHROMOSOME RECOMBINATION. Genetics 31: 449-453.

1345. Kaufmann, B.P.; Hollaender, A.; Gay, H. 1946. MODIFICATION OF THE FREQUENCY OF CHROMOSOMAL REARRANGEMENTS INDUCED BY X-RAYS IN *DROSOPHILA*. I. USE OF NEAR INFRA-RED RADIATION. Genetics 31: 349-367.

1346. Kaufmann, B.P.; Gay, H. 1947. THE INFLUENCE OF X-RAYS AND NEAR INFRA-RED RAYS ON RECESSIVE LETHALS IN *DROSOPHILA MELANOGASTER*. Proc. Nat. Acad. Sci., USA 33: 366-372.

1347. Kaufmann, B.P.; Gay, H. 1948. EFFECT OF NEAR INFRA-RED RADIATION ON THE PRODUCTION OF CHROMOSOME REARRANGEMENTS IN *DROSOPHILA* BY NITRO-GEN MUSTARD. Anat. Rec. 101: 670-671 (A).

1348. Kaufmann, B.P.; Gay, H. 1948. THE MODIFYING ACTION OF NEAR INFRARED RADIATION ON THE FREQUENCY OF INDUCED GENE AND CHROMOSOMAL CHANGES IN *DROSOPHILA MELANOGASTER*. Genetics 33: 112 (A).

1349. Kaufmann, B.P.; Gay, H.; Rothberg, H. Jr. 1949. THE INFLUENCE OF NEAR INFRARED RADIATION ON THE PRODUCTION BY NITROGEN MUSTARD OF CHROMO-SOME REARRANGEMENTS IN *DROSOPHILA*. J. Exp. Zool. 111: 415-436.

1350. Kaufmann, B.P.; Wilson, K. 1949. MODIFICATION OF THE FREQUENCY OF CHROMOSOMAL REARRANGEMENTS INDUCED BY X-RAYS IN *DROSOPHILA* IV. POSTTREATMENT WITH NEAR INFRARED RADIATION. Genetics 34: 425-436.

1351. Kaufmann, B.P.; McDonald, M.R.; Gay, H.; Rowan, M.E.; Moore, E.C. 1951. PATTERNS OF ORGANIZATION OF CELLULAR MATERIALS. Carnegie Inst. Washington Yearb. 50: 203-215.

1352. Kaufman, P.B.; Katz, J.M. 1961. GROWTH OF NODE-INTERNODE SEGMENTS OF *AVENA SATIVA* UNDER RED AND FAR-RED LIGHT REGIMES. Plant Physiol. 36: Suppl.-41 (A).

1353. Keerberg, H.; Keerberg, O.; Pärnik, T.; Viil, J.; Värk, E. 1971. CO_2 ASSIMILATION BY *PHASEOLUS* AND *ASPIDISTRA* LEAVES UNDER VARYING DENSITY OF BLUE AND RED RADIANT FLUX. Photosynthetica 5: 99-106.

1354. Keerberg, H.; Värk, E.; Keerberg, O.; Pärnik, T. 1971. THE EFFECT OF LIGHT QUALITY ON THE ^{14}C INCORPORATION INTO AMINO AND ORGANIC ACIDS DURING THE $^{14}CO_2$ ASSIMILATION BY BEAN LEAVES. Izv. Akad. Nauk. Est. SSR, Biol. 20: 350-352 (RUS).

1355. Kefford, N.P. 1962. AUXIN-GIBBERELLIN INTERACTION IN RICE COLEOPTILE ELONGATION. Plant Physiol. 37: 380-386.

1356. Keister, D.L.; Jagendorf, A.T.; San Pietro, A. 1962. DEVELOPMENT OF BEAN-LEAF TRANSHYDROGENASE IN ETIOLATED LEAVES. Biochim. Biophys. Acta 62: 332-337.

1357. Kende, H.; Lang, A. 1964. GIBBERELLINS AND LIGHT INHIBITION OF STEM GROWTH IN PEAS. Plant Physiol. 39: 435-440.

1358. Kendrick, R.E.; Frankland, B. 1968. KINETICS OF PHYTOCHROME DECAY IN *AMARANTHUS* SEEDLINGS. Planta 82: 317-320.

1359. Kendrick, R.E.; Frankland, B. 1969. PHOTOCONTROL OF GERMINATION IN *AMARANTHUS CAUDATUS*. Planta 85: 326-339.

1360. Kendrick, R.E.; Frankland, B. 1969. THE *IN VIVO* PROPERTIES OF *AMARANTHUS* PHYTOCHROME. Planta 86: 21-32.

1361. Kendrick, R.E.; Spruit, C.J.P.; Frankland, B. 1969. PHYTOCHROME IN SEEDS OF *AMARANTHUS CAUDATUS*. Planta 88: 293-302.

1362. Kendrick, R.E.; Hillman, W.S. 1970. DARK REVERSION OF PHYTOCHROME IN *SINAPIS ALBA* L. Plant Physiol. 46: Suppl.-2 (A).

1363. Kendrick, R.E.; Hillman, W.S. 1970. DARK REVERSION OF PHYTOCHROME IN *SINAPIS ALBA* L. Plant Physiol. 46: 596-598.

1364. Kendrick, R.E.; Hillman, W.S. 1971. IONIC RELATIONS AND PHYTOCHROME IN *PISUM SATIVUM* EPICOTYLS. Plant Physiol. 47: Suppl.-12, Abstr. No. 67 (A).

1365. Kendrick, R.E.; Hillman, W.S. 1971. ABSENCE OF PHYTOCHROME DARK REVERSION IN SEEDLINGS OF THE CENTROSPERMAE. Am. J. Bot. 58: 424-428.

1366. Kendrick, R.E. 1972. ASPECTS OF PHYTOCHROME DECAY IN ETIOLATED SEEDLINGS UNDER CONTINUOUS ILLUMINATION. Planta 102: 286-293.

1367. Kendrick, R.E.; Hillman, W.S. 1972. ION RELATIONS, CHLOROPHYLL SYNTHESIS AND THE QUESTION OF 'BULK' PHYTOCHROME IN *PISUM SATIVUM*. Physiol. Plant 26: 7-12.

1368. Kendrick, R.E.; Spruit, C.J.P. 1972. PHYTOCHROME INTERMEDIATES *IN VIVO*. Proc. VI Int. Congr. Photobiol. Abstr. No. 160 (A).

1369. Kendrick, R.E.; Spruit, C.J.P. 1972. PHYTOCHROME DECAY IN SEEDLINGS UNDER CONTINUOUS INCANDESCENT LIGHT. Planta 107: 341-350.

1370. Kendrick, R.E.; Spruit, C.J.P. 1972. LIGHT MAINTAINS HIGH LEVELS OF PHYTOCHROME INTERMEDIATES. Nature (London) New Biol. 237: 281-282.

1371. Kendrick, R.E.; Spruit, C.J.P. 1973. PHYTOCHROME INTERMEDIATES *IN VIVO*. I. EFFECTS OF TEMPERATURE, LIGHT INTENSITY, WAVELENGTH AND OXYGEN ON INTERMEDIATE ACCUMULATION. Photochem. Photobiol. 18: 139-144.

1372. Kendrick, R.E.; Spruit, C.J.P. 1973. PHYTOCHROME INTERMEDIATES *IN VIVO*. III. KINETIC ANALYSIS OF INTERMEDIATE REACTIONS AT LOW TEMPERATURE. Photochem. Photobiol. 18: 153-159.

1373. Kendrick, R.E.; Spruit, C.J.P. 1972. PHYTOCHROME PROPERTIES AND THE MOLECULAR ENVIRONMENT. Plant Physiol. 52: 327-331.

1374. Kendrick, R.E. 1974. PHYTOCHROME INTERMEDIATES IN FREEZE-DRIED TISSUE. Nature (London) 250: 159-161.

1375. Kendrick, R.E.; Spruit, C.J.P. 1974. INVERSE DARK REVERSION OF PHYTO-CHROME: AN EXPLANATION. Planta 120: 265-272.

1376. Kent, M.; Gortner, W. A. 1951. EFFECT OF PRE-ILLUMINATION ON THE RE-SPONSE OF SPLIT PEA STEMS TO GROWTH SUBSTANCES. Bot. Gaz. (Chicago) 112: 307-311.

1377. Khalatkar, A.S.; Thengane, R.J.; Rane, B.V.; Dnyansagar, V.R. 1974. LIGHT SENSITIVITY OF ETHYL METHANESULFONATE TREATMENT IN *HORDEUM VULGARE*. Mutat. Res. 25: 415-419.

1378. Khan, A.A.; Tolbert, N.E. 1965. REVERSAL OF INHIBITORS OF SEED GERMINA-TION BY RED LIGHT PLUS KINETIN. Physiol. Plant. 18: 41-43.

1379. Khan, A.A.; Tolbert, N.E. 1966. LIGHT-CONTROLLED CYCOCEL REVERSAL OF COUMARIN INHIBITION OF LETTUCE SEED GERMINATION AND ROOT GROWTH. Physiol. Plant. 19: 76-80.

1380. Khan, A.A. 1966. BREAKING OF DORMANCY IN *XANTHIUM* SEEDS BY KINETIN MEDIATED BY LIGHT AND DNA-DEPENDENT RNA SYNTHESIS. Physiol. Plant. 19: 869-874.

1381. Khan, A.A. 1967. ANTAGONISM BETWEEN CYTOKININS AND GERMINATION INHIBI-TORS. Nature (London) 216: 166-167.

1382. Khavkin, E.E. 1969. INDUCTION OF THE SYNTHESIS OF ENZYMES IN GROWTH PROCESSES AND MORPHOGENESIS OF PLANTS. Moscow (not obtained) (Re-ferred to by Rubin, L.B. et al. (1973) Biologia 8: 135-145).

1383. Khudairi, A.K. 1968. PHYSIOLOGICAL EFFECTS OF ASCORBIC ACID ON PLANTS. Plant Physiol. 43: Suppl.-48 (A).

1384. Khudairi, A.K. 1968. A POSSIBLE NEW PLANT HORMONE. Phytologia 17: 441-444.

1385. Khudairi, A.K.; Arboleda, O.P. 1971. PHYTOCHROME-MEDIATED CAROTENOID BIOSYNTHESIS AND ITS INFLUENCE BY PLANT HORMONES. Physiol. Plant. 24: 18-22.

1386. Khudairi, A.K.; Joglekar, R. 1971. PHYTOCHROME-MEDIATED ABSCISIC ACID SYNTHESIS IN TOMATOES. Plant Physiol. 47: Suppl.-11, Abstr. No. 64 (A).

1387. Khudairi, A.K.; Johnnykutty, A.T.; Agarwal, S. 1971. PHYTOCHROME-MEDIATED BUD DEVELOPMENT IN *PISUM SATIVUM*. Planta 101: 185-188.

1388. Khudairi, A.K. 1972. THE RIPENING OF TOMATOES, A MOLECULAR ECOLOGICAL APPROACH TO THE PHYSIOLOGY OF FRUIT RIPENING. Am. Sci. 60: 696-707 (R-D}.

1389. Khudairi, A.K.; Maeng, J. 1973. STUDIES ON THE FLOWERING MECHANISM IN *LEMNA*. II. THE DARK REACTION OF THE SHORT-DAY PLANT *LEMNA PERPUSILLA*. Physiol. Plant. 28: 271-277.

1390. Kidd, G.H.; Pratt, L.H. 1973. PHYTOCHROME DESTRUCTION. AN APPARENT RE-QUIREMENT FOR PROTEIN SYNTHESIS IN THE INDUCTION ON THE DESTRUCTION MECHANISM. Plant Physiol. 52: 309-311.

1391. Kimura, K. 1964. FLORAL INITIATION IN *PHARBITIS NIL* SUBJECTED TO CON-TINUOUS ILLUMINATION AT RELATIVELY LOW TEMPERATURES. III. EFFECT OF INTENSITY AND QUALITY OF LIGHT. Bot. Mag. 77: 115-121.

1392. Kimura, K. 1966. FLORAL INITIATION OF *PHARBITIS NIL* AT LOW TEMPERATURES Ber. Ohara Inst. Landwirtsch. Biol. Okayama Univ. 13: 39-88.

1393. Kimura, K. 1974. EFFECT OF LIGHT ON LEAF INCLINATION OF *TRITICUM AESTIVUM*. Ber. Ohara Inst. Landwirtsch. Biol. Okayama Univ. 16: 47-56.

1394. Kincaid, R.R. 1935. EFFECTS OF CERTAIN ENVIRONMENTAL FACTORS ON GERMI-NATION OF FLORIDA CIGAR-WRAPPER TOBACCO SEEDS. Fl. Agric. Exp. St. Bull. No. 277, 4-47.

1395. King, R.W. 1971. TIME MEASUREMENT IN THE PHOTOPERIODIC CONTROL OF FLOWERING. Ph.D. Thesis, Univ. Western Ontario, Canada.

1396. King, R.W.; Cumming, B.G. 1972. THE ROLE OF PHYTOCHROME IN PHOTOPERIOD-
       IC TIME MEASUREMENT AND ITS RELATION TO RHYTHMIC TIMEKEEPING IN THE
       CONTROL OF FLOWERING IN *CHENOPODIUM RUBRUM*. Planta 108: 39-57.

1397. King, R.W.; Cumming, B.G. 1972. RHYTHMS AS PHOTOPERIODIC TIMERS IN THE
       CONTROL OF FLOWERING *CHENOPODIUM RUBRUM* L. Planta 103: 281-301.

1398. King, R.W. 1974. PHYTOCHROME ACTION IN THE INDUCTION OF FLOWERING IN
       SHORT-DAY PLANTS: EFFECT OF PHOTOPERIOD QUALITY. Aust. J. Plant
       Physiol. 1: 445-457.

1399. Kinnersley, A.M.; Davies, P.J. 1974. LIGHT AND TEMPERATURE CONTROL OF
       HYPOCOTYL HAIR FORMATION IN *SINAPIS ALBA* L. Plant Physiol. 53:
       Suppl.-2, Abstr. No. 3.

1400. Kinzel, W. 1907. ÜBER DEN EINFLUSS DES LICHTES AUF DIE KEIMUNG "LICHT-
       HARTE" SAMEN. Ber. Dtsch. Bot. Ges. 25: 269-276.

1401. Kinzel, W. 1908. DIE WIRKUNG DES LICHTES AUF DIE KEIMUNG. Ber. Dtsch.
       Bot. Ges. 26: 105-115.

1402. Kinzel, W. 1908. LICHTKEIMUNG EINIGE BESTÄTIGENDE UND ERGÄNZENDE BEMER-
       KUNGEN ZU DEN VORLÄUFIGEN MITTEILUNGEN VON 1907 UND 1908. Ber.
       Dtsch. Bot. Ges. 26: 631-645.

1403. Kinzel, W. 1908. LICHTKEIMUNG, WEITERE BESTÄTIGENDE UND ERGÄNZENDE
       BEMERKUNGEN ZU DEN VORLÄUFIGEN MITTEILUNGEN VON 1907 UND 1908. Ber.
       Dtsch. Bot. Ges. 26: 654-665.

1404. Kinzel, W. 1909. LICHTKEIMUNG, ERLÄUTERUNGEN UND ERGÄNZUNGEN. Ber.
       Dtsch. Bot. Ges. 27: 536-545.

1405. Kirk, J.T.O.; Tilney-Bassett, R.A.F. 1967. *The Plastids*, W.H. Freeman
       and Co., London and San Francisco, pp. 457-471 (R).

1406. Kirkland, L.; Posner, H.B. 1974. THE ROLE OF LIGHT IN THE PHOTOPERIODIC
       INHIBITION OF FLOWER DEVELOPMENT IN *LEMNA PERPUSILLA* 6746. Plant
       Physiol. 53: Suppl.-3, Abstr. No. 10.

1407. Klebs, G. 1893. UEBER DEN EINFLUSS DES LICHTES AUF DIE FORTPFLANZUNG
       DER GEWÄCHSE. Biol. Centralblatt 13, Nr. 21/22: 641-656 (R).

1408. Klebs, G. 1905. ÜBER VARIATIONEN DER BLÜTEN. Jahrb. Wiss. Bot., pp.
       1-320.

1409. Klebs, G. 1917. ZUR ENTWICKELUNGS-PHYSIOLOGIE DER FARNPROTHALLIEN II,
       III. Sitzungsber. Heidelb. Akad. Wiss. Math. Naturwiss. Kl. 8:
       1-138.

1410. Klebs, G. 1918. ÜBER DIE BLÜTENBILDUNG VON *SEMPERVIVUM*. Flora 111-112: 128-151.

1411. Kleiber, H. 1964. DER EINFLUSS SICHTBARER STRAHLUNG AUF WACHSTUM UND DIFFERENZIERUNG DES HYPOKOTYLS UND DER KOTYLEDONEN VON *SINAPIS ALBA* L. Ph.D. Thesis, Univ. Freiburg, Germany.

1412. Kleiber, H.; Mohr, H. 1964. DER EINFLUSS SICHTBARER STRAHLUNG AUF DIE STOMATA-BILDUNG IN DER EPIDERMIS DER KOTYLEDONEN VON *SINAPIS ALBA* L. Z. Bot. 52: 78-85 (ENG Summary).

1413. Kleiber, H.; Mohr, H. 1967. VOM EINFLUSS DES PHYTOCHROMS AUF DIE XYLEMDIFFERENZIERUNG IM HYPOCOTYL DES SENFKEIMLINGS (*SINAPIS ALBA* L.) Planta 76: 85-92 (ENG Summary).

1414. Klein, A.O.; Filner, B. 1968. DURATION OF FAR-RED LIGHT SENSITIVITY IN DEVELOPING BEAN LEAVES. Plant Physiol. 43: Suppl.-49 (A).

1415. Klein, A.O. 1969. PERSISTENT PHOTOREVERSIBILITY OF LEAF DEVELOPMENT. Plant Physiol. 44: 897-902.

1416. Klein, R.M.; Klein, D.T. 1962. INTERACTION OF IONIZING AND VISIBLE RADIATION IN MUTATION INDUCTION IN *NEUROSPORA CRASSA*. Am. J. Bot. 49: 870-874.

1417. Klein, R.M.; Wansor, J. 1963. EFFECTS OF NON-IONIZING RADIATION ON EXPANSION OF DISKS FROM LEAVES OF DARK-GROWN BEAN PLANTS. Plant Physiol. 38: 5-10.

1418. Klein, R.M. 1965. PHOTOMORPHOGENESIS OF THE BEAN PLUMULAR HOOK. Physiol. Plant. 18: 1026-1033.

1419. Klein, R.M.; Edsall, P.C. 1966. SUBSTITUTION OF REDOX CHEMICALS FOR RADIATION IN PHYTOCHROME MEDIATED PHOTOMORPHOGENESIS. Plant Physiol. 41: 949-952.

1420. Klein, S.; Preiss, J.W. 1958. DEPTH CONTROLLED DEUTERON IRRADIATION OF *LACTUCA SATIVA* SEEDS. I. EFFECTS ON GERMINATION AND GROWTH. Plant Physiol. 33: 321-325.

1421. Klein, S.; Preiss, J.W. 1958. REVERSIBILITY OF THE RED-FAR-RED REACTION BY IRRADIATION AT DIFFERENT SITES. Nature (London) 181: 200-201.

1422. Klein, S.; Bryan, G.; Bogorad, L. 1964. EARLY STAGES IN THE DEVELOPMENT OF PLASTID FINE STRUCTURE IN RED AND FAR-RED LIGHT. J. Cell Biol. 22: 433-442.

1423. Klein, W.H.; Moh, C.C.; Withrow, R.B. 1955. COMPARATIVE RESPONSES OF THE BEAN HYPOCOTYL HOOK TO X-IRRADIATION AND VISIBLE RED ENERGY. Plant Physiol. 30: Suppl.-9 (A).

1424. Klein, W.H.; Withrow, R.B.; Elstad, V. 1956. THE ACTION SPECTRUM AND KINETICS OF FAR-RED BLOCKING OF THE RED INDUCED OPENING OF THE HYPOCOTYL HOOK OF BEAN. Plant Physiol. 31: Suppl.-13 (A).

1425. Klein, W.H.; Withrow, R.B.; Elstad, V.B. 1956. RESPONSE OF THE HYPOCOTYL HOOK OF BEAN SEEDLINGS TO RADIANT ENERGY AND OTHER FACTORS. Plant Physiol. 31: 289-294.

1426. Klein, W.H.; Withrow, R.B.; Elstad, V. 1957. KINETICS OF THE FAR-RED INACTIVATION OF PHOTOMORPHOGENESIS IN THE BEAN HOOK. Plant Physiol. 32: Suppl.-9 (A).

1427. Klein, W.H.; Withrow, R.B.; Elstad, V.; Price, L. 1957. PHOTOCONTROL OF GROWTH AND PIGMENT SYNTHESIS IN THE BEAN SEEDLING AS RELATED TO IRRADIANCE AND WAVELENGTH. Am. J. Bot. 44: 15-19.

1428. Klein, W.H.; Withrow, R.B.; Withrow, A.P.; Elstad, V. 1957. TIME COURSE OF FAR-RED INACTIVATION OF PHOTOMORPHOGENESIS. Science 125: 1146-1147.

1429. Klein, W.H. 1959. INTERACTION OF GROWTH FACTORS WITH PHOTOPROCESS IN SEEDLING GROWTH. *Photoperiodism and Related Phenomena in Plants and Animals*. Ed. R.B. Withrow, A.A.A.S. Washington, D.C., pp. 207-215.

1430. Klein, W.H. 1963. SOME RESPONSES OF THE BEAN HYPOCOTYL. Am. Biol. Teach. 25: 104-106 (A).

1431. Klein, W.H.; Price, L.; Mitrakos, K. 1963. LIGHT STIMULATED STARCH DEGRADATION IN PLASTIDS AND LEAF MORPHOGENESIS. Photochem. Photobiol. 2: 233-240.

1432. Klein, W.H.; Edwards, J.L.; Shropshire, W. Jr. 1967. SPECTROPHOTOMETRIC MEASUREMENTS OF PHYTOCHROME *IN VIVO* AND THEIR CORRELATION WITH PHOTOMORPHOGENIC RESPONSES OF *PHASEOLUS*. Plant Physiol. 42: 264-270.

1433. Klein-Eude, D.; Huault, C.; Rollin, P. 1971. INFLUENCE DE LA LUMIÈRE SUR L'ACTIVITÉ-PAL (= PHÉNYLALANINE AMMONIAC-LYASE, EC. 4.3.1.5.) DES COTYLÉDONS DE RADIS: ACTION DE LA CYCLOHEXIMIDE. C.R. Acad. Sci. Ser. D: 273: 1276-1278.

1434. Klein-Eude, D.; Rollin, P.; Huault, C. 1974. EFFECTS OF SOME TRANSLA-
TION AND TRANSCRIPTION INHIBITORS ON THE DEVELOPMENT OF THE PHENYLA-
LANINE AMMONIA-LYASE ACTIVITY INDUCED BY LIGHT IN RADISH COTYLEDONS.
Plant Sci. Lett. 2: 1-8.

1435. Kleshnin, A.F. 1943. ON THE ROLE OF SPECTRAL COMPOSITION OF LIGHT IN
PHOTOPERIODIC REACTION. Akad. Nauk. SSSR Dokl. 40: 208-211.

1436. Kleshnin, A.F. 1946. ROLE OF SPECTRA OF VISIBLE LIGHT IN PHOTOPERIODIC
AND FORMATIVE PROCESSES AT VARIOUS DEVELOPMENTAL PHASES. Akad. Nauk.
SSSR Dokl. 52: 813-816.

1437. Kleshnin, A. 1950. IMPORTANCE OF DIFFERENT PARTS OF THE SPECTRUM OF
PHYSIOLOGICAL RADIATION FOR GROWTH AND DEVELOPMENT OF PLANTS. Akad.
Nauk SSSR Dokl. 70: 891-894 (RUS).

1437.5 Kleudgen, H.K.; Lichtenthaler, H.K. 1974. INDUCTION AND REVERSION OF
PRENYL-LIPID SYNTHESIS IN ETIOLATED BARLEY SEEDLINGS BY RED AND FAR-
RED LIGHT. Proc. III Int. Congr. Photosynth. pp. 2017-2020.

1438. Kline, M.G.; Johnson, T.; Salisbury, F.B. 1966. RESPONSES TO VISIBLE
LIGHT: PLANTS. *Environmental Biology*, Ed. P.L. Altman and D.S.
Dittmer, Fed. Amer. Soc. Exper. Biol., Bethesda, Md., pp. 143-146
(R).

1439. Koevenig, J.L.; Jacobs, W.P. 1972. EFFECT OF LIGHT ON BASIPETAL MOVE-
MENT OF INDOLEACETIC ACID IN GREEN STEM SECTIONS OF *COLEUS*. Plant
Physiol. 49: 866-867.

1440. Kofranek, A.M.; Sachs, R.M. 1963. EFFECT OF FAR-RED DURING THE PHOTO-
PERIOD ON FLOWER INITIATION. Plant Physiol. 38: Suppl.-23 (A).

1441. Kofranek, A.M.; Sachs, R.M. 1964. EFFECT OF FAR-RED ILLUMINATION DURING
THE PHOTOPERIOD ON FLORAL INITIATION OF *CHENOPODIUM AMARANTICOLOR*.
Am. J. Bot. 51: 520-521.

1442. Kögl, F.; Haagen-Smit, A.J.; Van Hulssen, C.J. 1936. ÜBER DEN EINFLUSS
UNBEKANNTER AUSSERER FAKTOREN BEI VERSUCHEN MIT *AVENA SATIVA*. Hoppe-
Seyler's Z. Physiol. Chem. 241: 17-33.

1443. Kohl, F.G. 1886. DIE TRANSPIRATION DER PFLANZEN UND IHRE EINWIRKUNG AUF
DIE AUSBILDUNG PFLANZLICHER GEWEBE. Braunschweig, pp. 52-74.

1444. Kohl, F.G. 1895. ZUR MECHANIK DER SPALTÖFFNUNGSBEWEGUNG. Bot.
Beiblatt. Leopoldina: 4 pp. (not obtained).

1445. Kohlbecker, R. 1957. DIE ABHÄNGIGKEIT DES LÄNGENWACHSTUMS UND DER
PHOTOTROPISCHEN KRÜMMUNGEN VON DER LICHTQUALITÄT BEI KEIMWURZELN VON
SINAPIS ALBA. Z. Bot. 45: 507-524.

1446. Köhler, D. 1965. ÜBER DEN GIBBERELLINGEHALT VON ZWERG UND NORMALERBSEN
IM ROTLICHT UND DIE WIRKUNG VON CHLORCHOLINCHLORID AUF DAS WACHSTUM
DER ERBSEN. Planta 65: 218-224 (ENG Summary).

1447. Köhler, D. 1965. DIE WIRKUNG VON SCHWACHEM ROTLICHT UND CHLOROCHOLIN-
CHLORID AUF DEN GIBBERELLINGEHALT NORMALER ERBSENSÄMLINGE UND DIE
URSACHE DER UNTERSCHIEDLICHEN EMPFINDLICHTKEIT VON ZWERG UND NORMAL-
ERBSENSÄMLINGEN GEGEN IHR EIGENES GIBBERELLIN. Planta 67: 44-54
(ENG Summary).

1448. Köhler, D. 1966. DIE ABHÄNGIGKEIT DER GIBBERELLINPRODUKTION VON
NORMALERBSEN VOM PHYTOCHROM SYSTEM. Planta 69: 27-33 (ENG Summary).

1449. Köhler, D. 1966. VERÄNDERUNGEN DES GIBBERELLINGEHALTES VON SALATSAMEN
NACH BELICHTUNG. Planta 70: 42-45 (ENG Summary).

1450. Köhler, D.; Willert, K.v.; Lüttge, U. 1968. PHYTOCHROMABHÄNGIGE VER-
ÄNDERUNGEN DES WACHSTUMS UND DER IONENAUFNAHME ETIOLIERTER ERBSEN-
KEIMLINGE. Planta 83: 35-48 (ENG Summary).

1451. Köhler, D. 1969. PHYTOCHROMABHÄNGIGER IONENTRANSPORT IN ERBSENSÄMLIN-
GEN. Planta 84: 158-165 (ENG Summary).

1452. Köhler, D. 1970. DIE WIRKUNG DES ROTLICHTES AUF DAS WACHSTUM VON
ERBSENKEIMLINGEN UND IHREN GEHALT AN GIBBERELLINÄHNLICHEN SUBSTANZEN.
Z. Pflanzenphysiol. 62: 426-435 (ENG Summary).

1453. Köhler, D. 1970. ÜBER DEN ZUSAMMENHANG ZWISCHEN ACHSEN- UND BLATT-
WACHSTUM UND IONENAUFNAHME BEI KEIMLINGEN VON *PISUM SATIVUM*. Z.
Pflanzenphysiol. 63: 185-193 (ENG Summary).

1454. Köhler, K.H. 1972. ACTION OF INHIBITORS OF PROTEIN AND NUCLEIC ACID
SYNTHESIS ON LIGHT-DEPENDENT AND KINETIN-STIMULATED BETACYANIN
SYNTHESIS. Phytochemistry 11: 127-131.

1455. Köhler, K.H. 1972. PHOTOCONTROL OF BETACYANIN SYNTHESIS IN *AMARANTHUS
CAUDATUS* SEEDLINGS IN THE PRESENCE OF KINETIN. Phytochemistry 11:
133-137.

1456. Köhler, K.H. 1973. DIE STEUERUNG DER AMARTHINBIOSYNTHESE DURCH DAS
PHYTOCHROMSYSTEM (EINSCHLIESSLICH BESCHREIBUNG DER BESTRAHLUNGSANLAGE
UND DER LICHTENERGIEMESSUNG). Biol. Zentralb. 92: 307-336 (ENG
Summary).

1457. Koller, B.; Smith, H. 1972. RELATIONSHIP BETWEEN PHOTOMORPHOGENESIS AND RNA SYNTHESIS IN OAT AND PEA SEEDLINGS. Phytochemistry 11: 1295-1301.

1458. Koller, D.; Mayer, A.M.; Poljakoff-Mayber, A.; Klein, S. 1962. SEED GERMINATION. Annu. Rev. Plant Physiol. 13: 437-464 (R).

1459. Koller, D.; Poljakoff-Mayber, A.; Berg, A.; Diskin, T. 1963. GERMINA-TION-REGULATING MECHANISMS IN *CITRULLUS COLOCYNTHIS*. Am. J. Bot. 50: 597-603.

1460. Koller, D. 1964. THE SURVIVAL VALUE OF GERMINATION-REGULATING MECHA-NISMS IN THE FIELD. Herb. Abstr. 34: 1-7 (R).

1461. Koller, D.; Sachs, M.; Negbi, M. 1964. SPECTRAL SENSITIVITY OF SEED GERMINATION IN *ARTEMISIA MONOSPERMA*. Plant Cell Physiol. 5: 79-84.

1462. Koller, D.; Negbi, M.; Segal, N. 1966. KINETIC ANALYSIS OF SEED GERMI-NATION IN *ATRIPLEX DIMORPHOSTEGIA*. Jerusalem Hebrew Univ. Authority for Research and Development, Research Report Science, Agriculture 1965/66, pp. 274-275 (A).

1463. Koller, D. 1970. ANALYSIS OF THE DUAL ACTION OF WHITE LIGHT ON GERMINA-TION OF *ATRIPLEX DIMORPHOSTEGIA* (CHENOPODIACEAE). Isr. J. Bot. 19: 499-516.

1464. Koller, D. 1972. ENVIRONMENTAL CONTROL OF SEED GERMINATION. *SEED Bio-logy*, Ed. T.T. Kozlowski, Academic Press, New York and London 2: 1-101 (R).

1465. Kolli, S. 1969. CHEMICAL CONTROL OF FLOWERING. Bot. Rev. 35: 195-200 (R).

1466. Kommerell, E. 1927. QUANTITATIVE VERSUCHE ÜBER DEN EINFLUSS DES LICHTES VERSCHIEDENER WELLENLÄNGEN AUF DIE KEIMUNG VON SAMEN. Jahrb. Wiss. Bot. 66: 461-512.

1467. Kondo, N.; Fujii, T.; Yamaki, T. 1969. EFFECT OF LIGHT ON AUXIN TRANS-PORT AND ELONGATION OF *AVENA* MESOCOTYL. Dev. Growth Differ. 11: 46-61.

1468. Kondo, N.; Inoue, Y.; Shibata, K. 1973. PHYTOCHROME DISTRIBUTION IN *AVENA* SEEDLINGS MEASURED BY SCANNING A SINGLE SEEDLING. Plant Sci. Lett. 1: 165-168.

1469. Kondurushkin, I.A.; Shakhov, A.A. 1967. SOME DATA ON THE BIOLOGICAL
       INTERACTION OF THE VISIBLE AND INFRA-RED AREAS OF THE ELECTROMAGNETIC
       SPECTRUM. Elektron Obrab. Mater 5: 91-94 (RUS) (R).

1470. Koningsberger, V.J. 1922. TROPISMUS UND WACHSTUM, KAPITEL V. MONO-
       CHROMATISCHES LICHT. Rec. Trav. Bot. Neerl. 19: 71-101.

1471. Koningsberger, V.J. 1954. LIGHT AND LIFE. Proc. I Int. Congr. Photo-
       biol., pp. 7-20 (R).

1472. Konishi, M.; Galston, A.W. 1964. LIGHT-INDUCED CHANGES IN PHENOLIC
       INHIBITORS OF INDOLEACETIC ACID OXIDASE IN COTYLEDONS OF *PHARBITIS
       NIL*. Phytochemistry 3: 559-568.

1473. Konishi, M. 1969. RESISTANCE OF HYPOCOTYL OF *PHARBITIS NIL* TO HYPER-
       TONIC SOLUTIONS AND COLD TEMPERATURES AS AFFECTED BY FAR-RED LIGHT.
       Plant Physiol. 44: Suppl.-19, Abstr. No. 89 (A).

1474. Konishi, M. 1969. GROWTH STUDY ON HYPOCOTYLS OF JAPANESE MORNING GLORY
       AS INFLUENCED BY FAR-RED AND RED LIGHT. Proc. XI Int. Bot. Congr.,
       p. 114 (A).

1474.5 Konishi, M. 1972. DIFFERENCES BETWEEN EFFECTS OF SPECTRAL AND FLUORES-
       CENT OR FILTERED MONOCHROMATIC LIGHTS ON INDUCING PHOTOPERIODIC SEN-
       SITIVITY OF *PHARBITIS NIL*. Seibutsu Kankyo Chosetsu 10: 44-51.

1475. Könitz, W. 1958. BLÜHHEMMUNG BEI KURZTAGPFLANZEN DURCH HELLROT- UND
       DUNKELROTLICHT IN DER PHOTO- UND SKOTOPHILEN PHASE. Planta 51: 1-29.

1476. Konstantinova, T.N. 1966. PHOTOCHEMICAL AND DARK REACTIONS OF PLANT
       PHOTOPERIODICITY. Usp. Sovrem Biol. 61: 118-131 (RUS) (R).

1477. Konstantinova, T.N. 1969. PHOTOPERIODISM AS A SEQUENTIAL CHAIN OF LIGHT
       AND DARK REACTIONS. Izv. Akad. Nauk. SSSR Ser. Biol. (3), pp. 386-
       400 (RUS) (R).

1478. Kopcewicz, J. 1972. EFFECT OF COLOURED LIGHT IRRADIATION ON GERMINATION
       AND ENDOGENOUS GROWTH REGULATOR CONTENT IN SCOTS PINE (*PINUS SILVES-
       TRIS* L.). Bull. Acad. Pol. Sci. Ser. Sci. Biol. 20: 419-424.

1479. Kopcewicz, J.; Porazinski, Z. 1973. EFFECT OF RED LIGHT IRRADIATION ON
       METABOLISM OF FREE AND BOUND GIBBERELLINS IN SCOTS PINE (*PINUS
       SILVESTRIS* L.). Bull. Acad. Pol. Sci. Ser. Sci. Biol. 21: 383-387.

1480. Koukkari, W.L.; Hillman, W.S. 1966. PHYTOCHROME TRANSFORMATIONS IN
       NONSEEDLING TISSUES. Plant Physiol. 41: Suppl.-16 (A).

1481. Koukkari, W.L.; Hillman, W.S. 1966. PHYTOCHROME LEVELS ASSAYED BY *IN VIVO* SPECTROPHOTOMETRY IN MODIFIED UNDERGROUND STEMS AND STORAGE ROOTS. Physiol. Plant. 19: 1073-1078.

1482. Koukkari, W.L.; Hillman, W.S. 1967. EFFECTS OF TEMPERATURE AND AERATION ON PHYTOCHROME TRANSFORMATIONS IN *PASTINACA SATIVA* ROOT TISSUE. Am. J. Bot. 54: 1118-1122.

1483. Koukkari, W.L.; Hillman, W.S. 1968. PULVINI AS THE PHOTORECEPTORS IN THE PHYTOCHROME EFFECT ON NYCTINASTY IN *ALBIZZIA JULIBRISSIN*. Plant Physiol. 43: 698-704.

1484. Koukkari, W.L.; McEvoy, R.C. 1970. PHYTOCHROME AND OSMOTIC EFFECTS REGULATING PINNULE MOVEMENTS. Plant Physiol. 46: Suppl.-2, Abstr. No. 8 (A).

1485. Kowallik, W. 1962. ÜBER DIE WIRKUNG DES BLAUEN AND ROTEN SPEKTRAL-BEREICHS AUF DIE ZUSAMMENSETZUNG UND ZELLTEILUNG SYNCHRONISIERTER CHLORELLEN. Planta 58: 337-365 (ENG Summary).

1486. Kowallik, W. 1963. DIE ZELLTEILUNG VON *CHLORELLA* IM VERLAUFE EINER FARBLICHTKULTUR. Planta 60: 100-108.

1487. Kowallik, W. 1965. DIE PROTEINPRODUKTION VON *CHLORELLA* IM LICHT VERSCHIEDENER WELLENLÄNGEN. Planta 64: 191-200 (ENG Summary).

1488. Kowallik, W. 1966. EINFLUSS VERSCHIEDENER LICHTWELLENLÄNGEN AUF DIE ZUSAMMENSETZUNG VON *CHLORELLA* IN GLUCOSEKULTUR BEI GEHEMMTER PHOTO-SYNTHESE. Planta 69: 292-295 (ENG Summary).

1489. Kraml, M. 1971. DIE WIRKUNG KURZWELLIGEN LICHTES AUF PHYTOCHROMREAK-TIONEN VON *PISUM* UND *SINAPIS*. Z. Pflanzenphysiol. 65: 97-117 (ENG Summary).

1490. Kraml, M. 1974. DIFFERENT PHYTOCHROME PHOTOCONVERSION IN DRIED EMBRYOS OF OAT SEEDS AS INFLUENCED BY PRETREATMENT WITH RED LIGHT. Proc. Eur. Annu. Symp. Plant Photomorphogenesis, (Antwerpen) pp. 26-30.

1491. Kranz, A.R. 1973. HOMO-AND HETEROALLELIC GENE ACTION ON THE BIOSYNTHE-SIS OF CHLOROPHYLL, PRIMARY CAROTENOIDS, GIBBERELLIC ACID AND PHYTO-CHROME IN *ARABIDOPSIS THALIANA*. Genetics 74: Suppl. No. 2, part 2, S-145 (A).

1492. Kranz, A.R. 1974. GENE ANALYSIS OF SEED GERMINATION INDUCED BY PHYTO-CHROME (P_{fr}) AND/OR GIBBERELLIC ACID (GA_3) IN *ARABIDOPSIS THALIANA*. Arabidopsis Inf. Ser. 11: 4-5.

1493. Kranz, A.R. 1974. ISOLATION OF MUTANTS DEFECTIVE IN CERTAIN PHYTO-
CHROME-MEDIATED PHOTOMORPHOSIS. Arabidopsis Inf. Ser. 11: 19-20.

1494. Kraus, G. 1876. SITZUNGSBERICHTE DER NATURFORSCHENDEN GESELLSCHAFT ZU
HALLE. Bot. Ztg. 34: 503-508.

1495. Krinsky, N.I. 1974. MEMBRANE PHOTOCHEMISTRY AND PHOTOBIOLOGY. Photochem. Photobiol. 20: 533-534 (R).

1496. Kritsky, M.S. 1974. THE LIGHT-DEPENDENT PROCESSES IN FUNGI: A POSSIBLE
APPROACH TO SOME PROBLEMS OF PHOTOBIOLOGICAL EVOLUTION. *The origin
of life and evolutionary biochemistry*, Ed. K. Dose; S.W. Fox; G.A.
Deborin and T.E. Pavlovskaya. Plenum Press, New York, pp. 263-269
(R).

1497. Kroes, H.H. 1968. THE MECHANISM OF THE PHOTOREVERSIBLE PHYTOCHROME RE-
ACTION. Proc. V Int. Congr. Photobiol., p. 92 (A).

1498. Kroes, H.H. 1968. REVERSIBLE CHANGES IN THE CIRCULAR DICHROISM OF
PHYTOCHROME DURING PHOTOISOMERISATION OF THE PIGMENT. Biochem. Biophys. Res. Commun. 31: 877-883.

1499. Kroes, H.H. 1969. THE STRUCTURE OF THE PHYTOCHROME CHROMOPHORE. Paper
delivered at the Photomorphogenesis Meeting, Univ. of Reading.

1500. Kroes, H.H.; van Rooijen, A.; Geers, J.M.; Greuell, E.H.M. 1969. LARGE-
SCALE ISOLATION OF PHYTOCHROME FROM OAT SEEDLINGS. Biochim. Biophys.
Acta 175: 409-413.

1501. Kroes, H.H. 1970. THE STRUCTURE OF THE PIGMENT PHYTOCHROME. Physiol.
Veg. 8: 533-549.

1502. Kroes, H.H. 1970. A STUDY OF PHYTOCHROME, ITS ISOLATION, STRUCTURE AND
PHOTOCHEMICAL TRANSFORMATIONS. Meded. Landbouwhogesch. Wageningen
70-18: 1-112.

1503. Krotkov, G. 1964. THE INFLUENCE OF THE WAVELENGTH OF INCIDENT LIGHT ON
THE PATH OF CARBON IN PHOTOSYNTHESIS. Trans. R. Soc. Can. Sect. 3,
2: 205-215.

1504. Krug, H. 1962. BERICHT ÜBER EINE STUDIENREISE IN DIE U.S.A. Institute
für Pflanzenban und Saatguterzeugung der Forschungsanstalt für
Landwirtschaft. Braunschweig Volkenode, Germany (not obtained) (Referred to by Siegelman, H.W. (1964) *Biochemistry of Phenolic Compounds*, Ed. J.B. Harborne, Academic Press, New York and London, pp.
437-456) (R).

1505. Ku, P.K.; Mancinelli, A.L.   1972.   PHOTOCONTROL OF ANTHOCYANIN SYNTHESIS. I. ACTION OF SHORT, PROLONGED, AND INTERMITTENT IRRADIATIONS ON THE FORMATION OF ANTHOCYANINS IN CABBAGE, MUSTARD, AND TURNIP SEEDLINGS. Plant Physiol. 49: 212-217.

1506. Ku (Tai), P.K.   1973.   PHOTOCONTROL OF ANTHOCYANIN SYNTHESIS.   Ph.D. Thesis, Columbia Univ., New York.

1507. Kuiper, P.J.C.   1964.   DEPENDENCE UPON WAVELENGTH OF STOMATAL MOVEMENT IN EPIDERMAL TISSUE OF *SENECIO ODORIS*.   Plant Physiol. 39: 952-955.

1508. Kujawski, R.F.   1972.   SOME ASPECTS OF THE PHYSIOLOGY OF COILING IN SEEDLINGS OF *CUSCUTA GRONOVII* WILLD.   Ph.D. Thesis, State Univ. of New York, Albany.

1509. Kujawski, R.F.; Truscott, F.H.   1974.   PHOTOCONTROL OF HOOK OPENING IN *CUSCUTA GRONOVII* WILLD.   Plant Physiol. 53: 610-614.

1510. Kuperman, F.M.   1955.   LIGHT AS A FACTOR IN THE DEVELOPMENT OF THE PLANT AND THE MORPHOGENESIS OF PLANTS.   Jestastvoznanije v Skole 1 (RUS) (R) (not obtained) (Referred to by Duda, M. 1968. Biologia (Bratislava) 23: 777-792),

1511. Kuperman, F.M.   1956.   BIOLOGICAL BASIS OF WHEAT CULTURE.   3 Izd. M.G.U. (RUS) (R) (not obtained) (Referred to by Duda, M. 1968. Biologia (Bratislava) 23: 777-792).

1512. Kuperman, F.M.   1959.   FUNDAMENTALS OF THE REGULARITIES OF THE ONTOGENY OF PLANTS IN THE LIGHT AND THE THEORY OF THE DEVELOPMENT OF CITIES. Trudy Konferencii posvj. 40 Letiju Vel. Okt. Soc. Revol. Inst. Genetiki Akad. Nauk. SSSR 2 (RUS) (R) (not obtained) (Referred to by Duda, M. 1968. Biologia (Bratislava) 23: 777-792).

1513. Kuperman, F.M.   1961.   RESULTS OF THE INVESTIGATION OF ORGANOGENESIS OF INDIVIDUAL ECOTYPES OF MILLET UNDER THE CONDITIONS OF LIGHT CHAMBERS. Morphogenez rastenij I., Izd. M.G.U. (RUS) (not obtained) (Referred to by Duda, M. 1968. Biologia (Bratislava) 23: 777-792).

1514. Kurtz, E.B. Jr.; Alcorn, S.M.   1960.   SOME GERMINATION REQUIREMENTS OF SAGUARO CACTUS SEEDS.   J. Cactus Succulent Soc. Am. 32: 72-74.

1515. Küstner, H.   1931.   HORMONWIRKUNG BEI DEN PFLANZEN UND HORMONSTEIGERUNG DURCH ROTES LICHT.   Klin. Wochenschr. 10: 1585.

1516. Kuzmenko, A.A. 1937. THE EFFECT OF IRRADIATING GERMINATING TOBACCO SEEDS WITH LIGHT OF VARIOUS SPECTRAL COMPOSITION ON THE GROWTH AND DEVELOPMENT OF PLANTS. J. Inst. Bot. Akad. Nauk. Ukr. SSR No. 13-14: 179-196 (RUS) (ENG Summary).

1517. Kuznetsov, E.D.; Shakov, A.A. 1972. Proc. I Soviet scientific technical Conf. on renewed sources of energy, Vol. 3, Photoenergetics of plants Moscow (RUS) (not obtained) (R) (Referred to by Kuznetsov, E.D.; Shakov, A.A. 1974. Elektron. Obrab. Mater. 4: 66-68).

1518. Kuznetsov, E.D.; Shakov, A.A. 1974. LOW-ENERGY PHOTOSTIMULATION OF THE BIOSYNTHESIS OF PROTEIN IN PLANTS. Elektron. Obrab. Mater. 4: 66-68.

1519. Lackmann, I. 1971. WIRKUNGSSPEKTREN DER ANTHOCYANSYNTHESE IN GEWEBE-KULTUREN UND KEIMLINGEN VON *HAPLOPAPPUS GRACILIS*. Planta 98: 258-269 (ENG Summary).

1520. La Croix, L.J.; Canvin, D.T. 1963. THE ROLE OF LIGHT AND OTHER FACTORS IN THE GROWTH AND DIFFERENTIATION OF BARLEY EMBRYOS. Plant Physiol. 38: Suppl.-23 (A).

1521. Laetsch, W.M.; Briggs, W.R. 1961. PHOTOMORPHOGENETIC RESPONSES OF THE SPORELING OF WATER FERN *MARSILEA VESTITA*. Am. J. Bot. 48: 529 (A).

1522. Laetsch, W.M.; Briggs, W.R. 1962. PHOTOMORPHOGENETIC RESPONSES OF SPORELINGS OF *MARSILEA VESTITA*. Plant Physiol. 37: 142-148.

1523. Laetsch, W.M. 1963. OBSERVATIONS ON THE PHOTOMORPHOGENESIS OF CULTURED TISSUE. Am. J. Bot. 50: 616 (A).

1524. Laloraya, M.M.; Srivastava, H.N.; Tyagi, S.K. 1968. BIOCHEMICAL EVENTS IN PHOTOMORPHOGENETIC CONTROL OF SEEDLING GROWTH. Proc. V Int. Congr. Photobiol., p. 62 (A).

1525. Lambert, C. 1972. PHYTOCHROME ET MÉTABOLISME DE L'ARGININE DANS DES TISSUS DE TOPINAMBOUR CULTIVÉS *IN VITRO*. C.R. Acad. Sci. Ser D 275: 2639-2641.

1526. Landgraf, J.E. 1961. ÜBER DEN EINFLUSS DES LICHTES AUF DEN PROTEIN-STOFFWECHSEL BEI KEIMLINGEN VON *SINAPIS ALBA* L. Planta 57: 543-556 (ENG Summary).

1527. Lane, H.C.; Siegelman, H.W.; Butler, W.L.; Firer, E.L. 1962, EXTRACTION AND ASSAY OF PHYTOCHROME FROM GREEN PLANTS. Plant Physiol. 37: Suppl.-27, Abstr. No. 748 (A).

1528. Lane, H.C. 1963. EFFECT OF LIGHT QUALITY ON MATURITY IN THE MILO GROUP OF SORGHUM. Crop Sci. 3: 496-499.

1529. Lane, H.C.; Butler, W.L. 1963. STUDIES ON THE DARK TRANSFORMATION OF PHYTOCHROME. Plant Physiol. 38: Suppl.-5 (A).

1530. Lane, H.C.; Siegelman, H.W.; Butler, W.L.; Firer, E.M. 1963. DETECTION OF PHYTOCHROME IN GREEN PLANTS. Plant Physiol. 38: 414-416.

1531. Lane, H.C. 1964. EFFECTS OF LIGHT ON HOOK OPENING AND TWINING OF SEED-LINGS OF DODDER, CUSCUTA INDECORA CHOIS. Plant Physiol. 39: Suppl.-49 (A).

1532. Lane, H.C.; Cathey, H.M. 1965. THE DEPENDENCE OF FLOWERING IN SEVERAL LONG-DAY PLANTS ON THE SPECTRAL COMPOSITION OF LIGHT EXTENDING THE PHOTOPERIOD. Plant Physiol. 40: Suppl.-44-45 (A).

1533. Lane, H.C.; Cathey, H.M.; Evans, L.T. 1965. THE DEPENDENCE OF FLOWERING IN SEVERAL LONG-DAY PLANTS ON THE SPECTRAL COMPOSITION OF LIGHT EX-TENDING THE PHOTOPERIOD. Am. J. Bot. 52: 1006-1014.

1534. Lane, H.C.; Kasperbauer, M.J. 1965. PHOTOMORPHOGENIC RESPONSES OF DODDER SEEDLINGS. Plant Physiol. 40: 109-116.

1535. Lane, R.D. 1957. RESEARCH IN TREE PHYSIOLOGY PROVIDES PROMISING LEADS. Northeast. For. Exp. Stn. p. 22, Upper Darby (A).

1536. Lang, A. 1954. ENTWICKLUNGSPHYSIOLOGIE. Fortschr. Bot. 15: 400-475 (R).

1537. Lang, A. 1965. PHYSIOLOGY OF FLOWER INITIATION. Handbuch der Pflanzen-physiologie Ed. W. Ruhland, Berlin-Göttingen Heidelberg Springer 15/1, 1380-1536 (R).

1538. Lange, H.; Mohr, H. 1965. DIE HEMMUNG DER PHYTOCHROM-INDUZIERTEN ANTHO-CYANSYNTHESE DURCH ACTINOMYCIN D UND PUROMYCIN. Planta 67: 107-121 (ENG Summary).

1539. Lange, H.; Bienger, I.; Mohr, H. 1967. EINE NEUE BEWEISFÜHRUNG FÜR DIE HYPOTHESE EINER DIFFERENTIELLEN GENAKTIVIERUNG DURCH PHYTOCHROM 730. Planta 76: 359-366 (ENG Summary).

1540. Lange, H.; Steiner, A.M. 1968. INTERACTION BETWEEN HYDROXYPROLINE INHI-BITION AND PHYTOCHROME DEPENDENT ACCUMULATION OF ANTHOCYANIN IN MUS-TARD SEEDLINGS (SINAPIS ALBA L.). Naturwissenschaften 55: 138.

1541. Lange, H.; Shropshire, W. Jr.; Mohr, H. 1971. AN ANALYSIS OF PHYTO-CHROME-MEDIATED ANTHOCYANIN SYNTHESIS. Plant Physiol. 47: 649-655.

1542. Lange, S. 1929. ÜBER DEN EINFLUSS WEISSEN UND ROTEN LICHTES AUF DIE ENTWICKLUNG DES MESOKOTYLS BEI HAFERKEIMLINGEN. Jahrb. Wiss. Bot. 71: 1-25.

1543. Langewellpott-Kunze, D. 1970. ÜBER DEN EINFLUSS VON GENO- UND PLASMO-
TYPUS AUF DIE PHYTOCHROMGESTEUERTE SAMENKEIMUNG UND DIE CHLOROPHYLL-
SYNTHESE (UNTERSUCHUNGEN AN *RAIMANNIA OENOTHEREN*). Ph.D. Thesis,
Univ. Tübingen, Germany (not obtained) (referred to by Hachtel, W.
1972. Planta 102: 247-260).

1544. Langston, R.; Leopold, A.C. 1954. THE DARK FIXATION OF CARBON DIOXIDE
AS A FACTOR IN PHOTOPERIODISM. Plant Physiol. 29: 436-440.

1545. Larcher, G. 1971. ÉTUDE THÉORIQUE ET MISE AU POINT D'UN SPECTROPHOTO-
MÈTRE DIFFÉRENTIEL A DEUX LONGUEURS D'ONDE DE TRÈS GRANDE
SENSIBILITÉ. Nouv. Rev. Opt. Appl. 2: 331-336.

1546. Larcher, G.; Huault, C.; Malcoste, R. 1971. MISE EN ÉVIDENCE D'UNE
CORRÉLATION QUANTITATIVE ENTRE LE PHYTOCHROME ET L'ACTIVITÉ-PAL
(= PHÉNYLALANINE AMMONIAC-LYASE, EC. 4.3.1.5.) DANS LES COTYLÉDONS DE
RAPHANUS SATIVUS L. C.R. Acad. Sci. Ser. D 273: 2257-2260.

1547. Larpent, J.-P.; Jacques, R. 1972. CROISSANCE, CHLOROPHYLLES ET PHYTO-
CHROME CHEZ LE *DRAPARNALDIA MUTABILIS* (ROTH) CEDERG, CULTIVÉ EN
RADIATIONS MONOCHROMATIQUES. C.R. Acad. Sci. Ser. D 274: 1297-1299.

1548. Larpent, M.; Jacques, R. 1971. RÔLE DU PHYTOCHROME DANS LE DÉVELOPPE-
MENT DU PROTONÉMA DE *FUNARIA HYGROMETRICA* (HEDW). C.R. Acad. Sci.
Ser. D 273: 162-164.

1548.5 Larpent-Gourgaud, M.; Jacques, R. 1971-1972. PHYTOCHROME ET GERMINATION
DES PROPAGULES DU *TETRAPHIS PELLUCIDA* (L.) RABENH. Rev. Bryol.
Lichénol. 38: 265-267.

1549. Larpent-Gourgaud, M.; Larpent, J.-P.; Jacques, R. 1972. RÔLE DU PHYTO-
CHROME DANS LA GERMINATION ET LA CROISSANCE DU PROTONÉMA DE *TETRAPHIS
PELLUCIDA* (L.) RABENH. Physiol. Veg. 10: 553-558 (ENG Summary).

1549.5 Larpent-Gourgaud, M.; Larpent, J.-P.; Jacques, R. 1974. EFFET DU PHYTO-
CHROME SUR LE DÉVELOPPEMENT DES PROTONÉMAS DE BRYOPHYTES. Bull. Soc.
Bot. Fr. 121: 153-160 (R-D).

1550. Laudi, G.; Bonatti, P. 1967. RICERCHE COMPARATE SULLA MORFOLOGIA E
SULLA FISIOLOGIA DI *LARIX* E DI *PICEA*. AZIONE DELL'OSCURITA E DELLA
LUCE DI DIVERSA LUNGHEZZA D'ONDA SULLA GERMINAZIONE DEI SEMI. G.
Bot. Ital. 101: 25-31 (ENG Summary).

1551. Lawson, V.R. 1973. EXPERIMENTS ON THE MECHANISM OF CELL GROWTH AND
PHOTOMORPHOGENESIS IN COLEOPTILES. Ph.D. Thesis, The George Washington Univ., Washington, D.C.

1552. Lecharny, A.; Jacques, R. 1972. PHYTOCHROME ET VARIATIONS DE SENSIBI-
LITÉ AUX ÉCLAIREMENTS DE FAIBLE ÉNERGIE. C.R. Acad. Sci. Ser. D
275: 2227-2230.

1553. Lecharny, A.; Jacques, R. 1974. PHYTOCHROME ET CROISSANCE DES TIGES;
VARIATIONS DE L'EFFET DE LA LUMIÈRE EN FONCTION DU TEMPS ET DU LIEU
DE PHOTOPERCEPTION. Physiol. Veg. 12: 721-738.

1554. LeDeunff, Y. 1971. MISE EN ÉVIDENCE DU PHYTOCHROME CHEZ LES SEMENCES DE
RUMEX CRISPUS L. Physiol. Veg. 9: 201-208 (ENG Summary).

1555. LeDeunff, Y. 1973. PHYTOCHROME ET CHOC THERMIQUE DANS LA GERMINATION
DES SEMENCES DE RUMEX CRISPUS L. C.R. Acad. Sci. Ser. D 276: 2443-
2446.

1556. LeDeunff, Y. 1974. CHOCS THERMIQUES, PHYTOCHROME ET GERMINATION DES
SEMENCES DORMANTES DE RUMEX CRISPUS L. C.R. Acad. Sci. Ser. D 279:
1583-1586.

1557. LeDeunff, Y. 1974. RÔLE DU POTASSIUM SUR L'ADDITIVITÉ DES ACTIONS DUES
AU CHOC THERMIQUE ET AU PHYTOCHROME SUR LA LEVÉE DE DORMANCE SECON-
DAIRE DES SEMENCES DE RUMEX CRISPUS L. C.R. Acad. Sci. Ser. D 279:
1617-1619.

1558. Lee, O.Y.; Stadelmann, E. 1972. LIGHT AS A FACTOR IN WATER PERMEABILITY
CHANGES OF PISUM PARENCHYMA. Plant Physiol. 49: Suppl.-62, Abstr.
No. 349 (A).

1559. Leff, J. 1964. INTERACTION BETWEEN KINETIN AND LIGHT ON GERMINATION OF
GRAND RAPIDS LETTUCE SEEDS. Plant Physiol. 39: 299-303.

1560. Leggatt, C.W. 1948. A CONTRIBUTION TO THE STUDY OF DORMANCY IN SEEDS
LACTUCA SATIVA L. Can. J. Res. 26: 194-217.

1561. Leitgeb, H. 1880. STUDIEN ÜBER ENTWICKLUNG DER FARNE. Sitzungsber.
Akad. Wiss. Wien, Math. Naturwiss. Kl. Abt. 1 80: 201-227.

1562. LeNoir, W.C. Jr. 1967. THE EFFECT OF LIGHT ON THE CELLULAR COMPONENTS
OF POLARIZED GROWTH IN BEAN INTERNODES. Am. J. Bot. 54: 876-887.

1563. Leopold, A.C. 1951. PHOTOPERIODISM IN PLANTS. Q. Rev. Biol. 26:
247-263 (R).

1564. Leopold, A.C.; Guernsey, F.S. 1954. RESPIRATORY RESPONSES TO RED AND
INFRA-RED LIGHT. Physiol. Plant. 7: 30-40.

1565. Letouzé, R. 1972. PHYTOCHROME ET CROISSANCE DU BOUGEON AXILLAIRE CHEX
SALIX BABYLONICA L. C.R. Acad. Sci. Ser. D 275: 2663-2666.

1566. Letouzé, R. 1974. CROISSANCE DU BOURGEON AXILLAIRE D'UNE BOUTURE DE SAULE (*SALIX BABYLONICA* L.) EN CULTURE *IN VITRO*. DOMINANCE APICALE ET QUALITÉ DE LA LUMIÈRE. Physiol. Veg. 12: 397-412.

1567. Lewak, S.; Smolenska, G. 1968. LE SYSTÈME PHYTOCHROME DANS LA GERMINA-TION DES SEMENCES DE POMMIER. Physiol. Veg. 6: 403-408 (ENG Summary).

1568. Lhoste, J.M. 1972. SOME PHYSICAL ASPECTS OF THE PHYTOCHROME PHOTOTRANS-FORMATION. *Phytochrome*, Ed. K. Mitrakos and W. Shropshire, Jr.; Academic Press: London and New York, pp. 47-74 (R).

1569. Lichtenthaler, H.K.; Becker, K. 1971. CHANGES OF THE PLASTIDQUINONE AND CAROTENOID METABOLISM ASSOCIATED WITH THE FORMATION OF FUNCTIONING CHLOROPLASTS IN CONTINUOUS FAR-RED AND WHITE LIGHT. Proc. Int. Congr. Photosynth. Res. 2nd pp. 2451-2459.

1570. Lichtenthaler, H.K. 1973. REGULATION DER LIPOCHINONSYNTHESE IN CHLORO-PLASTEN. Ber. Dtsch. Bot. Ges. 86: 313-329 (R) (ENG Summary).

1571. Lie, T.A. 1969. NON-PHOTOSYNTHETIC EFFECTS OF RED AND FAR-RED LIGHT ON ROOT-NODULE FORMATION BY LEGUMINOUS PLANTS. Plant Soil 30: 391-404.

1572. Liebig, M. 1942. UNTERSUCHUNGEN ÜBER DIE ABHÄNGIGKEIT DER SPALTWEITE DER STOMATA VON INTENSITÄT UND QUALITÄT DER STRAHLUNG. Planta 33: 206-257.

1573. Liljenberg, C. 1966. THE EFFECT OF LIGHT ON THE PHYTOLIZATION OF CHLOROPHYLLIDE A AND THE SPECTRAL DEPENDENCE OF THE PROCESS. Physiol. Plant. 19: 848-853.

1574. Lindner, H. 1966. PHOTOMORPHOGENESE BEI *PISUM SATIVUM*. Ph.D. Thesis, Univ. Erlangen, Germany.

1575. Link, W. 1969. DIE REGULATION DER PROTEINSYNTHESE DURCH PHYTOCHROM (OBJEKTE: KEIMLINGE VON *SINAPIS ALBA* L.). Ph.D. Thesis, Univ. Freiburg, Germany.

1576. Linsbauer, K.; Abranowicz, E. 1909. UNTERSUCHUNGEN ÜBER DIE CHLORO-PLASTENBEWEGUNGEN. Sitzungsber. Akad. Wiss. Wien. Math. Naturwiss. Kl. Abt. 1, 118: 137-182.

1577. Linschitz, H.; Kasche, V.; Butler, W.L.; Siegelman, H.W. 1966. THE KINETICS OF PHYTOCHROME CONVERSION. J. Biol. Chem. 241: 3395-3403.

1578. Linschitz, H.; Kasche, V. 1967. KINETICS OF PHYTOCHROME CONVERSION: MULTIPLE PATHWAYS IN THE P_R TO P_{FR} REACTION, AS STUDIED BY DOUBLE-FLASH TECHNIQUE. Proc. Natl. Acad. Sci. USA 58: 1059-1064.

1579. Lion, J. 1968. THE INFLUENCE OF RED LIGHT ON GEOTROPISM OF DECAPITATED AVENA COLEOPTILES. Acta Bot. Neerl. 17: 416-422.

1579.5 Lips, S.H.; Roth-Bejerano, N. 1974. PLANT HORMONES AND THE ORGANIZATION OF MULTI-ENZYME SYSTEMS IN PLANT MICROBODIES. *Plant Growth Substances 1973*, Proc. VIII Int. Conf. Plant Growth Subst. Tokyo, pp. 719-724.

1580. Lisansky, S.G. 1972. ALTERING RATES OF DECAY OF PHOTOREVERSIBILITY OF PHYTOCHROME *IN VITRO*. Plant Physiol. 49: Suppl.-65, Abstr. No. 365 (A).

1581. Lisansky, S.G. 1973. CHEMICAL AGENTS AFFECTING PHYTOCHROME STABILITY *IN VITRO*. Ph.D. Thesis, Yale Univ., New Haven.

1582. Lisansky, S.G.; Galston, A.W. 1973. EFFECTS OF METAL IONS ON DECAY AND REVERSION OF PURIFIED PHYTOCHROME *IN VITRO*. Plant Physiol. 51: Suppl.-52, Abstr. No. 281 (A).

1583. Lisansky, S.G.; Galston, A.W. 1974. PHYTOCHROME STABILITY *IN VITRO*. I. EFFECT OF METAL IONS. Plant Physiol. 53: 352-359.

1584. Listowski, A. 1927. ÜBER DEN EINFLUSS VERSCHIEDENFARBIGEN LICHTES AUF DIE KEIMUNG DER SPOREN UND ENTWICKLUNG DER PROTONEMEN EINIGER MOOSE. Bull. Acad. Pol. Sci. Cl. 3, pp. 631-666.

1585. Liverman, J.; Bonner, J. 1953. THE INTERACTION OF AUXIN AND LIGHT IN THE GROWTH RESPONSES OF PLANTS. Am. Soc. Plant Physiol. Sept. 6-10, Madison, Wisconsin, p. 26 (A).

1586. Liverman, J.; Bonner, J. 1953. THE INTERACTION OF AUXIN AND LIGHT IN THE GROWTH RESPONSES OF PLANTS. Proc. Nat. Acad. Sci. USA 39: 905-916.

1587. Liverman, J.L.; Johnson, M.P.; Starr, L. 1955. REVERSIBLE PHOTOREACTION CONTROLLING EXPANSION OF ETIOLATED BEAN-LEAF DISKS. Science 121: 440-441.

1588. Liverman, J.L. 1955. THE PHYSIOLOGY OF FLOWERING. Annu. Rev. Plant Physiol. 6: 177-210 (R).

1589. Liverman, J.L.; Johnson, S.P. 1967. CONTROL OF ARRESTED FRUIT GROWTH IN TOMATO BY GIBBERELLINS. Science 125: 1086-1087.

1590. Liverman, J.L.; Scott, R.A. Jr. 1957. THE CONTROL OF ETIOLATED LEAF GROWTH BY LIGHT AND KININS. Plant Physiol. 32: Suppl.-48 (A).

1591. Liverman, J.L.; Johnson, S.P. 1958. THE CONTROL OF PLANT GROWTH BY AN INTERACTION OF LIGHTS AND CHEMICALS. Scientia (Milan) 93: 293-295.

1592. Liverman, J.L. 1959. CONTROL OF LEAF GROWTH BY AN INTERACTION OF CHEMICALS AND LIGHT. *Photoperiodism and Related Phenomena in Plants and Animals*, Ed. R.B. Withrow A.A.A.S. Washington, D.C., pp. 161-180.

1593. Liverman, J.L. 1960. CONTROL OF GROWTH AND REPRODUCTIVE PROCESSES BY RED AND FAR-RED LIGHT. Radiat. Res. Suppl. 2: 133-156 (R).

1594. Lloyd, F.E. 1908. THE PHYSIOLOGY OF STOMATA. Carnegie Inst. Washington Publ. No. 82, pp. 107-142.

1595. Lockhart, J.A. 1956. THE EFFECT OF LIGHT AND THE GIBBERELLINS ON STEM ELONGATION IN DWARF AND NORMAL PEA SEEDLINGS. Plant Physiol. 31: Suppl.-12 (A).

1596. Lockhart, J.A. 1956. REVERSAL OF THE LIGHT INHIBITION OF PEA STEM GROWTH BY THE GIBBERELLINS. Proc. Nat. Acad. Sci. USA 42: 841-848.

1597. Lockhart, J.A. 1957. THE LIGHT REQUIREMENT FOR A GIBBERELLIC ACID RESPONSE IN DWARF BEAN SEEDLINGS. Plant Physiol. 32: Suppl.-48 (A).

1598. Lockhart, J.A. 1958. THE RESPONSE OF VARIOUS SPECIES OF HIGHER PLANTS TO LIGHT AND GIBBERELLIC ACID. Physiol. Plant. 11: 478-486.

1599. Lockhart, J.A. 1958. THE INFLUENCE OF RED AND FAR-RED RADIATION ON THE RESPONSE OF *PHASEOLUS VULGARIS* TO GIBBERELLIC ACID. Physiol. Plant. 11: 487-492.

1600. Lockhart, J.A.; Gottschall, V. 1958. GROWTH RESPONSES OF *PISUM* IN RELATION TO LIGHT AND GIBBERELLIC ACID. Plant Physiol. 33: Suppl.-40 (A).

1601. Lockhart, J.A. 1959. THE INTRACELLULAR MECHANISM OF STEM GROWTH INHIBITION BY VISIBLE RADIATION. Proc. IX Int. Bot. Congr. 2: 233 (A).

1602. Lockhart, J.A. 1959. STUDIES ON THE MECHANISM OF STEM GROWTH INHIBITION BY VISIBLE RADIATION. Plant Physiol. 34: 457-460.

1603. Lockhart, J.A.; Gottschall, V. 1959. GROWTH RESPONSES OF ALASKA PEA SEEDLINGS TO VISIBLE RADIATION AND GIBBERELLIC ACID. Plant Physiol. 34: 460-465.

1604. Lockhart, J.A. 1959. THE HORMONAL MECHANISM OF GROWTH INHIBITION BY VISIBLE RADIATION. *Plant Growth Regulation*, IV Int. Conf. Plant Growth Regulation, The Iowa State University Press, Ames, pp. 543-557 (R).

1605. Lockhart, J.A. 1959. CONTROL OF STEM GROWTH BY LIGHT AND GIBBERELLIC ACID. *Chemical Agents and Growth*, Ed. Am. Assoc. Adv. Sci. 55: 217-221 (R).

1606. Lockhart, J.A. 1960. INTRACELLULAR MECHANISM OF GROWTH INHIBITION BY RADIANT ENERGY. Plant Physiol. 35: 129-135.

1607. Lockhart, J.A.; Deal, P.H. 1960. PREVENTION OF RED LIGHT INHIBITION OF STEM GROWTH IN THE CUCURBITACEAE BY GIBBERELLIN A_4. Naturwissenschaften 6: 141-142.

1608. Lockhart, J.A. 1961. ON THE HORMONAL MECHANISM OF PHOTOINHIBITION OF PLANT STEM GROWTH. Proc. III Congr. Photobiol., pp. 401-402 (A).

1609. Lockhart, J.A. 1961. PHOTOINHIBITION OF STEM ELONGATION BY FULL SOLAR RADIATION. Am. J. Bot. 48: 387-392.

1610. Lockhart, J.A. 1961. INTERACTIONS BETWEEN GIBBERELLIN AND VARIOUS ENVIRONMENTAL FACTORS ON STEM GROWTH. Am. J. Bot. 48: 516-525.

1611. Lockhart, J.A. 1961. MECHANISM OF THE PHOTOPERIODIC PROCESS IN HIGHER PLANTS. Handbuch der Pflanzenphysiologie, Ed. W. Ruhland, Berlin-Göttingen Heildelberg, Springer XVI: 390-438 (R).

1612. Lockhart, J.A. 1963. LIGHT AND HORMONES IN PLANT DEVELOPMENT. Am. Biol. Teach. 25: 110-112 (R).

1613. Lockhart, J.A. 1963. PHOTOMORPHOGENESIS IN PLANTS. Plant Sci. 7: 1-43 (R).

1614. Lockhart, J.A. 1964. PHYSIOLOGICAL STUDIES ON LIGHT SENSITIVE STEM GROWTH. Planta 62: 97-115.

1615. Lörcher, L. 1958. THE INITIATION AND REGULATION OF ENDOGENOUS-DIURNAL LEAF-MOVEMENT BY DIFFERENT SPECTRAL REGIONS OF LIGHT. Ph.D. Thesis, Univ. Tübingen, Germany (GER) (ENG Summary).

1616. Lörcher, L. 1958. DIE WIRKUNG VERSCHIEDENER LICHTQUALITÄTEN AUF DIE ENDOGENE TAGESRHYTHMIK VON *PHASEOLUS*. Z. Bot. 46: 209-241.

1617. Loercher, L. 1966. PHYTOCHROME CHANGES CORRELATED TO MESCOTYL INHIBITION IN ETIOLATED *AVENA* SEEDLINGS. Plant Physiol. 41: 932-936.

1618. Loercher, L. 1968. ENDURANCE OF RED LIGHT STIMULUS IN LETTUCE SEEDS DURING OSMOTIC INCUBATION. Plant Physiol. 43: Suppl.-22 (A).

1619. Loercher, L. 1974. CHANGING RED LIGHT SENSITIVITY OF EXCISED BEAN
HYPOCOTYL HOOKS. Plant Physiol. 53: Suppl.-2, Abstr. No. 4 (A).

1620. Loercher, L. 1974. PERSISTENCE OF RED LIGHT INDUCTION IN LETTUCE SEEDS
OF VARYING HYDRATION. Plant Physiol. 53: 503-506.

1621. Lona, F. 1956. L'ACIDO GIBBERELLICO DETERMINA LA GERMINAZIONE DEI SEMI
DI *LACTUCA SCARIOLA* IN FASE DI SCOTO-INHIBIZIONE. Ateneo Parmense
27: 641-644 (ENG, FR, GER Summaries).

1622. Lona, F.; Bocchi, A. 1956. INTERFERENZA DELL'ACIDO GIBBERELLICO
NELL'EFFETTO DELLA LUCE ROSSA E ROSSA-ESTREMA SULL'ALLUNGAMENTO DEL
FUSTO DI *PERILLA OCYMOIDES* L. Ateneo Parmense 27: 645-649 (ENG, FR,
GER Summaries).

1623. Lona, F. 1957. BRIEF ACCOUNTS ON THE PHYSIOLOGICAL ACTIVITIES OF
GIBBERELLIC ACID AND OTHER SUBSTANCES IN RELATION TO PHOTOTHERMAL
CONDITIONS. Union Int. Sci. Biol. Ser. B., 34: 141-167.

1624. Lona, F.; Bocchi, A. 1957. AZIONE DELL'ACIDO GIBBERELLICO SULL'ACCRES-
CIMENTO E FIORITURA DELLE PIANTE, GERMINAZIONE DEI SEMI E GERMOGLIA-
ZIONE DELLE GEMME, IN RAPPORTO ALLA REAZIONE A PARTICOLARI RADIA-
ZIONI. Proc. II Int. Congr. Photobiol. 443 (A).

1625. Lona, F. 1959. SOME ASPECTS OF PHOTOTHERMAL AND CHEMICAL CONTROL OF
GROWTH AND FLOWERING. *Photoperiodism and Related Phenomena in Plants
and Animals*, Ed. R.B. Withrow, A.A.A.S., Washington, D.C., pp. 351-
358 (R-D).

1626. Lona, F. 1961. INIBIZIONE DELLA NODULAZIONE RADICALE NEL PISELLO *METEOR*
COME CONSEGUENZA DEL TRATTAMENTO NICTOFASICO INTERMITTENTE CON LUCE
ROSSO-ESTREMA. Nuovo. G. Bot. Ital. 68: 228-232 (ENG Summary).

1627. Lona, F. 1962. POSTEFFETTO MORFOGENETICO PLURICICLICO DI UN BREVE
STIMOLO ROSSO-ESTREMO PRENICTOFASICO. Ateneo Parmense 33 Suppl.-6:
214-218 (ENG Summary).

1628. Lona, F. 1963. REAZIONE MORFOGENETICA DI *HYDROPHYLLUM VIRGINICUM* A
FATTORI LUMINOSI ED ORMONALI. Nuovo. G. Bot. Ital. 70: 553-560 (ENG
Summary).

1629. Lona, F.; Fioretti, L. 1964. MORPHOGENETIC POST-EFFECT OF A SINGLE
LIGHT STIMULUS DURING A SERIES OF PHOTOCYCLES. Proc. IV Int. Congr.
Photobiol. pp. 103-104 (A).

1630. Lourtioux, A. 1961. ACTION DES ÉCLAIREMENTS COLORÉS SUR LA FLORAISON DE *MYOSOTIS PALUSTRIS*. Prog. Photobiol. Proc. Int. Congr. 3rd Copenhagen, 1960, pp. 406-408.

1631. Loveys, B.R.; Wareing, P.F. 1971. THE RED LIGHT CONTROLLED PRODUCTION OF GIBBERELLIN IN ETIOLATED WHEAT LEAVES. Planta 98: 109-116.

1632. Loveys, B.R.; Wareing, P.F. 1971. THE HORMONAL CONTROL OF WHEAT LEAF UNROLLING. Planta 98: 117-127.

1633. Ludwig, F.; Ries, J.v. 1928. DIE BIOLOGISCHE BEDEUTUNG DER ROT- UND QUARZLICHTBESTRAHLUNG. Strahlentherapie 29: 581-591.

1634. Ludwig, F.; Reis, J.v. 1940. WIE WIRD DAS ZELLWACHSTUM DURCH HORMONE, VITAMINE, DURCH LICHT, D'ARSONVALISATION, KURZWELLEN UND RÖNTGEN-STRAHLEN BEEINFLUSST? VERSUCHE AN EMBRYONALEN, GEZÜCHTETEN UND PFLANZLICHEN ZELLEN. Strahlentherapie 67: 507-521.

1635. Ma, T.H.; Wolff, S. 1965. FAR-RED-INDUCED MITOTIC DELAY AND THE APPAR-ENT INCREASE OF X-RAY INDUCED CHROMATID ABERRATIONS IN *TRADESCANTIA* MICROSPORES. Radiat. Bot. 5: 293-298.

1636. Ma, T.H.; Snope, A.J.; Chang, T.Y. 1971. FAR-RED-LIGHT EFFECT ON ULTRA-VIOLET LIGHT INDUCED CHROMATID ABERRATIONS IN POLLEN TUBES OF *TRADES-CANTIA*. Radiat. Biol. 11: 39-43.

1637. Macfarlane, J.M. 1895. THE SENSITIVE MOVEMENTS OF SOME FLOWERING PLANTS UNDER COLORED SCREENS. Bot. Centralbl. 61: 136-146.

1638. Machlis, L. 1962. THE EFFECTS OF MINERAL SALTS, GLUCOSE, AND LIGHT ON THE GROWTH OF THE LIVERWORT, *SPHAEROCARPUS DONNELLII*. Physiol. Plant. 15: 354-362.

1639. MacKenzie, J.M. Jr.; Coleman, R.A.; Pratt, L.H. 1974. A SPECIFIC RE-VERSIBLE INTRACELLULAR LOCALIZATION OF PHYTOCHROME AS P_{fr}. Plant Physiol. 53: Suppl.-2, Abstr. No. 5 (A).

1640. Maeda, E.; Sugiura, T. 1969. EFFECTS OF MONOCHROMATIC LIGHT ON THE LAMINA INCLINATION IN RICE SEEDLINGS. Nippon Sakumotsu Gakkai Kiji 38: 615-621 (JAP) (ENG Summary).

1641. Maeda, M.; Imahori, K. 1968. LIGHT EFFECTS ON THE MORPHOGENESIS. Sci. Rep. Coll. Gen. Educ., Osaka Univ. 17: 23-31.

1642. Magness, J.R. 1928. OBSERVATIONS ON COLOR DEVELOPMENT IN APPLES. Proc. Wash. State Hortic. Assoc. 24: 128-130.

1643. Magness, J.R. 1928. OBSERVATIONS ON COLOR DEVELOPMENT IN APPLES. Proc. Am. Soc. Hortic. Sci. 25: 289-292.

1644. Maheshwari, S.C.; Lakshmi, S. 1973. THE ROLE OF LIGHT IN REGULATING PLANT GROWTH AND DEVELOPMENT. Proc. Indian Nat. Sci. Acad. Part B 39: 478-488 (R).

1645. Malcevsky, V.P. 1937. *Progress in Soviet Breeding*. (not obtained) (Referred to by Gortikova, N. (1938). Dokl. Akad. Nauk. SSSR 19: 417-419) (RUS).

1646. Malcolm, A.A.; Russell, D.W. 1974. EARLY CHANGES IN RNA METABOLISM IN ETIOLATED BEAN LEAVES IRRADIATED WITH RED LIGHT. *Mechanisms of Regulation of Plant Growth*, Eds. R.L. Bieleski, A.R. Ferguson, M.M. Cresswell, R. Soc. N.Z. Bull. 12: 333-338.

1647. Malcoste, R. 1968. UN PROBLÈME ÉCOLOGIQUE: LA GERMINATION DES SEMENCES DANS LES CONDITIONS NATURELLES. Ann. Biol. 7: 241-274 (R).

1648. Malcoste, R. 1968. L'INDUCTION DE LA GERMINATION DES GRAINES DE *NIGELLA DAMASCENA* L. PAR LA LUMIÈRE. C.R. Acad. Sci. Ser. D 267: 613-616.

1649. Malcoste, R. 1969. ETUDE PAR SPECTROPHOTOMÉTRIE *IN VIVO* DU PHYTOCHROME DE QUELQUES SEMENCES. C.R. Acad. Sci. Ser. D 269: 701-703.

1650. Malcoste, R. 1969. LE PHYTOCHROME DANS LES GRAINES DU *NEMOPHILA INSIGNIS*: ÉTUDE PAR SPECTROPHOTOMÉTRIE *IN VIVO*. C.R. Acad. Sci. Ser. D 269: 1415-1418.

1651. Malcoste, R. 1970. LE PHYTOCHROME, PHOTORÉCEPTEUR DES RADIATIONS VISIBLES CONTRÔLANT LA GERMINATION DES GRAINES DE *NEMOPHILA INSIGNIS* L. Physiol. Veg. 8: 531 (A).

1652. Malcoste, R.; Boisard, J. 1970. ETUDE DU PHYTOCHROME DANS LES GRAINES DE *CUCUMIS SATIVUS* (CORNICHON, VAR. VERT DE PARIS) PAR SPECTROPHOTO-MÉTRIE DIFFÉRENTIELLE *IN VIVO*. C.R. Acad. Sci. Ser. D 270: 331-334.

1653. Malcoste, R.; Boisard, J.; Rollin, P.; Spruit, C.J.P. 1970. PHYTOCHROME IN SEEDS OF SOME CUCURBITACEAE: *IN VIVO* SPECTROPHOTOMETRY. Meded. Landbouwhogesch. Wageningen 70-16: 1-16.

1654. Malcoste, R. 1971. KINETICS OF PHYTOCHROME IN RADISH COTYLEDONS *IN VIVO* SPECTROPHOTOMETRIC MEASUREMENTS. Proc. Eur. Annu. Symp. Plant Photo-morphogenesis (Athens), pp. 30-31 (A).

1655. Malcoste, R.; Larcher, G.; Huault, C. 1971. ETUDE DE CINÉTIQUES D'APPARITION ET DE DISPARITION DU PHYTOCHROME DANS LES COTYLÉDONS DE *RAPHANUS SATIVUS* L. C.R. Acad. Sci. Ser. D 273: 1197-1200.

1656. Malcoste, R.; Huault, C.; Larcher, G.; Rollin, P. 1972. EVOLUTION DU CONTENU EN PHYTOCHROME DES COTYLÉDONS DE RADIS, À L'OBSCURITÉ ET À LA LUMIÈRE MESURES PAR SPECTROPHOTOMÉTRIE *IN VIVO*. Physiol. Veg. 10: 575-587 (ENG Summary).

1657. Malcoste, R.; Tzanni, H.; Jacques, R.; Rollin, P. 1972. THE INFLUENCE OF BLUE LIGHT ON DARK-GERMINATING SEEDS OF *NEMOPHILA INSIGNIS*. Planta 103: 24-34.

1658. Malcoste, R. 1973. RECHERCHES SUR LE MÉTABOLISME DU PHYTOCHROME ET SES RELATIONS AVEC CERTAINES PHOTORÉPONSES. Ph.D. Thesis, Univ. Rouen, France.

1659. Manabe, K.; Furuya, M. 1971. FACTORS CONTROLLING RATES OF NONPHOTO-CHEMICAL TRANSFORMATION OF *PISUM* PHYTOCHROME *IN VITRO*. Plant Cell Physiol. 12: 95-101.

1660. Manabe, K.; Furuya, M. 1971. EFFECTS OF METALLIC IONS ON NONPHOTOCHEM-ICAL DECAY OF P_{fr} IN *AVENA* COLEOPTILES. Bot. Mag. 84: 417-423.

1661. Manabe, K.; Furuya, M. 1973. A RAPID PHYTOCHROME-DEPENDENT REDUCTION OF NICOTINAMIDE ADENINE DINUCLEOTIDE PHOSPHATE IN PARTICLE FRACTION FROM ETIOLATED BEAN HYPOCOTYL. Plant Physiol. 51: 982-983.

1662. Manabe, K.; Furuya, M. 1974. PHYTOCHROME-DEPENDENT REDUCTION OF NICOTI-NAMIDE NUCLEOTIDES IN THE MITOCHONDRIAL FRACTION ISOLATED FROM ETIOLATED PEA EPICOTYLS. Plant Physiol. 53: 343-347.

1663. Mancinelli, A.L. 1963. INHIBITION OF FLOWERING IN *XANTHIUM PENNSYLVANI-CUM* BY PROLONGED IRRADIATION WITH FAR-RED. Plant Physiol. 38: Suppl.-48 (A).

1664. Mancinelli, A.L.; Borthwick, H.A. 1964. AN INDUCED LIGHT REQUIREMENT FOR THE GERMINATION OF TOMATO SEEDS. Plant Physiol. 39: Suppl.-49 (A).

1665. Mancinelli, A.L.; Borthwick, H.A. 1964. PHOTOCONTROL OF GERMINATION AND PHYTOCHROME REACTION IN DARK-GERMINATING SEEDS OF *LACTUCA SATIVA* L. Ann. Bot. (Rome) 28: 9-24.

1666. Mancinelli, A.L. 1966. BROAD-SPECTRUM LIGHT SOURCES, PHOTOCONVERSION OF PHYTOCHROME AND SOME PHYSIOLOGICAL RESPONSES IN TOMATO SEED GERMI-NATION. Ann. Bot. (Rome) 28: 675-686.

1667. Mancinelli, A.L.; Borthwick, H.A.; Hendricks, S.B. 1966. PHYTOCHROME ACTION IN TOMATO-SEED GERMINATION. Bot. Gaz. (Chicago) 127: 1-5.

1668. Mancinelli, A.L.; Yaniv, Z.; Smith, P. 1966. PHYTOCHROME CONTROL OF
GERMINATION IN TOMATO SEEDS. Plant Physiol. 41: Suppl.-17-18 (A).

1669. Mancinelli, A.L.; Downs, R.J. 1967. INHIBITION OF FLOWERING OF
XANTHIUM PENSYLVANICUM WALLR. BY PROLONGED IRRADIATION WITH FAR RED.
Plant Physiol. 42: 95-98.

1670. Mancinelli, A.L.; Tolkowsky, A. 1967. CHANGES IN THE LEVEL OF PHYTO-
CHROME DURING THE GERMINATION OF CUCUMBER SEEDS. Plant Physiol.
42: Suppl.-9 (A).

1671. Mancinelli, A.L.; Yaniv, Z.; Smith, P. 1967. PHYTOCHROME AND SEED GER-
MINATION. I. TEMPERATURE DEPENDENCE AND RELATIVE P_{FR} LEVELS IN THE
GERMINATION OF DARK-GERMINATING TOMATO SEEDS. Plant Physiol. 42:
333-337.

1672. Mancinelli, A.L.; Tolkowsky, A. 1968. PHYTOCHROME AND SEED GERMINATION.
V. CHANGES OF PHYTOCHROME CONTENT DURING THE GERMINATION OF CUCUMBER
SEEDS. Plant Physiol. 43: 489-494.

1673. Mancinelli, A.L. 1969. PHYTOCHROME AND SEED GERMINATION. *Current
Topics Plant Science*, Ed. J.E. Gunckel, Academic Press, New York,
pp. 144-151 (R).

1674. Mancinelli, A.L.; Ku, P.-K. 1972. PHOTOCONTROL OF ANTHOCYANIN SYNTHESIS
IN CABBAGE AND MUSTARD SEEDLINGS. Plant Physiol. 49: Suppl.-63,
Abstr. No. 353 (A).

1675. Mancinelli, A.L.; Eisenstadt, F.A. 1973. PHYTOCHROME, TEMPERATURE AND
CUCUMBER SEED GERMINATION. Plant Physiol. 51: Suppl.-52, Abstr. No.
280 (A).

1676. Mancinelli, A.L.; Eisenstadt, F. 1974. PHYTOCHROME AND THE GERMINATION
OF *PHACELIA* AND *NEMOPHILA* SEEDS. Plant Physiol. 53: Suppl.-2,
Abstr. No. 8 (A).

1677. Mancinelli, A.L.; Ku (Tai), P.-K.; Susinno, R. 1974. PHOTOCONTROL OF
ANTHOCYANIN SYNTHESIS: PHYTOCHROME, CHLOROPHYLL AND ANTHOCYANIN
SYNTHESIS. Photochem. Photobiol. 20: 71-79.

1678. Manetas, J.; Mitrakos, K. 1971. CONTROL OF LIPID BIOSYNTHESIS BY PHYTO-
CHROME. Proc. Eur. Annu. Symp. Plant Photomorphogenesis, (Athens)
pp. 32-33 (A).

1679. Mann, J.D.; Jordon, L.S. 1966. CIPC INHIBITION OF THE PHYTOCHROME-
ENHANCED GERMINATION OF GRAND RAPIDS LETTUCE SEED. Plant Physiol.
41: Suppl.-18 (A).

1680. Mann, J.D.; Storey, W.B.; Jordon, L.S.; Day, B.E.; Haid, H. 1966. LIGHT DEPENDENCY IN SEED GERMINATION. Calif. Agric. 20: 6-7 (R-D).

1681. Mann, J.D.; Haid, H.; Jordon, L.S.; Day, B.E. 1967. INHIBITION OF THE ACTION OF PHYTOCHROME BY THE HERBICIDE CIPC. Nature (London) 213: 420-421.

1682. Manning, H.E. 1950. THE EFFECT OF ANTHOCYANIN FILTERS ON PLANT BEHAVIOR AND DEVELOPMENT. Butler Univ. Bot. Stud. 9: 203-211.

1683. Mansfield, T.A. 1964. STOMATAL SENSITIVITY IN *XANTHIUM PENNSYLVANICUM* WALL TO INTERRUPTIONS OF THE DARK PERIOD. Proc. IV Int. Congr. Photobiol., p. 104 (A).

1684. Mansfield, T.A. 1964. A STOMATAL LIGHT REACTION SENSITIVE TO WAVE-LENGTHS IN THE REGION OF 700 mµ. Nature (London) 201: 470-472.

1685. Mansfield, T.A. 1965. THE LOW INTENSITY LIGHT REACTION OF STOMATA: EFFECTS OF RED LIGHT ON RHYTHMIC STOMATAL BEHAVIOR IN *XANTHIUM PENNSYLVANICUM*. Proc. Soc. London Ser. B 162: 567-574.

1686. Mansfield, T.A.; Meidner, H. 1965. STOMATAL OPENING IN LIGHT OF DIFFERENT WAVELENGTHS: EFFECT OF BLUE LIGHT INDEPENDENT OF CARBON DIOXIDE CONCENTRATION. J. Exp. Bot. 17: 510-521.

1687. Mansfield, T.A. 1971. STOMATA IN NEW PERSPECTIVE. Sch. Sci. Rev. 53: 316-325 (R-D).

1688. Mantouvalos, G. 1969. THE ROLE OF PHYTOCHROME IN PLANT RESPIRATION. Ph.D. Thesis, Univ. Athens, Greece (GK) (not obtained).

1689. Mantouvalos, G.; Mitrakos, K. 1971. PHYTOCHROME ACTION ON THE INCORPO-RATION OF LABELLED TCA CYCLE ACIDS IN CORN LEAVES. Proc. Eur. Annu. Symp. Plant Photomorphogenesis (Athens) p. 34 (A).

1690. Mapson, L.W.; Swain, T. 1964. INFLUENCE OF RED AND FAR-RED LIGHT ON THE PHOTO-OXIDATION OF ASCORBIC ACID AND PHOTOREDUCTION OF ITS OXI-DIZED FORMS. Nature (London) 204: 886-887.

1691. Mapson, L.W. 1964. THE ASCORBIC ACID SYSTEM IN LEAVES: FURTHER OBSER-VATIONS OF PHOTOOXIDATION AND PHOTOREDUCTION. Phytochemistry 3: 429-445.

1692. Mapson, L.W.; Swain, T. 1966. CONTROL OF PHOTO-OXIDATION AND REDUCTION OF ASCORBATE BY PHYTOCHROME OR SIMILAR COMPOUND. Phytochemistry 5: 829-853.

1693. Marchal-Gabriac, B.; Veyron, P.; Rollin, P.; Boisard, J. 1974. MESURE DES PHOTOEQUILIBRES DU PHYTOCHROME DANS LES PLANTULES DE COURGE. Plant Sci. Lett. 3: 191-198 (ENG Summary).

1694. Marcus, A. 1959. PHOTOCONTROL OF THE FORMATION OF TPN TRIOSEPHOSPHATE DEHYDROGENASE. Proc. IX Int. Bot. Congr. 2: 252 (A).

1695. Marcus, A. 1960. PHOTOCONTROL OF FORMATION OF RED KIDNEY BEAN LEAF TRIPHOSPHOPYRIDINE NUCLEOTIDE LINKED TRIOSEPHOSPHATE DEHYDROGENASE. Plant Physiol. 35: 126-128.

1696. Marcus, A. 1971. ENZYME INDUCTION IN PLANTS. Annu. Rev. Plant Physiol. 22: 313-336 (R).

1697. Margaris, N. 1972. PHYTOCHROME ACTION OF THE FREE AMINO ACID METABOLISM IN PLANTS. Ph.D. Thesis, Univ. Athens, Greece (GK) (not obtained).

1698. Margulies, M.M. 1962. THE EFFECT OF LIGHT AND CHLORAMPHENICOL ON DEVELOPMENT OF PHOTOSYNTHETIC ACTIVITIES OF LEAVES. Plant Physiol. 37: Suppl.-39 (A).

1699. Margulies, M.M. 1965. RELATIONSHIP BETWEEN RED LIGHT MEDIATED GLYCERALDEHYDE-3-PHOSPHATE DEHYDROGENASE FORMATION AND LIGHT DEPENDENT DEVELOPMENT OF PHOTOSYNTHESIS. Plant Physiol. 40: 57-61.

1700. Marmé, D. 1969. PHOTOMETRISCHE MESSUNGEN AM PHYTOCHROMSYSTEM VON *SINAPIS ALBA* L. ALS GRUNDLAGE FÜR KORRELATIONEN PHYSIOLOGISCHER UND BIOPHYSIKALISCHER DATEN IM RAHMEN DER PHOTOMORPHOGENESE. Ph.D. Thesis, Univ. Freiburg, Germany.

1701. Marmé, D. 1969. PHOTOMETRISCHE MESSUNGEN AM PHYTOCHROMSYSTEM VON SENFKEIMLINGEN (*SINAPIS ALBA* L.). Planta 88: 43-57 (ENG Summary).

1702. Marmé, D. 1969. AN AUTOMATIC RECORDING DEVICE FOR MEASURING PHYTOCHROME WITH A DUAL WAVELENGTH RADIOSPECT. Planta 88: 58-60.

1703. Marmé, D.; Marchal, B.; Schäfer, E. 1971. A DETAILED ANALYSIS OF PHYTOCHROME DECAY AND DARK REVERSION IN MUSTARD COTYLEDONS. Planta 100: 331-336.

1704. Marmé, D.; Schäfer, E.; Marchal, B. 1971. SHORT TIME ANALYSIS OF THE PHYTOCHROME DECAY IN MUSTARD SEEDLINGS WHICH SHOWS A STRONG DEVIATION FROM A FIRST ORDER KINETICS. Proc. Eur. Annu. Symp. Plant Photomorphogenesis, (Athens), p. 35 (A).

1705. Marmé, D.; Schäfer, E.; Trillmich, F.; Hertel, R. 1971. EVIDENCE FOR MEMBRANE BOUND PHYTOCHROME IN MAIZE COLEOPTILES. Proc. Eur. Annu. Symp. Plant Photomorphogenesis, (Athens), p. 36 (A).

1706. Marmé, D.; Schäfer, E. 1972. ON THE LOCALIZATION AND ORIENTATION OF PHYTOCHROME MOLECULES IN CORN COLEOPTILES (*ZEA MAYS* L.). Z. Pflanzenphysiol. 67: 192-194.

1707. Marmé, D.; Boisard, J.; Briggs, W.R. 1973. BINDING PROPERTIES *IN VITRO* OF PHYTOCHROME TO A MEMBRANE FRACTION. Proc. Nat. Acad. Sci. USA 70: 3861-3865.

1708. Marmé, D. 1974. BINDING PROPERTIES OF PLANT PHOTORECEPTOR PHYTOCHROME TO BIOLOGICAL MEMBRANES. Proc. Eur. Annu. Symp. Plant Photomorphogenesis, (Antwerpen), pp. 4-7.

1709. Marmé, D. 1974. BINDING PROPERTIES OF THE PLANT PHOTORECEPTOR PHYTOCHROME TO MEMBRANES. J. Supramol. Struct. 2: 751-768.

1710. Marmé, D.; MacKenzie, J.M. Jr.; Boisard, J.; Briggs, W.R. 1974. THE ISOLATION AND PARTIAL CHARACTERIZATION OF A MEMBRANE FRACTION CONTAINING PHYTOCHROME. Plant Physiol. 54: 263-271.

1711. Marsh, P.B.; Taylor, E.E.; Bassler, L.M. 1959. A GUIDE TO THE LITERATURE ON CERTAIN EFFECTS OF LIGHT ON FUNGI: REPRODUCTION, MORPHOLOGY, PIGMENTATION, AND PHOTOTROPIC PHENOMENA. Plant Dis. Rep. Suppl.-261: 250-312 (R).

1712. Martin, J.H. 1972. ETHANOL INHIBITION OF RED FAR-RED REACTIONS IN GERMINATING LIGHT SENSITIVE LETTUCE SEEDS. Plant Physiol. 49: Suppl.-64 Abstr. No. 359 (A).

1713. Marushige, K.; Marushige, Y. 1963. CHANGES IN THE GROWTH AND PHOTOPERIODIC SENSITIVITY OF *PHARBITIS NIL* SEEDLINGS IN RELATION TO LOW INTENSITY LIGHT. Bot. Mag. 76: 181-190.

1714. Marushige, K.; Takimoto, A. 1967. PREPARATION FOR RESPONSE TO PHOTOPERIOD. *Physiology of Flowering in Pharbitis nil*, Ed. S. Imamura, Jpn. Soc. Plant Physiol., Tokyo, pp. 29-36 (R).

1715. Masoner, M.; Unser, G.; Mohr, H. 1972. ACCUMULATION OF PROTOCHLOROPHYLL AND CHLOROPHYLL A AS CONTROLLED BY PHOTOMORPHOGENICALLY EFFECTIVE LIGHT. Planta 105: 267-272.

1716. Masuda, Y.; Pjon, C.-J.; Furuya, M. 1970. PHYTOCHROME ACTION IN *ORYZA SATIVA* L. V. EFFECTS OF DECAPITATION AND RED AND FAR-RED LIGHT ON CELL WALL EXTENSIBILITY. Planta 90: 236-242.

1717. Masulli, O. 1909. INFLUENZA DELLE VARIE RADIAZIONI LUMINOSE SULLE PIANTE. Bull. Orto. Bot. Univ. Napoli 2: 329-402.

1718. Masulli, O. 1910. INFLUENZA DELLE VARIE RADIAZIONE LUMINOSE SULLE
PIANTE. Z. Bot. 2: 633-634 (A) (GER).

1719. Mathon, C. Ch.; Stroun, M. 1960. LUMIÉRE ET FLORASON. Presses univer-
sitaires de France, Paris (R) (not obtained) [referred to by Shulgin,
I.A. (1964), Fiziol. Rast. 11: 398-408].

1720. Matsuo, E. 1974. STUDIES ON GROWTH AND DEVELOPMENT OF BULBS IN THE
EASTER LILY (*LILIUM LONGIFLORUM* THUNB.) II. EFFECT OF RED, ORANGE
AND BLUE FLUORESCENT LIGHTS AND DARKNESS DURING THE SCALING ON THE
GROWTH BEHAVIOUR OF SCALE BULBLETS. Kyushu Daigaku Nogakubu Gakygei
Zasshi 4: 197-201 (JAP) (ENG Summary).

1721. Mayer, A.M.; Neuman, G.; Evenari, M. 1959. THE EFFECT OF LIGHT AND
GIBBERELLIC ACID ON THE ELONGATION OF LETTUCE HYPOCOTYLS. Bull. Res.
Counc. Isr. Sect. D: 7: 97-100.

1722. Mayer, A.M. 1960. GERMINATION RESEARCH AT THE HEBREW UNIVERSITY JERUSA-
LEM, ISRAEL - A REVIEW. Indian J. Plant Physiol. 3: 13-23 (R).

1723. Mayer, A.M.; Poljakoff-Mayber, A. 1963. *The Germination of Seeds*.
Pergamon Press Oxford, New York, pp. 1-100 (R).

1724. Mayer, F. 1964. LICHTORIENTIERTE CHLOROPLASTEN-VERLAGERUNGEN BEI
SELAGINELLA MARTENSII. Z. Bot. 52: 346-381 (ENG Summary).

1725. Mayer, F. 1966. LICHTINDUZIERTE CHLOROPLASTEN-VERLAGERUNGEN BEI
SELAGINELLA MARTENSII. Z. Pflanzenphysiol. 55: 65-70 (ENG Summary).

1726. Mazzolani, G. 1963. ESIGENZE QUALITATIVE E QUANTITATIVE DI LUCE NELLA
GERMINAZIONE DI SEMI NON FOTOBLASTICI DI *LACTUCA SATIVA* L. Ann.
Bot. (Rome) 27: 493-500 (ENG Summary).

1727. Mazzolani, G.; Gardano, G. 1965. INIBIZIONE DELLA GERMINAZIONE DI SEMI
DI *LACTUCA SATIVA* L. PER MEZZO DI UNA REAZIONE A BASSA ENERGIA DOVUTA
A LUCE BLU. Ann. Bot. (Rome) 28: 373-378 (ENG Summary).

1728. Mazzolani, G.; Gardano, G. 1965. SIMILARITÀ DELL'EFFETTO DELL'ACIDO
GIBBERELLICO CON QUELLO DELLA LUCE ROSSA E REVERSIBILITÀ DEL SISTEMA
GIBBERELLINA = ER NELLA GERMINAZIONE DEI SEMI DI *LACTUCA SATIVA* L.
Ann. Bot. (Rome) 28: 379-383 (ENG Summary).

1729. Mazzolani. G.; Gardano, G. 1965. INIBIZIONE DELLA GERMINAZIONE DEI SEMI
DI *LACTUCA SATIVA* L. DA LUCE BLU E COMPARAZIONE CON IL COMPORTAMENTO
ALL 'ER. Ann. Bot. (Rome) 28: 385-390 (ENG Summary).

1730. Mazzolani, G. 1966. FLUTTUAZIONE NATURALE DELLA GERMINABILITÀ E RISPOSTE A TRATTAMENTI CON LUCE ER E BLU DEI SEMI *LACTUCA SATIVA* L. Ann. Bot. (Rome) 28: 731-738 (ENG Summary).

1731. McArthur, J.A.; Briggs, W.R. 1968. PHYTOCHROME RELATIONSHIPS IN THE DARK-GROWN PEA SEEDLING. Proc. V. Int. Congr. Photobiol., p. 91 (A).

1732. McArthur, J.A. 1968. PHYTOCHROME RELATIONSHIPS IN THE DARK-GROWN PEA SEEDLING. Ph.D. Thesis, Stanford Univ., Stanford.

1733. McArthur, J.A.; Briggs, W.R. 1970. PHYTOCHROME APPEARANCE AND DISTRI- BUTION IN THE EMBRYONIC AXIS AND SEEDLING OF ALASKA PEAS. Planta 91: 146-154.

1734. McArthur, J.A.; Hopkins, D.W.; Butler, W.L. 1970. PHYTOCHROME FROM GREEN OATS. Plant Physiol. 46: Suppl.-3, Abstr. No. 12 (A).

1735. McArthur, J.A.; Briggs, W.R. 1971. *IN VIVO* PHYTOCHROME REVERSION IN IMMATURE TISSUE OF ALASKA PEA SEEDLING. Plant Physiol. 48: 46-49.

1736. McClure, J.W. 1968. PHOTOCONTROL OF *SPIRODELA INTERMEDIA* FLAVONOIDS. Plant Physiol. 43: 193-200.

1737. McClure, J.W.; Wilson, K.G. 1970. PHOTOCONTROL OF C-GLYCOSYLFLAVONES IN BARLEY SEEDLINGS. Phytochemistry 9: 763-773.

1738. McClure, J.W. 1974. PHYTOCHROME CONTROL OF OSCILLATING LEVELS OF PHENYLALANINE AMMONIA LYASE IN *HORDEUM VULGARE* SHOOTS. Phytochemis- try 13: 1065-1069.

1739. McClure, J.W. 1974. ACTION SPECTRA FOR PHENYLALANINE AMMONIA LYASE IN *HORDEUM VULGARE*. Phytochemistry 13: 1071-1073.

1740. McCullough, J.M. 1968. PHYSIOLOGICAL PREDETERMINATION OF GERMINATION RESPONSES IN *ARABIDOPSIS THALIANA* (L.) HEYNH. Ph.D. Thesis, George Washington Univ., Washington, D.C.

1741. McCullough, J.M.; Shropshire, W. Jr. 1970. PHYSIOLOGICAL PREDETERMINA- TION OF GERMINATION RESPONSES IN *ARABIDOPSIS THALIANA* (L.) HEYNH. Plant Cell Physiol. 11: 139-148.

1742. McDonough, W.T. 1965. SOME EFFECTS OF THIOL GROUP REAGENTS ON THE IN- DUCTION OF GERMINATION IN *VERBASCUM THAPSUS* L. Plant Physiol. 40: Suppl.-76 (A).

1743. McDonough, W.T. 1965. SOME EFFECTS OF PHOSPHON ON GERMINATION INDUCED BY RED RADIATION AND GIBBERELLIC ACID IN SEEDS OF *VERBASCUM THAPSUS*. Plant Physiol. 40: 575-577.

1744. McDonough, W.T. 1966. THIOL GROUP REAGENTS AS INHIBITORS OF INDUCED GERMINATION. Ad. Front. Plant Sci. 16: 161-166.

1745. McDonough, W.T. 1967. MODIFICATION OF PHOTOCONTROL OF GERMINATION. Radiat. Res. 31: 74-78.

1746. McDonough, W.T. 1967. PHYTOCHROME-MEDIATED GERMINATION: EFFECTS OF BRIEF HIGH TEMPERATURE TREATMENTS. Photochem. Photobiol. 6: 919-921.

1747. McElroy, W.D.; Swanson, C.P. 1951. THE THEORY OF RATE PROCESSES AND GENE MUTATION. Q. Rev. Biol. 26: 348-363 (R).

1748. McEvoy, R.C.; Koukkari, W.L. 1972. EFFECTS OF ETHYLENEDIAMINETETRA-ACETIC ACID, AUXIN AND GIBBERELLIC ACID ON PHYTOCHROME CONTROLLED NYCTINASTY IN *ALBIZZIA JULIBRISSIN*. Physiol. Plant. 26: 143-147.

1749. McIlvaine, H.R.C.; Popp, H.W. 1940. FURTHER STUDIES ON GROWTH SUB-STANCES IN RELATION TO THE MECHANISM OF THE ACTION OF RADIATION ON PLANTS. J. Agric. Res. Washington, D.C. 60: 207-215.

1750. McKenzie, J.S.; Weiser, C.J.; Burke, M.J. 1974. EFFECTS OF RED AND FAR RED LIGHT ON THE INITIATION OF COLD ACCLUMATION IN *CORNUS STOLONIFERA* MICHX. Plant Physiol. 53: 783-789.

1751. McLemore, B.F.; Hansbrough, T. 1970. INFLUENCE OF LIGHT ON GERMINATION OF *PINUS PALUSTRIS* SEEDS. Physiol. Plant. 23: 1-10.

1752. McLemore, B.F. 1971. LIGHT REQUIREMENTS FOR GERMINATION OF LOBLOLLY PINE SEEDS. For. Sci. 17: 285-286.

1753. McNitt, R.E.; Glessner, L.; Shen-Miller, J. 1974. SPECTRAL EFFECTS ON CORN-ROOT GEOTROPISM AND PREFERENTIAL DISTRIBUTION OF ORGANELLES. Plant Physiol. 53: Suppl.-46, Abstr. No. 258 (A).

1754. Mego, J.L.; Jagendorf, A.T. 1961. EFFECT OF LIGHT ON GROWTH OF BLACK VALENTINE BEAN PLASTIDS. Biochim. Biophys. Acta 53: 237-254.

1755. Meidner, H. 1968. THE COMPARATIVE EFFECTS OF BLUE AND RED LIGHT ON THE STOMATA OF *ALLIUM CEPA* L. AND *XANTHIUM PENNSYLVANICUM*. J. Exp. Bot. 19: 146-151.

1756. Meijer, G. 1957. THE INFLUENCE OF LIGHT QUALITY ON THE FLOWERING RE-SPONSE OF *SALVIA OCCIDENTALIS*. Acta Bot. Neerl. 6: 395-406.

1757. Meijer, G.; Van der Veen, R. 1957. WAVELENGTH DEPENDENCE ON PHOTOPERI-ODIC RESPONSES. Acta Bot. Neerl. 6: 429-433.

1758. Meijer, G. 1958. INFLUENCE OF LIGHT ON THE ELONGATION OF GHERKIN SEEDLINGS. Acta Bot. Neerl. 7: 614-620.

1759. Meijer, G. 1958. THE INFLUENCE OF LIGHT AND OF GROWTH REGULATORS ON THE ELONGATION OF GHERKIN SEEDLINGS. Acta Bot. Neerl. 7: 621-626.

1760. Meijer, G. 1958. THE INFLUENCE OF LIGHT QUALITY ON THE PHOTOPERIODIC RESPONSE OF *SALVIA OCCIDENTALIS*. Acta Bot. Neerl. 7: 801-806.

1761. Meijer, G. 1959. THE INFLUENCE OF LIGHT OF DIFFERENT SPECTRAL REGIONS ON THE ELONGATION OF INTERNODES. Proc. IX Int. Bot. Congr. 2: 259-260 (A).

1762. Meijer, G. 1959. THE SPECTRAL DEPENDENCE OF FLOWERING AND ELONGATION. Acta Bot. Neerl. 8: 189-246 (Ph.D. Thesis, Univ. Utrecht, Netherlands).

1763. Meijer, G. 1959. PHOTOMORPHOGENESIS IN DIFFERENT SPECTRAL REGIONS. *Photoperiod and Related Phenoma in Plants and Animals*, Ed. R.B. Withrow, A.A.A.S., Washington, D.C., pp. 101-109.

1764. Meijer, G.; Van der Veen, R. 1960. DUAL EFFECT OF NIGHTBREAK LIGHT. Acta Bot. Neerl. 9: 220-223.

1765. Meijer, G.; Van der Veen, R. 1961. DUAL EFFECT OF RED LIGHT ON THE PHOTOPERIODIC RESPONSE OF *SALVIA OCCIDENTALIS*. Proc. III Int. Congr. Photobiol., pp. 387-388.

1766. Meijer, G. 1962. PHOTOMORPHOGENESIS INFLUENCED BY LIGHT OF DIFFERENT SPECTRAL REGIONS. Adv. Front. Plant Sci. 1: 129-140 (R).

1767. Meijer, G.; Engelsma, G. 1964. THE INFLUENCE OF A PRE-IRRADIATION ON THE PHOTOINHIBITION OF HYPOCOTYL ELONGATION. Proc. IV Int. Congr. Photobiol., p. 105 (A).

1768. Meijer, G.; Engelsma, G. 1965. THE SYNERGISTIC INFLUENCE OF A PRE-IRRADIATION ON THE PHOTOINHIBITION ON GHERKIN SEEDLINGS. Photochem. Photobiol. 4: 251-258.

1769. Meijer, G. 1966. LUMIÈRE ET CROISSANCE EN LONGUEUR. Photochem. Photobiol. 5: 373-374 (A) (R).

1770. Meijer, G. 1966. THE INFLUENCE OF LIGHT ON PLANT DEVELOPMENT. *Les Congres et Colloqué de l'Université de Liege* 38: 141-149 (R).

1771. Meijer, G. 1968. RAPID GROWTH INHIBITION OF GHERKIN HYPOCOTYLS IN BLUE LIGHT. Acta Bot. Neerl. 17: 9-14.

1772. Meischke, D. 1936. ÜBER DEN EINFLUSS DER STRAHLUNG AUF LICHT- UND DUNKELKEIMER. Jahrb. Wiss. Bot. 83: 359-405.

1773. Melnichuk, Yu.P. 1968. STRUCTURE OF PHYTOCHROME. Rost. Ustoichivst. Rast. Akad. Nauk. Ukr. SSR Resput. Mezhvedom. 5b, No. 4 52-58 (R) (RUS).

1774. Melnichuk, Yu.P.; Skripchenko, L.M.; Gladun, A.A.; Kalinin, F.L. 1969. ON THE MECHANISM OF ACTION OF PHYTOCHROME P_{fr} AND SYNTHESIS OF POLYRIBOSOMS IN ETIOLATED PEA SEEDLINGS. Fiziol. Biokhim. Kul't. Rast. 1: 37-39 (RUS) (ENG Summary).

1775. Melnichuk, Yu.P.; Kalinin, F.L.; Gladun, A.A.; Gorda, M.V. 1971. STUDY OF LYSINE HISTONE IN TISSUES OF ETIOLATED SEEDLINGS OF PLANTS DIFFERING IN A PHYTOCHROME STATE. Fiziol. Biokhim. Kul't Rast. 3: 408-411 (RUS) (ENG Summary).

1776. Melnichuk, Yu.P. 1973. PHYTOCHROME AS THE FACTOR REGULATING GROWTH AND MORPHOGENESIS OF PLANTS. Regul. Metab. Rastit. Kletki, pp. 159-183 (RUS) (R).

1777. Melnichuk, Yu.P.; Gladun, A.A.; Kalinin, F.L. 1973. NUCLEAR AND CYTO-PLASMIC PROTEINS OF WHEAT SEEDLINGS IN DEPENDENCE ON PHYTOCHROME FORMS. Fiziol. Biokhim. Kul't. Rast. 5: 462-467 (RUS) (ENG Summary).

1778. Menhenett, R. 1972. HORMONAL AND PHYTOCHROME-INDUCED UNROLLING OF BARLEY LEAVES. Ph.D. Thesis, Australian National Univ., Canberra, Australia.

1779. Menhenett, R.; Carr, D.J. 1973. GROWTH INHIBITORS FROM ETIOLATED LEAVES OF BARLEY (*HORDEUM VULGARE* L.). Aust. J. Biol. Sci. 26: 527-537.

1780. Mer, C.L. 1959. A STUDY OF THE GROWTH AND PHOTOPERCEPTIVITY OF ETIO-LATED OAT SEEDLINGS. J. Exp. Bot. 10: 220-232.

1781. Mer, C.L.; Dixon, P.F. 1962. MANGANESE SUPPLY IN RELATION TO THE GROWTH AND PHOTOSENSITIVITY OF ETIOLATED OAT SEEDLINGS. Ann. Bot. (London) 26: 1-11.

1782. Mer, C.L.; Causton, D.R. 1963. CARBON DIOXIDE: A FACTOR INFLUENCING CELL DIVISION. Nature (London) 199: 360-362.

1783. Mer, C.L. 1966. THE INHIBITION OF CELL DIVISION IN THE MESOCOTYL OF ETIOLATED OAT PLANTS BY LIGHT OF DIFFERENT FREQUENCIES. Ann. Bot. (London) 30: 17-23.

1784. Mertz, D. 1971. THE EFFECT OF VISIBLE RADIATION AND GIBBERELLINS A_1, A_3 AND A_5 ON GROWTH OF THE THIRD INTERNODE OF 7 DAY-OLD ETIOLATED PROGRESS PEA SEEDLING. Plant Physiol. 47: Suppl.-11, Abstr. No. 65 (A).

1785. Mertz, D.; Lutz, J. 1973. THE GROWTH PROMOTING EFFECT OF RED LIGHT ON INTERNODE ELONGATION OF PROGRESS SEEDLINGS. Plant Cell Physiol. 14: 275-284.

1786. Meyer, F.J. 1920. DIE LICHTPHYSIOLOGIE DER PFLANZEN. Naturwissenschaften 8: 842-851 (R).

1787. Michel, J.-P.; Montgareuil, P.G. de 1970. PHOSPHORYLATIONS ASSOCIÉES À L'ACTIVATION PAR LE ROUGE LOINTAIN D'UNE CAPACITÉ STABLE EN OXYGÈNE PHOTOSYNTHÉTIQUE. C.R. Acad. Sci. Ser. D. 270: 2655-2658.

1788. Michel, J.P.; Thibault, P. 1970. EFFET ANTAGONISTE ROUGE-ROUGE LOINTAIN AU NIVEAU DES PHOTOPHOSPHORYLATIONS ASSOCIÉES À L'ACTIVATION DU DÉGAGEMENT D'OXYGÈNE PHOTOSYNTHÉTIQUE. C.R. Acad. Sci. Ser. D. 271: 976-979.

1789. Michel, J.P.; Thibault, P. 1973. ETUDE CINETIQUE DE LA SYNTHESE D'ATP *IN VIVO* EN LUMIERE MONO - ET BIOCHROMATIQUE CHEZ *ZEA MAYS*: EFFET ANTAGONISTE ROUGE-ROUGE LOINTAIN. Biochim. Biophys. Acta 305: 390-396 (ENG Summary).

1790. Miller, C.O. 1956. SIMILARITY OF SOME KINETIN AND RED LIGHT EFFECTS. Plant Physiol. 31: 318-319.

1791. Miller, C.O. 1958. THE RELATIONSHIP OF THE KINETIN AND RED-LIGHT PROMOTIONS OF LETTUCE SEED GERMINATION. Plant Physiol. 33: 115-117.

1792. Miller, C.O. 1961. KINETIN AND RELATED COMPOUNDS IN PLANT GROWTH. Annu. Rev. Plant Physiol. 12: 395-408 (R).

1793. Miller, C.O.; Downs, R.J.; Siegelman, H.W. 1965. A RAPID PROCEDURE FOR THE VISIBLE DETECTION OF PHYTOCHROME. BioScience 15: 596-597, 615.

1794. Miller, D.H.; Machlis, L. 1966. STIMULATION OF THE GROWTH RATE OF THE LIVERWORT, *SPHAEROCARPOS DONNELLII*, BY LIGHT. Plant Physiol. 41: Suppl.-15 (A).

1795. Miller, D.H.; Machlis, L. 1967. PHYTOCHROME-MEDIATED CHLOROPHYLL SYNTHESIS IN THE LIVERWORT *SPHAEROCARPOS DONNELLII*. Plant Physiol. 42: Suppl.-10 (A).

1796. Miller, D.H.; Machlis, L. 1968. EFFECTS OF LIGHT ON THE GROWTH AND DEVELOPMENT OF THE LIVERWORT, *SPHAEROCARPOS DONNELLII* AUST. Plant Physiol. 43: 714-722.

1797. Miller, D.H.; Machlis, L. 1968. LIGHT MEDIATED CHANGES IN THE CHLOROPLASTS OF THE LIVERWORT, *SPHAEROCARPOS DONNELLII* AUST. PLANT Physiol. 43: 723-729.

1798. Miller, J.H. 1961. THE EFFECT OF AUXIN AND GUANINE ON GELL EXPANSION AND CELL DIVISION IN THE GAMETOPHYTE OF THE FERN, *ONOCLEA SENSIBILIS*. Am. J. Bot. 48: 816-819.

1799. Miller, J.H.; Miller, P.M. 1961. THE EFFECT OF DIFFERENT LIGHT CONDITIONS AND SUCROSE ON THE GROWTH AND DEVELOPMENT OF THE GAMETOPHYTE OF THE FERN, *ONOCLEA SENSIBILIS*. Am. J. Bot. 48: 154-159.

1800. Miller, J.H.; Wright, D.R. 1961. AN AGE-DEPENDENT CHANGE IN THE RESPONSE OF FERN GAMETOPHYTES TO RED LIGHT. Science 134: 1629.

1801. Miller, J.H.; Miller, P.M. 1963. EFFECTS OF RED AND FAR-RED ILLUMINATION ON THE ELONGATION OF FERN PROTONEMATA AND RHIZOIDS. Plant Cell Physiol. 4: 65-72.

1802. Miller, J.H.; Miller, P.M. 1964. BLUE LIGHT IN THE DEVELOPMENT OF FERN GAMETOPHYTES AND ITS INTERACTION WITH FAR-RED AND RED LIGHT. Am. J. Bot. 51: 329-334.

1803. Miller, J.H.; Miller, P.M. 1965. THE RELATIONSHIP BETWEEN THE PROMOTION OF ELONGATION OF FERN PROTONEMATA BY LIGHT AND GROWTH SUBSTANCES. Am. J. Bot. 52: 871-876.

1804. Miller, J.H.; Miller, P.M. 1967. ACTION SPECTRA FOR LIGHT-INDUCED ELONGATION IN FERN PROTONEMATA. Physiol. Plant. 20: 128-138.

1805. Miller, J.H.; Miller, P.M. 1967. INTERACTION OF PHOTOMORPHOGENETIC PIGMENTS IN FERN GAMETOPHYTES: PHYTOCHROME AND A YELLOW-LIGHT-ABSORBING PIGMENT. Plant Cell Physiol. 8: 765-769.

1806. Miller, J.H.; Stephani, M.C. 1971. EFFECTS OF COLCHICINE AND LIGHT ON CELL FORM IN FERN GAMETOPHYTES. IMPLICATIONS FOR A MECHANISM OF LIGHT-INDUCED CELL ELONGATION. Physiol. Plant. 24: 264-271.

1807. Miller, J.H.; Greany, R.H. 1974. DETERMINATION OF RHIZOID ORIENTATION BY LIGHT AND DARKNESS IN GERMINATING SPORES OF *ONOCLEA SENSIBILIS*. Am. J. Bot. 61: 296-302.

1808. Miller, J.H.; Miller, P.M. 1974. ETHYLENE AND THE RESPONSES TO LIGHT OF RICE SEEDLINGS. Physiol. Plant. 30: 206-211.

1809. Miller, J.M.; Whitenberg, D.C. 1971. RED AND FAR-RED EFFECT ON OXIDATIVE PHOSPHORYLATION BY BEEF HEART MITOCHONDRIA. Texas J. Sci. 23: 142-145.

1810. Miller, N.R.; Nast, C.G.; Dunn, S. 1968. MODIFICATIONS OF THE ANATOMY
AND GROWTH OF A CULTIVAR OF *PHASEOLUS VULGARIS* L. BY LIGHT QUALITY.
Adv. Front. Plant Sci. 19: 73-79.

1811. Miller, P.M.; Miller, J.H. 1966. TEMPERATURE DEPENDENCE OF THE EFFECTS
OF LIGHT AND AUXIN ON THE ELONGATION OF FERN PROTONEMATA. Plant Cell
Physiol. 7: 485-488.

1812. Mirande, M. 1922. INFLUENCE DE LA LUMIÈRE SUR LA FORMATION DE L'ANTHO-
CYANINE DANS LES ÉCAILLES DES BULBES DE LIS. C.R. Acad. Sci. Ser. D:
175: 496-498.

1813. Mishra, D.; Kar, M. 1973. EFFECT OF BENZIMIDAZOLE AND NICKEL IONS IN
THE CONTROL OF *ORYZA SATIVA* LEAF SENESCENCE BY RED AND FAR-RED LIGHT.
Phytochemistry 12: 1521-1522.

1814. Mishra, D.; Pradhan, P. 1973. REGULATION OF SENESCENCE IN DETACHED RICE
LEAVES BY LIGHT, BENZIMIDAZOLE AND KINETIN. Exp. Gerontol. 8:
153-155.

1815. Mitra, G.C.; Allsopp, A.; Wareing, P.F. 1959. I. THE EFFECTS OF LIGHT
OF VARIOUS QUALITIES ON THE DEVELOPMENT OF THE PROTONEMA AND BUD FOR-
MATION IN *POHLIA NUTANS* (HEDW.) LINDB. Phytomorphology 9: 47-55.

1816. Mitra, G.C.; Misra, L.P.; Kaul, K.N. 1962. EFFECTS OF COCONUT MILK AND
KINETIN ON THE DEVELOPMENT OF THE PROTONEMA AND BUD FORMATION IN
POHLIA NUTANS. Nature (London) 195: 1219-1220.

1817. Mitra, G.C.; Misra, L.P.; Prabha, C. 1965. INTERACTION OF RED AND BLUE
LIGHT ON THE DEVELOPMENT OF THE PROTONEMA AND BUD FORMATION IN *POHLIA
NUTANS*. Planta 65: 42-48.

1818. Mitrakos, K. 1961. THE PARTICIPATION OF THE RED FAR-RED REACTION SYSTEM
IN CHLOROPHYLL-METABOLISM. Physiol. Plant. 14: 497-503.

1819. Mitrakos, K. 1963. CHLOROPHYLL METABOLISM AND ITS RELATIONSHIP TO
PHOTOPERIODISM, ENDOGENOUS DAILY RHYTHM AND RED, FAR-RED REACTION
SYSTEM. Photochem. Photobiol. 2: 223-231 (R).

1820. Mitrakos, K.; Klein, W.H.; Price, L. 1965. SOLUBLE SUGAR CHANGES IN
ETIOLATED CORN LEAF TISSUE AS INFLUENCED BY RED-LIGHT TREATMENT.
Planta 66: 207-215.

1821. Mitrakos, K.; Price, L.; Klein, W.H.; Steiner, A. 1967. RED-LIGHT EF-
FECT ON TRACER DISTRIBUTION IN ETIOLATED LEAF TISSUE. Planta 76:
190-196.

1822. Mitrakos, K.; Klein, W.H.; Price, L. 1969. BIOCHEMICAL ASPECTS OF RED AND FAR-RED RESPONSES IN PLANT TISSUES. Proc. Int. Symp. Plant Stimulation (Sofia) pp. 1217-1228 (R).

1823. Mitrakos, K.; Mantouvalos, G.; Margaris, N.; Vrettou, S. 1969. ON THE BIOCHEMISTRY OF THE PHYTOCHROME MORPHOGENESIS. Proc. XI Int. Bot. Congr., p. 149 (A).

1824. Mitrakos, K. 1972. PHYTOCHROME ACTION ON INTERMEDIARY METABOLISM. *Phytochrome*: Ed. K. Mitrakos and W. Shropshire, Jr., Academic Press: New York and London, pp. 587-612 (R).

1825. Mitrakos, K.; Mantouvalos, G. 1972. *IN VIVO* GLUCOSE BREAKDOWN UNDER ACTIVATED AND NON-ACTIVATED PHYTOCHROME. Z. Pflanzenphysiol. 67: 97-104.

1826. Mitrakos, K.; Margaris, N. 1974. PHYTOCHROME EFFECT ON FREE AMINO ACID METABOLISM OF HIGHER PLANTS. Planta 116: 17-25.

1827. Miyachi, S. 1969. REGULATION OF PHOTOSYNTHETIC CARBON METABOLISM BY WAVELENGTH, LIGHT INTENSITY AND OXYGEN. Proc. XI Int. Bot. Congr., p. 149 (A).

1828. Miyachi, S.; Hogetsu, D. 1970. EFFECTS OF PREILLUMINATION WITH LIGHT OF DIFFERENT WAVELENGTHS ON SUBSEQUENT DARK CO_2-FIXATION IN *CHLORELLA* CELLS. Can. J. Bot. 48: 1203-1207.

1829. Miyata, H. 1970. ENDOGENOUS LIGHT-ON RHYTHM IN RESPIRATION OF A LONG-DAY DUCKWEED, *LEMNA GIBBA* G_3. Plant Cell Physiol. 11: 293-301.

1830. Miyoshi, Y.; Furuya, M.; Takimoto, A. 1974. DARK TRANSFORMATIONS OF PHYTOCHROME IN COTYLEDONS OF *PHARBITIS NIL*. Plant Cell Physiol. 15: 1115-1123.

1831. Moh, C.C.; Withrow, R.B. 1955. THE POTENTIATING EFFECT OF NEAR INFRARED ON X-RAY-INDUCED CHROMOSOME BREAKAGE IN BROAD BEAN. Plant Physiol. 30: Suppl.-9 (A).

1832. Moh, C.C.; Withrow, R.B. 1957. INTERACTION OF RED AND FAR-RED RADIANT ENERGY IN MODIFYING X-RAY-INDUCED CHROMATID ABERRATIONS IN BROAD BEAN. Plant Physiol. 32: Suppl.-11 (A).

1833. Moh, C.C.; Withrow, R.B. 1959. NONIONIZING RADIANT ENERGY AS AN AGENT IN ALTERING THE INCIDENCE OF X-RAY-INDUCED CHROMATID ABERRATIONS II. REVERSAL OF THE FAR-RED POTENTIATING EFFECT IN *VICIA* BY RED RADIANT ENERGY. Radiat. Res. 10: 13-19.

1834. Moh, C.C.; Withrow, R.B. 1959. NONIONIZING RADIANT ENERGY AS AN AGENT IN ALTERING THE INCIDENCE OF X-RAY-INDUCED CHROMATID ABERRATIONS III. ACTION SPECTRUM FOR FAR-RED POTENTIATION. Radiat. Res. 11: 18-23.

1835. Mohr, H. 1956. DIE BEEINFLUSSUNG DER KEIMUNG VON FARNSPOREN DURCH LICHT UND ANDERE FAKTOREN. Planta 46: 534-551.

1836. Mohr, H. 1956. DIE ABHÄNGIGKEIT DES PROTONEMAWACHSTUMS UND DER PROTO-NEMAPOLARITÄT BEI FARNEN VOM LICHT. Planta 47: 127-158.

1837. Mohr, H. 1957. DER EINFLUSS MONOCHROMATISCHER STRAHLUNG AUF DAS LÄNGEN-WACHSTUM DES HYPOCOTYLS UND AUF DIE ANTHOCYANBILDUNG BEI KEIMLINGEN VON SINAPIS ALBA L. (=BRASSICA ALBA BOISS). Planta 49: 389-405.

1838. Mohr, H. 1958. NEUE STUDIEN ÜBER MORPHOGENETISCH WICHTIGE PIGMENT-SYSTEME IN PFLANZEN. Naturwissenschaften 45: 448-449.

1839. Mohr, H.; Lünenschloss, A. 1958. WEITERE STUDIEN ZUR PHOTOMORPHOGENESE DER KEIMLINGE VON SINAPIS ALBA (L.). Naturwissenschaften 45: 578-579.

1840. Mohr, H. 1959. THE PHOTOCHEMICAL CONTROL OF ANTHOCYANIN SYNTHESIS AND CORRELATED PHOTOMORPHOGENESIS IN DARK-GROWN SEEDLINGS OF SINAPIS ALBA L. Proc. IX Int. Bot. Congr. 2: 267-268 (A).

1841. Mohr, H. 1959. DER LICHTEINFLUSS AUF DIE HAARBILDUNG AM HYPOKOTYL VON SINAPIS ALBA L. Planta 53: 109-124 (ENG Summary).

1842. Mohr, H. 1959. DER LICHTEINFLUSS AUF DAS WACHSTUM DER KEIMBLÄTTER BEI SINAPIS ALBA L. Planta 53: 219-245 (ENG Summary).

1843. Mohr, H. 1960. PHOTOMORPHOGENETISCHE REAKTIONSSYSTEME IN PFLANZEN 1. TEIL: DAS REVERSIBLE HELLROT-DUNKELROT-REAKTIONSSYSTEM UND DAS BLAU-DUNKELROT-REAKTIONSSYSTEM. Ergeb. Biol. 22: 67-107 (R).

1844. Mohr, H. 1960. PHOTOMORPHOGENETISCHE REAKTIONSSYSTEME IN PFLANZEN 2. TEIL: DER EINFLUSS KURZWELLIGEN LICHTS AUF WACHSTUM UND ENTWICKLUNG. Ergeb. Biol. 23: 47-95 (R).

1845. Mohr, H. 1960. STRAHLUNG UND PFLANZE EINE ALLGEMEINE ÜBERSICHT. Stud. Gen. 13: 464-476 (R).

1846. Mohr, H.; Noblé, A. 1960. DIE STEUERUNG DER SCHLIESSUNG UND ÖFFNUNG DES PLUMULA-HAKENS BEI KEIMLINGEN VON LACTUCA SATIVA DURCH SICHTBARE STRAHLUNG. Planta 55: 327-342 (ENG Summary).

1847. Mohr, H.; Peters, E. 1960. DER PHOTOTROPISMUS UND DAS LICHTABHÄHGIGE LÄNGENWACHSTUM DES HYPOKOTYLS VON SINAPIS ALBA L. Planta 55: 637-646 (ENG Summary).

1848.   Mohr, H.; Pichler, I.   1960.   DER EINFLUSS HELLROTER UND DUNKELROTER
        STRAHLUNG AUF DIE GEOTROPISCHE REAKTION DER KEIMLINGE VON *SINAPIS
        ALBA* L.   Planta 55: 57-66 (ENG Summary).

1849.   Mohr, H.; Wehrung, M.   1960.   DIE STEUERUNG DES HYPOKOTYLWACHSTUMS BEI
        DEN KEIMLINGEN VON *LACTUCA SATIVA* L. DURCH SICHTBARE STRAHLUNG.
        Planta 55: 438-450 (ENG Summary).

1850.   Mohr, H.   1961.   WIRKUNGEN KURZWELLIGEN LICHTES.   Handbuch der Pflanzen-
        physiologie. Ed. W. Ruhland, Berlin-Göttingen Heidelberg, Springer
        XVI: 439-531 (R).

1851.   Mohr, H.   1961.   PHOTOCHEMICAL CONTROL OF ANTHOCYANIN SYNTHESIS AND
        CORRELATED PHOTOMORPHOGENESIS IN DARK-GROWN SEEDLINGS OF *SINAPIS ALBA*
        L.   Recent Adv. Bot., pp. 1025-1028 (R).

1852.   Mohr, H.   1961.   NON-PHOTOSYNTHETIC CONTROL OF GROWTH AND MORPHOGENESIS
        OF SEEDLINGS BY VISIBLE RADIATION.   *Effects of Ionizing Radiation on
        Seeds* 1960. A Symposium.   I.A.E.A. Bull. pp. 181-188 (R).

1853.   Mohr, H.   1961.   THE EFFECTS OF LONG VISIBLE AND NEAR INFRARED RADIATION
        ON PLANTS.   Proc. III Int. Congr. Photobiol., pp. 44-49 (R).

1854.   Mohr, H.   1961.   LIGHT AND PLANTS.   Universitas 4: 427-433 (R).

1855.   Mohr, H.; Appuhn, U.   1961.   ZUR WECHSELWIRKUNG VON LICHT UND GIBBEREL-
        LINSÄURE.   Naturwissenschaften 48: 483.

1856.   Mohr, H.   1962.   DIE PHOTOMORPHOGENESE DER DIKOTYLEN-KEIMLINGE.   Ber.
        Dtsch. Bot. Ges. 75: 454-455 (R).

1857.   Mohr, H.   1962.   PRIMARY EFFECTS OF LIGHT ON GROWTH.   Annu. Rev. Plant
        Physiol. 13: 465-488 (R).

1858.   Mohr, H.   1962.   LUZ Y PLANTA.   Universitas 1: 75-82 (R).

1859.   Mohr, H.; Appuhn, U.   1962.   DIE STEUERUNG DES HYPOCOTYLWACHSTUMS VON
        SINAPIS ALBA L. DURCH LICHT UND GIBBERELLINSÄURE.   Planta 59: 49-67
        (ENG Summary).

1860.   Mohr, H.; Barth, C.   1962.   EIN VERGLEICH DER PHOTOMORPHOGENESE DER
        GAMETOPHYTEN VON *ALSOPHILA AUSTRALIS* (BR) UND *DRYOPTERIS FILIX-MAS*
        (L.) SCHOTT.   Planta 58: 580-593 (ENG Summary).

1861.   Mohr, H.; Haug, A.   1962.   DIE HISTOLOGISCHEN VORGÄNGE WÄHREND DER LICHT-
        ABHÄNGIGEN SCHLIESSUNG UND ÖFFNUNG DES PLUMULAHAKENS BEI DEN KEIM-
        LINGEN VON *LACTUCA SATIVA* L.   Planta 59: 151-164 (ENG Summary).

1862. Mohr, H.; Ohlenroth, K. 1962. PHOTOSYNTHESE UND PHOTOMORPHOGENESE BEI FARNVORKEIMEN VON *DRYOPTERIS FILIX-MAS*. Planta 57: 656-664 (ENG Summary).

1863. Mohr, H.; Pinnig, E. 1962. DER EINFLUSS DES LICHTES AUF DIE BILDUNG VON BLATTPRIMORDIEN AM VEGETATIONSKEGEL DER KEIMLINGE VON *SINAPIS ALBA* L. Planta 58: 569-579 (ENG Summary).

1864. Mohr, H. 1963. LICHT UND PFLANZE-NEUE ERKENNTNISSE DER PHOTOBIOLOGIE. Universitas 18: 293-300 (R).

1865. Mohr, H. 1963. DIE KONTROLLE DER FARN- UND MOOSSPORENKEIMUNG DURCH LICHT. Proc. Int. Symp. Physiol. Ecol. Biochem. Germination, Greifswald; Ernst-Moritz-Arndt-University, 1963 (abridged version) (R) (Publ. in Full, 1967).

1866. Mohr, H. 1963. DIE STEUERUNG DER PFLANZLICHEN ENTWICKLUNG DURCH LICHT. Umschau 63: 20-24 (R).

1867. Mohr, H. 1963. THE INFLUENCE OF VISIBLE RADIATION ON THE GERMINATION OF ARCHEGONIATE SPORES AND THE GROWTH OF THE FERN PROTONEMA. J. Linn. Soc. London, Bot. 58: 287-296 (R).

1868. Mohr, H. 1963. DIE PHOTOMORPHOGENESE DER DIKOTYLENKEIMLINGE. Naturwiss. Rundsch. 16: 1-9 (R).

1869. Mohr, H.; Appuhn, U. 1963. DIE KEIMUNG VON *LACTUCA* - ACHÄNEN UNTER DEM EINFLUSS DES PHYTOCHROMSYSTEMS UND DER HOCHENERGIEREAKTION DER PHOTOMORPHOGENESE. Planta 60: 274-288 (ENG Summary).

1870. Mohr, H.; Van Nes, E. 1963. DER EINFLUSS SICHTBARER STRAHLUNG AUF DIE FLAVONOIDSYNTHESE UND MORPHOGENESE DER BUCHWEIZEN-KEIMLINGE (*FAGOPYRUM ESCULENTUM* MOENCH.) I. SYNTHESE VON ANTHOCYAN. Z. Bot. 51: 1-16 (ENG Summary).

1871. Mohr, H. 1964. THE HIGH ENERGY REACTION OF PHOTOMORPHOGENESIS. Proc. X Int. Bot. Congr., pp. 186-187 (A).

1872. Mohr, H. 1964. THE CONTROL OF PLANT GROWTH AND DEVELOPMENT BY LIGHT. Biol. Rev. Cambridge Philos. Soc. 39: 87-112 (R).

1873. Mohr, H.; Holl, G. 1964. DIE REGULATION DER ZELLAKTIVITÄT BEI FARNVORKEIMEN DURCH LICHT. Z. Bot. 52: 209-221 (ENG Summary).

1874. Mohr, H.; Meyer, U.; Hartmann, K. 1964. DIE BEEINFLUSSUNG DER FARNSPOREN-KEIMUNG (*OSMUNDA CINNAMOMEA* L. UND *O. CLAYTONIANA* L.) ÜBER DAS PHYTOCHROMSYSTEM UND DIE PHOTOSYNTHESE. Planta 60: 483-496 (ENG Summary).

1875. Mohr, H. 1965. STEUERUNG DER PFLANZLICHEN ENTWICKLUNG DURCH LICHT. Naturwiss. Rundsch. 18: 101-108 (R).

1876. Mohr, H. 1965. DIE REGULATION DER ANTHOCYANSYNTHESE DURCH LICHT. Beitr. Biochem. Physiol. Naturst. 299-316 (R).

1877. Mohr, H. 1965. DIE KONTROLLE DER FARN- UND MOOSSPORENKEIMUNG DURCH LICHT. Biol. Rundsch. 2: 153-164 (R).

1878. Mohr, H. 1965. DIE STEUERUNG DER ENTWICKLUNG DURCH LICHT AM BEISPIEL DER FARNGAMETOPHYTEN. Ber. Dtsch. Bot. Ges. 78: 54-68 (R-D).

1879. Mohr, H.; Lange, H. 1965. DIE HEMMUNG DER LICHTINDUZIERTEN ANTHOCYAN-SYNTHESE DURCH ACTINOMYCIN D. Naturwissenschaften 52: 261.

1880. Mohr, H.; Schlickewei, I.; Lange, H. 1965. DIE HEMMUNG DES PHYTOCHROM-INDUZIERTEN KOTYLEDONENWACHSTUMS DURCH ACTINOMYCIN D. Z. Naturforsch. Teil B. 20: 819-821.

1881. Mohr, H.; Wagner, E.; Hartmann, K.M. 1965. ZUR DEUTUNG DER HOCHENERGIE-REAKTION DER PHOTOMORPHOGENESE (=HER) AUF DER BASIS DES PHYTOCHROM-SYSTEMS. Naturwissenschaften 52: 209.

1882. Mohr, H. 1966. UNTERSUCHUNGEN ZUR PHYTOCHROMINDUZIERTEN PHOTOMORPHO-GENESE DES SENFKEIMLINGS (*SINAPIS ALBA* L.). Z. Pflanzenphysiol. 54: 63-83 (R-D) (ENG Summary).

1883. Mohr, H. 1966. DIE STEUERUNG DER ENTWICKLUNG DURCH LICHT. Scientia 60: 244-250 (R).

1884. Mohr, H. 1966. DIFFERENTIAL GENE ACTIVATION AS A MODE OF ACTION OF PHYTOCHROME 730. Photochem. Photobiol. 5: 469-483 (R-D).

1885. Mohr, H.; Senf, R. 1966. DIE HEMMUNG DER PHYTOCHROM-INDUZIERTEN ANTHO-CYANSYNTHESE DURCH PUROMYCIN UND 2-THIOURACIL. Planta 71: 195-203 (ENG Summary).

1886. Mohr, H. 1967. DIE KONTROLLE DER FARN- UND MOOSSPORENKEIMUNG DURCH LICHT. Proc. Int. Symp. Physiol. Ecol. Biochem. Germination, Ed. H. Borriss, Greifswald; Ernst-Moritz-Arndt-University 1967 1: 909-921 (R).

1887. Mohr, H.; Bienger, I. 1967. EXPERIMENTE ZUR WIRKUNG VON ACTINOMYCIN D AUF DIE DURCH PHYTOCHROM BEWIRKTE ANTHOCYANSYNTHESE. Planta 75: 180-184 (ENG Summary).

1888. Mohr, H.; Holderied, Ch.; Link, W.; Roth, K. 1967. PROTEIN- UND RNS-GEHALT DES HYPOCOTYLS BEIM STATIONÄREN WACHSTUM IM DUNKELN UND UNTER DEM EINFLUSS VON PHYTOCHROM (KEIMLINGE VON *SINAPIS ALBA* L.). Planta 76: 348-358 (ENG Summary).

1889. Mohr, H. 1968. INTRODUCTORY LECTURE ON PHOTOMORPHOGENESIS. Proc. V Int. Congr. Photobiol., p. 99 (A) (R).

1890. Mohr, H. 1968. DIE STEUERUNG DER ENTWICKLUNG DURCH DAS PHYTOCHROM-SYSTEM. Arbeitsgem. Forsch. Landes Nordrhein-Westfalen Nat. Ing. Gesellschaftswiss. [Veroeff.] 183: 39-75 (R).

1891. Mohr, H.; Huault, C.; Lange, H.; Lohmann, L.; Rissland, I.; Weidner, M. 1968. LAG-PHASES IN PHYTOCHROME-MEDIATED ENZYME SYNTHESIS (PAL). Planta 83: 267-275.

1892. Mohr, H.; Roth, K.; Link, W. 1968. RNA AND PROTEIN SYNTHESIS IN CONNECTION WITH PHYTOCHROME-MEDIATED CONTROL OF HYPOCOTYL LENGTHENING IN MUSTARD SEEDLINGS. Plant Physiol. 43: Suppl.-15 (A).

1893. Mohr, H. 1969. CONTROL OF ENZYME SYNTHESIS BY PHYTOCHROME. Proc. XI Int. Bot. Congr., p. 150 (A).

1894. Mohr, H. 1969. PHOTOMORPHOGENESIS. *Physiology of Plant Growth and Development* Ed. M.B. Wilkins, McGraw-Hill, New York, pp. 508-556 (R).

1895. Mohr, H. 1969. PHOTOMORPHOGENESIS. Proc. V Int. Congr. Photobiol., pp. 99-141 (R-D).

1896. Mohr, H. 1969. LIGHT AND MORPHOGENESIS. *Biology and the Physical Sciences*, Ed. S. Devons, Columbia Univ. Press, New York, pp. 209-237 (R).

1897. Mohr, H. 1970. MECHANISM OF ACTION OF PHYTOCHROME. Biochem. J. 119: 3p-4p (R).

1898. Mohr, H. 1970. REGULATION DER ENZYMSYNTHESE BEI DER HÖHEREN PFLANZE. Naturwiss. Rundsch. 23: 187-195 (R-D).

1899. Mohr, H. 1971. BIOCHEMISCHE MODELLSYSTEME FÜR DIFFERENZIERUNGSVORGÄNGE. Umschau: 71: 547-551 (R).

1900. Mohr, H.; Bienger, I.; Lange, H. 1971. PRIMARY REACTION OF PHYTOCHROME. Nature (London) 230: 56-58.

1901. Mohr, H.; Sitte, P. 1971. *MOLEKULARE GRUNDLAGEN DER ENTWICKLUNG MÜNCHEN*: BLV.

1901.5 Mohr, H. 1972. *LECTURES ON PHOTOMORPHOGENESIS*, Springer-Verlag, Berlin, Heidelberg, New York.

1902. Mohr, H.; Oelze-Karow, H. 1973. ZUM MECHANISMUS DER PHYTOCHROMWIRKUNG. Biol. Unserer Zeit. 3: 137-147 (R).

1903. Mohr, H. 1974. ADVANCES IN PHYTOCHROME RESEARCH. Photochem. Photobiol. 20: 539-542.

1904. Mohr, H. 1974. THE ROLE OF PHYTOCHROME IN CONTROLLING ENZYME LEVELS IN PLANTS. MTP Int. Rev. Sci. Biochem. Ser. One, 9: 37-81.

1905. Mohr, H.; Drumm, H.; Kasemir, H. 1974. LICHT UND FARBSTOFFE. Ber. Dtsch. Bot. Ges. 87: 49-69 (ENG Summary).

1906. Mohr, H.; Peter, K. 1974. IS PHYTOCHROME-MEDIATED ENZYME "INDUCTION" A MODULATION OF THE DARK PROCESS? Proc. Eur. Annu. Symp. Plant Photo-morphogenesis, (Antwerpen), pp. 60-63.

1907. Möller, J.; Van Poucke, M. 1970. GEL ELECTROPHORETIC COMPARISON OF LIGHT-INDUCED ASCORBIC ACID OXIDASE FROM MUSTARD SEEDLINGS AND FROM PUMPKIN TISSUE. Phytochemistry 9: 1803-1805.

1908. Mondain-Monval, O.D. 1963. ÉTUDE DE L'ACTION DE LA LUMIÈRE SUR LA GERMINATION DES GRAINES DE TOMATE (*LYCOPERSICUM ESCULENTUM* MILLER) VARIÉTÉ MARMANDE. C.R. Acad. Sci. Ser. D. 257: 3646-3648.

1909. Monéger, R. 1968. INCORPORATIONS DE RADIO-ACTIVITÉ, À PARTIR DE BICAR-BONATE ^{14}C ET D'ACÉTATE 2-^{14}C DE SODIUM, DANS LES CAROTÉNOÏDES DE FRONDES ÉTIOLÉES DE *SPIRODELA POLYRRHIZA* SCHLEID. EXPOSÉES À DES RADIATIONS OLIGOCHROMATIQUES. C.R. Acad. Sci. Ser. D. 267: 605-608.

1910. Monéger, R. 1968. CONTRIBUTION À L'ÉTUDE DE L'INFLUENCE EXERCÉE PAR LA LUMIÈRE SUR LA BIOSYNTHÈSE DES CAROTÉNOÏDES CHEZ LA *SPIRODELA POLYRRHIZA* (L.) SCHLEIDEN. Physiol. Veg. 6: 165-202.

1911. Monéger, R.; Jacques, R. 1968. ACTION DE RADIATIONS OLIGOCHROMATIQUES SUR LES TENEURS EN CAROTÉNOÏDES DES FRONDES ÉTIOLÉES DE *SPIRODELA POLYRRHIZA* SCHLEID. C.R. Acad. Sci. Ser. D. 267: 313-316.

1912. Monéger, R.; Michanol, Y. 1968. UN MÉCANISME POSSIBLE D'ACTION DE LA LUMIÈRE SUR LES BIOSYNTHÈSES DE CAROTÉNOIDES CHEZ LES VÉGÉTAUX SUPÉRIEURS CHLOROPHYLLIENS. Bull. Soc. Fr. Physiol. Veg. 14: 473-497 (R).

1913. Monselise, S.P. 1962. CITRUS SEED BIOLOGY. Proc. XVI Int. Hortic. Congr. 4: 559-565.

1914. Monselise, S.P.; Kadman-Zahavi, A. 1964. MORPHOGENIC RESPONSES OF EPICOTYL HOOK, PRIMARY LEAVES AND FIRST INTERNODE OF CITRUS SEEDLINGS TO IRRADIATION WITH FAR-RED AND RED LIGHT. Proc. IV Int. Congr. Photobiol., p. 106 (A).

1915. Monselise, S.P.; Kadman-Zahavi, A. 1965. MORPHOGENETIC RESPONSES OF EPICOTYL HOOK, PRIMARY LEAVES AND FIRST INTERNODE OF CITRUS SEEDLINGS TO IRRADIANCE. Photochem. Photobiol. 4: 549-553.

1916. Montemartini, L. 1911. INTORNO ALL'INFLUENZA DEI RAGGI ULTRAVIOLETTI SULLO SVILUPPO DEGLI ORGANI DI RIPRODUZIONE DELLE PIANTE. Atti Ist. Bot. Univ. Pavia, Ser. 2, 9: 13-23.

1917. Moore, P.H.; Hamner, K.C. 1966. ACTION OF RED AND FAR-RED LIGHT BREAKS ON THE FLOWERING RESPONSE OF *XANTHIUM* GIVEN DURING 48-HOUR DARK PERIODS. Plant Physiol. 41: Suppl.-30 (A).

1918. Moore, P.H.; Reid, H.B.; Hamner, K.C. 1967. FLOWERING RESPONSES OF *XANTHIUM PENSYLVANICUM* TO LONG DARK PERIODS. Plant Physiol. 42: 503-509.

1919. Moraes, W.B.C.; Vicente, M.; Meneghini, M. 1967. UM EFEITO, DEPENDENTE DA LUZ E DA PRESENCA DOS COTILÉDONES, OPÔSTO À ABERTURA DA ALCA DO HIPOCÔTILO DE "SEEDLINGS" DE FEIJÃO. Arq. Inst. Biol. Sao Paulo 34: 73-81 (ENG Summary).

1920. Morgan, P.W.; Powell, R.D. 1969. EFFECT OF COUMARIN ON RED LIGHT-STIMULATED BEAN LEAF DISK EXPANSION AND LETTUCE SEED GERMINATION ASSOCIATED WITH MODIFICATION OF ETHYLENE PRODUCTION. Proc. Assoc. South. Agric. Work. 66th, p. 246 (A).

1921. Morgan, P.W.; Powell, R.D. 1969. EFFECT OF COUMARIN ON RED LIGHT-STIMULATED BEAN LEAF DISK EXPANSION AND LETTUCE SEED GERMINATION ASSOCIATED WITH MODIFICATION OF ETHYLENE PRODUCTION. Plant Physiol. 44: Suppl.-31, Abstr. No. 147 (A).

1922. Morgan, P.W.; Powell, R.D. 1970. INVOLVEMENT OF ETHYLENE IN RESPONSES OF ETIOLATED BEAN HYPOCOTYL HOOK TO COUMARIN. Plant Physiol. 45: 553-557.

1923. Morren, C. [note after by A. Brongniart] 1832. SUR L'INFLUENCE DES RAYONS COLORÉS SUR LA GERMINATION DES PLANTES. Ann. Sc. Nat. 27: 201-205.

1924. Morton, J.S. 1970. DEVELOPMENTAL PHYSIOLOGY OF THE MESOCOTYL OF *ZEA Mays*. Ph.D. Thesis, George Washington Univ., Washington, D.C.

1925. Moshkov, B.S. 1950. THE EFFECT OF INDIVIDUAL REGIONS OF THE SPECTRUM OF PHYSIOLOGICAL RADIATION ON THE GROWTH AND DEVELOPMENT OF CERTAIN PLANTS. Dokl. Akad. Nauk. SSSR 71: 171-174 (RUS).

1926. Moshkov, B.S. 1961. PHOTOPERIODISM IN PLANTS. Moscow. (not obtained), (referred to by Rubin, L.B. et. al., Biologia 8: 135-145 (1973)) (R) (RUS).

1927. Moshkov, B.S. 1962. YIELDS OF MAXIMUM PRODUCING AND EARLY RIPENING PLANTS IN ARTIFICIAL CONDITIONS. Agrobiologiya 5: 742-755 (RUS).

1928. Moshkov, B.S.; Yulanovskaya, M.V. 1962. THE EFFECTS OF SPECTRAL COMPOSITION OF LIGHT ON THE PHOTOPERIODICAL REACTION OF OIL-BEARING PERILLA. Sb. Tr. Agronomical Physics #9 (RUS) (not obtained).

1929. Moshkov, B.S.; Mikhailov, A.P. 1964. THE CHARACTER OF THE INTERRELATIONS OF LIGHT AND FAR-RED RADIATION WITH THE DARK PROCESSES OF THE RHYTHMIC ACTIVITIES OF PLANT REACTIONS. Dokl. Vaskniil 4: 11-14 (RUS).

1930. Moshkov, B.S. 1966. RAISING PLANTS UNDER ARTIFICIAL ILLUMINATION. Izd. "Kolos", L. (RUS) (R) (not obtained).

1931. Moshkov, B.S.; Pumpyanskaya, S.L.; Fukshanskii, L. Ya. 1967. CONCERNING THE CONSTRUCTION OF A MODEL OF THE PHOTOPERIODIC REACTION IN PLANTS. Dokl. Akad. Nauk SSSR 173: 963-966 (RUS) (R-D).

1932. Moshkov, B.S.; Pumpyanskaya, S.L.; Fukshanskii, L. Ya. 1967. MODEL OF THE PHOTOPERIODIC MECHANISM IN PLANTS. Fiziol. Rast. 14: 983-989 (RUS).

1933. Moshkov, B.S. 1968. STUDIES OF THE EFFECTS OF THE SPECTRAL QUALITY OF LIGHT ON THE INDUCTION AND POST INDUCTION PERIODS ON THE ONTOGENY OF PLANTS. Sb. Tr. Agron. Fiz. 15: 43-48 (RUS) (R-D).

1934. Moshkov, B.S.; Pumpyanskaya, S.L.; Fukshanskii, L. Ya. 1968. CONCERNING A MODEL SCHEME FOR THE PHOTOPERIODIC REACTION IN PLANTS. Sb. Tr. Agron. Fiz. 15: 5-42 (RUS) (R-D).

1935. Moshkov, B.S.; Pumpyanskaya, S.L.; Fukshanskii, L. Ya. 1969. SOME QUALITATIVE RESULTS OF THE ANALYSIS OF A GENERAL MODEL OF PHOTOPERIODISM. Fiziol. Rast. 16: 41-48 (RUS) (R-D) (ENG Summary).

1936. Moshkov, B.S.; Pumpyanskaya, S.L.; Fukshanskii, L. Ya. 1970. MODEL OF PHOTOPERIODISM AND MEANS FOR OPTIMIZING THE PRODUCTIVITY OF PLANTS. Vazhneishie Probl. Fotosint. Rastenievod 1970, pp. 90-96 (RUS).

1937. Mouravieff, I. 1958. ACTION DE LA LUMIÈRE SUR LA CELLULE VÉGÉTALE 1.
       PRODUCTION DU MOUVEMENT D'OUVERTURE STOMATIQUE PAR LA LUMIÈRE DES
       DIVERSES RÉGIONS DU SPECTRE. Bull. Soc. Bot. Fr. 105: 467-475.

1938. Mouravieff, I. 1960. POLARISATION PHOTOTACTIQUE DU PROTOPLASME DANS
       LES CELLULES ÉPIDERMIQUES D'*APONOGETON DISTACHYUS* L. C.R. Acad.
       Sci. Ser. D. 250: 1104-1105.

1939. Mouravieff, I. 1965. SUR LES RÉACTIONS DES CELLULES STOMATIQUES AU
       RAYONNEMENT ULTRAVIOLET PROCHE EN PRÉSENCE OU EN ABSENCE DU GAZ
       CARBONIQUE. C.R. Acad. Sci. Ser. D. 260: 5392-5395.

1939.5 Mousseron-Canet, M.; Mani, J.-C. 1972. PHOTOCHROMISM. *Photochemistry
       and Molecular Reactions*. Israel Program for Scientific Translations,
       Jerusalem, pp. 189-201 (R).

1940. Mugele, F.; Haupt, W. 1961. DIE TEMPERATURABHÄNGIGKEIT DER CHLOROPLAS-
       TENBEWEGUNG. Naturwissenschaften 48: 531-532.

1941. Mugele, F. 1962. DER EINFLUSS DER TEMPERATUR AUF DIE LICHTINDUZIERTE
       CHLOROPLASTENBEWEGUNG. Z. Bot. 50: 368-388 (ENG Summary).

1942. Muir, R.M. 1970. THE CONTROL OF GROWTH BY THE SYNTHESIS OF IAA AND ITS
       CONJUGATION. *Plant Growth Substances* 1970, Ed. D.J. Carr, Springer-
       Verlag; Berlin, Heidelberg and New York, pp. 96-101.

1943. Muir, R.M.; Chang, K.C. 1974. EFFECT OF RED LIGHT ON COLEOPTILE
       GROWTH. Plant Physiol. 54: 286-288.

1944. Mumford, F.E.; Smith, D.H.; Heytler, P.G. 1964. THE EFFECT OF RED
       LIGHT ON THE FLAVONOID COMPOSITION OF ETIOLATED PEA PLUMULES.
       Biochem. J. 91: 517-522.

1945. Mumford, F.E. 1966. STUDIES ON THE PHYTOCHROME DARK REACTION *IN VITRO*.
       Biochemistry 5: 522-524.

1946. Mumford, F.E.; Jenner, E.L. 1966. PURIFICATION AND CHARACTERIZATION OF
       PHYTOCHROME FROM OAT SEEDLINGS. Biochemistry 5: 3657-3662.

1947. Mumford, F.E.; Mitchell, W.D. 1967. STUDIES ON THE PHYTOCHROME DARK
       REACTION *IN VITRO*. Plant Physiol. 42: Suppl.-10 (A).

1948. Mumford, F.E.; Anderson, G.R.; Jenner, E.L. 1968. THE EFFECT OF pH ON
       THE PHYTOCHROME DARK REACTION *IN VITRO*. Plant Physiol. 43: Suppl.-
       15 (A).

1949. Mumford, F.E.; Jenner, E.L. 1971. CATALYSIS OF THE PHYTOCHROME DARK
       REACTION BY REDUCING AGENTS. Plant Physiol. 47: Suppl.-1, Abstr.
       No. 4 (A).

1950. Mumford, F.E.; Jenner, E.L. 1971. CATALYSIS OF THE PHYTOCHROME DARK REACTION BY REDUCING AGENTS. Biochemistry 10: 98-101.

1951. Mumford, F.E. 1973. STUDIES ON SULFHYDRYL GROUPS IN PHYTOCHROME. Plant Physiol. 51: Suppl.-52, Abstr. No. 282 (A).

1952. Murneek, A.E. 1948. HISTORY OF RESEARCH IN PHOTOPERIODISM. *Vernalization and Photoperiodism*, A Symposium, Lotsya 1: 39-61, Chronica Botanica Co. Waltham, Mass. (R).

1953. Nabors, M.W. 1970. THE GROWTH PHYSICS AND WATER RELATIONS OF RED LIGHT-INDUCED GERMINATION IN LETTUCE SEEDS. Ph.D. Thesis, Mich. State Univ., East Lansing.

1954. Nabors, M.W.; Lang, A. 1971. THE GROWTH PHYSICS AND WATER RELATIONS OF RED-LIGHT-INDUCED GERMINATION IN LETTUCE SEEDS. I. EMBRYOS GERMINATING IN OSMOTICUM. Planta 101: 1-25.

1955. Nabors, M.W.; Lang, A. 1971. THE GROWTH PHYSICS AND WATER RELATIONS OF RED-LIGHT-INDUCED GERMINATION IN LETTUCE SEEDS. II. EMBRYOS GERMINATING IN WATER. Planta 101: 26-42.

1956. Nabors, M.W.; Kugrens, P.; Ross, C. 1974. PHOTODORMANT LETTUCE SEEDS: PHYTOCHROME-INDUCED PROTEIN AND LIPID DEGRADATION. Planta 117: 361-365.

1957. Nagata, Y. 1973. RHIZOID DIFFERENTIATION IN *SPIROGYRA* II. PHOTOREVERSIBILITY OF RHIZOID INDUCTION BY RED AND FAR-RED LIGHT. Plant Cell Physiol. 14: 543-554.

1958. Nakamura, S. 1954. GERMINATION OF THE EDIBLE BURDOCK (*ARCTIUM LAPPA* L.) SEEDS. II. EFFECT OF THE WAVE LENGTH OF RADIATION ON THE GERMINATION. Engei Gakkai Zasshi 23: 108-114 (JAP) (Eng Summary).

1959. Nakamura, S.; Okasako, Y.; Yamada, E. 1955. EFFECT OF LIGHT ON THE GERMINATION OF VEGETABLE SEEDS. Engei Gakkai Zasshi 24: 17-28 (JAP) (ENG Summary).

1960. Nakata, S.; Lockhart, J.A. 1966. EFFECTS OF RED AND FAR-RED RADIATION ON CELL DIVISION AND ELONGATION IN THE STEM OF PINTO BEAN SEEDLINGS. Am. J. Bot. 53: 12-20.

1961. Nakayama, S. 1958. STUDIES ON THE DARK PROCESS IN THE PHOTOPERIODIC RESPONSE OF *PHARBITIS* SEEDLINGS. Sci. Rep. Tohoku Imp. Univ., Ser. 4, 24: 137-183.

1962.   Nakayama, S.   1958.   PHOTOREVERSIBLE CONTROL OF FLOWERING AT THE START
         OF INDUCTIVE DARK PERIOD IN *PHARBITIS NIL*.   Seitaigaku Kenkyu 14:
         325-326.

1963.   Nakayama, S.; Borthwick, H.A.; Hendricks, S.B.   1960.   FAILURE OF PHOTO-
         REVERSIBLE CONTROL OF FLOWERING IN *PHARBITIS NIL*.   Bot. Gaz.
         (Chicago) 121: 237-243.

1964.   Nakayama, S.; Tobita, H.; Okumura, F.S.   1962.   ANTAGONISM OF KINETIN AND
         FAR-RED LIGHT OR β-INDOLEACETIC ACID IN THE FLOWERING OF *PHARBITIS*
         SEEDLINGS.   Phyton (Buenos Aires) 19: 43-48.

1965.   Naqvi, S.M.; Gordon, S. A.   1966.   AUXIN TRANSPORT IN *ZEA MAYS* L. COLEOP-
         TILES I.   INFLUENCE OF GRAVITY ON THE TRANSPORT OF INDOLEACETIC ACID-
         $2-{}^{14}C$.   Plant Physiol. 41: 1113-1118.

1966.   Naundorf, G.   1940.   UNTERSUCHUNGEN ÜBER DEN PHOTOTROPISMUS DER KEIM-
         WURZEL VON *HELIANTHUS ANNUUS*.   Planta 30: 639-663.

1967.   Naylor, A.W.   1941.   EFFECTS OF SOME ENVIRONMENTAL FACTORS ON PHOTOPERI-
         ODIC INDUCTION OF BEET AND DILL.   Bot. Gaz. (Chicago) 102: 557-575.

1968.   Naylor, A.W.   1961.   THE PHOTOPERIODIC CONTROL OF PLANT BEHAVIOR.
         Handbuch der Pflanzenphysiologie, Ed. W. Ruhland, Springer-Verlag,
         Berlin-Göttingen, Heidelberg, 16: 331-389 (R).

1969.   Nebel, B.J.; Naylor, A.W.   1964.   DIFFERENTIATION OF BUDS ON MOSS PROTO-
         NEMATA: PHYTOCHROME CONTROL FOLLOWING A CUMULATIVE LIGHT EFFECT.
         Plant Physiol. 39: Suppl.-51 (A).

1970.   Nebel, B.J.   1966.   ACTION SPECTRUM FOR PHOTOTROPISM IN PROTONEMA OF THE
         MOSS *PHYSCOMITRIUM PYRIFORME*.   Plant Physiol. 41: Suppl.-15 (A).

1971.   Nebel, B.J.   1967.   ACTION SPECTRA FOR PHOTOGROWTH AND PHOTOTROPISM IN
         PROTONEMATA OF THE MOSS *PHYSCOMITRIUM TURBINATUM*.   Plant Physiol. 42:
         Suppl.-10 (A).

1972.   Nebel, B.J.   1968.   ACTION SPECTRA FOR PHOTOGROWTH AND PHOTOTROPISM IN
         PROTONEMATA OF THE MOSS *PHYSCOMITRIUM TURBINATUM*.   Planta 81:
         287-302.

1973.   Nebel, B.J.   1969.   RESPONSES OF MOSS PROTONEMATA TO RED AND FAR-RED
         POLARIZED LIGHT: EVIDENCE FOR DISC-SHAPED PHYTOCHROME PHOTORECEPTORS.
         Plant Physiol. 44: Suppl.-19, Abstr. No. 90 (A).

1974.   Nebel, B.J.   1969.   RESPONSES OF MOSS PROTONEMATA TO RED AND FAR-RED
         POLARIZED LIGHT: EVIDENCE FOR DISC-SHAPED PHYTOCHROME PHOTORECEPTORS.
         Planta 87: 170-179.

1975. Negbi, M.; Koller, D. 1964. DUAL ACTION OF WHITE LIGHT IN THE PHOTO-
CONTROL OF GERMINATION OF *ORYZOPSIS MILIACEAE*. Plant Physiol. 39:
247-253.

1976. Negbi, M.; Black, M.; Bewley, J.D. 1968. FAR-RED SENSITIVE DARK PRO-
CESSES ESSENTIAL FOR LIGHT- AND GIBBERELLIN-INDUCED GERMINATION OF
LETTUCE SEED. Plant Physiol. 43: 35-40.

1977. Negbi, M.; Briggs, W.R. 1973. THE EFFECT OF CALCIUM ON DARK REACTIONS
OF PHYTOCHROME. Plant Physiol. 51: Suppl.-52, Abstr. No. 283 (A).

1978. Negm, F.B. 1972. STUDIES ON THE INTERACTION OF ETHYLENE, CARBON DI-
OXIDE, AND PHYTOCHROME IN OVERCOMING THERMODORMANCY OF LETTUCE SEEDS.
Ph.D. Thesis, Univ. Calif., Riverside.

1979. Negm, F.B.; Smith, O.E.; Kumamoto, J. 1973. THE ROLE OF PHYTOCHROME IN
AN INTERACTION WITH ETHYLENE AND CARBON DIOXIDE IN OVERCOMING
LETTUCE SEED THERMODORMANCY. Plant Physiol. 51: 1089-1094.

1980. Nesković, M.; Ćulafić, L. 1967. EFFECT OF LIGHT ON THE CONTENT OF
GROWTH SUBSTANCES IN PEA SHOOTS. Proc. Eur. Annu. Symp., Plant
Photomorphogenesis (Hvar), p. 75 (A).

1981. Nesković, M.; Konjević, R. 1972. THE EFFECT OF PHYTOCHROME ON ENDO-
GENOUS GIBBERELLINS AND SOME MACROMOLECULAR COMPOUNDS IN PEAS.
Proc. VI Int. Congr. Photobiol. Abstr. No. 169 (A).

1982. Nesković, M.; Konjević, R. 1974. THE NON-REVERSIBLE EFFECTS OF RED AND
FAR RED LIGHT ON THE CONTENT OF GIBBERELLIN-LIKE SUBSTANCES IN PEA
INTERNODES. J. Exp. Bot. 25: 733-739.

1983. Nesković, M.; Sjaus, T. 1974. THE ROLE OF ENDOGENOUS GIBBERELLIN-LIKE
SUBSTANCES AND INHIBITORS IN THE GROWTH OF PEA INTERNODES. Biol.
Plant. (Praha) 16: 57-66.

1984. Neuscheler-Wirth, H. 1970. PHOTOMORPHOGENESE UND PHOTOTROPISMUS BEI
MOUGEOTIA. Z. Pflanzenphysiol. 63: 238-260 (ENG Summary).

1985. Neuscheler-Wirth, H. 1971. DIE LICHTORIENTIERTE CHLOROPLASTENBEWEGUNG
VON *MOUGEOTIA* IN ABHÄNGIGKEIT VON DER VORKULTUR, VOM LICHT-DUNKEL-
WECHSEL UND VOM ZELLALTER. Z. Pflanzenphysiol. 65: 130-139 (ENG
Summary).

1986. Newman, D.W. 1971. THE EFFECT OF RED AND FAR RED LIGHT ON THE DESATU-
RATION OF FATTY ACIDS IN BARLEY LEAVES. Plant Physiol. 48: 300-302.

1987. Newman, D.W.; Rowell, B.W.; Byrd, K. 1973. LIPID TRANSFORMATIONS IN
GREENING AND SENESCING LEAF TISSUE. Plant Physiol. 51: 229-233.

1988. Newman, I.A.; Briggs, W.R. 1971. PHYTOCHROME MEDIATED ELECTRIC POTEN-
TIAL CHANGES ON OAT SEEDLINGS. Plant Physiol. 47: Suppl.-1, Abstr.
No. 6 (A).

1989. Newman, I.A.; Briggs, W.R. 1972. PHYTOCHROME-MEDIATED ELECTRIC POTEN-
TIAL CHANGES IN OAT SEEDLINGS. Plant Physiol. 50: 687-693.

1990. Newman, I.A. 1974. ELECTRIC RESPONSES OF OATS TO PHYTOCHROME TRANSFOR-
MATION. *Mechanisms of Regulation of Plant Growth*, Eds. R.L.
Bieleski; A.R. Ferguson; M.M. Cresswell. R. Soc. N.Z. Bull. 12:
355-360.

1991. Ng, M.Y.L.; Thimann, K.V.; Gordon, S.A. 1961. THE ACTION SPECTRUM FOR
ANTHOCYANIN FORMATION IN *SPIRODELA OLIGORRHIZA*. Plant Physiol. 36:
Suppl.-46 (A).

1992. Ng, Y.L.; Thimann, K.V.; Gordon, S.A. 1964. THE BIOGENESIS OF ANTHO-
CYANINS X. THE ACTION SPECTRUM FOR ANTHOCYANIN FORMATION IN *SPIRODELA
OLIGORRHIZA*. Arch. Biochem. Biophys. 107: 550-558.

1993. Nichiporovich, A.A. 1953. PRODUCTS OF PHOTOSYNTHESIS AND PHYSIOLOGICAL
ROLE OF PHOTOSYNTHETIC APPARATUS IN PLANTS. Trudy Inst. Fiziol.
Rast. im: K.A. Timiryazeva, Akad. Nauk SSSR 8: 3-41 (RUS) (not
obtained).

1994. Nichiporovich, A.A.; Andreyeva, T.F.; Voskresenskaya, N.P.; Nezgovorova,
L.A.; Novitzky, Y.I. 1957. VARIOUS WAYS OF TRANSFORMATION OF CAR-
BON ASSIMILATED BY PLANTS IN THE PROCESS OF PHOTOSYNTHESIS. Proc. of
the first (UNESCO) Int. Conf. Radio. Isotopes Scientific Research,
Paris 4: 411-431.

1995. Nichiporovich, A.A.; Voskresenskaya, N.P.; Butenko, R.G. 1961. EFFECT
OF RADIATION OF VARIOUS WAVE LENGTH REGIONS ON PLANT COMPOSITION.
Rec. Adv. Bot. 2: 1039-1046 (R-D).

1996. Niemann, G.J. 1967. A RED-LIGHT-DEPENDENT COMPOUND IN *PISUM SATIVUM*.
Acta Bot. Neerl. 16: 180-181.

1997. Ninnemann, H.; Halbsguth, W. 1965. ROLLE DES PHYTOCHROMS BEIM ETIOLE-
MENT VON *MARCHANTIA POLYMORPHA*. Naturwissenschaften 52: 110-111.

1998. Ninnemann, H. 1967. ÜBER DIE BETEILIGUNG VON WUCHSSTOFFEN, PHYTOCHROM,
NUCLEINSÄURE- UND PROTEIN-SYNTHESE BEIM ETIOLEMENT DER BRUTKÖRPER
VON *MARCHANTIA POLYMORPHA*. Biol. Zentralbl. 86: 303-364 (ENG
Summary).

1999. Nitsch, C.; Nitsch, J.P. 1966. EFFET DE LA LUMIÈRE SUR L'INDUCTION DE LA PHÉNYLALANINE-DÉAMINASE DANS LES TISSUS DE TUBERCULE D'*HELIANTHUS TUBEROSUS* L. C.R. Acad. Sci. Ser. D. 262: 1102-1105.

2000. Nitsch, J.P.; Nitsch, C. 1956. AUXIN-DEPENDENT GROWTH OF EXCISED *HELIANTHUS TUBEROSUS* TISSUES. Am. J. Bot. 43: 839-851.

2001. Nitsch, J.P.; Somogyi, L. 1958. LE PHOTOPÉRIODISME DES PLANTES LIGNEUSES. Ann. Soc. Nat. Hortic. Fr. 466-490.

2002. Nitsch, J.P. 1959. RÉACTIONS PHOTOPÉRIODIQUES CHEZ LES PLANTES LIGNEUSES. Bull. Soc. Bot. Fr. 106: 259-287.

2003. Nitsch, J.P.; Nitsch, C. 1962. ACTIVITÉS COMPARÉES DE NEUF GIBBÉREL-LINES SUR TROIS TESTS BIOLOGIQUES. Physiol. Veg. 4: 85-97 (ENG Summary).

2004. Nitsch, J.P. 1963. THE MEDIATION OF CLIMATIC EFFECTS THROUGH ENDOGENOUS REGULATING SUBSTANCES. Symp. on Environmental Control of Plant Growth, Canberra, Australia, August, 1962 pp. 175-194 (R).

2005. Nobbe, F. 1881. ÜBER DEN WASSERVERBRAUCH ZWEIJÄHRIGER ERLEN UNTER VERSCHIEDENEN BELEUCHTUNGS-BEDINGUNGEN. Landwitsch. Vers-Stn. 26: 354-355.

2006. Nuernbergk, E. 1925. BEITRÄGE ZUR PHYSIOLOGIE DES TAGESSCHLAFS DER PFLANZEN. Botanische abhandlungen 1: 4-138.

2007. Nuernbergk, E.L. 1954. DAS WIRKUNGSSPEKTRUM DES PHOTOPERIODISMUS UND PHOTOFORMATIVEN EFFEKTENS. ZUR TECHNIK DER STRAHLUNGSMESSUNGEN. Z. Bot. 42: 247-282 (R).

2008. Nwachuku, N.I.C.; Lockhart, J.A. 1964. HYPOCOTYL ELONGATION IN MUSTARD AND MUNG BEAN SEEDLINGS AS INFLUENCED BY LIGHT, GIBBERELLIN, AND CHLOROCHOLINE CHLORIDE. Physiol. Plant. 17: 725-736.

2009. Nyman, B. 1958. ON THE REASONS FOR PINE SEEDS' NEED OF LIGHT DURING GERMINATION. Rep. I Swedish Conf. Cell Res. (1957) Ark. Zool. Ser. 2, 11: 122-123.

2010. Nyman, B. 1961. EFFECT OF RED AND FAR-RED IRRADIATION ON THE GERMINA-TION PROCESS IN SEEDS OF *PINUS SYLVESTRIS* L. Nature (London) 191: 1219-1220.

2011. Nyman, B. 1963. STUDIES ON THE GERMINATION IN SEEDS OF SCOTS PINE (*PINUS SILVESTRIS* L.) WITH SPECIAL REFERENCE TO THE LIGHT FACTOR. Stud. For. Suec. 2: 1-164.

2012. Nyman, B. 1967. HELLROT-DUNKELROTEFFEKTE AUF DIE SAMENKEIMUNG DER
KIEFER. Proc. Int. Symp. Physiol. Ecol. Biochem. Germination,
Ed. H. Borriss, Griefswald; Ernst-Moritz-Arndt University 1967 1:
pp. 171-173.

2013. Nyman, B. 1969. STUDIES ON SUGARS AND STARCH IN LICHT- AND DARK-GERMI-
NATED SEEDS OF SCOTS PINE (*PINUS SILVESTRIS*). Physiol. Plant. 22:
441-452 (R).

2014. Oberdorfer, U. 1973. DIE ZWEIFACHE WIRKUNG VON PHYTOCHROM AUF BILDUNG
UND AKKUMULATION VON CHLOROPHYLL A. Ph.D. Thesis, Univ. Freiburg,
Germany.

2015. Oda, Y. 1962. EFFECT OF LIGHT QUALITY ON FLOWERING OF *LEMNA PERPUSILLA*
6746. Plant Cell Physiol. 3: 415-417.

2016. Oelze-Karow, H. 1969. DIE REPRESSION DER LIPOXYGENASE-SYNTHESE DURCH
PHYTOCHROM WÄHREND DER PHOTOMORPHOGENESE DES SENFKEIMLINGS (*SINAPIS
ALBA* L.) EIN SCHWELLENWERT-PHÄNOMEN. Ph.D. Thesis, Univ. Freiburg,
Germany.

2017. Oelze-Karow, H.; Mohr, H. 1970. EXPERIMENTS REGARDING THE PROBLEM OF
DIFFERENTIATION IN MULTICELLULAR SYSTEMS. Z. Naturforsch. Teil B.
25: 1282-1286.

2018. Oelze-Karow, H.; Schopfer, P.; Mohr, H. 1970. PHYTOCHROME-MEDIATED
REPRESSION OF ENZYME SYNTHESIS (LIPOXYGENASE): A THRESHOLD PHENOME-
NON. Proc. Nat. Acad. Sci. USA 65: 51-57.

2019. Oelze-Karow, H.; Mohr, H. 1971. DOUBLE ACTION MECHANISM IN PHYTOCHROME
MEDIATED DIFFERENTIATION. Proc. Eur. Annu. Symp. Plant Photomorphogenesis, (Athens), p. 37 (A).

2020. Oelze-Karow, H.; Mohr, H. 1972. REPRESSION OF LIPOXYGENASE SYNTHESIS
IN PLANT TISSUE THROUGH A THRESHOLD MECHANISM (COTYLEDONS OF MUS-
TARD SEEDLINGS). Proc. VI Int. Congr. Photobiol. Abstr. No. 162
(A).

2021. Oelze-Karow, H.; Mohr, H. 1973. QUANTITATIVE CORRELATION BETWEEN
SPECTROPHOTOMETRIC PHYTOCHROME ASSAY AND PHYSIOLOGICAL RESPONSE.
Photochem. Photobiol. 18: 319-330.

2022. Oelze-Karow, H.; Mohr, H. 1974. INTERORGAN CORRELATION IN A PHYTO-
CHROME-MEDIATED RESPONSE IN THE MUSTARD SEEDLING. Proc. Eur. Annu.
Symp. Plant Photomorphogenesis, (Antwerpen), pp. 126-127.

2023. Oelze-Karow, H.; Mohr, H. 1974. INTERORGAN CORRELATION IN A PHYTO-CHROME-MEDIATED RESPONSE IN THE MUSTARD SEEDLING. Photochem. Photo-biol. 20: 127-131.

2024. Ogasawara, N.; Miyachi, S. 1970. REGULATION OF CO_2-FIXATION IN *CHLORELLA* BY LIGHT OF VARIED WAVELENGTHS AND INTENSITIES. Plant Cell Physiol. 11: 1-14.

2025. Ogasawara, N.; Miyachi, S. 1970. EFFECTS OF DISALICYLIDENEPROPANDIA-MINE AND NEAR FAR-RED LIGHT ON $^{14}CO_2$-FIXATION IN *CHLORELLA* CELLS. Plant Cell Physiol. 11: 411-416.

2026. Ogasawara, N.; Miyachi, S. 1971. EFFECTS OF DARK PREINCUBATION AND CHLORAMPHENICOL ON BLUE-LIGHT INDUCED CO_2 INCORPORATION IN *CHLORELLA* CELLS. Plant Cell Physiol. 12: 675-682.

2027. Ogawa, Y. 1961. ÜBER DIE WIRKUNG VON KINETIN AUF DIE BLÜTENBILDUNG VON *PHARBITIS NIL* CHOIS. Plant Cell Physiol. 2: 343-359.

2028. Ogawara, K.; Ono, K. 1957. REVERSIBLE PHOTOCONTROL OF THE GERMINATION IN LIGHT-FAVORED TOBACCO SEEDS. Bull. Sch. Educ., Okayama Univ., No. 4: 52-67.

2029. Ogawara, K.; Ono, K. 1958. EFFECTS OF LIGHT ON THE GERMINATION OF *PETUNIA HYBRIDA* SEEDS. Engei Gakkai Zasshi 27: 276-281 (JAP) (ENG Summary).

2030. Ogawara, K.; Ono, K. 1961. INTERACTION OF GIBBERELLIN, KINETIN AND POTASSIUM NITRATE IN THE GERMINATION OF LIGHT-SENSITIVE TOBACCO SEEDS. Plant Cell Physiol. 2: 87-98.

2031. Ohlenroth, K. 1963. PROTEINSYNTHESE UND PHOTOMORPHOGENESE EIN BEITRAG ZUR KAUSALANALYZE DER MORPHOGENESE VON FARNGAMETOPHYTEN (*DRYOPTERIS FILIX-MAS*). Ph.D. Thesis, Univ. Freiburg, Germany.

2032. Ohlenroth, K.; Mohr, H. 1963. DIE STEUERUNG DER PROTEINSYNTHESE UND DER MORPHOGENESE BEI FARNVORKEIMEN DURCH LICHT. Planta 59: 427-441 (ENG Summary).

2033. Ohlenroth, K.; Mohr, H. 1964. DIE STEUERUNG DER PROTEINSYNTHESE DURCH BLAULICHT UND HELLROT IN DEN VORKEIMEN VON *DRYOPTERIS FILIX-MAS* (L.) SCHOTT. Planta 62: 160-170 (ENG Summary).

2034. Ohno, Y.; Fujiwara, A. 1967. PHOTOINHIBITION OF ELONGATION GROWTH OF ROOTS IN RICE SEEDLINGS. Plant Cell Physiol. 8: 141-150.

2035. O'Kelley, J.C.; Durant, J.P.; Stockdale, D.L. 1974. BLUE AND GREEN
LIGHT EFFECTS, AND THEIR PHOTOREVERSIBILITY, UPON ZOOSPORE PRODUCTION
AND THE SYNCHRONIZED CYCLE IN *PROTOSIPHON BOTRYOIDES* KLEBS. Photo-
chem. Photobiol. 20: 47-51.

2036. Okoloko, G.E. 1969. RIBONUCLEIC ACID METABOLISM IN THE PEA EPICOTYL IN
RELATION TO PHYTOCHROME AND HORMONE REGULATED ELONGATION. Ph.D.
Thesis, Univ. Calif., Riverside.

2037. Okoloko, G.E.; Lewis, L.N.; Reid, B.R. 1970. CHANGES IN NUCLEIC ACIDS
IN PHYTOCHROME-DEPENDENT ELONGATION OF THE ALASKA PEA EPICOTYL.
Plant Physiol. 46: 660-665.

2038. Okuntsov, M.M.; Kotlyarova, G.M. 1964. PHOTOCHEMICAL BIOSYNTHESIS OF
ASCORBIC ACID IN PLANT LEAVES. Rabotyl Probl. Lab. Kafedre Fiziol.
i Biokhim. Rast., Tomskii Univ., pp. 34-68 (RUS).

2039. Okuntsov, M.M.; Ronzhina, O.A.; Simonova, E.I. 1970. EFFECT OF RED
LIGHT ON CHLOROPHYLL BIOSYNTHESIS IN ETIOLATED PLANTS. Vopr. Fotosint., pp. 188-192 (RUS).

2040. Olatoye, S.T.; Hall, M.A. 1973. INTERACTION OF ETHYLENE AND LIGHT ON
DORMANT WEED SEEDS. Proc. Easter Sch. Agric. Sci. 19th, Univ.
Nottingham, pp. 233-249.

2041. Ono, K.; Ogawara, K. 1959. STUDIES ON THE GERMINATION OF *DIGITALIS
PURPUREA* SEEDS. Bull. Sch. Educ. Okayama Univ., No. 8, pp. 103-109.

2042. Oota, Y. 1970. PERIODICAL GROWTH RESPONSE OF *LEMNA GIBBA* G3 TO LIGHT-
BREAK. Plant Cell Physiol. 11: 417-425.

2043. Orlandini, M.; Malcoste, R. 1972. ETUDE DU PHYTOCHROME DES GRAINES DE
PINUS NIGRA ARN PAR SPECTROPHOTOMÉTRIE BICHROMATIQUE *IN VIVO*. Planta
105: 310-316 (ENG Summary).

2044. Orsenigo, M.; Marziani, G.; Albergoni, F. 1966. RICERCHE SULLA MORFO-
GENESI DEI PLASTIDI CLOROFILLIANI II. EFFETTO DELLA LUCE ROSSO CHIARA
E ROSSO SCURA SULL'EVOLUZIONE DEL PLASTIDIO "EZIOLATO". Nuovo Gi.
Bot. Ital. 73: 1-10 (ENG Summary).

2045. Orth, R. 1937. ZUR KEIMUNGSPHYSIOLOGIE DER FARNSPOREN IN VERSCHIEDENEN
SPEKTRALBEZIRKEN. Jahrb. Wiss. Bot. 84: 358-426.

2046. Ortwerth, B.J.; Koeppe, O.J. 1966. LIGHT DEPENDENT INCREASE OF TRIO-
SEPHOSPHATE DEHYDROGENASE IN PEA LEAVES. Plant Physiol. 41:
1213-1217.

2047. Paetz, K.W. 1930. UNTERSUCHUNGEN ÜBER DIE ZUSAMMENHÄNGE ZWISCHEN STOMATÄREN ÖFFNUNGSWEITE UND BEKANNTEN INTENSITÄTEN BESTIMMTER SPEKTRALBEZIRKE. Planta 10: 611-665.

2048. Paleg, L.G. 1965. PHYSIOLOGICAL EFFECTS OF GIBBERELLINS. Annu. Rev. Plant Physiol. 16: 291-322 (R).

2049. Paleg, L.G.; Aspinall, D. 1970. FIELD CONTROL OF PLANT GROWTH AND DE- VELOPMENT THROUGH THE LASER ACTIVATION OF PHYTOCHROME. Nature (London) 228: 970-973.

2050. Panasyuk, N.V.; Vasileiko, O.V. 1973. EFFECT OF RED AND FAR RED LIGHT ON SEED GERMINATION OF INTRODUCED TREE SPECIES. UKR Bot. Zh. 30: 784-786 (UKR) (Eng Summary).

2051. Pandey, S.B. 1965. INTERACTION BETWEEN SEED COLOUR AND LIGHT ON GERMI- NATION. Sci. Cult. 31: 586-587.

2052. Pandey, S.B. 1969. PHOTOCONTROL OF SEED GERMINATION IN *ANAGALLIS ARVENSIS* LINN. Trop. Ecol. 10: 96-138.

2053. Papenfuss, H.D.; Salisbury, F.B. 1966. LIGHT PROMOTION OF FLOWERING AND TIME MEASUREMENT IN *XANTHIUM*. Z. Pflanzenphysiol. 54: 195-202.

2054. Parker, M.W.; Hendricks, S.B.; Borthwick, H.A.; Scully, N.J. 1945. ACTION SPECTRUM FOR THE PHOTOPERIODIC CONTROL OF FLORAL INITIATION IN BILOXI SOYBEAN. Science 102: 152-155.

2055. Parker, M.W.; Hendricks, S.B.; Borthwick, H.A.; Scully, N.J. 1946. ACTION SPECTRUM FOR THE PHOTOPERIODIC CONTROL OF FLORAL INITIATION OF SHORT-DAY PLANTS. Bot. Gaz. (Chicago) 108: 1-26.

2056. Parker, M.W.; Hendricks, S.B.; Borthwick, H.A.; Went, F.W. 1949. SPECTRAL SENSITIVITIES FOR LEAF AND STEM GROWTH OF ETIOLATED PEA SEEDLINGS AND THEIR SIMILARITY TO ACTION SPECTRA FOR PHOTOPERIODISM. Am. J. Bot. 36: 194-204.

2057. Parker, M.W.; Borthwick, H.A. 1950. INFLUENCE OF LIGHT ON PLANT GROWTH. Annu. Rev. Plant Physiol. 1: 43-58 (R).

2058. Parker, M.W.; Hendricks, S.B.; Borthwick, H.A. 1950. ACTION SPECTRUM FOR THE PHOTOPERIODIC CONTROL OF FLORAL INITIATION OF THE LONG-DAY PLANT *HYOSCYAMUS NIGER*. Bot. Gaz. (Chicago) 111: 242-252.

2059. Parker, M.W.; Hendricks, S.B.; Borthwick, H.A.; Jenner, C.E. 1952. PHOTOPERIODIC RESPONSES OF PLANTS AND ANIMALS. Nature (London) 169: 242-243 (R).

2060. Paul, R.; Furuya, M. 1973. PHYTOCHROME ACTION IN *ORYZA SATIVA* L. VI. RED FAR-RED REVERSIBLE EFFECT ON EARLY DEVELOPMENT OF COLEOPTILES. Bot. Mag. 86: 203-211.

2061. Payer, H.D. 1968. DER EINFLUSS DER LICHTQUALITÄT AUF DIE AUFNAHME VON $^{14}CO_2$ UND AUF DIE VERTEILUNG DES ^{14}C IM STOFFWECHSEL (UNTERSUCHUNGEN AN FARNGAMETOPHYTEN, *DRYOPTERIS FILIX-MAS* (L.) SCHOTT. Ph.D. Thesis, Univ. Freiburg, Germany.

2062. Payer, H.D. 1969. UNTERSUCHUNGEN ZUR KOMPARTIMENTIERUNG DER FREIEN AMINOSÄURE ALANIN IN DEN FARNVORKEIMEN VON *DRYOPTERIS FILIX-MAS* (L.) SCHOTT IM ROTLICHT UND IM BLAULICHT. Planta 86: 103-115 (ENG Summary).

2063. Payer, H.D.; Mohr, H. 1969. EIN SPEZIFISCHER EINFLUSS VON BLAULICHT AUF DEN EINBAU VON PHOTOSYNTHETISCH ASSIMILIERTEM ^{14}C IN DAS PROTEIN VON FARNVORKEIMEN (*DRYOPTERIS FILIX-MAS* (L.) SCHOTT). Planta 86: 286-294 (ENG Summary).

2064. Payer, H.D.; Sotriffer, U.; Mohr, H. 1969. DIE AUFNAHME VON $^{14}CO_2$ UND DIE VERTEILUNG DES ^{14}C AUF FREIE AMINOSÄUREN UND AUF PROTEINAMINO-SÄUREN IM HELLROT UND IM BLAULICHT. [OBJEKT: FARNVORKEIME VON *DRYOPTERIS FILIX-MAS* (L. SCHOTT)]. Planta 85: 270-283 (ENG Summary).

2065. Pearce, G.W.; Streeter, L.R. 1931. A REPORT ON THE EFFECT OF LIGHT ON PIGMENT FORMATION IN APPLES. J. Biol. Chem. 92: 743-749.

2066. Pecket, R.C.; Bassim, T.A.H. 1974. MECHANISM OF PHYTOCHROME ACTION IN THE CONTROL OF BIOSYNTHESIS OF ANTHOCYANIN IN *BRASSICA OLERACEA*. Phytochemistry 13: 815-821.

2067. Pecket, R.C.; Bassim, T.A.H. 1974. THE EFFECT OF KINETIN IN RELATION TO PHOTOCONTROL OF ANTHOCYANIN BIOSYNTHESIS IN *BRASSICA OLERACEA*. Phytochemistry 13: 1395-1399.

2068. Penel, C.; Greppin, H. 1973. ACTION DES LUMIÈRES ROUGE ET INFRA-ROUGE SUR L'ACTIVITÉ PEROXYDASIQUE DES FEUILLES D'ÉPINARDS AVANT ET APRÈS L'INDUCTION FLORALE. Ber. Schweiz. Bot. Ges. 83: 253-261 (ENG, GER Summary).

2069. Penel, C.; Greppin, H. 1974. VARIATION DE LA PHOTOSTIMULATION DE L'ACTIVITÉ DES PEROXYDASES BASIQUES CHEZ L'ÉPINARD. Plant Sci. Lett. 3: 75-80 (ENG Summary).

2070. Perrin, G. 1908. INFLUENCE DES CONDITIONS EXTÉRIEURES SUR LE DÉVELOPPE-
MENT ET LA SEXUALITÉ DES PROTHALLES DE POLYPODIACÉES. C.R. Acad.
Sci. Ser. D. 147: 433-435.

2071. Peter, K.; Mohr, H. 1974. CONTROL OF PHENYLALANINE AMMONIA-LYASE AND
ASCORBATE OXIDASE IN THE MUSTARD SEEDLING BY LIGHT AND HOAGLAND'S
NUTRIENT SOLUTION. Z. Naturforsch. Teil C. 29: 222-228.

2072. Peterson, D.M. 1969. HOOK OPENING: REGULATION BY RED LIGHT, AUXIN AND
ETHYLENE. Proc. XI Int. Bot. Congr., p. 168 (A).

2073. Pfaff, W.; Schopfer, P. 1974. PHYTOCHROM-INDUZIERTE REGENERATION VON
ADVENTIVWURZELN BEIM SENFKEIMLING (*SINAPIS ALBA* L.). Planta 117:
269-278 (ENG Summary).

2074. Pfeffer, W. 1904. PFLANZENPHYSIOLOGIE, EIN HANDBUCH DER LEHRE VOM
STOFFWECHSEL UND KRAFTWECHSEL IN DER PFLANZE. Leipzig, Verlag
Wilhelm Engelmann, 2 Aufl. pp. 117-122; 252-278 (R).

2075. Pfeiffer, N.E. 1928. ANATOMICAL STUDY OF PLANTS GROWN UNDER GLASSES
TRANSMITTING LIGHT OF VARIOUS RANGES OF WAVE LENGTHS. Bot. Gaz.
(Chicago) 85: 427-436.

2076. Phillips, I.D.J.; Vlitos, A.J.; Cutler, H. 1959. THE INFLUENCE OF
GIBBERELLIC ACID UPON THE ENDOGENOUS GROWTH SUBSTANCES OF THE ALASKA
PEA. Contrib. Boyce Thompson Inst. 20: 111-120.

2077. Piattelli, M.; Giudici de Nicola, M.; Castrogiovanni, V. 1969. PHOTO-
CONTROL OF AMARANTHIN SYNTHESIS IN *AMARANTHUS TRICOLOR*. Phytochemistry 8: 731-736.

2078. Piattelli, M.; Giudici de Nicola, M.; Castrogiovanni, V. 1970. THE
INHIBITION BY ACTINOMYCIN D AND PUROMYCIN OF LIGHT-STIMULATED
AMARANTHIN SYNTHESIS. Phytochemistry 9: 785-789.

2079. Piattelli, M.; Giudici de Nicola, M.; Castrogiovanni, V. 1971. THE
EFFECT OF KINETIN ON AMARANTHIN SYNTHESIS IN *AMARANTHUS TRICOLOR* IN
DARKNESS. Phytochemistry 10: 289-293.

2080. Pick, H. 1883. UEBER DIE BEDEUTUNG DES ROTHEN FARBSTOFFES BEI DEN
PHANEROGAMEN UND DIE BEZIEHUNGEN DESSELBEN ZUR STÄRKEWANDERUNG. Bot.
Zentral. 16: 281-284; 314-318; 343-347; 375-383.

2081. Pike, C.S. 1971. STUDIES ON A NEUTRAL OAT PROTEASE AND ON PHYTOCHROME
DARK REACTIONS. Ph.D. Thesis, Harvard Univ., Cambridge.

2082. Pike, C.S.; Briggs, W.R. 1971. PARTIAL PURIFICATION AND PROPERTIES OF A PHYTOCHROME-DESTROYING PROTEASE FROM ETIOLATED *AVENA* SHOOTS. Plant Physiol. 47: Suppl.-1, Abstr. No. 1 (A).

2083. Pike, C.S.; Briggs, W.R. 1972. THE DARK REACTIONS OF RYE PHYTOCHROME *IN VIVO* AND *IN VITRO*. Plant Physiol. 49: 514-520.

2084. Pike, C.S.; Briggs, W.R. 1972. PARTIAL PURIFICATION AND CHARACTERIZATION OF A PHYTOCHROME-DEGRADING NEUTRAL PROTEASE FROM ETIOLATED OAT SHOOTS. Plant Physiol. 49: 521-530.

2085. Pike, C.S.; Kirschner, R.L. 1974. INVOLVEMENT OF REGULATORY MOLECULES IN THE PHYTOCHROME CONTROL OF BEAN BUD ATP LEVELS. Plant Physiol. 53: Suppl.-45, Abstr. No. 254 (A).

2086. Pilet, P.E. 1951. CONTRIBUTION À L'ÉTUDE DES HORMONES DE CROISSANCE (AUXINES) DANS LA RACINE DE *LENS CULINARIS* MEDIKUS. Mem. Soc. Vaudoise Sci. Nat. 10: 137-244.

2087. Pine, K.S. 1971. REGULATION OF POLYRIBOSOME FORMATION IN ETIOLATED BEAN LEAVES BY LIGHT. Ph.D. Thesis, Brandeis Univ., Waltham.

2088. Pine, K.; Klein, A.O. 1972. REGULATION OF POLYSOME FORMATION IN ETIOLATED BEAN LEAVES BY LIGHT. Dev. Biol. 28: 280-289.

2089. Piringer, A.A.; Downs, R.J.; Hendricks, S.B.; Borthwick, H.A. 1954. A REVERSIBLE PHOTOREACTION CONTROLLING PHOTOPERIODIC RESPONSE, SEED GERMINATION AND OTHER PHENOMENA. Proc. VIII Int. Bot. Congr. 321-323 (A) (R).

2090. Piringer, A.A.; Heinze, P.H. 1954. EFFECT OF LIGHT ON THE FORMATION OF A PIGMENT IN THE TOMATO FRUIT CUTICLE. Plant Physiol. 29: 467-472.

2091. Piringer, A.A.; Downs, R.J. 1959. PHOTOPERIOD CONTROL OF FLOWER DEVELOPMENT IN *CARYOPTERIS*. Plant Physiol. 34: Suppl.-4 (A).

2092. Piringer, A.A. 1961. PHOTOPERIOD, SUPPLEMENTAL LIGHT, AND ROOTING OF CUTTINGS. Proc. II Annu. Meet. West. Plant Propagators Conf., 4 pp. (R).

2093. Piringer, A.A. 1962. PHOTOPERIODIC RESPONSES OF VEGETABLE PLANTS. Proc. Plant Sci. Symp. Campbell Soup Co., pp. 173-184 (R).

2094. Piringer, A.A.; Downs, R.J.; Borthwick, H.A. 1963. PHOTOCONTROL OF GROWTH AND FLOWERING OF *CARYOPTERIS*. Am. J. Bot. 50: 86-90.

2095. Pirson, A.; Kowallik, W. 1960. WIRKUNG DES BLAUEN UND ROTEN SPEKTRALBEREICHES AUF DIE ZUSAMMENSETZUNG VON *CHLORELLA* BEI ANZUCHT IM LICHT-DUNKEL-WECHSEL. Naturwissenschaften 47: 476-477.

2096. Pirson, A.; Kowallik, W. 1964. SPECTRAL RESPONSES TO LIGHT BY UNI-
CELLULAR PLANTS. Photochem. Photobiol. 3: 489-497.

2097. Pittauer, G. 1912. ÜBER DEN EINFLUSS VERSCHIEDENER BELICHTUNG UND
EXTREMER TEMPERATUREN AUF DEN VERLAUF DER KEIMUNG FORSTLICHEN
SAATGUTES. Centratbl. Gesamte Forstwes. 38: 157-172, 213-224.

2098. Pizzolongo, P. 1965. SUL COMPORTAMENTO DELLE PLANTULE DI *CUSCUTA
PENTAGONA* ENGEL. A LUCE MONOCHROMATICA ED AL BUIO. Ann. Fac. Sci.
Agric. Univ. Studi. Napoli, Portici 1: 116-125 (ENG Summary).

2099. Pjon, C.-J.; Furuya, M. 1967. PHYTOCHROME ACTION IN *ORYZA SATIVA* L. I.
GROWTH RESPONSES OF ETIOLATED COLEOPTILES TO RED, FAR-RED AND BLUE
LIGHT. Plant Cell Physiol. 8: 709-718.

2100. Pjon, C.-J.; Furuya, M. 1968. PHYTOCHROME ACTION IN *ORYZA SATIVA* L.
II. THE SPECTROPHOTOMETRIC VERSUS THE PHYSIOLOGICAL STATUS OF PHYTO-
CHROME IN COLEOPTILES. Planta 81: 303-313.

2101. Pjon, C.-J.; Furuya, M. 1974. PHYTOCHROME ACTION IN *ORYZA SATIVA* L.
VII. EFFECTS OF LIGHT AND AERATION ON COLEOPTILE GROWTH UNDER SUB-
MERGED CONDITIONS. Plant Cell Physiol. 15: 663-668.

2102. Pleasanton, A.J. 1871. *ON THE INFLUENCE OF THE BLUE COLOR OF THE SKY
IN DEVELOPING ANIMAL AND VEGETABLE LIFE.* Inquirer Book and Job
Print, Philadelphia, 24 pp.

2103. Polevaya, V.S. 1967. EFFECT OF LIGHT OF DIFFERENT SPECTRAL COMPOSI-
TIONS ON THE GROWTH OF ISOLATED CARROT TISSUE CULTURES. Fiziol.
Rast. 14: 48-56 (RUS) (Consultants Bureau English Translation,
pp. 41-48).

2104. Polevaya, V.S. 1967. EFFECT OF LIGHT OF VARIOUS SPECTRAL COMPOSITIONS
ON SOME ASPECTS OF AUXIN METABOLISM IN CULTURES OF ISOLATED CARROT
TISSUE. Fiziol. Rast. 14: 582-591 (RUS) (Consultants Bureau English
Translation, pp. 496-503).

2105. Poljakoff-Mayber, A. 1952. GERMINATION INHIBITORS AND PLANT ENZYME
SYSTEMS I. CATALASE. Bull. Res. Counc. Isr. Sect. D. 2: 239-245.

2106. Poljakoff-Mayber, A. 1958. THE EFFECT OF EOSIN ON GERMINATION OF
LETTUCE SEEDS. Bull. Res. Counc. Isr. Sect. D. 6: 82-85.

2107. Poljakoff-Mayber, A.; Evenari, M.; Neumann, G. 1958. EFFECT OF RED
LIGHT AND GIBBERELLIC ACID ON THE TEMPERATURE-INHIBITED GERMINATION
OF LETTUCE SEEDS. Bull. Res. Counc. Isr. Sect. D. 6: 99-102.

2108. Ponce, M.; Wulff, R. 1973. FOTOCONTROL DE LA GERMINACION EN SEMILLAS DE *JUSSIAEA PERUVIANA*. Acta Cient. Venez. Suppl. 24: 34 (A).

2109. Popp, H.W. 1926. A PHYSIOLOGICAL STUDY OF THE EFFECT OF LIGHT OF VARIOUS RANGES OF WAVE LENGTH ON THE GROWTH OF PLANTS. Am. J. Bot. 13: 706-736.

2110. Popp, H.W.; Brown, F. 1936. EFFECTS OF DIFFERENT REGIONS OF THE VISIBLE SPECTRUM UPON SEED PLANTS. *Biological Effects of Radiation*, Ed. B.M. Dugger, McGraw-Hill, New York, II: 763-790 (R).

2111. Popp, H.W.; Brown, F. 1936. THE EFFECT OF ULTRA-VIOLET RADIATION UPON SEED PLANTS. *Biological Effects of Radiation*, Ed. B.M. Duggar, McGraw-Hill, New York, II: 853-887 (R).

2112. Popp, H.W.; McIlvaine, H.R.C. 1937. RADIATION AND PLANT GROWTH SUBSTANCES. Am. J. Bot. 24: 738 (A).

2113. Popp, H.W.; McIlvaine, H.R.C. 1937. GROWTH SUBSTANCES IN RELATION TO THE MECHANISM OF THE ACTION OF RADIATION ON PLANTS. J. Agr. Res. Washington, D.C. 55: 931-936.

2114. Popp, H.W.; Charlton, F.B. 1938. EFFECTS OF ULTRAVIOLET RADIATION UPON GERMINATION AND SEEDLING DEVELOPMENT. Pa. Agric. Exp. Stn. Bull. No. 366: 1-50.

2115. Porath, D.; Ben-Shaul, Y. 1972. SPECTROPHOTOMETRIC SURVEY OF PHYTOCHROME IN *SPIRODELA* SPP. Proc. VI Int. Congr. Photobiol. Abstr. No. 159 (A).

2116. Porath, D.; Ben-Shaul, Y. 1973. GROWTH, GREENING, AND PHYTOCHROME IN ETIOLATED *SPIRODELA* (LEMNACEAE). Plant Physiol. 51: 474-477.

2117. Posner, H.B. 1969. ELONGATION AND SPECTROPHOTOMETRICALLY ASSAYABLE PHYTOCHROME OF X-IRRADIATED STEM SEGMENTS FROM ETIOLATED *PISUM SATIVUM*. Radiat. Bot. 9: 353-355.

2118. Possingham, J.V. 1973. EFFECT OF LIGHT QUALITY ON CHLOROPLAST REPLICATION IN SPINACH. J. Exp. Bot. 24: 1247-1260.

2119. Poulson, R.; Beevers, L. 1969. THE INFLUENCE OF GROWTH REGULATORS ON THE UNROLLING OF BARLEY LEAF SECTIONS. Plant Physiol. 44: Suppl.-29, Abstr. No. 137 (A).

2120. Powell, R.D. 1958. EFFECT OF LIGHT AND TEMPERATURE ON GERMINATION OF TOBACCO SEED. Plant Physiol. 33: Suppl.-23 (A).

2121. Powell, R.D.; Griffith, M.M. 1960. SOME ANATOMICAL EFFECTS OF KINETIN
AND RED LIGHT ON DISKS OF BEAN LEAVES. Plant Physiol. 35: 273-275.

2122. Powell, R.D.; Griffith, M.M. 1961. THE EFFECT OF γ-RADIATION ON RED
LIGHT INDUCED GROWTH OF BEAN LEAVES TREATED WITH KINETIN AND
GIBBERELLIN. Plant Physiol. 36: Suppl.-43 (A).

2123. Powell, R.D. 1963. A SIMPLE EXPERIMENT FOR STUDYING THE EFFECT OF RED
AND FAR-RED LIGHT ON GROWTH OF LEAF DISKS. Am. Biol. Teach. 25:
107-109.

2124. Powell, R.D.; Griffith, M.M. 1963. EFFECTS OF KINETIN, RED LIGHT, AND
GAMMA RADIATION ON GROWTH OF DISKS OF BEAN LEAVES. Bot. Gaz.
(Chicago) 124: 274-278.

2125. Powell, R.D.; Morgan, P.W. 1970. FACTORS INVOLVED IN THE OPENING OF
THE HYPOCOTYL HOOK OF COTTON AND BEANS. Plant Physiol. 45: 548-552.

2126. Prantl, K. 1879. UEBER DEN EINFLUSS DES LICHTES AUF DIE BILATERALITÄT
DER FARNPROTHALLIEN. Bot. Ztg. 37: 697-703.

2127. Pratt, L.H.; Briggs, W.R. 1966. PHOTOCHEMICAL AND NONPHOTOCHEMICAL
REACTIONS OF PHYTOCHROME *IN VIVO*. Plant Physiol. 41: 467-474.

2128. Pratt, L.H.; Butler, W.L. 1968. SPECTRAL INTERMEDIATES OF PHYTOCHROME
TRANSFORMATION ISOLATED AT LOW TEMPERATURES. Proc. V Int. Congr.
Photobiol., p. 92 (A).

2129. Pratt, L.H.; Butler, W.L. 1968. STABILIZATION OF PHYTOCHROME INTER-
MEDIATES BY LOW TEMPERATURE. Photochem. Photobiol. 8: 477-485.

2130. Pratt, L.H.; Butler, W.L. 1969. TEMPERATURE DEPENDENCE OF PHYTOCHROME
TRANSFORMATION. Proc. XI Int. Bot. Congr., p. 173 (A).

2131. Pratt, L.H.; Butler, W.L. 1969. THE PHOTOTRANSFORMATION OF PHYTOCHROME
BY ULTRAVIOLET LIGHT. Plant Physiol. 44: Suppl.-18-19, Abstr. No.
86 (A).

2132. Pratt, L.H.; Butler, W.L. 1970. THE TEMPERATURE DEPENDENCE OF PHYTO-
CHROME TRANSFORMATIONS. Photochem. Photobiol. 11: 361-369.

2133. Pratt, L.H.; Butler, W.L. 1970. PHYTOCHROME CONVERSION BY ULTRAVIOLET
LIGHT. Photochem. Photobiol. 11: 503-509.

2134. Pratt, L.H. 1971. PHYTOCHROME LOCALIZATION BY AN UNLABELED ANTIBODY
ENZYME METHOD. Plant Physiol. 47: Suppl.-1, Abstr. No. 5 (A).

2135. Pratt, L.H.; Coleman, R.A. 1971. IMMUNOCYTOCHEMICAL LOCALIZATION OF
PHYTOCHROME. Proc. Nat. Acad. Sci. USA 68: 2431-2435.

2136. Pratt, L.H. 1973. MOLECULAR PROPERTIES OF PHYTOCHROME. What's New in Plant Physiol. 5: No. 5, 1-4 (R).

2137. Pratt, L.H. 1973. COMPARATIVE IMMUNOCHEMISTRY OF PHYTOCHROME. Plant Physiol. 51: 203-209.

2138. Pratt, L.H.; Coleman, R.A.; Kidd, G. 1973. AN IMMUNOLOGICAL APPROACH TO THE STUDY OF THE *IN VIVO* PHYTOCHROME DESTRUCTION REACTION. Plant Physiol. 51: Suppl.-53, Abstr. No. 285 (A).

2139. Pratt, L.H.; Coleman, R.A. 1974. PHYTOCHROME DISTRIBUTION IN ETIOLATED GRASS SEEDLINGS AS ASSAYED BY AN INDIRECT ANTIBODY-LABELLING METHOD. Am. J. Bot. 61: 195-202.

2140. Pratt, L.H.; Kidd, G.H.; Coleman, R.A. 1974. AN IMMUNOCHEMICAL CHARACTERIZATION OF THE PHYTOCHROME DESTRUCTION REACTION. Biochim. Biophys. Acta 365: 93-107.

2141. Preusse, M.; Wiegand, O.F. 1966. RESPONSES OF PERFUSED WHOLE SEEDLINGS OF *AVENA SATIVA* TO INDOLEACETIC ACID IN RED LIGHT AND DARKNESS. Plant Physiol. 41: Suppl.-16 (A).

2142. Price, L.; Klein, W.H. 1961. RED, FAR-RED RESPONSE AND CHLOROPHYLL SYNTHESIS. Plant Physiol. 36: 733-735.

2143. Price, L.; Klein, W.H. 1962. CHLOROPHYLL SYNTHESIS IN X-IRRADIATED ETIOLATED BEAN LEAF TISSUE. Radiat. Bot. 1962: 269-275.

2144. Price, L.; Mitrakos, K.; Klein, W.H. 1963. PHYTOCHROME MEDIATED CARBOHYDRATE RESPONSES IN ETIOLATED CORN LEAF SECTIONS. Plant Physiol. 38: Suppl.-5 (A).

2145. Price, L.; Mitrakos, K.; Klein, W.H. 1964. SYMPOSIUM ON PHOTOMORPHOGENESIS IN PLANTS III. PHOTOMORPHOGENESIS AND CARBOHYDRATE CHANGES IN ETIOLATED LEAF TISSUE. Q. Rev. Biol. 39: 11-18.

2146. Price, L.; Mitrakos, K.; Klein, W.H. 1965. SOME KINETICAL ASPECTS OF LIGHT-INDUCED CARBOHYDRATE UTILIZATION IN ETIOLATED LEAF TISSUE. Physiol. Plant. 18: 540-549.

2147. Pringsheim, E.G.; Pringsheim, O. 1935. PHYSIOLOGISCHE STUDIEN AN MOOSEN. 3. DIE ZÜCHTUNG VON LAUBMOOSPROTONEMEN IM DUNKELN. Jahrb. Wiss. Bot. 82: 311-332.

2148. Proctor, J.T.A. 1970. PHOTOCONTROL OF ANTHOCYANIN SYNTHESIS IN THE APPLE AND IN THE MUNG BEAN. Ph.D. Thesis, Cornell Univ., Ithaca.

2149. Pumpyanskaya, S.L.   1966.   INTERACTION OF HIGH-ENERGY, AND LOW ENERGY
REACTIONS AS THE MECHANISM OF ADAPTATION OF PLANTS TO SEASONAL
CHANGES OF EXTERNAL CONDITIONS.   Dokl. Acad. Nauk SSSR 168: 1427-
1429 (RUS) (R).

2150. Pumpyanskaya, S.L.   1967.   CONCERNING A POSSIBLE MECHANISM OF SEASONAL
RHYTHMS IN HIGHER PLANTS.   *Oscillatory Processes in Biological and
Chemical Systems*, Moscow, Izol. "Nayka" pp. 366-374 (RUS) (not
obtained).

2151. Purves, W.K.   1961.   DARK REACTIONS IN THE FLOWERING OF *LEMNA PERPUSILLA*
6746.   Planta 56: 684-690.

2152. Purves, W.K.; Briggs, W.R.   1968.   KINETICALLY SEPARABLE FORMS OF PHYTO-
CHROME DETECTED *IN VITRO* AND *IN VIVO*.   Proc. V Int. Congr. Photobiol., p. 93 (A).

2153. Purves, W.K.; Briggs, W.R.   1968.   KINETICALLY DISTINGUISHABLE POPULA-
TIONS OF PHYTOCHROME.   Plant Physiol. 43: 1259-1263.

2154. Pyrkosch, G.   1936.   LICHT UND TRANSPIRATIONSWIDERSTAND. 1. TEIL: DIE
TRANSPIRATIONSWIDERSTÄNDE IM MONOCHROMATISCHEN LICHT.   Protoplasma
26: 418-437.

2155. Quail, P.H.; Schäfer, E.; Marmé, D.   1972.   *DE NOVO* SYNTHESIS OF PHYTO-
CHROME.   Proc. VI Int. Congr. Photobiol., p. 156 (A).

2156. Quail, P.H.; Marmé, D.; Schäfer, E.   1973.   PARTICLE-BOUND PHYTOCHROME
FROM MAIZE AND PUMPKIN.   Nature (London) New Biol. 245: 189-191.

2157. Quail, P.H.; Schäfer, E.; Marmé, D.   1973.   *DE NOVO* SYNTHESIS OF PHYTO-
CHROME IN PUMPKIN HOOKS.   Plant Physiol. 52: 124-127.

2158. Quail, P.H.; Schäfer, E.; Marmé, D.   1973.   TURNOVER OF PHYTOCHROME IN
PUMPKIN COTYLEDONS.   Plant Physiol. 52: 128-131.

2159. Quail, P.H.   1974.   PARTICLE-BOUND PHYTOCHROME: SPECTRAL PROPERTIES OF
BOUND AND UNBOUND FRACTIONS.   Planta 118: 345-355.

2160. Quail, P.H.   1974.   *IN VITRO* BINDING OF PHYTOCHROME TO A PARTICULATE
FRACTION: A FUNCTION OF LIGHT DOSE AND STEADY-STATE P_{fr} LEVEL.
Planta 118: 357-360.

2161. Quail, P.H.; Schäfer, E.   1974.   PARTICLE-BOUND PHYTOCHROME: A FUNCTION
OF LIGHT DOSE AND STEADY-STATE P_{fr} CONCENTRATION.   *Mechanisms of
Regulation of Plant Growth*, Eds. R.L. Bieleski, A.R. Ferguson;
M.M. Cresswell; Roy. Soc. N.Z. Bull. 12: 351-354.

2162. Quail, P.H.; Schäfer, E. 1974. PARTICLE-BOUND PHYTOCHROME: A FUNCTION OF LIGHT DOSE AND STEADY-STATE LEVEL OF THE FAR-RED-ABSORBING FORM. J. Membr. Biol. 15: 393-404.

2163. Queiroz, O. 1968. ACTION DU PHOTOPÉRIODISME SUR L'ACTIVITÉ ENZYMATIQUE DANS LA SYNTHÈSE OU LA DÉGRADATION DE L'ACIDE MALIQUE CHEZ *KALANCHOË BLOSSFELDIANA*. C.R. Acad. Sci. Ser. D. 266: 1260-1262.

2164. Queiroz, O. 1968. SUR LE MÉTABOLISME ACIDE DES CRASSULACÉES III VARIATIONS D'ACTIVITÉ ENZYMATIQUE SOUS L'ACTION DU PHOTOPÉRIODISME ET DU THERMOPÉRIODISME. Physiol. Veg. 6: 117-136.

2165. Queiroz, O. 1969. EVIDENCES OF PHOTOPERIODIC CONTROL OF ENZYME ACTIVITY IN CRASSULACEAN ACID METABOLISM: CIRCADIAN RHYTHMS IN PEP CARBOXYLASE ACTIVITY AND CHANGES IN MALIC DEHYDROGENASE ISOZYMES, INDUCED BY SHORT DAYS IN *KALANCHOË BLOSSFELDIANA*. Proc. XI Int. Bot. Congr., p. 175 (A).

2166. Queiroz, O. 1969. PHOTOPERIODISME ET ACTIVITE ENZYMATIQUE (PEP CARBOXYLASE ET ENZYME MALIQUE) DANS LES FEUILLES DE *KALANCHOË BLOSSFELDIANA*. Phytochemistry 8: 1655-1663.

2167. Queiroz, O.; Trippi, V.S. 1969. ACTION DU PHOTOPÉRIODISME SUR L'ACTIVITÉ ENZYMATIQUE: LES ISOZYMES DE LA MALIQUE DÉSHYDROGÉNASE. C.R. Acad. Sci. Ser. D. 268: 2060-2062.

2168. Queiroz, O. 1970. SUR LE MÉTABOLISME ACIDE DES CRASSULACÉES IV. RÉFLEXIONS SUR LES PHÉNOMÈNES OSCILLATOIRES AU NIVEAU ENZYMATIQUE ET SUR LA COMPARTIMENTATION MÉTABOLIQUE, SOUS L'ACTION DU PHOTOPÉRIODISME. Physiol. Veg. 8: 75-110 (R).

2169. Queiroz, O.; Morel, C.; Celati, C. 1971. PHOTOPÉRIODISME ET ACTIVITÉ ENZYMATIQUE: ADAPTATION À LONG TERME, D'UN RÉSEAU MÉTABOLIQUE COMPLEXE, AUX CHANGEMENTS DE PHOTOPÉRIODE. C.R. Acad. Sci. Ser. D. 272: 3045-3048.

2170. Queiroz, O. 1972. CIRCADIAN RHYTHMS IN ENZYME ACTIVITY AND PHYTOCHROME. *Phytochrome*, Ed. K. Mitrakos and W. Shropshire, Jr., Academic Press: London and New York, pp. 295-316 (R).

2171. Queiroz, O. 1974. CIRCADIAN RHYTHMS AND METABOLIC PATTERNS. Annu. Rev. Plant Physiol. 25: 115-134 (R).

2172. Queiroz, O.; Morel, C. 1974. PHOTOPERIODISM AND ENZYME ACTIVITY. TOWARDS A MODEL FOR THE CONTROL OF CIRCADIAN METABOLIC RHYTHMS IN THE CRASSULACEAN ACID METABOLISM. Plant Physiol. 53: 596-602.

2173. Racusen, R.; Etherton, B. 1971. AN INVESTIGATION OF POSSIBLE PHYTO-
CHROME MEDIATED BIOELECTRIC POTENTIALS IN SINGLE CELLS OF MUNG BEAN
ROOTS. Plant Physiol. 47: Suppl.-2, Abstr. No. 7 (A).

2174. Racusen, R.; Miller, K. 1972. PHYTOCHROME-INDUCED ADHESION OF MUNG
BEAN ROOT TIPS TO PLATINUM ELECTRODES IN A DIRECT CURRENT FIELD.
Plant Physiol. 49: 654-655.

2175. Racusen, R.H. 1973. MEMBRANE PROTEIN CONFORMATIONAL CHANGES AS A
MECHANISM FOR THE PHYTOCHROME-INDUCED FIXED CHARGE REVERSAL IN ROOT
CAP CELLS OF MUNG BEAN. Plant Physiol. 51: Suppl.-51, Abstr. No.
277 (A).

2176. Racusen, R.H.; Etherton, B. 1973. THE ROLE OF ROOT CAP CELL FIXED
CHARGES IN PHYTOCHROME MEDIATED MUNG BEAN ROOT TIP ADHERENCE PHE-
NOMENA. Plant Physiol. 51: Suppl.-51, Abstr. No. 276 (A).

2177. Racusen, R.H.; Satter, R.L. 1974. EXTERNAL AND INTERNAL ELECTRICAL
CHANGES IN PULVINAR REGIONS OF *SAMANEA SAMAN*. Plant Physiol. 53:
Suppl.-45, Abstr. No. 253 (A).

2178. Raghavan, V. 1968. EFFECTS OF LIGHT QUALITY AND ACTINOMYCIN D ON THE
DISTRIBUTION AND METABOLISM OF RNA AND PROTEIN IN THE SUBCELLULAR
FRACTIONS OF BRACKEN FERN GAMETOPHYTES. Proc. V Int. Congr.
Photobiol., p. 155 (A).

2179. Raghavan, V. 1968. RNA AND PROTEIN METABOLISM IN THE PARTICULATE
FRACTIONS OF THE GAMETOPHYTES OF BRACKEN FERN DURING GROWTH IN RED
AND BLUE LIGHT. Planta 81: 38-48.

2180. Raghavan, V. 1969. ROLE OF LIGHT QUALITY AND RNA SYNTHESIS IN THE CON-
TROL OF GROWTH PATTERN IN FERN GAMETOPHYTES. Proc. XI Int. Bot.
Congr., p. 175 (A).

2181. Raghavan, V. 1969. INTERACTION OF LIGHT QUALITY AND NUCLEASES IN THE
GROWTH OF THE GAMETOPHYTES OF *ASPLENIUM NIDUS*. Am. J. Bot. 56:
871-879.

2182. Raghavan, V. 1969. PHOTOCONTROL OF GROWTH PATTERN IN A TISSUE ISOLATED
FROM THE GAMETOPHYTES OF BRACKEN FERN. Plant Cell Physiol. 10:
481-484.

2183. Raghavan, V. 1971. PHYTOCHROME CONTROL OF GERMINATION OF THE SPORES OF
ASPLENIUM NIDUS. Plant Physiol. 48: 100-102.

2184. Raghavan, V.; DeMaggio, A.E. 1971. ENHANCEMENT OF PROTEIN SYNTHESIS IN ISOLATED CHLOROPLASTS BY IRRADIATION OF FERN GAMETOPHYTES WITH BLUE LIGHT. Plant Physiol. 48: 82-85.

2185. Raghavan, V. 1973. BLUE LIGHT INTERFERENCE IN THE PHYTOCHROME-CONTROLLED GERMINATION OF THE SPORES OF *CHEILANTHES FARINOSA*. Plant Physiol. 51: 306-311.

2186. Railton, I.D.; Wareing, P.F. 1973. EFFECTS OF DAYLENGTH ON GIBBERELLIN LEVELS IN LEAVES OF A SHORT-DAY OBLIGATE POTATO SPECIES, *SOLANUM ANDIGENA*. Plant Physiol. 51: Suppl.-57, Abstr. No. 204 (A).

2187. Railton, I.D.; Wareing, P.F. 1973. EFFECTS OF DAYLENGTH ON ENDOGENOUS GIBBERELLINS IN *SOLANUM ANDIGENA* III. GIBBERELLIN PRODUCTION BY THE LEAVES. Physiol. Plant. 29: 430-433.

2188. Raschke, K. 1967. DER EINFLUSS VON ROT- UND BLAULICHT AUF DIE ÖFFNUNGS- UND SCHLIESSGESCHWINDIGKEIT DER STOMATA VON *ZEA MAYS*. Naturwissenschaften 54: 72-73.

2189. Raschke, K.; Fellows, M.P. 1972. TRANSIENT STOMATAL RESPONSES TO RED LIGHT MEDIATED BY PHYTOCHROME. Plant Research '71 MSU/AEC Plant Res. Lab. Mich. State Univ. 38-41.

2190. Rast, D.; Skrivanová, R.; Wohlpart, A. 1972. BETALAIN SYNTHESIS IN *CENTROSPERMAE* SEEDLINGS: THE ACTION OF LIGHT ON BETACYANIN FORMATION. Ber. Schweiz. Bot. Ges. 82: 213-222.

2191. Rast, D.; Skrivanová. R.; Bachofen, R. 1973. REPLACEMENT OF LIGHT BY DIBUTYRYL-C-AMP AND C-AMP IN BETACYANIN SYNTHESIS. Phytochemistry 12: 2669-2672.

2192. Rasumov, V.I. 1933. THE SIGNIFICANCE OF THE QUALITY OF LIGHT IN PHOTO-PERIODICAL RESPONSE. Tr. Prikl. Bot. Genet. Sel. Ser. 3: 217-251 (RUS) (ENG Summary).

2193. Rasumov, V.I. 1941. COLLECTION OF TRANSACTIONS ON PLANT PHYSIOLOGY IN MEMORY OF K. A. TIMIRYAZEV. Izd. Akad. Nauk. SSSR, referred to by Kleshnin, A.F. p. 283 (1946). Dokl. Akad. Nauk SSSR 52: 813-816 (RUS) (not obtained).

2194. Rauwenhoff, N.W.P. 1878. SUR LES CAUSES DES FORMES ANORMALES DES PLANTES QUI CROISSENT DANS L'OBSCURITÉ. Ann. Sci. Nat. Bot. Ser. 6, 5: 267-322.

2195. Raven, C.W. 1971. ON THE REVERSIBILITY OF THE PHYTOCHROME INDUCED
SYNTHESIS OF CHLOROPHYLL. Proc. Eur. Ann. Symp. Plant Photomorphogenesis, (Athens), p. 39 (A).

2196. Raven, C.W. 1971. SYNTHESIS OF CHLOROPHYLL AT DIFFERENT INTENSITIES OF
MONOCHROMATIC LIGHT. Proc. Int. Congr. Photosynth. Res. 2: 2325-
2332.

2197. Raven, C.W.; Spruit, C.J.P. 1972. INDUCTION OF RAPID CHLOROPHYLL
ACCUMULATION IN DARK GROWN SEEDLINGS. I. ACTION SPECTRUM FOR PEA.
Acta Bot. Neerl. 21: 219-230.

2198. Raven, C.W.; Spruit, C.J.P. 1972. INDUCTION OF RAPID CHLOROPHYLL
ACCUMULATION IN DARK GROWN SEEDLINGS II. PHOTOREVERSIBILITY. Acta
Bot. Neerl. 21: 640-654.

2199. Raven, C.W. 1973. CHLOROPHYLL FORMATION AND PHYTOCHROME. Ph.D. Thesis,
Agic. Univ., Wageningen, Netherlands.

2200. Raven, C.W.; Spruit, C.J.P. 1973. INDUCTION OF RAPID CHLOROPHYLL
ACCUMULATION IN DARK GROWN SEEDLINGS. III. TRANSPORT MODEL FOR
PHYTOCHROME ACTION. Acta Bot. Neerl. 22: 135-143.

2201. Raven, C.W.; Shropshire, W., Jr. 1974. DOSE-RESPONSE CURVES FOR PHYTO-
CHROME CONTROL OF CHLOROPHYLL FORMATION IN DARK GROWN AND DE-
EIOLATED PEA SEEDLINGS. Plant Physiol. 53: Suppl. 2, Abstr. No. 8
(A).

2202. Reed, W.A.; Bonner, B.A. 1971. INVESTIGATIONS ON THE RAPID PHYTOCHROME
INDUCED INHIBITION OF *TROPAEOLUM* STEM ELONGATION. Plant Physiol.
47: Suppl.-2, Abstr. No. 10 (A).

2203. Reed, W.A. 1973. STUDIES ON THE MECHANISM OF THE CONTROL OF GROWTH BY
PHYTOCHROME IN *TROPAEOLUM MAJUS*. Ph.D. Thesis, Univ. Calif., Davis.

2204. Reid, D.M.; Clements, J.B. 1968. RNA AND PROTEIN SYNTHESIS: PRE-
REQUISITES OF RED LIGHT-INDUCED GIBBERELLIN SYNTHESIS. Nature
(London) 219: 607-609.

2205. Reid, D.M.; Clements, J.B.; Carr, D.J. 1968. RED LIGHT INDUCTION OF
GIBBERELLIN SYNTHESIS IN LEAVES. Nature (London) 217: 580-582.

2206. Reid, D.M.; Clements, J.B.; Garrett, M.K.; Carr, D.J. 1968. THE ROLE
OF GIBBERELLINS IN PHYTOCHROME MEDIATED RESPONSES. Proc. V Int.
Congr. Photobiol., p. 156 (A).

2207. Reid, D.M.; Tuing, M.S.; Durley, R.C.; Railton, I.D. 1972. RED-LIGHT-
ENHANCED CONVERSION OF TRITIATED GIBBERELLIN A 9 INTO OTHER GIBBER-
ELLIN-LIKE SUBSTANCES IN HOMOGENATES OF ETIOLATED BARLEY LEAVES.
Planta 108: 67-75.

2208. Reid, D.M.; Tuing, M.S.; Railton, I.D. 1974. PHYTOCHROME CONTROL OF
GIBBERELLIN LEVELS IN BARLEY LEAVES. *Plant Growth Substances 1973*,
Proc. VIII Int. Conf. Plant Growth Subst., Tokyo pp. 325-331.

2209. Reid, H.B. 1966. FLOWERING OF *XANTHIUM* IN RESPONSE TO RED AND FAR-RED
LIGHT INTERRUPTIONS GIVEN IN LONG DARK PERIODS. Plant Physiol. 41:
Suppl.-29-30 (A).

2210. Reid, H.B.; Moore, P.H.; Hamner, K.C. 1967. CONTROL OF FLOWERING OF
XANTHIUM PENSYLVANICUM BY RED AND FAR-RED LIGHT. Plant Physiol.
42: 532-540.

2211. Reinert, J.; Clauss, H.; Ardenne, R.V. 1964. ANTHOCYANBILDUNG IN
GEWEBEKULTUREN VON *HAPLOPAPPUS GRACILIS* IN LICHT VERSCHIEDENER
QUALITÄT. Naturwissenschaften 51: 87.

2212. Reinert, R.A.; Kasperbauer, M.J. 1966. INFLUENCE OF RED AND FAR-RED
LIGHT ON VIRUS CONTENT OF CALLUS TISSUES CULTURED FROM *NICOTIANA
TABACUM*. Phytopathology 56: 1108-1109.

2213. Reisch, K.W.; Kiplinger, D.C. 1958. PRELIMINARY STUDIES ON THE EFFECT
OF FAR-RED RADIATION ON THE FLOWERING OF THE GREENHOUSE CHRYSANTHE-
MUM. Proc. Am. Soc. Hortic. Sci. 72: 498-502.

2214. Remer, W. 1904. DER EINFLUSS DES LICHTES AUF DIE KEIMUNG BEI *PHACELIA
TANACETIFOLIA* BENTH. Ber. Dtsch. Bot. Ges. 22: 328-339.

2215. Rentschler, H.G. 1967. PHOTOPERIODISCHE INDUKTION DER MONOSPOREN-
BILDUNG BEI *PORPHYRA TENERA* KJELLM. (RHODOPHYTA-BANGIOPHYCEAE).
Planta 76: 65-74 (ENG Summary).

2216. Resühr, B. 1939. BEITRÄGE ZUR LICHTKEIMUNG VON *AMARANTUS CAUDATUS* L.
UND *PHACELIA TANACETIFOLIA* BENTH. Planta 30: 471-506.

2217. Rethy, R. 1968. RED (R), FAR-RED (FR) PHOTOREVERSIBLE EFFECTS ON THE
GROWTH OF *CHARA* SPORELINGS. Z. Pflanzenphysiol. 59: 100-102.

2218. Rezk, M.R. 1967. STUDIES ON THE LIGHT SENSITIVITY OF *PLANTAGO MAJOR* L.
SEEDS. II. THE EFFECT OF RED LIGHT ALONE AND MEDIATED BY CHEMICALS.
Acta Bot. (Szeged) 13: 39-44.

2219. Rice, H.V. 1971. PURIFICATION AND PARTIAL CHARACTERIZATION OF OAT AND
RYE PHYTOCHROME. Ph.D. Thesis, Harvard Univ., Cambridge.

2220. Rice, H.V.; Briggs, W.R. 1973. PARTIAL CHARACTERIZATION OF OAT AND RYE
PHYTOCHROME. Plant Physiol. 51: 927-938.

2221. Rice, H.V.; Briggs, W.R. 1973. IMMUNOCHEMISTRY OF PHYTOCHROME. Plant
Physiol. 51: 939-945.

2222. Rice, H.V.; Briggs, W.R.; Jackson-White, C.J. 1973. PURIFICATION OF
OAT AND RYE PHYTOCHROME. Plant Physiol. 51: 917-926.

2223. Richardson, N. 1970. STUDIES ON THE PHOTOBIOLOGY OF *BANGIA FUSCOPUR-
PUREA*. J. Phycol. 6: 215-219.

2224. Richardson, S.D. 1958. RADICLE ELONGATION OF *PSEUDOTSUGA MENZIESII* IN
RELATION TO LIGHT AND GIBBERELLIC ACID. Nature (London) 181: 429-
430.

2225. Richter, G. 1962. DIE WIRKUNG VON BLAUER UND ROTER STRAHLUNG AUF DIE
MORPHOGENESE VON *ACETABULARIA*. Naturwissenschaften 49: 238.

2226. Richter, G.; Kirschstein, M.J. 1966. REGENERATION UND PHOTOSYNTHESE-
LEISTUNG KERNHALTIGER ZELL-TEILSTÜCKE VON *ACETABULARIA* IN BLAUER
UND ROTER STRAHLUNG. Z. Pflanzenphysiol. 54: 106-117.

2227. Ries, E. 1970. BEZIEHUNGEN ZWISCHEN GASWECHSEL UND ^{14}C-EINBAU MONO-
CHROMATISCH BESTRAHLTER ALGENZELLEN. Ph.D. Thesis, Eberhard-Karls
Univ., Tübingen, Germany (not obtained). [Referred to by
Voskresenskaya, N.P. (1972)] Annu. Rev. Plant Physiol. 23: 219-234.

2228. Rissland, I.; Mohr, H. 1967. PHYTOCHROM-INDUZIERTE ENZYMBILDUNG
(PHENYLALANINDESAMINASE) EIN SCHNELL ABLAUFENDER PROZESS. Planta
77: 239-249 (ENG Summary).

2229. Ritter, J.W. 1808. BEMERKUNGEN ÜBER PFLANZENERREGBARKEIT IM ALLGEMEI-
NEN UND BESONDERN. J. Chem. Physik. Mineral. 6: 456-482.

2230. Röbbelen, G. 1968. GENBEDINGTE ROTLICHT-EMPFINDLICHKEIT DER CHLORO-
PLASTENDIFFERENZIERUNG BEI *ARABIDOPSIS*. Planta 80: 237-254 (ENG
Summary).

2231. Robinson, C. 1974. RED LIGHT EFFECTS IN CUCUMBER SEED GERMINATION.
Plant Physiol. 53: Suppl.-45, Abstr. No. 250.

2232. Roesel, H.A.; Haber, A.H. 1963. STUDIES OF EFFECTS OF LIGHT ON GROWTH
PATTERN AND OF GIBBERELLIN SENSITIVITY IN RELATION TO AGE, GROWTH
RATE, AND ILLUMINATION IN INTACT WHEAT COLEOPTILES. Plant Physiol.
38: 523-532.

2233. Roh, S.M.; Wilkins, H.F. 1972. PHYTOCHROME AND HIGH ENERGY REACTION SYSTEMS IN THE GROWTH AND FLOWERING OF *LILIUM LONGIFLORUM* THUNB. Plant Physiol. 49: Suppl.-54, Abstr. No. 303 (A).

2234. Roh, S.M.; Wilkins, H.R. 1974. DECAY AND DARK REVERSION OF PHYTOCHROME IN *LILIUM LONGIFLORUM* THUNB. CV. NELLIE WHITE. HortScience 9: 37-38.

2235. Roh, S.M.; Wilkins, H.F. 1974. RED AND FAR-RED TREATMENTS ACCELERATE SHOOT EMERGENCE FROM BULBS OF *LILIUM LONGIFLORUM* THUNB. CV. NELLIE WHITE. HortScience 9: 38-39.

2236. Rohrbaugh, L.M. 1942. EFFECTS OF LIGHT QUALITY ON GROWTH AND MINERAL NUTRITION OF BEAN. Bot. Gaz. (Chicago) 104: 133-151.

2237. Rollin, P. 1958. ACTION QUALITATIVE DE LA LUMIÈRE SUR LA GERMINATION DES GRAINES DE *PLACELIA TANACETIFOLIA*. C.R. Acad. Sci. Ser. D. 247: 1484-1487.

2238. Rollin, P. 1959. INFLUENCE DE L'ACIDE GIBBERELLIQUE SUR LA GERMINATION DES SEMENCES PHOTOSENSIBLES. Bull. Soc. Fr. Physiol. Veg. 5: 24-26.

2239. Rollin, P.; Martin, M. 1961. INFLUENCE DE LA LUMIÈRE SUR LA GERMINA-TION DES GRAINES DE *PHACELIA TANACETIFOLIA* BENTH (HYDROPHYLLACÉES). Prog. Photobiol., Proc. Int. Congr. 3rd, Copenhagen, 1960, pp. 408-410.

2240. Rollin, P. 1963. INFLUENCE DE LA LUMIÈRE ET DE LA TEMPERATURE SUR LA GERMINATION. Ph.D. Thesis, Univ. Paris, France.

2241. Rollin, P. 1963. OBSERVATIONS SUR LA DIFFÉRENCE DE NATURE DE DEUX PHOTORÉACTIONS CONTRÔLANT LA GERMINATION DES AKÈNES DE *LACTUCA SATIVA* VAR. (REINE DE MAI.). C.R. Acad. Sci. Ser. D. 257: 3642-3645.

2242. Rollin, P.; Bidault, Y. 1963. ETUDE DES FACTEURS DETERMINANT LA GER-MINATION DES GRAINES DE *LYTHRUM SALICARIA* (LYTHRACEES). Photochem. Photobiol. 2: 59-71.

2243. Rollin, P. 1964. LES RÉACTIONS DE PHOTOMORPHOGENÈSE CHEZ LES PLANTULES DE *PHACELIA TANACETIFOLIA*. I. ACTION D'UN SYSTÈME A FAIBLE ÉNERGIE. Ann. Physiol. Veg. 6: 5-16 (ENG Summary).

2244. Rollin, P. 1964. LES RÉACTIONS DE PHOTOMORPHOGENÈSE CHEZ LES PLANTULES DE *PHACELIA TANACETIFOLIA*. Ann. Physiol. Veg. 6: 149-158 (ENG Summary).

2245. Rollin, P. 1964. REMARQUES CONCERNANT L'ACTION DE LA LUMIÈRE SUR LA GERMINATION. Can. J. Bot. 42: 463-471 (ENG Summary).

2246. Rollin, P. 1964. INFLUENCE DE LA LUMIÈRE SUR LA MORPHOGENÈSE DES VÉGÉTAUX. Annee. Biol. 3-4: 95-135 (R).

2247. Rollin, P. 1964. INTERPRETATION OF THE DIFFERENT TYPES OF ACTION OF FAR-RED LIGHT ON THE MORPHOGENESIS OF PLANTS. Isr. J. Bot. 13: 193-198 (R).

2248. Rollin, P. 1964. INFLUENCE OF FAR-RED LIGHT ON MORPHOGENESIS IN PLANTS. Proc. IV Int. Congr. Photobiol., p. 107 (A).

2249. Rollin, P. 1965. LA PHYSIOLOGIE DE LA GERMINATION. Centre de Documentation Universitaire Paris, 64 pp. (R).

2250. Rollin, P. 1965. SYMP SUR LA LUMIÈRET LA MORPHOGENESE DES PLANTES. Symp. Nov. 1965, Ronen (not obtained).

2251. Rollin, P. 1966. THE INFLUENCE OF LIGHT UPON SEED GERMINATION. POSSIBLE INTERPRETATIONS OF DATA. Photochem. Photobiol. 5: 367-371.

2252. Rollin, P. 1966. INFLUENCE DE LA LUMIÈRE SUR LES MOUVEMENTS DE NUTATION DES PLANTULES. Photochem. Photobiol. 5: 375-376 (ENG Summary).

2253. Rollin, P.; Maignan, G. 1966. LA NÉCESSITÉ DU PHYTOCHROME P_{rl} $(=P_{730})$ POUR LA GERMINATION DES AKÈNES DE *LACTUCA SATIVA* L. VARIÉTÉ "REINE DE MAI". C.R. Acad. Sci. Ser. D. 263: 756-759.

2254. Rollin, P. 1967. LA PHOTOMORPHOGÉNÈSE DES VÉGÉTAUX, UN PROBLÈME DE BIOLOGIE MOLÉCULAIRE. Bull. Soc. Linn. Normandie 8: 108-182 (ENG Summary) (R).

2255. Rollin, P. 1967. INHIBITION OF GERMINATION AND FAR-RED LIGHT: THREE DIFFERENT ACTIONS. Proc. Eur. Annu. Symp. Plant Photomorphogenesis, (Hvar), pp. 85-87.

2256. Rollin, P.; Maignan, G. 1967. PHYTOCHROME AND THE PHOTOINHIBITION OF GERMINATION. Nature (London) 214: 741-742.

2257. Rollin, P. 1968. LA PHOTOSENSIBILITÉ DES GRAINES. Bull. Soc. Fr. Physiol. Veg. 14: 47-63 (R).

2258. Rollin, P. 1970. *Phytochrome, Photomorphogénèse et Photopériodisme*. Monogr. Physiol. Veg. 1-136 (R).

2259. Rollin, P.; Huault, C. 1970. INFLUENCE DE LA LUMIÈRE VISIBLE SUR LA CROISSANCE ET LA DIFFÉRENCIATION CELLULAIRE. Mem. Soc. Bot. Fr. 1970, 21-26 (Eng Summary) (R).

2260. Rollin, P.; Malcoste, R.; Eude, D. 1970. LE RÔLE DU PHYTOCHROME DANS LA GERMINATION DES GRAINES DE *NEMOPHILA INSIGNIS* (L.). Planta 91: 227-234 (ENG Summary).

2261. Rollin, P. 1972. PHYTOCHROME CONTROL OF SEED GERMINATION. *Phytochrome*, Ed. K. Mitrakos and W. Shropshire, Jr., Academic Press: London and New York, pp. 229-254 (R).

2262. Rollin, P. 1974. LE PHYTOCHROME ET LE RÔLE DE LA LUMIÈRE DANS LA GER-MINATION. *La Germination des Semences*. Publ. Ganthier-villars. pp. 45-58.

2263. Rombach, J. 1961. GROWTH OF *LEMNA MINOR* AS INFLUENCED BY LIGHT AND KINETIN. *Prog. Photobiol.* Proc. Int. Congr. 3rd, Copenhagen, 1960, pp. 379-380.

2264. Rombach, J. 1965. THE INFLUENCE OF THE PHYTOCHROME REACTION ON THE GROWTH OF *LEMNA MINOR* L. Meded. Landbouwhogesch. Wageningen 65-14: 1-11.

2265. Rombach, J. 1966. THE PHYTOCHROME REACTION IN *LEMNA MINOR* L. Photo-chem. Photobiol. 5: 383-384.

2266. Rombach, J. 1968. PHYTOCHROME CONTENT OF *LEMNA MINOR* AND OTHER LEMNACEAE AS INFLUENCED BY LIGHT TREATMENT AND CULTURE CONDITIONS. Proc. V Int. Congr. Photobiol., p. 93 (A).

2267. Rombach, J.; Spruit, C.J.P. 1968. ON PHYTOCHROME IN *LEMNA MINOR* AND OTHER LEMNACEAE. Acta Bot. Neerl. 17: 445-454.

2268. Rombach, J. 1971. ON THE INTERACTION OF KINETIN AND PHYTOCHROME IN *LEMNA MINOR* GROWING IN THE DARK. Acta Bot. Neerl. 20: 636-645.

2269. Rombach, J. 1974. THIAMINE REQUIREMENT AND PHYTOCHROME IN *LEMNA MINOR* L. Proc. Eur. Annu. Symp. Plant Photomorphogenesis, (Antwerpen), pp. 83-85.

2270. Rombach, J. 1974. GROWTH STIMULATION BY CYTOKININS, THIAMINE AND PHYTO-CHROME IN *LEMNA MINOR* L. IN DARKNESS AND IN LIGHT. Acta Bot. Neerl. 23: 348 (A).

2271. Romberger, J.A. 1963. POSSIBLE MECHANISMS OF GROWTH AND DORMANCY CON-TROL. *Meristems, Growth and Development in Woody Plants*. Tech. Bull. No. 1293, USDA Forest Service, pp. 100-119 (R).

2272. Roodenburg, J.W.M. 1930. KUNSTLICHTCULTUUR. Landbouwhogesch. Wagen-ingen, Laboratorium Twinbouwplantenteelt No. 14: 1-68 (ENG Summary).

2273. Roodenburg, J.W.M. 1940. DAS VERHALTEN VON PFLANZEN IN VERSCHIEDEN-FARBIGEM LICHT. Recl. Trav. Bot. Neerl. 37: 301-376.

2274. Roodenburg, J.W.M. 1947. DAGLENGTE, BLOEMVORMING EN BLOEI. Vakbl. Biol. 27: 65-76 (R).

2275. Roodenburg, J.W.M. 1954. THE PHYSIOLOGICAL LENGTH OF THE PHOTOPERIOD. Proc. VIII Bot. Congr., pp. 318-319 (R).

2276. Roth, K.; Link, W.; Mohr, H. 1970. RNS-UND PROTEINSYNTHESE IM ZUSAM-MENHANG MIT DER REGULATION DES ZELLSTRECKUNGSWACHSTUMS. Cytobiologie 1: 248-258 (ENG Summary).

2277. Roth-Bejerano, N.; Koller, D.; Negbi, M. 1966. MEDIATION OF PHYTOCHROME IN THE INDUCTIVE ACTION OF LOW TEMPERATURE ON DARK GERMINATION OF LETTUCE SEED AT SUPRA-OPTIMAL TEMPERATURE. Plant Physiol. 41: 962-964.

2278. Roth-Bejerano, N.; Koller, D.; Negbi, M. 1971. PHOTOCONTROL OF GERMINATION IN *HYOSCYAMUS DESERTORUM*, A KINETIC ANALYSIS. Isr. J. Bot. 20: 28-40.

2279. Roussel, L. '1973. UN NOUVEAU VENU EN PHYSIOLOGIE VÉGÉTALE: LE PHYTOCHROME. Bois For. Trop. 119: 53-57 (R).

2280. Roux, S.J.; Hillman, W.S. 1969. ALDEHYDE EFFECTS ON PHYTOCHROME. Proc. XI Int. Bot. Congr., p. 184 (A).

2281. Roux, S.J.; Hillman, W.S. 1969. THE EFFECT OF GLUTARALDEHYDE AND TWO MONOALDEHYDES ON PHYTOCHROME. Arch. Biochem. Biophys. 131: 423-429.

2282. Roux, S.J.; Hillman, W.S. 1970. AMINO ACID ANALYSES OF GLUTARALDEHYDE-REACTED PHYTOCHROME. Plant Physiol. 46: Suppl.-3, Abstr. No. 14 (A).

2283. Roux, S. 1971. NEW OBSERVATIONS ON THE PURIFICATION AND PROPERTIES OF PHYTOCHROME FROM OATS. Proc. Eur. Annu. Symp. Plant Photomorphogenesis, (Athens), pp. 40-42 (A).

2284. Roux, S.J., Jr. 1971. CHEMICAL APPROACHES TO THE STRUCTURAL PROPERTIES OF PHYTOCHROME. Ph.D. Thesis, Yale Univ., New Haven.

2285. Roux, S.J. 1972. CHEMICAL EVIDENCE FOR CONFORMATIONAL DIFFERENCES BETWEEN THE RED AND FAR-RED-ABSORBING FORMS OF OAT PHYTOCHROME. Biochemistry 11: 1930-1936.

2286. Roux, S.; Yguerabide, J. 1972. PHYTOCHROME IN ARTIFICIAL MEMBRANES. Plant Physiol. 49: Suppl.-65, Abstr. No. 364 (A).

2287. Roux, S.J.; Yguerabide, J. 1973. PHOTOREVERSIBLE CONDUCTANCE CHANGES INDUCED BY PHYTOCHROME IN MODEL LIPID MEMBRANES. Proc. Nat. Acad. Sci. USA 70: 762-764.

2288. Roux, S.J. 1974. CONDUCTANCE CHANGES INDUCED BY THE GLYCOPROTEIN PHYTO-CHROME IN MODEL MEMBRANES. Proc. Eur. Annu. Symp. Plant Photomorphogenesis, (Antwerpen), pp. 1-3.

2289. Rubin, B.A.; Chernavina, I.A.; Dorofeeva, E.V. 1958. CYTOCHEMICAL PECULIARITIES OF GROWTH IN WHEAT IN RELATION TO ILLUMINATION. Nauchn. Dokl. Vyssh. Shk. Biol. Nauki 1958, pp. 165-168 (RUS).

2290. Rubin, L.B.; Eremeyeva, O.V.; Fraikin, G. Ya. THE EFFECTS OF LIGHT ON THE CONSUMPTION OF OXYGEN BY CELLS OF *PSEUDOMONAS FLUORESCENS*. Scientific Reports, Upper School Biological Sciences No. 9: 78-82 (RUS) (not obtained).

2291. Rubin, L.B.; Eremeyeva, O.V.; Fraikin, G. Ya.; Shvinka, Yu. E. 1972. EVIDENCE FOR THE EXISTENCE OF PHYTOCHROME SYSTEM OF REGULATION IN MICROORGANISMS. Proc. VI Int. Congr. Photobiol., Abstr. No. 175 (A).

2292. Rubin, L.B.; Shvinka, Yu. E.; Adamova, N.P. 1972. THE EFFECTS OF THE SPECTRAL QUALITY OF LIGHT ON REPRODUCTION, BIOSYNTHESIS OF PROTEIN AND SOME OF THE FIRST REACTIONS OF PHOTOSYNTHESIS IN *ECTOTHIORHO-DOSPIRA SHAPOSHRIKOVII*. Dokl. Akad. Nauk SSSR Biol. 202: 459-465 (RUS).

2293. Rubin, L.B.; Eremeyeva, O.V.; Fraikin, G. Ya.; Shvinka, Yu. E. 1973. PHOTOCHROMIC SYSTEMS OF REGULATION AND THEIR ROLE IN THE DEVELOPMENT OF MICROORGANISMS. Scientific Reports, Upper School, Biological Sciences No. 3: 49-55 (RUS) (not obtained).

2294. Rubin, L.B.; Shvinka, Yu. E.; Fraikin, G. Ya. 1973. ON PHOTOREGULATORY SYSTEMS IN PLANTS. Biologia 8: 135-145 (RUS) (ENG Summary) (R).

2295. Rubinstein, B. 1968. PHYTOCHROME-INDUCED ENZYME FORMATION IN CHLOROPLASTS. Ph.D. Thesis, U. Calif., Berkeley.

2296. Rubinstein, B. 1969. ANALYSIS OF HYPOCOTYL HOOK UNBENDING IN BEAN. Plant Physiol. 44: Suppl.-18, Abstr. No. 84 (A).

2297. Rubinstein, B.; Drury, K.S.; Park, R.B. 1969. EVIDENCE FOR BOUND PHYTOCHROME IN OAT SEEDLINGS. Plant Physiol. 44: 105-109.

2298. Rubinstein, B. 1970. PHYTOCHROME CONTROL OF AUXIN EFFECTS IN BEAN HYPOCOTYL HOOKS. Plant Physiol. 46: Suppl.-1, Abstr. No. 5 (A).

2299. Rubinstein, B. 1971. THE ROLE OF VARIOUS REGIONS OF THE BEAN HYPOCOTYL ON RED LIGHT-INDUCED HOOK OPENING. Plant Physiol. 48: 183-186.

2300. Rubinstein, B. 1971. AUXIN AND RED LIGHT IN THE CONTROL OF HYPOCOTYL HOOK OPENING IN BEANS. Plant Physiol. 48: 187-192.

2301. Rubinstein, B. 1972. CHARACTERISTICS OF HOOK FORMATION BY BEAN SEED-LINGS. Plant Physiol. 49: 640-643.

2302. Rüdiger, W.; Correll, D.L. 1969. ÜBER DIE STRUKTUR DES PHYTOCHROM-CHROMOPHORS UND SEINE PROTEIN-BINDUNG. Justus Liebigs. Ann. Chem. 723: 208-212 (ENG Summary).

2303. Rüdiger, W. 1972. ISOLATION AND PURIFICATION OF PHYTOCHROME. *Phytochrome*, Ed. K. Mitrakos and W. Shropshire, Jr., Academic Press: London and New York, pp. 107-125 (R).

2304. Rüdiger, W. 1972. CHEMISTRY OF PHYTOCHROME CHROMOPHORE. *Phytochrome*, Ed. K. Mitrakos and W. Shropshire, Jr., Academic Press: London and New York, pp. 129-141 (R).

2305. Rudolph, E. 1965. UNTERSUCHUNGEN ÜBER DEN EINFLUSS DER PHOTOREAKTIONS-SYSTEME AUF DIE CHLOROPHYLLSYNTHESE. Planta 66: 75-94 (ENG Summary).

2306. Ruge, U. 1952. ÜBER DIE BEDEUTUNG DES CHLOROPHYLLS FÜR DIE ENTWICKLUNG DER ADVENTIVWURZELN. Ber. Dtsch. Bot. Ges. 65: 338-340.

2307. Ruge, U. 1953. DIE SYNTHESE DER BIOS- WUCHSSTOFFE IN VERSCHIEDENEN SPEKTRALBEREICHEN. Naturwissenschaften 40: 225-226.

2308. Ruge, U. 1957. DER ASCORBINSÄUREGEHALT VON *TRADESCANTIA*-BLÄTTERN IN ABHÄNGIGKEIT VON DER WELLENLÄNGE DES LICHTES. Naturwissenschaften 44: 13-14.

2309. Ruge, U. 1958. DIE LICHTPHYSIOLOGISCHEN GRUNDLAGEN DER PFLANZEN BELEUCHTUNG. Angew. Bot. 32: 207-220 (R).

2310. Ruge, U. 1960. DER AUXIN-GEHALT VON *TRADESCANTIA*-BLÄTTERN IN ABHÄNGIG-KEIT VON DER WELLENLÄNGE DES LICHTES. Naturwissenschaften 47: 381-382.

2311. Ruge, U.; Brunner, H. 1972. ÜBER DIE BEDEUTUNG DES HELLROT/DUNKELROT-SYSTEMS FÜR DIE ENTWICKLUNG DER ADVENTIVWURZELN. Z. Pflanzenphysiol. 67: 93-96 (ENG Summary).

2312. Russell, D.W. 1966. STUDIES ON THE BIOCHEMISTRY OF PHOTOMORPHOGENESIS IN THE PEA PLANT. Ph.D. Thesis, Yale Univ., New Haven.

2313. Russell, D.W.; Galston, A.W. 1967. FLAVONOID COMPLEXES IN *PISUM SATI-VUM*. IV. THE EFFECT OF RED LIGHT ON SYNTHESIS OF KAEMPFEROL COMPLEXES AND ON GROWTH IN SUB-APICAL INTERNODE TISSUES. Phytochemistry 6: 791-797.

2314. Russell, D.W.; Galston, A.W. 1968. BLOCKAGE BY GIBBERELLIC ACID OF PHYTOCHROME EFFECTS ON GROWTH, AUXIN RESPONSES, AND FLAVONOID SYNTHE-SIS IN ETIOLATED PEA INTERNODES. Plant Physiol. 43: Suppl.-15 (A).

2315. Russell, D.W.; Galston, A.W. 1968. COMPARATIVE ANALYSIS OF PHYTOCHROME-MEDIATED GROWTH RESPONSES IN INTERNODES OF DWARF AND TALL PEA PLANTS. Planta 78: 1-10.

2316. Russell, D.W.; Galston, A.W. 1969. BLOCKAGE BY GIBBERELLIC ACID OF PHYTOCHROME EFFECTS ON GROWTH, AUXIN RESPONSES, AND FLAVONOID SYNTHE-SIS IN ETIOLATED PEA INTERNODES. Plant Physiol. 44: 1211-1216.

2317. Sabnis, H.; Mer, C.L. 1969. ANALYTICAL STUDIES OF THE GROWTH OF THE ETIOLATED SEEDLINGS OF *AVENA SATIVA* III. THE PHOTOSENSITIVITY OF THE MESOCOTYL IN RELATION TO PHOSPHATE NUTRITION. New Phytol. 68: 105-111.

2318. Sachs, J. 1857. UEBER DAS BEWEGUNGSORGAN UND DIE PERIODISCHEN BEWEGUN-GEN DER BLÄTTER VON *PHASEOLUS* UND *OXALIS*. Bot. Ztg. 15: 809-815.

2319. Sachs, J. 1864. WIRKUNGEN FARBIGEN LICHTS AUF PFLANZEN. Bot. Ztg. 22: 353-358 and Taf. XIII (R).

2320. Sachs, J. 1864. WIRKUNGEN FARBIGEN LICHTS AUF PFLANZEN. Bot. Ztg. 22: 361-372.

2321. Sachs, J. 1887. ÜBER DIE WIRKUNG DER ULTRAVIOLETTEN STRAHLEN AUF DIE BLÜTHENBILDUNG. Arbeit des Botan. Institut in Wurzburg III Heft. 3, pp. 372-388.

2322. Sagromsky, H. 1965. EINFLUSS VON LICHT AUF DIE KEIMUNG VON KÜRBISSAMEN. Kulturpflanze 13: 509-515.

2323. Saidov, A.S.; Polevoi, V.V. 1971. INFLUENCE OF RED AND FAR-RED LIGHT ON THE SYNTHESIS OF PIGMENTS AND ABSORPTION OF OXYGEN IN ETIOLATED LEAVES OF *PHASEOLUS AUREUS*. Vestn. Leningr. Univ., Biol., pp. 140-142 (RUS) (ENG Summary).

2324. Saidov, A.S.; Polevoi, V.V.; Maksemov, G.B. 1971. EFFECT OF RED AND FAR-RED LIGHT ON THE GROWTH OF ETIOLATED SEEDLINGS OF MUNG BEAN (*PHASEOLUS AUREUS* ROXB.). Fiziol. Biokhim. Kult. Rast. 3: 508-511 (RUS) (ENG Summary).

2325. Saidov, A.S.; Magomedov, I.M.; Polevoi, V.V. 1972. ACTION OF RED AND LONG-WAVELENGTH RED LIGHT ON THE GROWTH OF ETIOLATED SHOOTS OF *PHASEOLUS AUREUS* AND ON THE DARK FIXATION OF CARBON DIOXIDE. Vestn. Leningr. Univ., Biol., pp. 135-137 (RUS) (Eng Summary).

2326. Saidov, A.S.; Polevoi, V.V.; Makhlina, A.M. 1973. THE EFFECT OF RED
       AND FAR RED LIGHT ON THE REDOX POTENTIAL AND THE CONTENT OF SULF-
       HYDRYL GROUPS IN DETACHED LEAVES OF ETIOLATED BEAN (*PHASEOLUS AUREUS*
       ROXB.) SEEDLINGS. Dokl. Akad. Nauk. SSSR 208: 995-997 (RUS) (English
       Translation; Consultants Bureau, Plenum Publishing Corp. N.Y., N.Y.,
       Dokl. Bot. Sci. 208/210: 29-31).

2327. Sale, P.J.M. 1959. THE INFLUENCE OF LIGHT WAVELENGTH AND GIBBERELLIN
       ACID ON PLANT MORPHOGENESIS. Ph.D. Thesis, Univ. Reading, Great
       Britian (not obtained) (Referred to by Vince, D.; Blake, J.; and
       Spencer, R. (1964) Physiol. Plant. 17: 119-125).

2328. Sale, P.J.M.; Vince, D. 1959. DURATION OF IRRADIATION AS A FACTOR
       AFFECTING THE RESPONSE OF INTERNODES TO WAVE-LENGTH. Proc. IX Int.
       Bot. Congr. 340 (A).

2329. Sale, P.J.M.; Vince, D. 1959. EFFECTS OF WAVE-LENGTH AND TIME OF IRRA-
       DIATION ON INTERNODE LENGTH IN *PISUM SATIVUM* AND *TROPAEOLUM MAJUS*.
       Nature (London) 183: 1174-1175.

2330. Sale, P.J.M.; Vince, D. 1960. EFFECTS OF LIGHT AND GIBBERELLIC ACID ON
       INTERNODE GROWTH IN *PISUM SATIVUM*. Physiol. Plant. 13: 664-673.

2331. Sale, P.J.M.; Vince, D. 1963. SOME EFFECTS OF LIGHT ON LEAF GROWTH IN
       PISUM SATIVUM AND *TROPAEOLUM MAJUS*. Photochem. Photobiol. 2:
       401-405.

2332. Sale, P.J.M.; Vince, D.; Prue, J.E. 1964. KINETICS OF THE PHOTO-
       INHIBITION OF STEM GROWTH IN *PISUM SATIVUM* AND *TROPAEOLUM MAJUS*.
       Photochem. Photobiol. 3: 61-65.

2333. Saleh, M. 1972. EFFECTS OF LIGHT UPON QUANTITY AND QUALITY OF *MATRI-
       CARIA CHAMOMILLA* L. OIL. PART 2: PRELIMINARY STUDY OF SUPPLEMENTARY
       COLOURED LIGHT EFFECTS UPON CONTROLLED CONDITIONS. Pharmazie 27:
       608-611.

2334. Salisbury, F.B.; Bonner, J. 1956. THE REACTIONS OF THE PHOTOINDUCTIVE
       DARK PERIOD. Plant Physiol. 31: 141-146.

2335. Salisbury, F.B. 1959. GROWTH REGULATORS AND FLOWERING. II. THE COBAL-
       TOUS ION. Plant Physiol. 34: 598-604.

2336. Salisbury, F.B. 1961. PHOTOPERIODISM AND THE FLOWERING PROCESS. Annu.
       Rev. Plant Physiol. 12: 293-326 (R).

2337. Salisbury, F.B. 1963. *THE FLOWERING PROCESS*. Pergamon Press, New
       York, N.Y. (R-D).

2338. Salisbury, F.B. 1964. RECENT DEVELOPMENTS IN FLOWER INDUCTION. Proc. X Int. Bot. Cong., p. 187, Abstr. No. 433 (A).

2339. Salisbury, F.B. 1965. THE INITIATION OF FLOWERING. Endeavour 24: 74-80 (R).

2340. Salisbury, F.B. 1965. TIME MEASUREMENT AND THE LIGHT PERIOD IN FLOWER-ING. Planta 66: 1-26.

2341. Sánchez, R.A. 1965. EL FOTOCONTROL EN EL PROCESO DE GERMINACIÓN. Cienc. Invest. 21: 147-160.

2342. Sánchez, R.A. 1967. SOME OBSERVATIONS ABOUT THE EFFECT OF LIGHT ON THE LEAF SHAPE IN *TARAXACUM OFFICINALE* L. Meded. Landbouwhosch. Wageningen 67-16: 1-11.

2343. Sánchez, R. 1971. PHYTOCHROME INVOLVEMENT IN THE CONTROL OF LEAF SHAPE OF *TARAXACUM OFFICINALE* L. Experientia 27: 1234-1237.

2344. Sander, C.; Laber, L.J.; Bell, W.D.; Hamilton, R.H. 1968. LIGHT SENSI-TIVITY OF PLASTIDS AND PLASTID PIGMENTS PRESENT IN THE ALBESCENT MAIZE MUTANT. Plant Physiol. 43: 693-697.

2345. Sandmeier, M.; Nitsch, J.P. 1963. PHOTOBIOLOGIE DU MESOCOTYL D'AVOINE. I. ACTION DES RADIATIONS ROUGE CLAIR ET ROUGE SOMBRE. Photochem. Photobiol. 2: 479-491 (ENG Summary).

2346. Sandmeier, M.; Nitsch, J.P. 1966. PHOTOBIOLOGIE DU MÉSCOTYLE D'AVOINE II. STIMULATION DE L'ÉLONGATION PAR LA LUMIÈRE ROUGE-SOMBRE EN PRÉSENCE DE DIVERSES GIBBÉRELLINES. Photochem. Photobiol. 5: 75-81 (ENG Summary).

2347. Sandmeier, M. 1967. ANNULATION DES EFFETS PRODUITS PAR LA LUMIÈRE SUR L'ALLONGEMENT DE SEGMENTS DE MÉSCOTYLES D'AVOINE PAR TROIS INHIBI-TEURS DE LA FORMATION DE L'ADÉNOSINE TRIPHOSPHATE (ATP). C.R. Acad. Sci. Ser. D. 265: 1948-1951.

2348. Sandmeier, M.; Nitsch, J.P. 1967. PHOTOBIOLOGIE DU MÉSOCOTYLE D'AVOINE - III. DOUBLE EFFET DE LA LUMIÈRE BLEUE. Photochem. Photobiol. 6: 269-285 (ENG Summary).

2349. Sandmeier, M. 1968. PHOTOBIOLOGIE DU MESOCOTYLE D'AVOINE-IV SPECTRES D'ACTION ET EFFICACITE QUANTIQUE DE LA LUMIÈRE. Photochem. Photo-biol. 7: 391-401 (ENG Summary).

2350. Sandmeier, M.; Ivart, J. 1972. MODIFICATION DU TAUX DES NUCLEOTIDES
ADENYLIQUES (ATP, ADP ET AMP), PAR UN ECLAIREMENT DE LUMIERE ROUGE-
CLAIR (660 nm). Photochem. Photobiol. 16: 51-59 (ENG Summary).

2351. Sarafis, V. 1972. THE COMPARATIVE PHOTOBIOLOGY OF SPORE GERMINATION IN
THE POLYTRICHIDAE. Proc. VI Int. Congr. Photobiol., Abstr. No. 190
(A).

2352. Satter, R.L.; Wetherell, D.F. 1967. THE CONTROL OF PLANT GROWTH BY RED
AND FAR-RED IRRADIATION. Bull. Inst. Cellular Biol. Univ. Conn. 9:
1-9 (R).

2353. Satter, R.L.; Wetherell, D.F. 1968. PHOTOMORPHOGENESIS IN *SINNINGIA
SPECIOSA*, CV. QUEEN VICTORIA I. CHARACTERIZATION OF PHYTOCHROME CON-
TROL. Plant Physiol. 43: 953-960.

2354. Satter, R.L.; Wetherell, D.F. 1968. PHOTOMORPHOGENESIS IN *SINNINGIA
SPECIOSA*, CV. QUEEN VICTORIA II. STEM ELONGATION: INTERACTION OF A
PHYTOCHROME CONTROLLED PROCESS AND A RED-REQUIRING, ENERGY DEPENDENT
REACTION. Plant Physiol. 43: 961-967.

2355. Satter, R.L.; Sabnis, D.D.; Galston, A.W. 1969. ON THE MECHANISM OF
PHYTOCHROME CONTROL OF NYCTINASTIC LEAFLET CLOSURE IN *ALBIZZIA
JULIBISSIN*. Plant Physiol. 44: Suppl.-18, Abstr. No. 83 (A).

2356. Satter, R.L.; Galston, A.W. 1970. PHYTOCHROME CONTROLLED NYCTINASTY IN
ALBIZZIA JULIBRISSIN II. K^+ FLUX AS A BASIS FOR LEAFLET CLOSURE.
Plant Physiol. 46: Suppl.-2, Abstr. No. 7 (A).

2357. Satter, R.L.; Marinoff, P.; Galston, A.W. 1970. PHYTOCHROME CONTROLLED
NYCTINASTY IN *ALBIZZIA JULIBRISSIN* II. POTASSIUM FLUX AS A BASIS FOR
LEAFLET MOVEMENT. Am. J. Bot. 57: 916-926.

2358. Satter, R.L.; Sabnis, D.D.; Galston, A.W. 1970. PHYTOCHROME CONTROLLED
NYCTINASTY IN *ALBIZZIA JULIBRISSIN* I. ANATOMY AND FINE STRUCTURE OF
THE PULVINULE. Am. J. Bot. 57: 374-381.

2359. Satter, R.L.; Galston, A.W. 1971. RHYTHMIC, PHYTOCHROME AND HORMONAL
CONTROL OF *ALBIZZIA* LEAFLET MOVEMENT AND K FLUX. Plant Physiol. 47:
Suppl.-2, Abstr. No. 9 (A).

2360. Satter, R.L.; Galston, A.W. 1971. PHYTOCHROME-CONTROLLED NYCTINASTY IN
ALBIZZIA JULIBRISSIN. III. INTERACTIONS BETWEEN AN ENDOGENOUS RHYTHM
AND PHYTOCHROME IN CONTROL OF POTASSIUM FLUX AND LEAFLET MOVEMENT.
Plant Physiol. 48: 740-746.

2361. Satter, R.L.; Galston, A.W. 1971. POTASSIUM FLUX: A COMMON FEATURE OF *ALBIZZIA* LEAFLET MOVEMENT CONTROLLED BY PHYTOCHROME OR ENDOGENOUS RHYTHM. Science 174: 518-519.

2362. Satter, R.L.; Applewhite, P.B.; Galston, A.W. 1972. JOINT RHYTHMIC AND PHYTOCHROME ACTION IN CONTROL OF LEAF MOVEMENTS AND POTASSIUM FLUX. Proc. VI Int. Congr. Photobiol., Abstr. No. 163 (A).

2363. Satter, R.L.; Applewhite, P.B.; Galston, A.W. 1972. IAA-DEPENDENT ACETYLCHOLINE-INDEPENDENT LEAFLET MOVEMENT IN *ALBIZZIA*. Plant Physiol. 49: Suppl.-53, Abstr. No. 298 (A).

2364. Satter, R.L.; Applewhite, P.B.; Galston, A.W. 1972. PHYTOCHROME-CON-TROLLED NYCTINASTY IN *ALBIZZIA JULIBRISSIN*. V. EVIDENCE AGAINST ACETYLCHOLINE PARTICIPATION. Plant Physiol. 50: 523-525.

2365. Satter, R.L.; Marinoff, P.; Galston, A.W. 1972. PHYTOCHROME-CONTROLLED NYCINASTY IN *ALBIZZIA JULIBRISSIN*. IV. AUXIN EFFECTS ON LEAFLET MOVE-MENT AND K FLUX. Plant Physiol. 50: 235-241.

2366. Satter, R.L.; Applewhite, P.B.; Kreis, D.J., Jr.; Galston, A.W. 1973. RHYTHMIC LEAFLET MOVEMENT IN *ALBIZZIA JULIBRISSIN*: EFFECT OF ELECTROLYTES AND TEMPERATURE ALTERATION. Plant Physiol. 52: 202-207.

2367. Satter, R.L.; Galston, A.W. 1973. LEAF MOVEMENTS: ROSETTA STONE OF PLANT BEHAVIOR? BioScience 23: 407-416 (R).

2368. Satter, R.L.; Applewhite, P.B.; Galston, A.W. 1974. RHYTHMIC POTASSIUM FLUX IN *ALBIZZIA*: EFFECT OF AMINOPHYLLINE, CATIONS, AND INHIBITIONS OF RESPIRATION AND PROTEIN SYNTHESIS. Plant Physiol. 54: 280-285.

2369. Satter, R.L.; Geballe, G.T.; Galston, A.W. 1974. POTASSIUM FLUX AND LEAF MOVEMENT IN *SAMANEA SAMAN* II. PHYTOCHROME CONTROLLED MOVEMENT. J. Gen. Physiol. 64: 431-442.

2370. Saunders, J.A.; McClure, J.W. 1973. ACETYLCHOLINE INHIBITION OF PHYTOCHROME-MEDIATED INCREASES IN A FLAVONOID AND IN PHENYLALANINE AMMONIA-LYASE ACTIVITY OF ETIOLATED BARLEY PLUMULES. Plant Physiol. 51: 407-408.

2371. Sawhney, R.; Cumming, B.G. 1973. THE ROLE OF PHOTOSYNTHESIS AND HER IN THE FLOWERING OF A SD PLANT, *CHENOPODIUM RUBRUM*. Plant Physiol. 51: Suppl.-29, Abstr. No. 157 (A).

2372. Sayre, J.D. 1929. OPENING OF STOMATA IN DIFFERENT RANGES OF WAVE LENGTHS OF LIGHT. Plant Physiol. 4: 323-328.

2373. Scarth, G.W.; Shaw, M. 1951. STOMATAL MOVEMENT AND PHOTOSYNTHESIS IN
       PELARGONIUM. I. EFFECTS OF LIGHT AND CARBON DIOXIDE. Plant Physiol.
       26: 207-225.

2374. Schäfer, E. 1971. DETAILIERTE PHOTOMETRISCHE MESSUNGEN *IN VIVO* AM
       PHYTOCHROMSYSTEM VON *SINAPIS ALBA* L. UND *CUCURBITA PEPO* L. Ph.D.
       Thesis, Univ. Freiburg, Germany.

2375. Schäfer, E.; Marmé, D.; Marchal, B. 1971. ANALYSIS OF THE PHYTOCHROME
       PHOTOTRANSFORMATION KINETICS IN MUSTARD SEEDLINGS. Proc. Eur. Annu.
       Symp. Plant Photomorphogenesis, (Athens), p. 43 (A).

2376. Schäfer, E.; Marmé, D.; Marchal, B. 1971. STUDIES OF THE TIME DEPEND-
       ENCE OF THE PHYTOCHROME SYSTEM IN MUSTARD SEEDLINGS. Proc. Eur.
       Annu. Symp. Plant Photomorphogenesis, (Athens), p. 44 (A).

2377. Schäfer, E.; Marchal, B.; Marmé, D. 1971. ON THE PHYTOCHROME PHOTO-
       TRANSFORMATION KINETICS IN MUSTARD SEEDLINGS. Planta 101: 265-276.

2378. Schäfer, E.; Marchal, B.; Marmé, D. 1972. *IN VIVO* MEASUREMENTS OF THE
       PHYTOCHROME PHOTOSTATIONARY STATE IN FAR RED LIGHT. Photochem.
       Photobiol. 15: 457-464.

2379. Schäfer, E.; Schmidt, W.; Quail, P.; Marmé, D. 1972. SPECTROSCOPY OF
       PHYTOCHROME IN TURBID MATERIALS. Proc. VI Int. Congr. Photobiol.,
       Abstr. No. 157 (A).

2380. Schäfer, E.; Schmidt, W.; Mohr, H. 1973. COMPARATIVE MEASUREMENTS OF
       PHYTOCHROME IN COTYLEDONS AND HYPOCOTYL HOOK OF MUSTARD (*SINAPIS
       ALBA* L.). Photochem. Photobiol. 18: 331-334.

2381. Schäfer, E. 1974. IRRADIANCE DEPENDENCE OF THE PHYTOCHROME SYSTEM.
       Proc. Eur. Annu. Symp. Plant Photomorphogenesis, (Antwerpen),
       pp. 20-21.

2381.5. Schäfer, E. 1974. EVIDENCE FOR BINDING OF PHYTOCHROME TO MEMBRANES.
       Membrane Transport in Plants. Ed. U. Zimmerman and J. Dainty,
       Springer-Verlag, Berlin, Heidelberg, New York, pp. 435-440 (R).

2382. Schäfer, E.; Mohr, H. 1974. IRRADIANCE DEPENDENCY OF THE PHYTOCHROME
       SYSTEM IN COTYLEDONS OF MUSTARD (*SINAPIS ALBA* L.). J. Math. Biol.
       1: 9-15.

2383. Schäfer, E.; Schmidt, W. 1974. TEMPERATURE DEPENDENCE OF PHYTOCHROME
       DARK REACTIONS. Planta 116: 257-266.

2384. Schanz, F. 1918. EINFLUSS DES LICHTES AUF DIE GESTALTUNG DER VEGETA-
       TION. Ber. Dtsch. Bot. Ges. 36: 619-632.

2385. Schanz, F. 1918. WIRKUNGEN DES LICHTS AUF DIE PFLANZE. Biol. Centralbl. 38: 283-296.

2386. Schanz, F. 1919. WIRKUNGEN DES LICHTS VERSCHIEDENER WELLENLÄNGE AUF DIE PFLANZEN. Ber. Dtsch. Bot. Ges. 37: 430-442.

2387. Schappelle, N.A. 1933. A STUDY TO DETERMINE THE RANGE OF WAVE-LENGTH MOST EFFECTIVE IN STIMULATING REPRODUCTIVE GROWTH IN *MARCHANTIA*. Am. J. Bot. 20: 677 (A).

2388. Schappelle, N.A. 1936. EFFECT OF NARROW RANGES OF WAVE LENGTHS OF RADIANT ENERGY, AND OTHER FACTORS, ON THE REPRODUCTIVE GROWTH OF LONG-DAY AND SHORT-DAY PLANTS. Cornell Univ. Agric. Exp. Stu. Mem. 185: 1-33.

2389. Scharff, O. 1962. EFFECTS OF RED AND FAR-RED LIGHT ON THE HYPOCOTYL OF *PICEA ABIES*. Physiol. Plant. 15: 804-814.

2390. Scheibe, J.; Lang, A. 1965. LETTUCE SEED GERMINATION: EVIDENCE FOR A REVERSIBLE LIGHT-INDUCED INCREASE IN GROWTH POTENTIAL AND FOR PHYTOCHROME MEDIATION OF THE LOW TEMPERATURE EFFECT. Plant Physiol. 40: 485-492.

2391. Scheibe, J.E., Jr. 1966. STUDIES ON PHOTOBLASTIC GERMINATION IN LETTUCE SEED. Ph.D. Thesis, Calif. Inst. Technol., Pasadena.

2392. Scheibe, J.; Lang, A. 1967. LETTUCE SEED GERMINATION: A PHYTOCHROME-MEDIATED INCREASE IN THE GROWTH RATE OF LETTUCE SEED RADICLES. Planta 72: 348-354.

2393. Scheibe, J.; Hendricks, S.B. 1968. AN OBSERVATION ON POSSIBLE PHOTO-OXIDATION OF ASCORBIC ACID IN STRAWBERRY LEAVES. Phytochemistry 7: 31-33.

2394. Scheibe, J.; Lane, A. 1969. LETTUCE SEED GERMINATION: EFFECTS OF HIGH TEMPERATURE AND OF REPEATED FAR-RED TREATMENT IN RELATION TO PHYTOCHROME. Photochem. Photobiol. 9: 143-150.

2395. Scheibe, J. 1972. PHOTOREVERSIBLE PIGMENT: OCCURRENCE IN A BLUE-GREEN ALGA. Science 176: 1037-1039.

2396. Scherf, H.; Zenk, M.H. 1967. INDUCTION OF ANTHOCYANIN AND PHENYLALANINE AMMONIA-LYASE FORMATION BY A HIGH ENERGY LIGHT REACTION AND ITS CONTROL THROUGH THE PHYTOCHROME SYSTEM. Z. Pflanzenphysiol. 56: 203-206.

2397. Scherf, H.; Zenk, M.H. 1967. DER EINFLUSS DES LICHTES AUF DIE FLAVO-
NOIDSYNTHESE UND DIE ENZYMINDUKTION BEI *FAGOPYRUM ESCULENTUM* MOENCH.
Z. Pflanzenphysiol. 57: 401-418 (ENG Summary).

2398. Schmidt, P. 1870. ÜBER EINIGE WIRKUNGEN DES LICHTES AUF PFLANZEN.
Ph.D. Thesis, Breslau, pp. 27-38.

2399. Schmidt, W.; Marmé, D.; Quail, P.; Schäfer, E. 1973. PHYTOCHROME:
FIRST-ORDER PHOTOTRANSFORMATION KINETICS *IN VIVO*. Planta 111:
329-336.

2400. Schmidt, W. 1974. A VARIABLE AUTOMATIC RECORDING DEVICE FOR MEASURING
PHYTOCHROME WITH THE PERKIN-ELMER SPECTROPHOTOMETER MODEL 356. Anal.
Biochem. 59: 91-97.

2401. Schmidt, W.; Schäfer, E. 1974. DEPENDENCE OF PHYTOCHROME DARK REACTIONS
ON THE INITIAL PHOTOSTATIONARY STATE. Planta 116: 267-272.

2402. Schnarrenberger, C.; Mohr, H. 1967. DIE WECHSELWIRKUNG VON HELLROT,
DUNKELROT, UND BLAULICHT BEI DER PHOTOMORPHOGENESE VON FARNGAMETO-
PHYTEN [*DRYOPTERIS FILIX-MAS* (L.) SCHOTT]. Planta 75: 114-124
(ENG Summary).

2403. Schnarrenberger, C.; Mohr, H. 1967. PHYTOCHROME-MEDIATED SYNTHESIS OF
CAROTENOIDS IN MUSTARD SEEDLINGS (*SINAPIS ALBA* L.). Naturwissenschaften 54: 648-649.

2404. Schnarrenberger, C. 1969. DIE REGULATION DER CAROTINOIDSYNTHESE DURCH
PHYTOCHROM (P_{DR}) ALS BEISPIEL FÜR DIE REGULATION EINER "POSITIVEN
PHOTOMORPHOSE MIT DUNKELSYNTHESE". Ph.D. Thesis, Univ. Freiburg,
Germany.

2405. Schnarrenberger, C.; Mohr, H. 1969. PHYTOCHROME-MEDIATED SYNTHESIS OF
CAROTENOIDS IN SEEDLINGS. Progr. Photosynthesis Res. 2: 675-680.

2406. Schnarrenberger, C.; Mohr, H. 1970. CAROTENOID SYNTHESIS IN MUSTARD
SEEDLINGS AS CONTROLLED BY PHYTOCHROME AND INHIBITORS. Planta 94:
296-307.

2407. Schneider, C.L. 1941. THE EFFECT OF RED LIGHT ON GROWTH OF THE *AVENA*
SEEDLING WITH SPECTRAL REFERENCE TO THE FIRST INTERNODE. Am. J.
Bot. 28: 878-886.

2408. Schneider, M.J.; Borthwick, H.A.; Hendricks, S.B. 1966. LIGHT-MEDIATED
CONTROL OF NASTIC LEAF MOVEMENTS, FLOWERING, AND STEM LENGTHENING IN
HYOSCYAMUS NIGER. Plant Physiol. 41: Suppl.-15-16 (A).

2409. Schneider, M.J.; Borthwick, H.A.; Hendricks, S.B. 1967. PHOTOMORPHO-
GENIC CONTROL OF STEM LENGTHENING AND FLOWERING IN THREE LONG-DAY
PLANTS. Plant Physiol. 42: Suppl.-9 (A).

2410. Schneider, M.J.; Borthwick, H.A.; Hendricks, S.B. 1967. EFFECTS OF
RADIATION ON FLOWERING OF *HYOSCYAMUS NIGER*. Am. J. Bot. 54: 1241-
1249.

2411. Schneider, M.J.; Fondeville, J.C.; Borthwick, H.A.; Hendricks, S.B.
1967. PHOTOCONTROL OF *MIMOSA PUDICA* L. LEAF MOVEMENT. Plant
Physiol. 42: Suppl.-10 (A).

2412. Schneider, M.J.; Stimson, W.R. 1970. THE CONTRIBUTION OF PHOTOSYNTHESIS
TO THE HIGH ENERGY REACTION CONTROLLING PLANT DEVELOPMENT. Plant
Physiol. 46: Suppl.-25, Abstr. No. 134 (A).

2413. Schneider, M.J.; Stimson, W.R. 1971. FURTHER EVIDENCE FOR PHOTOSYNTHE-
TIC INVOLVEMENT IN A HIGH ENERGY REACTION (HER) RESPONSE. Plant
Physiol. 47: Suppl.-2, Abstr. No. 12 (A).

2414. Schneider, M.J.; Stimson, W.R. 1971. CONTRIBUTIONS OF PHOTOSYNTHESIS
AND PHYTOCHROME TO THE FORMATION OF ANTHOCYANIN IN TURNIP SEEDLINGS.
Plant Physiol. 48: 312-315.

2415. Schneider, M.J.; Stimson, W.R. 1972. PHYTOCHROME AND PHOTOSYSTEM I:
A MODEL FOR THEIR INTERACTION IN HIGH ENERGY RESPONSES. Plant
Physiol. 49: Suppl.-53, Abstr. No. 297 (A).

2416. Schneider, M.J.; Stimson, W. 1972. PHYTOCHROME AND PHOTOSYSTEM I INTER-
ACTION IN A HIGH-ENERGY PHOTORESPONSE. Proc. Nat. Acad. Sci. USA
69: 2150-2154.

2417. Scholz, A.; Haupt, W. 1968. LICHTORIENTIERTE CHLOROPLASTENBEWEGUNG BEI
DER GRÜNALGE *HORMIDIUM FLACCIDUM*. DIE BETEILIGUNG VON CHLOROPLASTEN-
PIGMENTEN. Naturwissenschaften 55: 186-187.

2418. Schönbohm, E. 1962. ÜBER DIE "NEGATIVE PHOTOTAXIS" DER *MOUGEOTIA*-
CHLOROPLASTEN. Ph.D. Thesis, Univ. Tübingen, Germany (not obtained)
(Referred to by Mugele, F. (1962), Z. Botan. 50: 368-388).

2419. Schönbohm, E. 1963. UNTERSUCHUNGEN ÜBER DIE STARKLICHTBEWEGUNG DES
MOUGEOTIA-CHLOROPLASTEN. Z. Bot. 51: 233-276 (ENG Summary).

2420. Schönbohm, E. 1964. DIE WIRKUNG KURZWELLIGER STRAHLUNG AUF DEN
HELLROT-DUNKELROT-ANTAGONISMUS BEI EINIGEN PHOTOMORPHOSEN AN
TRITICUM VULGARE UND *LACTUCA SATIVA*. Z. Bot. 52: 335-345 (ENG
Summary).

2421. Schönbohm, E. 1965. DIE BEEINFLUSSUNG DER NEGATIVEN PHOTOTAXIS DES
       MOUGEOTIA-CHLOROPLASTEN DURCH LINEAR POLARISIERTE LANGWELLIGE
       STRAHLUNG. Z. Pflanzenphysiol. 53: 344-355 (ENG Summary).

2422. Schönbohm, E. 1966. DER EINFLUSS VON ROTLICHT AUF DIE NEGATIVE PHOTO-
       TAXIS DES *MOUGEOTIA*-CHLOROPLASTEN: DIE BEDEUTUNG EINES GRADIENTEN
       VON P_{730} FÜR DIE ORIENTIERUNG. Z. Pflanzenphysiol. 55: 278-286
       (ENG Summary).

2423. Schönbohm, E. 1966. DIE BEDEUTUNG DES PHYTOCHROMSYSTEMS FÜR DIE
       NEGATIVE PHOTOTAXIS DES *MOUGEOTIA*-CHLOROPLASTEN. Ber. Dtsch. Bot.
       Ges. 79: 131-138.

2424. Schönbohm, E. 1967. DIE BEDEUTUNG DES GRADIENTEN VON PHYTOCHROM 730 UND
       DIE TONISCHE WIRKUNG VON BLAULICHT BEI DER NEGATIVEN PHOTOTAXIS DES
       MOUGEOTIA-CHLOROPLASTEN. Z. Pflanzenphysiol. 56: 282-291 (ENG
       Summary).

2425. Schönbohm, E. 1967. DIE HEMMUNG DER POSITIVEN UND NEGATIVEN PHOTOTAXIS
       DES *MOUGEOTIA*-CHLOROPLASTEN DURCH JODID-IONEN. Z. Pflanzenphysiol.
       56: 366-374 (ENG Summary).

2426. Schönbohm, E. 1968. AKTIONSDICHROISMUS BEI DER STARKLICHTBEWEGUNG DES
       CHLOROPLASTEN VON *MOUGEOTIA* SPEC. Ber. Dtsch. Bot. Ges. 81: 203-209
       (ENG Summary).

2427. Schönbohm, E. 1969. UNTERSUCHUNGEN ÜBER DEN EINFLUSS VON PHOTOSYNTHESE-
       HEMMSTOFFEN UND HALOGENIDEN AUF DIE STARKLICHT-UND SCHWACHLICHTBEWE-
       GUNG DES CHLOROPLASTEN VON *MOUGEOTIA* SPEC. Z. Pflanzenphysiol. 60:
       255-269 (ENG Summary).

2428. Schönbohm, E. 1969. DIE HEMMUNG DER LICHTINDUZIERTEN BEWEGUNG DES
       MOUGEOTIA-CHLOROPLASTEN DURCH P-CHLORMERCURIBENZOAT (VERSUCHE ZUR
       MECHANIK DER CHLOROPLASTENBEWEGUNG). Z. Pflanzenphysiol. 61:
       250-260 (ENG Summary).

2429. Schönbohm, E. 1970. SEKUNDÄRREAKTIONEN BEI DER CHLOROPLASTENBEWEGUNG.
       Ber. Dtsch. Bot. Ges. 83: 629-632 (R).

2430. Schönbohm, E. 1971. UNTERSUCHUNGEN ZUM PHOTORECEPTORPROBLEM BEIM
       TONISCHEN BLAULICHT-EFFEKT DER STARKLICHTBEWEGUNG DES *MOUGEOTIA*-
       CHLOROPLASTEN. Z. Pflanzenphysiol. 66: 20-33 (ENG Summary).

2431. Schönbohm, E. 1972. EXPERIMENTS ON THE MECHANISM OF CHLOROPLAST MOVE-
       MENT IN LIGHT ORIENTED CHLOROPLAST ARRANGEMENT. Acta Protozool. 11:
       211-224 (R).

2432. Schönbohm, E. 1972. DIE WIRKUNG VON SH-BLOCKERN SOWIE VON LICHT UND DUNKEL AUF DIE VERANKERUNG DER *MOUGEOTIA*-CHLOROPLASTEN IM CYTOPLASMATISCHEN WANDBELAG. Z. Pflanzenphysiol. 66: 113-132 (ENG Summary).

2433. Schönbohm, E. 1973. DIE LICHTINDUZIERTE VERANKERUNG DER PLASTIDEN IM CYTOPLASMATISCHEN WANDBELAG: EINE PHYTOCHROMGESTEUERTE KURZZEITREAKTION. Ber. Dtsch. Bot. Ges. 86: 423-430 (ENG Summary).

2434. Schopfer, P.; Mohr, H. 1965. DIE REGULATION DES ASCORBINSÄUREGEHALTS VON KEIMPFLANZEN ÜBER DAS PHYTOCHROMSYSTEM. Naturwissenschaften 52: 265-266.

2435. Schopfer, P. 1966. UNTERSUCHANGEN ZUR PHYTOCHROMINDUZIERTEN PHOTOMORPHOGENESE DES SENFKEIMLINGS (*SINAPIS ALBA* L.). Ph.D. Thesis, Univ. Freiburg, Germany.

2436. Schopfer, P. 1966. DER EINFLUSS VON PHYTOCHROM AUF DIE STATIONÄREN KONZENTRATIONEN VON ASCORBINSÄURE UND DEHYDROASCORBINSÄURE BEIM SENFKEIMLING (*SINAPIS ALBA* L.). Planta 69: 158-177 (ENG Summary).

2437. Schopfer, P.; Mohr, H. 1966. DIE WIRKUNG VON PHYTOCHROM UND ACTINOMYCIN D AUF DAS HYPOKOTYLWACHSTUM VON SENFKEIMLINGEN (*SINAPIS ALBA* L.). Naturwissenschaften 53: 231.

2438. Schopfer, P. 1967. DIE HEMMUNG DER PHYTOCHROMINDUZIERTEN PHOTOMORPHOGENESE ("POSITIVE" PHOTOMORPHOSEN) DES SENFKEIMLINGS (*SINAPIS ALBA* L.) DURCH ACTINOMYCIN D UND PUROMYCIN. Planta 72: 297-305 (ENG Summary).

2439. Schopfer, P. 1967. DER EINFLUSS VON ACTINOMYCIN D UND PUROMYCIN AUF DIE PHYTOCHROMINDUZIERTE WACHSTUMSHEMMUNG DES HYPOKOTYLS BEIM SENFKEIMLING (*SINAPIS ALBA* L.). Planta 72: 306-320 (ENG Summary).

2440. Schopfer, P. 1967. WEITERE UNTERSUCHUNGEN ZUR PHYTOCHROMINDUZIERTEN AKKUMULATION VON ASCORBINSÄURE BEIM SENFKEIMLING (*SINAPIS ALBA* L.). Planta 74: 210-227 (ENG Summary).

2441. Schopfer, P. 1969. DIE HEMMUNG DES STRECKUNGSWACHSTUMS DURCH PHYTOCHROM EIN STOFFAUFNAHME ERFORDERNDER PROZESS. Planta 85: 383-388 (ENG Summary).

2442. Schopfer, P. 1971. CONTROL OF HYPOCOTYL GROWTH BY A P_{fr} THRESHOLD MECHANISM. Proc. Eur. Annu. Symp. Plant Photomorphogenesis, (Athens), pp. 45-46 (A).

2443. Schopfer, P. 1971. DIE PHENYLALANINAMMONIUMLYASE (PAL, EC 4.3.1.5) DES SENFKEIMLINGS (*SINAPIS ALBA* L.) EIN ELEKTROPHORETISCH EINHEITLICHES ENZYM. Planta 99: 339-346 (ENG Summary).

2444. Schopfer, P.; Hock, B. 1971. NACHWEIS DER PHYTOCHROM-INDUZIERTEN *DE NOVO*-SYNTHESE VON PHENYLALANINAMMONIUMLYASE (PAL, E.C. 4.3.1.5) IN KEIMLINGEN VON *SINAPIS ALBA* L. DURCH DICHTEMARKIERUNG MIT DEUTERIUM. Planta 96: 248-253 (ENG Summary).

2445. Schopfer, P.; Oelze-Karow. H. 1971. NACHWEIS EINER SCHWELLENWERTSREGU-LATION DURCH PHYTOCHROM BEI DER PHOTOMODULATION DES HYPOKOTYL-STRECKUNGSWACHSTUMS VON SENFKEIMLINGEN (*SINAPIS ALBA* L.). Planta 100: 167-180 (ENG Summary).

2446. Schopfer, P. 1972. PHYTOCHROME II: PROPERTIES AND FUNCTION *IN VIVO*. Proc. VI Int. Congr. Photobiol. Abstr. No. 021 (A) (R).

2447. Schopfer, P. 1972. PHYTOCHROME AND THE CONTROL OF ENZYME ACTIVITY. *Phytochrome*, Ed. K. Mitrakos and W. Shropshire, Jr. Academic Press: London and New York, pp. 485-514 (R).

2448. Schopfer, P. 1972. ROLE OF PHYTOCHROME IN THE CONTROL OF ENZYME ACTIVI-TY IN HIGHER PLANTS: PHOTOMODULATION AND PHOTODETERMINATION OF ENZYME SYNTHESIS. Symp. Biol. Hung. 13: 115-126 (R).

2449. Schopfer, P.; Mohr, H. 1972. PHYTOCHROME-MEDIATED INDUCTION OF PHENYLALANINE AMMONIA-LYASE IN MUSTARD SEEDLINGS. Plant Physiol. 49: 8-10.

2450. Schopfer, P. 1973. MODULATION UND DETERMINATION DER ENZYMBILDUNG ALS REGULATIONSPRINZIPIEN BEI DER PHYTOCHROMABHÄNGIGEN PHOTOMORPHOGENESE. Ber. Dtsch. Bot. Ges. 86: 271-286 (ENG Summary) (R).

2451. Schopfer, P.; Plachy, C. 1973. DIE ORGANSPEZIFISCHE PHOTODETERMINATION DER ENTWICKLUNG VON PEROXYDASEAKTIVITÄT IM SENFKEIMLUNG (*SINAPIS ALBA* L.) DURCH PHYTOCHROM. I. KINETISCHE ANALYSE. Z. Naturforsch. 28: 296-301 (ENG Summary).

2452. Schopfer, P.; Acton, G.J. 1974. PHYTOCHROME-MEDIATED ENZYME *DE NOVO* SYNTHESIS (PAL) IN MUSTARD COTYLEDONS. Proc. Eur. Annu. Symp. Plant Photomorphogenesis, (Antwerpen), pp. 64-65.

2453. Schopfer, P.; Pfaff, W. 1974. PHYTOCHROME-INDUCED REGENERATION OF ADVENTITIOUS ROOTS IN THE MUSTARD SEEDLING (*SINAPIS ALBA* L.). Proc. Eur. Annu. Symp. Plant Photomorphogenesis, (Antwerpen), p. 124.

2454. Schulz, M.R.; Klein, R.M. 1963. EFFECTS OF VISIBLE AND ULTRAVIOLET RADIATION ON THE GERMINATION OF *PHACELIA TANACETIFOLIA*. Am. J. Bot. 50: 430-434.

2455. Schulz, M.R.; Klein, R.M. 1965. ON THE MECHANISMS OF LIGHT-INDUCED GERMINATION INHIBITION OF *PHACELIA TANACETIFOLIA*. Am. J. Bot. 52: 278-281.

2456. Schulz, N. 1901. UEBER DIE EINWIRKUNG DES LICHTES AUF DIE KEIMUNGS-FÄHIGKEIT DER SPOREN DER MOOSE, FARNE, UND SCHACHFELHALME. Beih. Bot. Zentralbl. XI: 81-97.

2457. Schulz, R. 1964. DIE WIRKUNG VERSCHIEDENER LICHT QUALITÄTEN UND INTENSITÄTEN BEI DER PHOTOINDUKTION DER DORSIVENTRALITÄT BEI KEIMEN-DEN BRUTKÖRPERN VON *MARCHANTIA POLYMORPHA* L. Ph.D. Thesis, Univ. Frankfurt/Main, Germany (not obtained) (referred to by Ninnerman, H. (1967) Biol. Zentralbl. 86: 303-364).

2458. Schwabe, W.W. 1964. LIGHT AND DARK REACTIONS. Proc. X Int. Bot. Congr. pp. 188-189 (A).

2459. Schwabe, W.W.; Wilson, J.R. 1965. EFFECTS OF PHOTOPERIOD ON THE APPARENT VISCOSITY OF LEAF CYTOPLASM IN *KALANCHOË BLOSSFELDIANA*. 2. SOME LONG- AND SHORT-TERM EFFECTS OF DAYLENGTH AND SPECTRAL COMPOSI-TION OF LIGHT. Ann. Bot. (London) 29: 383-406.

2460. Schwabe, W.W. 1968. THE INITIATION OF FLOWERING. Sci. Prog. Oxford 56: 325-336 (R).

2461. Schwabe, W.W.; Valio, I.F.M. 1970. GROWTH AND DORMANCY IN *LUNULARIA CRUCIATA* (L.) DUM. VI. GROWTH REGULATION BY DAYLENGTH, BY RED, FAR-RED, AND BLUE LIGHT, AND BY APPLIED GROWTH REGULATORS AND CHELATING AGENTS. J. Exp. Bot. 21: 122-137.

2462. Schwemmle, B. 1969. DAS PROBLEM DER BLÜTENBILDUNG. Naturwiss. Rundsch. 22: 47-53 (R).

2463. Scott, E.G.; Carter, J.E.; Street, H.E. 1961. STUDIES OF THE GROWTH IN CULTURE OF EXCISED WHEAT ROOTS III. THE QUANTITATIVE AND QUALITATIVE REQUIREMENT FOR LIGHT. Physiol. Plant. 14: 725-733.

2464. Scott, N.S.; Nair, H.; Smillie, R.M. 1971. THE EFFECT OF RED IRRADIA-TION ON PLASTID RIBOSOMAL RNA SYNTHESIS IN DARK-GROWN PEA SEEDLINGS. Plant Physiol. 47: 385-388.

2465. Scott, N.S.; Munns, R.; Graham, D.; Smillie, R.M. 1971. ORIGIN AND SYNTHESIS OF CHLOROPLAST RIBOSOMAL RNA AND PHOTOREGULATION DURING CHLOROPLAST BIOGENESIS. *The Autonomy and Biogenesis of Mitochondria and Chloroplasts*, Ed. N.K. Boardman, A.W. Linnane and R.M. Smillie, North Holland, Amsterdam, pp. 383-392.

2466. Scott, R.A., Jr.; Liverman, J.L. 1956. PROMOTION OF LEAF EXPANSION BY KINETIN AND BENZYLAMINOPURINE. Plant Physiol. 31: 321-322.

2467. Scott, R.A., Jr. 1957. BIOCHEMICAL AND PHOTOCHEMICAL CONTROL OF LEAF DISK EXPANSION. Ph.D. Thesis, Tex. A&M Univ.

2468. Scott, R.A.; Liverman, J.L. 1957. CONTROL OF ETIOLATED BEAN LEAF-DISK EXPANSION BY GIBBERELLINS AND ADENINE. Science 126: 122-124.

2469. Scott, T.K.; Wilkins, M.B. 1969. AUXIN TRANSPORT IN ROOTS. IV. EFFECTS OF LIGHT ON IAA MOVEMENT AND GEOTROPIC RESPONSIVENESS IN *ZEA* ROOTS. Planta 87: 249-258.

2470. Seitz, K. 1964. DAS WIRKUNGSSPEKTRUM DER PHOTODINESE BEI *ELODEA CANADENSIS*. Protoplasma 58: 621-640 (ENG Summary).

2471. Seitz, K. 1967. WIRKUNGSSPEKTREN FÜR DIE STARKLICHTBEWEGUNG DER CHLOROPLASTEN, DIE PHOTODINESE UND DIE LICHTABHÄNGIGE VISKOSITÄT-SÄNDERUNG BEI *VALLISNERIA SPIRALIS* SSP. *TORTA*. Z. Pflanzenphysiol. 56: 246-261 (ENG Summary).

2472. Seitz, K. 1967. EINE ANALYSE DER FÜR DIE LICHTABHÄNGIGEN BEWEGUNGEN DER CHLOROPLASTEN VERANTWORTLICHEN PHOTOREZEPTORSYSTEME BEI *VALLISNERIA SPIRALIS* SSP. *TORTA*. Z. Pflanzenphysiol. 57: 96-104 (ENG Summary).

2473. Seitz, K. 1970. ÜBER DEN MECHANISMUS DER LICHTINDUZIERTEN ORIENTIE-RUNGSBEWEGUNG DER CHLOROPLASTEN. Ber. Dtsch. Bot. Ges. 83: 193-198 (R).

2474. Seitz, K. 1970. ZUR FRAGE DER JODID-WIRKUNG AUF DIE STARKLICHTBEWEGUNG DER CHLOROPLASTEN VON *VALLISNERIA SPIRALIS* SSP. *TORTA*. Z. Pflanzen-physiol. 62: 63-69 (ENG Summary).

2475. Seitz, K. 1970. DIE STARKLICHTBEWEGUNG DER CHLOROPLASTEN VON *VALLISNERIA* IN ABHÄNGIGKEIT VON HEMMSTOFFEN DER OXYDATIVEN PHOSPHORYLIERUNG. Z. Pflanzenphysiol. 63: 401-407 (ENG Summary).

2476. Seitz, K. 1971. DIE URSACHE DER PHOTOTAXIS DER CHLOROPLASTEN: EIN ATP-
GRADIENT? (VERSUCHE ZUM PRIMÄRPROZESS DER STARKLICHTBEWEGUNG BEI
VALLISNERIA). Z. Pflanzenphysiol. 64: 241-256 (ENG Summary).

2477. Seitz, K. 1972. PRIMARY PROCESSES CONTROLLING THE LIGHT INDUCED MOVE-
MENT OF CHLOROPLASTS. Acta Protozool. 11: 225-235 (R).

2478. Seitz, K. 1974. IRRADIANCE DEPENDENT FAR-RED EFFECTS UPON RED INDUCED
ANTHOCYANIN SYNTHESIS IN *SINAPIS ALBA*. Proc. Eur. Annu. Symp. Plant
Photomorphogenesis, (Antwerpen), pp. 31-32.

2479. Seitz, K. 1974. IRRADIANCE DEPENDENT FAR-RED EFFECTS UPON RED INDUCED
GERMINATION OF LETTUCE SEEDS. Z. Pflanzenphysiol. 71: 49-56.

2480. Selman, I.W.; Ahmed, E.O.S. 1962. SOME EFFECTS OF FAR-RED IRRADIATION
AND GIBBERELLIC ACID ON THE GROWTH OF TOMATO PLANTS. Ann. Appl.
Biol. 50: 479-485.

2481. Sen, N. 1969. ACTION OF LIGHT IN THE GERMINATION OF SEEDS AND SEEDLING
GROWTH IN SOME *ASCLEPIADACEAE*. Acta Bot. Acad. Sci. Hung. 15:
327-335.

2482. Sen, S.P. 1962. THE ROLE OF CARBON DIOXIDE FIXATION IN PHOTOPERIODISM-
THE EFFECT OF DARK INTERRUPTION TREATMENTS. Indian J. Plant Physiol.
5: 202-217.

2483. Senebier, J. 1782. MEMOIRES PHYSIO-CHIMIQUES. 2: 55-75, 103-104.

2484. Senn, G. 1908. *DIE GESTALTS UND LAGEVERÄNDERUNG DER PFLANZENCHROMATO-
PHOREN*. Leipzig. Verlag Wilhelm Engelmann, 397 pp. and Tables.

2485. Setty, S.L.; Jaffe, M.J. 1970. PHYTOCHROME CONTROLLED CONTRACTION AND
RECOVERY OF CONTRACTILE VACUOLE IN THE MOTOR CELLS OF *MIMOSA PUDICA*
L. Am. J. Bot. 57: 762 (A).

2486. Setty, S.; Jaffe, M.J. 1972. PHYTOCHROME-CONTROLLED RAPID CONTRACTION
AND RECOVERY OF CONTRACTILE VACUOLES IN THE MOTOR CELLS OF *MIMOSA
PUDICA* AS AN INTRACELLULAR CORRELATE OF NYCTINASTY. Planta 108:
121-131.

2487. Shakhov, A.A.; Kuznetsov, E.D. 1972. CHANGE IN THE HISTONE LEVEL
DURING STIMULATION OF BIOSYNTHESIS BY RED LIGHT. Elektron, Obrab.
Mater 3: 72-75 (RUS).

2488. Shapiro, S. 1958. THE ROLE OF LIGHT IN THE GROWTH OF ROOT PRIMORDIA IN
THE STEM OF THE LOMBARDY POPLAR. *The Physiology of Forest Trees*,
Ed. K.V. Thimann, The Ronald Press, New York, pp. 445-465.

2489. Sheard, C.; Higgins, G.M. 1927. THE INFLUENCE OF SELECTIVE AND
       GENERAL IRRADIATION BY A QUARTZ MERCURY ARC LAMP UPON THE GERMINATION
       AND GROWTH OF SEEDS. Science 65: 282-284.

2490. Sheard, C.; Higgins, G.M.; Foster, W.T. 1930. THE GERMINATION OF SEEDS,
       GROWTH OF PLANTS AND DEVELOPMENT OF CHLOROPHYLL AS INFLUENCED BY
       SELECTIVE SOLAR IRRADIATION. Science 71: 291-293.

2491. Sheehan, T.J.; Teas, H.J. 1957. PRELIMINARY PHOTO AND CHEMICAL STUDIES
       ON FLORAL INDUCTION IN CHRYSANTHEMUMS. Fla. State Hortic. Soc.,
       pp. 398-402.

2492. Shen-Miller, J. 1973. SPECTRAL SENSITIVITY OF CORN ROOT GEOTROPISM.
       Plant Physiol. 51: Suppl.-52, Abstr. No. 279 (A).

2493. Shen-Miller, J. 1974. SPECTRAL SENSITIVITY OF CORN ROOT GEOTROPISM.
       Plant Growth Substances 1973, Proc. VIII Int. Conf. Plant Growth
       Subst., Tokyo, pp. 1095-1103.

2494. Sherwin, J.E.; Furuya, M. 1973. A RED-FAR RED REVERSIBLE EFFECT ON
       UPTAKE OF EXOGENOUS INDOLEACETIC ACID IN ETIOLATED RICE COLEOPTILES.
       Plant Physiol. 51: 295-298.

2495. Shirley, H.L. 1929. THE INFLUENCE OF LIGHT INTENSITY AND LIGHT QUALITY
       UPON THE GROWTH OF PLANTS. Am. J. Bot. 16: 354-390.

2496. Shiyan, P.N.; Lebedev, S.I.; Litse, R.A. 1968. INTERRELATION BETWEEN
       LIGHT AND PHOSPHORUS NUTRITION OF PLANTS. Nauk Pr., Ukr. Silskogo-
       spod. Akad. 4: 35-41 (RUS) (not obtained).

2497. Shinohara, T.; Yamamoto, Y.; Kitano, H.; Fukuda, M. 1974. INTERACTIONS
       OF LIGHT AND OZONE INJURY IN TOBACCO. Nippon Sakumotsu Gakkai Kiji
       43: 433-438.

2498. Shlyk, A.A.; Savchenko, G.E.; Stanishevenkaya, E.M.; Shevchuk, S.N.;
       Gaponenko, V.I.; Gatikh, O.A. 1966. ROLE OF PHYTOCHROME IN THE
       CHLOROPHYLL METABOLISM OF GREEN PLANTS. Dokl. Akad. Nauk. SSSR
       171: 1443-1446 (RUS).

2499. Shlyk, A.A.; Shevchuk, S.N.; Gaponeko, V.I. 1974. INVESTIGATION OF
       PHYTOCHROME SYSTEM EFFECT ON PROCESS OF CHLOROPHYLL FORMATION IN
       POST-ETIOLATED LEAVES. Dokl. Akad. Nauk SSSR 215: 1003-1006 (RUS).

2500. Shropshire, W., Jr.; Klein, W.H.; Elstad, V.B. 1961. ACTION SPECTRA
       OF PHOTOMORPHOGENIC INDUCTION AND PHOTOINACTIVATION OF GERMINATION
       IN *ARABIDOPSIS THALIANA*. Plant Cell Physiol. 2: 63-69.

2501. Shropshire, W., Jr.; Klein, W.H.; Edwards, J.L. 1964. PHOTOMORPHOGENE-
SIS INDUCED BY FLAVINMONONUCLEOTIDE FLUORESCENCE. Physiol. Plant.
17: 676-682.

2502. Shropshire, W., Jr.; Mohr, H. 1970. GRADIENT FORMATION OF ANTHOCYANIN
IN SEEDLINGS OF *FAGOPYRUM* AND *SINAPIS* UNILATERALLY EXPOSED TO RED
AND FAR-RED LIGHT. Photochem. Photobiol. 12: 145-149.

2503. Shropshire, W., Jr.; Lange, H.; Mohr, H. 1971. AN ANALYSIS OF PHYTO-
CHROME MEDIATED ANTHOCYANIN SYNTHESIS. Plant Physiol. 47: Suppl.-2,
Abstr. No. 11 (A).

2504. Shropshire, W., Jr. 1972. PHYTOCHROME, A PHOTOCHROMIC SENSOR. Photophysiology 7: 33-72 (R).

2505. Shropshire, W., Jr. 1972. ACTION SPECTROSCOPY. *Phytochrome*: Ed. K.
Mitrakos and W. Shropshire, Jr., Academic Press: London and New
York, pp. 161-181 (R).

2506. Shropshire, W., Jr. 1973. PHOTOINDUCED PARENTAL CONTROL OF SEED GERMI-
NATION AND THE SPECTRAL QUALITY OF SOLAR RADIATION. Sol. Energy 15:
99-105.

2507. Shropshire, W., Jr. 1974. PHOTOTROPISM INTRODUCTORY LECTURE. Proc. VI
Int. Congr. Photobiol., Abstr. No. 024 (R-D).

2508. Shternberg, M.B. 1965. *PLANT GROWTH AND NUCLEIN METABOLISM REGULATORS*.
Science Publishing house, Moscow, pp. 65-102 (RUS) (R).

2509. Shuck, A.L. 1935. LIGHT AS A FACTOR INFLUENCING THE DORMANCY OF LET-
TUCE SEEDS. Plant Physiol. 10: 193-196.

2510. Shulgin, I.A. 1962. ON THE ROLE OF INFRA-RED RADIATION IN THE ACTIVI-
TIES OF PLANTS. Dokl. Akad. Nauk. USSR 146: 484-487 (RUS) (R).

2511. Shulgin, I.A.; Kuperman, F.M.; Mertsalov, S.M. 1963. EFFECT OF SPEC-
TRAL COMPOSITION, RADIATION INTENSITY AND DURATION OF PHOTOPERIODS
ON THE DEVELOPMENT, GROWTH AND MORPHOGENESIS OF RADISH PLANTS.
Vestn. Skh. Nauki Moscow 8: 21-33 (RUS) (ENG, FR, GR, Summaries).

2512. Shulgin, I.A. 1964. ON THE EFFECT OF VISUAL AND INFRA-RED RADIATION ON
THE GROWTH AND DEVELOPMENT OF RADISH. Fiziol. Rast. 11: 398-408
Consultants Bureau Eng. Translation, pp. 339-348.

2513. Shulgin, I.A. 1965. INFLUENCE OF SPECTRAL COMPOSITION AND LIGHT INTEN-
SITY ON THE DEVELOPMENT OF PLANTS DURING VARIOUS PHOTOPERIODS.
Fiziol. Rast. 12: 289-300 (RUS) Consultants Bureau Eng. Translation,
pp. 245-254.

200

2514. Shulgin, I.A.; Scherbina, I.P. 1968. EFFICIENCY OF LIGHT OF DIFFERENT SPECTRAL ENERGY DISTRIBUTION IN REACTIONS OF PHOTOMORPHOGENESIS. Dokl. Akad. Nauk. SSSR 179: 479-482 (RUS).

2515. Shumate, W.H. 1965. FLORAL INHIBITION OF BILOXI SOYBEAN DURING A 72 HOUR CYCLE. Ph.D. Thesis, Univ. Calif., Los Angeles.

2516. Shumate, W.H.; Reid, H.B.; Hamner, K.C. 1967. FLORAL INHIBITION OF BILOXI SOYBEAN DURING A 72 HOUR CYCLE. Plant Physiol. 42: 1511-1518.

2516.5 Shupilova, G.A. 1974. ABSORBING ACTION OF ROOTS DURING ILLUMINATION OF PLANTS BY LIGHT OF VARIOUS SPECTRAL COMPOSITIONS. Biol. Biofiz. Mater. Itogovoi Nauchn. Konf. Zakonchennym 1973 Godu. Temain. 1973: 132-138 (RUS) (not obtained).

2517. Sidaway, G.H. 1969. ELECTROSTATIC INFLUENCE ON PHYTOCHROME MEDIATED PHOTOMORPHOGENESIS. Int. J. Biometeorol. 13: 219-230.

2518. Sidaway, G.H. 1970. ELECTROSTATIC SENSITIVITY OF THE PHOTO-RECEPTIVE MECHANISM IN GERMINATING "GRAND RAPIDS" LETTUCE SEED. Planta 90: 295-298.

2519. Siegelman, H.W.; Hendricks, S.B. 1956. TWO PHOTOCHEMICALLY DISTINCT CONTROLS OF ANTHOCYANIN FORMATION IN *BRASSICA* SEEDLINGS. Plant Physiol. 31: Suppl.-13 (A).

2520. Siegelman, H.W.; Hendricks, S.B. 1957. PHOTOCONTROL OF ANTHOCYANIN SYNTHESIS IN APPLE HYPODERMIS. Plant Physiol. 32: Suppl.-9 (A).

2521. Siegelman, H.W.; Hendricks, S.B. 1957. PHOTOCONTROL OF ANTHOCYANIN FORMATION IN TURNIP AND RED CABBAGE SEEDLINGS. Plant Physiol. 32: 393-398.

2522. Siegelman, H.W.; Hendricks, S.B. 1958. PHOTOCONTROL OF ANTHOCYANIN SYNTHESIS IN APPLE SKIN. Plant Physiol. 33: 185-190.

2523. Siegelman, H.W. 1961. BIOSYNTHESIS OF ANTHOCYANIN AND RELATED COM-POUNDS. Recent Adv. Bot. 2: 1028-1031.

2524. Siegelman, H.W.; Firer, E.M.; Butler, W.L.; Hendricks, S.B. 1961. PARTIAL PURIFICATION OF PHYTOCHROME. Plant Physiol. 36: Suppl.-42 (A).

2525. Siegelman, H.W.; Firer, E.M.; Butler, W.L.; Hendricks, S.B. 1962. PHYTOCHROME FROM CORN AND BARLEY SEEDLINGS. Plant Physiol. 37: Suppl.-27, Abstr. No. 749 (A).

2526. Siegelman, H.W. 1964. DENATURATION OF PHYTOCHROME. Proc. IV Int. Congr. Photobiol., p. 85 (A).

2527. Siegelman, H.W. 1964. PHYSIOLOGICAL STUDIES ON PHENOLIC BIOSYNTHESIS. *Biochemistry of Phenolic Compounds*, Ed. J.B. Harborne, Academic Press: London and New York, pp. 437-456 (R).

2528. Siegelman, H.W.; Butler, W.L. 1964. PURIFICATION AND PROPERTIES OF PHYTOCHROME. Proc. X Int. Bot. Congr., p. 185 (A).

2529. Siegelman, H.W.; Firer, E.M. 1964. PURIFICATION OF PHYTOCHROME FROM OAT SEEDLINGS. Biochemistry 3: 418-423.

2530. Siegelman, H.W.; Hendricks, S.B. 1964. PHYTOCHROME AND ITS CONTROL OF PLANT GROWTH AND DEVELOPMENT. Adv. Enzymol. Relat. Subj. Biochem. 26: 1-33 (R).

2531. Siegelman, H.W.; Butler, W.L. 1965. PROPERTIES OF PHYTOCHROME. Annu. Rev. Plant Physiol. 16: 383-392 (R).

2532. Siegelman, H.W.; Hendricks, S.B. 1965. PURIFICATION AND PROPERTIES OF PHYTOCHROME: A CHROMOPROTEIN REGULATING PLANT GROWTH. Fed. Proc. Fed. Am. Soc. Exp. Biol. 24: 863-867.

2533. Siegelman, H.W.; Turner, B.C.; Hendricks, S.B. 1965. THE CHROMOPHORE OF PHYTOCHROME. Plant Physiol. 40: Suppl.-53 (A).

2534. Siegelman, H.W.; Turner, B.C.; Hendricks, S.B. 1966. THE CHROMOPHORE OF PHYTOCHROME. Plant Physiol. 41: 1289-1292.

2535. Siegelman, H.W.; Chapman, D.J.; Cole, W.J. 1968. THE BILE PIGMENTS OF PLANTS. *Porphyrins and Related Compounds*, Ed. T.W. Goodwin, Academic Press: London and New York, pp. 107-120 (R).

2536. Siegelman, H.W. 1969. PHYTOCHROME. *Physiology of Plant Growth and Development*, Ed. M.B. Wilkins, McGraw-Hill, New York, pp. 487-506 (R).

2537. Sierp, H. 1918. EIN BEITRAG ZUR KENNTNIS DES EINFLUSSES DES LICHTES AUF DAS WACHSTUM DER KOLEOPTILE VON *AVENA SATIVA*. Z. Bot. 10: 641-729.

2538. Sierp, H. 1933. UNTERSUCHUNGEN ÜBER DIE ÖFFNUNGSBEWEGUNG DER STOMATA IN VERSCHIEDENEN SPEKTRALBEZIRKEN. Flora 128: 269-285.

2539. Simon, S.V. 1928. ZUR KEIMUNGSPHYSIOLOGIE DER WINTERKNOSPEN VON *HYDROCHARIS MORSUS RANAE* L.: ZUGLEICHEIN BEITRAG ZUR FRAGE DER JAHRESPERIODIZITÄT. Jahrb. Wiss. Bot. 68: 11-205.

2540. Simon, S.V. 1931. WEITERE UNTERSUCHUNGEN ZUR KEIMUNGSPHYSIOLOGIE DER WINTERKNOSPEN VON *HYDROCHARIS*. I. ÜBER ABSTUMPFUNGSERSCHEINUNGEN INFOLGE EINER ZUM AUSTREIBEN NICHT HINREICHENDEN BELICHTUNG. Jahrb. Wiss. Bot. 75: 622-641.

2541. Simon, S.V. 1934. WEITERE UNTERSUCHUNGEN ZUR KEIMUNGSPHYSIOLOGIE DER WINTERKNOSPEN VON *HYDROCHARIS* II-IV. Jahrb. Wiss. Bot. 79: 296-310.

2542. Simpson, G.M.; Wain, R.L. 1961. A RELATIONSHIP BETWEEN GIBBERELLIC ACID AND LIGHT IN THE CONTROL OF INTERNODE EXTENSION OF DWARF PEAS (*PISUM SATIVUM*). J. Exp. Bot. 12: 207-216.

2543. Singh, G.; Garg, O.P. 1971. EFFECT OF RED, FAR-RED RADIATIONS ON GER-MINATION OF COTTON SEEDS. Plant Cell Physiol. 12: 411-415.

2544. Sircar, S.M.; Biswas, M. 1960. VIABILITY AND GERMINATION INHIBITOR OF THE SEED OF RICE. Nature (London) 187: 620-621.

2545. Sisler, E.C.; Klein, W.H. 1960. EFFECT OF RED AND FAR-RED IRRADIATION OF NUCLEOTIDE PHOSPHATE AND ADENOSINE TRIPHOSPHATE IN SEEDLINGS. Plant Physiol. 35: Suppl.-32 (A).

2546. Sisler, E.C.; Klein, W.H.; Gettens, R. 1961. THE EFFECT OF RED AND FAR-RED RADIANT ENERGY AND DELTA-AMINO-LEVULINIC ACID ON THE LAG PHASE OF CHLOROPHYLL SYNTHESIS IN BEAN SEEDLINGS. Plant Physiol. 36: Suppl.-42 (A).

2547. Sisler, E.C.; Klein, W.H. 1961. EFFECT OF RED AND FAR-RED IRRADIATION ON NUCLEOTIDE PHOSPHATE AND ADENOSINE TRIPHOSPHATE LEVELS IN DARK-GROWN BEAN AND *AVENA* SEEDLINGS. Physiol. Plant. 14: 115-123.

2548. Sisler, E.C.; Klein, W.H. 1963. THE EFFECT OF AGE AND VARIOUS CHEMI-CALS OF THE LAG PHASE OF CHLOROPHYLL SYNTHESIS IN DARK-GROWN BEAN SEEDLINGS. Physiol. Plant. 16: 315-322.

2549. Sivori, E.; Went, F.W. 1944. PHOTOPERIODICITY OF *BAERIA CHRYSOSTOMA*. Bot. Gaz. (Chicago) 105: 321-329.

2550. Skinner, C.G.; Shive, W. 1959. STIMULATION OF LETTUCE SEED GERMINATION BY 6-(SUBSTITUTED) PURINES. Plant Physiol. 34: 1-3.

2551. Slabecka-Szweykowska, A. 1955. ON THE INFLUENCE OF THE WAVE LENGTH OF LIGHT ON THE BIOGENESIS OF ANTHOCYANIN PIGMENT IN THE *VITIS VINIFERA* TISSUE *IN VITRO*. Acta Soc. Bot. Pol. 24: 3-11 (POL) (ENG Summary).

2552. Slabecka-Szweykowska, A. 1955. THE INFLUENCE OF LIGHT ON THE BIOGENE-SIS OF RUBROBRASSICIN IN SEEDLINGS OF RED CABBAGE. Acta Soc. Bot. Pol. 24: 13-26 (POL) (ENG Summary).

2553. Smillie, R.M.; Scott, N.S. 1969. ORGANELLE BIOSYNTHESIS: THE CHLORO-
PLAST. *Progress in Molecular and Submolecular Biology*, Ed. F.E.
Hahn, Springer-Verlag, Berlin 1: 136-202 (R).

2554. Smith, D.H., Jr.; Mumford, F.E.; Castle, J.E. 1961. IAA OXIDASE INHIBI-
TOR FROM ETIOLATED PEA EIPCOTYLS. Plant Physiol. 36: Suppl.-47 (A).

2555. Smith, H.; Frankland, B. 1966. SPECIFIC INHIBITION BY URACIL DERIVA-
TIVES OF THE MECHANISM OF DORMANCY RELEASE BY LIGHT-SENSITIVE LET-
TUCE SEEDS. Nature (London) 211: 1323-1324.

2556. Smith, H.; Koller, B.; Attridge, T.H.; Harper, D.B. 1968. RNA AND
ENZYME SYNTHESIS IN RELATION TO THE FUNCTION OF PHYTOCHROME. Proc.
V Int. Congr. Photobiol., p. 155 (A).

2557. Smith, H. 1970. PHYTOCHROME AND PHOTOMORPHOGENESIS IN PLANTS. Nature
(London) 227: 665-668 (R).

2558. Smith, H.; Attridge, T.H. 1970. INCREASED PHENYLALANINE AMMONIA-LYASE
ACTIVITY DUE TO LIGHT TREATMENT AND ITS SIGNIFICANCE FOR THE MODE OF
ACTION OF PHYTOCHROME. Phytochemistry 9: 487-495.

2559. Smith, H.; Harper, D.B. 1970. THE EFFECTS OF SHORT- AND LONG-TERM
IRRADIATION ON THE FLAVONOID COMPLEMENT OF THE TERMINAL BUDS OF
PISUM SATIVUM VAR. ALASKA. Phytochemistry 9: 477-485.

2560. Smith, H. 1972. THE PHOTOCONTROL OF FLAVONOID BIOSYNTHESIS. *Phytochrome*: Ed. K. Mitrakos and W. Shropshire, Jr., Academic Press:
London and New York, pp. 433-481 (R).

2561. Smith, H. 1972. PHYTOCHROME, HORMONES AND MEMBRANES. Nature (London)
236: 425 (R).

2562. Smith, H. 1973. LIGHT QUALITY AND GERMINATION: ECOLOGICAL IMPLICATIONS.
Proc. Easter Sch. Agric. Sci., Univ. Nottingham Ed. W. Heydecker,
pp. 219-231 (R).

2562.5 Smith, H. 1973. REGULATORY MECHANISMS IN THE PHOTOCONTROL OF FLAVONOID
BIOSYNTHESIS. *Biosynthesis and its Control in Plants*, Ed. B.V.
Milborrow, Academic Press: London and New York, pp. 303-321 (R).

2563. Smith, H. 1974. THE PHOTOCONTROL OF POLYSOME LEVELS IN BEAN LEAVES.
Proc. Eur. Annu. Symp. Plant Photomorphogenesis, (Antwerpen), pp.
106-112.

2564. Smith, H. 1974. PHYTOCHROMES AND PLANT RHYTHMS. Biol. Hum. Aff. 39:
12-16.

2565. Smith, H. 1974. BIOCHEMISTRY OF PHOTOMORPHOGENESIS. MTP Int. Rev. Sci. Biochem. Ser. 1, 11: 159-197.

2566. Smith, R.G. 1973. PHOTOTRANSFORMATION STUDIES ON PHYTOCHROME. Ph.D. Thesis, Brandeis Univ., Waltham.

2567. Smoleńska, G.; Lewak, S. 1971. GIBBERELLINS AND THE PHOTOSENSITIVITY OF ISOLATED EMBRYOS FROM NON-STRATIFIED APPLE SEEDS. Planta 99: 144-153.

2568. Smoleńska, G.; Lewak, S. 1974. THE ROLE OF LIPASES IN THE GERMINATION OF DORMANT APPLE EMBRYOS. Planta 116: 361-370.

2569. Sobota, A.E.; Partanen, C.R. 1966. THE GROWTH AND DIVISION OF CELLS IN RELATION TO MORPHOGENESIS IN FERN GAMETOPHYTES. I. PHOTOMORPHOGENETIC STUDIES IN *PTERIDIUM AQUILINUM*. Can. J. Bot. 44: 497-506.

2570. Soeder, C.J.; Schulze, G.; Thiele, D. 1966. A NEW TYPE OF "LIGHT INHIBITION", OCCURRING IN SYNCHRONOUS CULTURES OF *CHLORELLA*. Verh. Int. Ver. Theor. Ange. Limnol. 16: 1595-1601.

2571. Song, P.S.; Chae, Q.; Lightner, D.A.; Briggs, W.R.; Hopkins, D. 1973. FLUORESCENCE CHARACTERISTICS OF PHYTOCHROME AND BILIVERDINS. J. Am. Chem. Soc. 95: 7892-7894.

2572. Song, P.S. 1974. PHOTOREACTIVITY OF PHOTORECEPTOR MOLECULES, FLAVINS, CAROTENOIDS, AND PHYTOCHROME. Proc. II Annu. Meet. Am. Soc. Photobiol., p. 142, Abstr. No. FPM-B3 (A).

2573. Soriano, A. 1953. ESTUDIOS SOBRE GERMINACIÓN. I. Rev. Invest. Agri. 7: 315-340.

2574. Soriano, A.; Sánchez, R.A.; De Eilberg, B.A. 1964. FACTORS AND PROCESSES IN THE GERMINATION OF *DATURA FEROX* L. Can. J. Bot. 42: 1189-1203.

2575. Speer, H.L.; Palmer, D.S. 1972. THE EFFECT OF RED AND FAR-RED LIGHT ON SUBSEQUENT ENZYME ACTIVITY IN *AVENA* COLEOPTILES. Physiol. Plant. 26: 233-238.

2576. Speer, H.L. 1973. THE EFFECT OF ARSENATE AND OTHER INHIBITORS ON EARLY EVENTS DURING THE GERMINATION OF LETTUCE SEEDS (*LACTUCA SATIVA* L.). Plant Physiol. 52: 142-146.

2577. Speer, H.L.; Hsiao, A.I.; Vidaver, W. 1974. EFFECTS OF GERMINATION-PROMOTING SUBSTANCES GIVEN IN CONJUNCTION WITH RED LIGHT ON THE PHYTOCHROME-MEDIATED GERMINATION OF DORMANT LETTUCE SEEDS (*LACTUCA SATIVA* L.). Plant Physiol. 54: 852-854.

2578. Spruit, C.J.P. 1965. ABSORPTION SPECTRUM CHANGES DURING DARK DECAY OF
PHYTOCHROME - 730 IN PLANTS. Meded. Landbouwhogesch. Wageningen
65-12: 1-6.

2579. Spurit, C.J.P. 1966. THERMAL REACTIONS FOLLOWING ILLUMINATION OF PHYTO-
CHROME. Meded. Landbouwhogesch. Wageningen 66-15: 1-7.

2580. Spruit, C.J.P. 1966. SPECTRAL OBSERVATIONS RELATED TO THE RED- FAR RED
ANTAGONISM IN PLANTS. Curr. Photosynth. Proc. West. Eur. Conf. 2nd,
1965, pp. 67-74.

2581. Spruit, C.J.P. 1966. PHOTOREVERSIBLE PIGMENT TRANSFORMATIONS IN ETIO-
LATED PLANTS. Biochim. Biophys. Acta 112: 186-188.

2582. Spruit, C.J.P. 1966. LOW-TEMPERATURE ACTION SPECTRA FOR TRANSFORMATIONS
OF PHOTOPERIODIC PIGMENTS. Biochim. Biophys. Acta 120: 454-456.

2583. Spruit, C.J.P. 1967. SPECTROSCOPY OF PHYTOCHROME DECAY AND REVERSAL
IN VIVO. Proc. Eur. Annu. Symp. Plant Photomorphogenesis, (Hvar),
pp. 7-10.

2584. Spruit, C.J.P. 1967. ABNORMAL PHYTOCHROME SPECTRUM IN LEAVES. Biochim.
Biophys. Acta 143: 260-262.

2585. Spruit, C.J.P. 1967. PHYTOCHROME DECAY AND REVERSAL IN LEAVES AND STEM
SECTIONS OF ETIOLATED PEA SEEDLINGS. Meded. Landbouwhogesch.
Wageningen 67-14: 1-6.

2586. Spruit, C.J.P. 1967. PHOTOREACTIONS IN PHYTOCHROME-CONTAINING EXTRACTS
FROM ETIOLATED PEA SEEDLINGS. Meded. Landbouwhogesch. Wageningen
67-15: 1-9.

2587. Spruit, C.J.P. 1968. SPECTROSCOPY OF PHYTOCHROME *IN VIVO* AND *IN VITRO*.
Proc. V Int. Congr. Photobiol., p. 100 (A).

2588. Spruit, C.J.P.; Boisard, J.; Rollin, P. 1968. SPECTROPHOTOMETRIC PHYTO-
CHROME IN IMBIBED SEEDS OF DARK GERMINATING PLANTS. Plant Physiol.
43: Suppl.-15 (A).

2589. Spruit, C.J.P.; Mancinelli, A.L. 1969. PHYTOCHROME IN CUCUMBER SEEDS.
Planta 88: 303-310.

2590. Spruit, C.J.P. 1970. SPECTROPHOTOMETERS FOR THE STUDY OF PHYTOCHROME
IN VIVO. Meded. Landbouwhogesch. Wageningen 70-14: 1-18.

2591. Spruit, C.J.P.; Raven, C.W. 1970. REGENERATION OF PROTOCHLOROPHYLL IN
DARK GROWN SEEDLINGS FOLLOWING ILLUMINATION WITH RED AND FAR RED
LIGHT. Acta Bot. Neerl. 19: 165-174.

2592. Spruit, C.J.P. 1971. THE PHYTOCHROME PARADOXES; CAN WE UNDERSTAND THEM? Proc. Eur. Annu. Symp. Plant Photomorphogenesis, (Athens), pp. 47-48 (A).

2593. Spruit, C.J.P. 1971. PHOTOREACTIVE PIGMENTS IN FLOWER PETALS. Proc. Int. Congr. Photosynth. Res. 2nd, pp. 1673-1680.

2594. Spruit, C.J.P. 1971. SENSITIVE QUASI-CONTINUOUS MEASUREMENT OF PHOTO-INDUCED TRANSMISSION CHANGES. Meded. Landbouwhogesch. Wageningen 71-21: 1-6.

2595. Spruit, C.J.P. 1972. ESTIMATION OF PHYTOCHROME BY SPECTROPHOTOMETRY *IN VIVO*: INSTRUMENTATION AND INTERPRETATION. *Phytochrome*: Ed. K. Mitrakos and W. Shropshire, Jr., Academic Press: London and New York, pp. 77-104 (R).

2596. Spruit, C.J.P.; Kendrick, R.E. 1972. ON THE KINETICS OF PHYTOCHROME PHOTOCONVERSION *IN VIVO*. Planta 103: 319-326.

2597. Spruit, C.J.P.; Spruit, H.C. 1972. DIFFERENCE SPECTRUM DISTORTION IN NON-HOMOGENEOUS PIGMENT ASSOCIATIONS: ABNORMAL PHYTOCHROME SPECTRA *IN VIVO*. Biochim. Biophys. Acta 275: 401-413.

2598. Spruit, C.J.P.; Kendrick, R.E. 1973. PHYTOCHROME INTERMEDIATES *IN VIVO* II. CHARACTERISATION OF INTERMEDIATES BY DIFFERENCE SPECTROPHOTOME-TRY. Photochem. Photobiol. 18: 145-152.

2599. Stabenau, H. 1972. AKTIVITÄTSÄNDERUNGEN VON ENZYMEN BEI *CHLOROGONIUM ELONGATUM* UNTER DEM EINFLUSS VON ROTEM UND BLAUEM LICHT. Z. Pflanzenphysiol. 67: 105-112 (ENG Summary).

2600. Stafford, H.A. 1948. STUDIES ON THE GROWTH AND XYLARY DEVELOPMENT OF *PHLEUM PRATENSE* SEEDLINGS IN DARKNESS AND IN LIGHT. Am. J. Bot. 35: 706-715.

2601. Stahl, E. 1897. UEBER DEN PFLANZENSCHLAF UND VERWANDTE ERSCHEINUNGEN. Bot. Zeit. 55: 71-109.

2602. Stanko, S.A.; Gvozdikovskaya, A.T. 1967. EFFECT OF PULSED, CONCENTRATED SUNLIGHT ON THE BIOSYNTHESIS OF AMINO ACIDS AND SUGARS, AND ON THE UPTAKE AND INCLUSION INTO ORGANIC COMPOUNDS OF NITROGEN, PHOSPHORUS, AND POTASSIUM BY GREEN WHEAT SPROUTS. Tr. Lab. Evol. Ekol. Fiziol. Akad. Nauk SSSR, Inst. Fiziol. Rast. 6: 120-140 (RUS).

2603. Stanko, S.A.; Kuznetsova, G.K. 1972. EFFECT OF THE PRESOWING IRRADIA-
TION OF SEEDS BY PULSED CONCENTRATED ELECTRIC LIGHT ON THE SOLASODINE
LEVEL IN NIGHTSHADE. Elektron. Obrab. Mater 1: 73-77 (RUS).

2604. Stanley, R.G.; Butler, W.L. 1961. LIFE PROCESSES OF THE LIVING SEED.
Yearbook of Agriculture, pp. 88-94 (R).

2605. Stasny, J.T.; Mumford, F.E. 1971. ELECTRON MICROSCOPIC OBSERVATIONS OF
PURIFIED OAT PHYTOCHROME. Proc. Electron Microsc. Soc. Am. 29:
362-363.

2606. Steer, B.T.; Gibbs, M. 1969. CHANGES IN SUCCINYL CoA SYNTHETASE
ACTIVITY IN ETIOLATED BEAN LEAVES CAUSED BY ILLUMINATION. Plant
Physiol. 44: 775-780.

2607. Steer, B.T.; Gibbs, M. 1969. DELTA-AMINOLEVULINIC ACID DEHYDRASE IN
GREENING BEAN LEAVES. Plant Physiol. 44: 781-783.

2608. Stein, G. 1954. ÉTATS MÉTASTABLES DANS LES SYSTÈMES BIOLOGIQUES IRRA-
DIES. J. Chim. Phys. 51: 133-136 (R-D).

2609. Stein, G.; Richter, R. 1961. THE EFFECT OF X-RAY IRRADIATION IN CON-
JUNCTION WITH RED AND FAR-RED LIGHT ON LETTUCE SEED GERMINATION.
Effects of Ionizing Radiation on Seeds 1960 Symp. Int. Atomic Energy
Agency, Vienna, pp. 197-199.

2610. Steiner, A.M. 1963. DER EINFLUSS DES LICHTES AUF MORPHOGENESE UND
CHLOROPLASTENENTWICKLUNG DER GAMETOPHYTEN VON *SPHAEROCARPUS
DONNELLII* AUST. Z. Bot. 51: 399-423 (ENG Summary).

2611. Steiner, A.M. 1964. DER EINFLUSS VON LICHT UND TEMPERATUR AUF DIE
SPORENKEIMUNG BEI *SPHAEROCARPUS DONNELLII* AUST. (HEPATICAE). Z.
Bot. 52: 245-282 (ENG Summary).

2612. Steiner, A.; Klein, W.H.; Price, L.; Mitrakos, K. 1965. THE INFLUENCE
OF RED LIGHT ON THE DISTRIBUTION OF ^{14}C IN ETIOLATED CORN LEAF SEC-
TIONS. Plant Physiol. 40: Suppl.-54 (A).

2613. Steiner, A.M. 1967. PHYTOCHROME ACTION ELICITED BY SHORT WAVELENGTH
IRRADIATION IN POLAROTROPISM OF GERMLINGS OF A FERN AND A LIVERWORT.
ACTION SPECTRA. Proc. Eur. Annu. Symp. Plant Photomorphogenesis,
(Hvar), pp. 113-116.

2614. Steiner, A.M. 1967. DOSE-RESPONSE CURVES FOR POLAROTROPISM IN GERM-
LINGS OF A FERN AND A LIVERWORT. Naturwissenschaften 54: 497.

2615. Steiner, A.M. 1967. ACTION SPECTRA FOR POLAROTROPISM IN GERMLINGS OF A
FERN AND A LIVERWORT. Naturwissenschaften 18: 497-498.

2616. Steiner, A.M. 1968. ÄNDERUNGEN IM KOHLENHYDRATGEHALT DER ORGANE DES
       SENFKEIMLINGS (*SINAPIS ALBA* L.) IM DAUER-DUNKELROT UNTER DEM EINFLUSS
       VON PHYTOCHROM. Z. Pflanzenphysiol. 59: 401-414 (ENG Summary).

2617. Steiner, A.M. 1968. RASCH ABLAUFENDE ÄNDERUNGEN IM GEHALT AN LÖSLICHEN
       ZUCKERN UND ZELLWANDKOHLENHYDRATEN BEI DER PHYTOCHROMINDUZIERTEN
       PHOTOMORPHOGENESE DES SENFKEIMLINGS (*SINAPIS ALBA* L.). Planta 82:
       223-234 (ENG Summary).

2618. Steiner, A.M.; Lange, H. 1968. INTERACTION BETWEEN HYDROXYPROLINE AND
       PHYTOCHROME CONTROLLING HYPOCOTYL ELONGATION IN MUSTARD SEEDLINGS
       (*SINAPIS ALBA* L.). Naturwissenschaften 55: 187-188.

2619. Steiner, A.; Price, L.; Mitrakos, K.; Klein, W.H. 1968. RED LIGHT
       EFFECTS ON UPTAKE OF ^{14}C AND ^{32}P INTO ETIOLATED CORN LEAF TISSUE
       DURING PHOTOMORPHOGENIC LEAF OPENING. Physiol. Plant. 21: 895-901.

2620. Steiner, A.M. 1969. PHYTOCHROME ACTION IN BLUE-UV-MEDIATED POLAROTRO-
       PISM OF GERMLINGS OF A FERN AND A LIVERWORT. Proc. XI Int. Bot.
       Congr., p. 209 (A).

2621. Steiner, A.M. 1969. INFLUENCE OF SUBSTRATE RESERVES ON CELL GROWTH AND
       CELL-WALL SYNTHESIS HYPOCOTYL OF *SINAPIS ALBA* L. Naturwissenschaften
       56: 423.

2622. Steiner, A.M. 1969. AFTER-RIPENING IN SEEDS OF *SINAPIS ALBA* L. Natur-
       wissenschaften 56: 423-424.

2623. Steiner, A.M. 1969. INFLUENCE OF DIFFERENT LIGHT QUALITIES ON THE
       ACCUMULATION OF ANTHOCYANIN-3-MONOGLUCOSIDES AND THEIR TURNOVER IN
       PETALS OF *PETUNIA HYBRIDA*. Naturwissenschaften 57: 549-550.

2624. Steiner, A.M. 1969. DIE ZELLWANDZUSAMMENSETZUNG VON HYPOKOTYLEN DES
       SENFKEIMLINGS (*SINAPIS ALBA* L.) BEI WACHSTUMSHEMMUNG DURCH INHIBI-
       TOREN ODER PHYTOCHROM. Planta 84: 348-352 (ENG Summary).

2625. Steiner, A.M. 1969. DOSE RESPONSE BEHAVIOUR FOR POLAROTROPISM OF THE
       GERM TUBE OF THE LIVERWORT *SPHAEROCARPOS DONNELLII* AUST. Planta 86:
       334-342.

2626. Steiner, A.M. 1969. ACTION SPECTRUM FOR POLAROTROPISM OF THE GERM TUBE
       OF THE LIVERWORT *SPHAEROCARPOS DONNELLII* AUST. Planta 86: 343-352.

2627. Steiner, A.M. 1969. CHANGES OF THE ENDOGENOUS RHYTHM IN PHYTOCHROME
       MEDIATED SPORE GERMINATION OF THE LIVERWORT *SPHAEROCARPOS* DURING
       SPORE AFTER-RIPENING. Z. Pflanzenphysiol. 61: 184-191.

2628. Steiner, A.M. 1969. DOSE RESPONSE BEHAVIOUR FOR POLAROTROPISM OF THE CHLORONEMA OF THE FERN *DRYOPTERIS FILIX-MAS* (L.) SCHOTT. Photochem. Photobiol. 9: 493-506.

2629. Steiner, A.M. 1969. ACTION SPECTRUM FOR POLAROTROPISM IN THE CHLORONEMA OF THE FERN *DRYOPTERIS FILIX-MAS* (L.) SCHOTT. Photochem. Photobiol. 9: 507-513.

2630. Steiner, A.M. 1970. RED LIGHT INTERACTIONS WITH BLUE AND ULTRAVIOLET LIGHT IN POLAROTROPISM OF GERMLINGS OF A FERN AND A LIVERWORT. Photochem. Photobiol. 12: 169-174.

2631. Steiner, A.M. 1971. LIGHT CONTROL OF ACCUMULATION AND TURNOVER OF THE ANTHOCYANIN-3-MONOGLUCOSIDES IN PETALS OF PETUNIA. Proc. Eur. Annu. Symp. Plant Photomorphogenesis, (Athens), pp. 49-51 (A).

2632. Steiner, A.M. 1972. DER EINFLUSS VON LICHT VERSCHIEDENER WELLENLÄNGE AUF DIE AKKUMULATION UND DEN UMSATZ VON ANTHOCYAN-3-MONOGLUCOSIDEN IN ISOLIERTEN PETALEN VON *PETUNIA HYBRIDA*. Z. Pflanzenphysiol. 66: 133-154 (ENG Summary).

2633. Steiner, A.M. 1972. DER EINFLUSS DER LICHTINTENSITÄT AUF DIE AKKUMULATION EINZELNER ANTHOCYANE IN ISOLIERTEN PETALEN VON *PETUNIA HYBRIDA*. Z. Pflanzenphysiol. 68: 266-271 (ENG Summary).

2634. Steiner, A.M. 1974. ANTHOCYANIN ACCUMULATION AND COMPOSITION IN SEEDLINGS OF DIFFERENT CULTIVARS OF *SINAPIS ALBA* L. Z. Pflanzenphysiol. 71: 186-188.

2635. Stelzner, G.; Hartisch, J. 1938. ENTWICKLUNGSPHYSIOLOGISCHE UNTERSUCHUNGEN AN GETREIDE. Angew. Bot. 20: 156-178.

2636. Stephan, J. 1928. UNTERSUCHUNGEN ÜBER DIE LICHTWIRKUNG BESTIMMTER SPEKTRALBEZIRKE UND BEKANNTER STRAHLUNGSINTENSITÄTEN AUF DIE KEIMUNG UND DAS WACHSTUM EINIGER FARNE UND MOOSE. Planta 5: 381-443.

2637. Stephan, J. 1928. DER EINFLUSS VON LICHTQUALITÄT UND QUANTITÄT (EINSCHLIESSLICH ULTRAROT) AUF DAS WACHSTUM DER BRUTKÖRPER VON *MARCHANTIA POLYMORPHA*. Planta 6: 510-518.

2638. Stephan, J. 1928. ZUR KEIMUNG VON *PHACELIA TANACETIFOLIA* BENTH. Ber. Dtsch. Bot. Ges. 46: 499-508.

2639. Stephan, J. 1929. ENTWICKLUNGSPHYSIOLOGISCHE UNTERSUCHUNGEN AN EINIGEN FARNEN I. Jahrb. Wiss. Bot. 70: 707-742.

2640. Stewart, S.; Wiegand, O.F. 1968. COMPARISON OF RED LIGHT EFFECTS ON SECTIONS AND INTACT COLEOPTILES OF *AVENA*. Plant Physiol. 43: Suppl.-14 (A).

2641. Stewart, S.L. III. 1970. INHIBITION AND PROMOTION OF GROWTH BY RED LIGHT IN THE *AVENA* COLEOPTILE. Ph.D. Thesis, Univ. Texas, Austin.

2642. Stickland, R.G.; Sunderland, N. 1972. PHOTOCONTROL OF GROWTH AND OF ANTHOCYANIN AND CHLOROGENIC ACID PRODUCTION IN CULTURED CALLUS TISSUES OF *HAPLOPAPPUS GRACILIS*. Ann. Bot. (London) 36: 671-685.

2643. Stimson, W.R. 1972. PHOTOSYNTHESIS AND PHYTOCHROME IN THE PHOTOCONTROL OF ANTHOCYANIN FORMATION BY *BRASSICA RAPA*. Ph.D. Thesis, Columbia Univ., New York.

2644. Stoklasa, J. 1911. ÜBER DEN EINFLUSS DER ULTRAVIOLETTEN STRAHLEN AUF DIE VEGETATION. Centralbla Bakt. II. Abt. 31: 477-495.

2645. Stoklasa, J. 1914. ÜBER DIE EINWIRKUNG DER ULTRAVIOLETTEN STRAHLEN AUF DIE CHLOROPHYLLHALTIGE ZELLE. Z. Pflanzenkr. 24: 193-204.

2646. Stolwijk, J.A.J. 1951. PHOTOPERIODISCHE EN FORMATIEVE EFFECTEN VAN SUPPLEMENTAIRE BELICHTING MET VERSCHILLENDE SPECTRALE GEBIEDEN. Handel. Ned. Nat. Geneeskd. Congr. 32, pp. 87-88 (A).

2647. Stolwijk, J.A.J. 1952. PHOTOPERIODIC AND FORMATIVE EFFECTS OF VARIOUS WAVELENGTH REGIONS IN *COSMOS BIPINNATUS*, *SPINACIA OLERACEA*, *SINAPIS ALBA*, AND *PISUM SATIVUM* I. Proc. K. Ned. Akad. Wet. Ser. C. 55: 489-497.

2648. Stolwijk, J.A.J. 1952. PHOTOPERIODIC AND FORMATIVE EFFECTS OF VARIOUS WAVELENGTH REGIONS IN *COSMOS BIPINNATUS*, *SPINACIA OLERACEA*, *SINAPIS ALBA*, AND *PISUM SATIVUM* II. Proc. K. Ned. Akad. Wet. Ser. C. 55: 498-502.

2649. Stolwijk, J.A.J. 1954. WAVE LENGTH DEPENDENCE OF PHOTOMORPHOGENESIS IN PLANTS. Meded. Landbouwhogesch. Wageningen 54-5: 181-244.

2650. Stolwijk, J.A.J. 1954. ANTAGONISTIC EFFECTS OF SUPPLEMENTARY LIGHT OF VARIOUS WAVE LENGTH REGIONS. Proc. VIII Int. Bot. Congr., pp. 320-321 (R).

2651. Stolwijk, J.A.J. 1954. SOME CHARACTERISTICS OF INTERNODE ELONGATION. Proc. I Int. Congr. Photobiol., pp. 78-82 (R).

2652. Stolwijk, J.A.J.; Zeevaart, J.A.D. 1955. WAVE LENGTH DEPENDENCE OF DIFFERENT LIGHT REACTIONS GOVERNING FLOWERING IN *HYOSCYAMUS NIGER*. Proc. K. Ned. Akad. Wet. Ser. C. 58: 386-396.

2653. Stone, B.P. 1968. PHYSIOLOGICAL STUDIES OF THE GERMINATION OF PHOTO-
SENSITIVE LETTUCE SEED. Ph.D. Thesis, Univ. Tenn. (obtained from
Diss. Abstr. Int. B, (1969) 30: 1003-1004).

2654. Stoppel, T.; Trumpf, C. 1922. BEITRAG ZUM PROBLEM DER SCHLAFBEWEGUNGEN
VON *PHASEOLUS MULTIFLORUS*. Mitt. Inst. Allg. Bot. Hamburg 5: 1-16.

2655. Stoutjesdijk, Ph. 1972. SPECTRAL TRANSMISSION CURVES OF SOME TYPES OF
LEAF CANOPIES WITH A NOTE ON SEED GERMINATION. Acta Bot. Neerl. 21:
185-191.

2656. Stoutjesdijk, Ph. 1972. A NOTE ON THE SPECTRAL TRANSMISSION OF LIGHT BY
TROPICAL RAINFOREST. Acta Bot. Neerl. 21: 346-350.

2656.5 Stowe, B.B.; Obreiter, J.B. 1962. GROWTH PROMOTION IN PEA STEM SECTIONS
II. BY NATURAL OILS AND ISOPRENOID VITAMINS. Plant Physiol. 37:
158-164.

2657. Strain, H.H. 1938. FORMATION OF CAROTENOIDS AND CHLOROPHYLLS IN ETIO-
LATED BARLEY SEEDLINGS EXPOSED TO RED LIGHT. Plant Physiol. 13:
413-418.

2658. Street, H.E. 1953. FACTORS CONTROLLING MERISTEMATIC ACTIVITY IN EXCISED
ROOTS III. LIGHT AS A FACTOR IN THE 'LOCATION EFFECT' NOTED WITH
ROOTS OF *LYCOPERSICUM ESCULENTUM* MILL. Physiol. Plant. 6: 466-479.

2659. Strohmer, F.; Stift, A. 1904. ÜBER DEN EINFLUSS DER LICHTFARBE AUF
DAS WACHSTUM DER ZUCKERRÜBE. Öst.-Ung. Zeitschrift Zucker, I,
pp. 17-52.

2660. Stroun, M. 1959. RELATIONSHIP BETWEEN THE LENGTH OF DAY, THE LIGHT
SPECTRUM, AND THE STATE OF DIFFERENTIATION OF FLORAL PRIMORDIA IN
LONG-DAY CEREALS. Proc. IX Int. Bot. Congr., pp. 384-385 (A).

2661. Stroun, M.; Schopfer, J.F.; Chodat, F. 1959. RELATIONS ENTRE LA DURÉE
DE LA PHOTOPÉRIODE, LA QUALITÉ DE LA LUMIÈRE ET LE DÉVELOPPEMENT DES
CÉRÉALES. Bull. Soc. Bot. Fr. 106: 309-321 (ENG Summary).

2662. Stroun, M.; Mathon, C.-Ch.; Sandmeier, M.; Chodat, F.; Giroud, A. 1961.
LONG-DAY EFFECT AS A FUNCTION OF INTERRELATIONS BETWEEN LIGHT
QUALITY, DURATION OF PHOTOPERIOD, AND DEVELOPMENT PHASES IN *PERILLA
NANKINENSIS* VOSS. Proc. III Int. Congr. Photobiol., pp. 384-386.

2663. Sudakov, V.L. 1970. APPARATUS FOR THE SPECTROPHOTOMETRIC STUDY OF
PHYTOCHROME. Sb. Tr. Agron. Fiz. 21: 114-117 (RUS).

2664. Sudakov, V.L. 1972. NEOGENESIS OF PHYTOCHROME IN ETIOLATED PEA SHOOTS.
Dokl. Akad. Nauk. SSSR 206: 1250-1252 (RUS).

2665. Sugai, M.; Furuya, M. 1967. PHOTOMORPHOGENESIS IN *PTERIS VITTATA* I. PHYTOCHROME-MEDIATED SPORE GERMINATION AND BLUE LIGHT INTERACTION. Plant Cell Physiol. 8: 737-748.

2666. Sugai, M.; Furuya, M. 1968. PHOTOMORPHOGENESIS IN *PTERIS VITTATA* II. RECOVERY FROM BLUE-LIGHT-INDUCED INHIBITION OF SPORE GERMINATION. Plant Cell Physiol. 9: 671-680.

2667. Sugai, M. 1970. PHOTOMORPHOGENESIS IN *PTERIS VITTATA*. III. PROTECTIVE ACTION OF ETHANOL ON BLUE-LIGHT-INDUCED INHIBITION OF SPORE GERMINA- TION. Dev. Growth Differ. 12: 13-20.

2668. Sugai, M. 1971. PHOTOMORPHOGENESIS IN *PTERIS VITTATA*. IV. ACTION SPEC- TRA FOR INHIBITION OF PHYTOCHROME-DEPENDENT SPORE GERMINATION. Plant Cell Physiol. 12: 103-109.

2669. Sugawara, T. 1939. STUDIES ON THE FORMATION OF ASCORBIC ACID (VITAMIN C) IN PLANTS 2. THE INFLUENCE OF RADIATION OF DIFFERENT WAVE-LENGTHS ON THE ASCORBIC ACID CONTENTS IN ETIOLATED SEEDLINGS. Jpn. J. Bot. 10: 325-333.

2670. Sugiura, M. 1963. EFFECT OF RED AND FAR-RED LIGHT ON PROTEIN AND PHOS- PHATE METABOLISM IN TOBACCO LEAF DISKS. Bot. Mag. 76: 174-180.

2671. Surrey, K. 1961. SPECTRAL RESPONSE OF PHOSPHATE METABOLISM IN GERMI- NATING LETTUCE SEED. Plant Physiol. 36: Suppl.-47 (A).

2672. Surrey, K. 1962. SPECTRAL RESPONSE OF PHOSPHATE METABOLISM IN GERMI- NATING LETTUCE SEEDS. U.S. A.E.C. Rep. No. ANL-6535, pp. 147-154.

2673. Surrey, K. 1962. ACTION AND INTERACTION OF MONOCHROMATIC LIGHT ON PHOSPHATE METABOLISM OF GERMINATING LETTUCE SEEDS. Can. J. Bot. 40: 965-974.

2674. Surrey, K.; Gordon, S.A. 1962. INFLUENCE OF LIGHT ON PHOSPHATE METABO- LISM IN LETTUCE SEED: SPECTRAL RESPONSE RED, FAR-RED INTERACTION. Plant Physiol. 37: 327-332.

2675. Surrey, K.; Barr, E.M. 1966. LIGHT-DEPENDENT MODIFICATIONS IN THE METABOLIC RESPONSES OF SQUASH SEEDLINGS. Plant Physiol. 41: 780-786.

2676. Surrey, K. 1967. SPECTRAL RESPONSE AND INTERACTION OF VARIOUS WAVE- LENGTHS ON THE PHOSPHATE METABOLISM OF GERMINATING LETTUCE SEEDS. Proc. Int. Symp. Physiol. Ecol. Biochem. Germination, Ed. H. Borriss, Greifswald; Ernst-Moritz-Arndt-University 1967 1: 663-671.

2677. Surrey, K. 1967. ACTION AND INTERACTION OF RED AND FAR-RED RADIATION ON LIPOXIDASE METABOLISM OF SQUASH SEEDLINGS. Plant Physiol. 42: 421-424.

2678. Surrey, K. 1967. CHLOROPHYLL SYNTHESIS IN SQUASH SEEDLINGS: ACTION AND INTERACTION OF RED AND FAR-RED IRRADIATION. Can. J. Bot. 45: 929-938.

2679. Suzuki, H.; Furuya, M. 1968. PHYTOCHROME, AND PHOTOMORPHOGENIC REACTIONS. Nippon Butsuri Gakkaishi 23: 317-319 (JAP) (R).

2680. Suzuki, H.; Hamanaka, T. 1969. ON THE MOLECULAR MECHANISM FOR LIGHT CAPTURE IN RHODOPSIN AND PHYTOCHROME SYSTEMS. J. Phys. Soc. Jpn. 26: 1462-1472.

2681. Suzuki, H.; Sugimoto, T.; Nakachi, K. 1973. ON THE MODELS FOR PHYTOCHROME CHROMOPHORE. J. Phys. Soc. Jpn. 34: 1045-1053.

2682. Suzuki, Y.; Saito, T. 1969. PHOTO-, THERMO- AND CHEMICAL-INDUCTION IN SEED GERMINATION OF *PHYSALIS ALKEKENGI*. Sci. Rep. Fac. Ant. Sci. Fukushima Univ. No. 19: 37-46.

2683. Suzuki, Y.; Takahashi, N. 1969. RED AND FAR-RED REVERSIBLE PHOTOREACTIONS ON SEED GERMINATION OF *CUCUMIS SATIVA*. Plant Cell Physiol. 10: 475-479.

2684. Swanson, C.P.; Hollaender, A. 1946. THE FREQUENCY OF X-RAY-INDUCED CHROMATID BREAKS IN *TRADESCANTIA* AS MODIFIED BY NEAR INFRARED RADIATION. Proc. Nat. Acad. Sci. USA 32: 295-302.

2685. Swanson, C.P. 1947. THE EFFECT OF INFRARED TREATMENT ON THE PRODUCTION OF X-RAY INDUCED CHANGES IN THE CHROMOSOMES OF *TRADESCANTIA*. Am. J. Bot. 34: 590 (A).

2686. Swanson, C.P. 1949. FURTHER STUDIES ON THE EFFECT OF INFRA-RED RADIATION OF X-RAY-INDUCED CHROMATID ABERRATIONS IN *TRADESCANTIA*. Proc. Nat. Acad. Sci. USA 35: 237-244.

2687. Swanson, C.P.; Yost, H.T., Jr. 1951. THE ACTION OF INFRARED RADIATION ON THE CHROMOSOMES OF *TRADESCANTIA*. Genetics 36: 579 (A).

2688. Swanson, C.P.; Yost, H.T., Jr. 1951. THE INDUCTION OF ACTIVATED, STABLE STATES IN THE CHROMOSOMES OF *TRADESCANTIA* BY INFRARED AND X-RAYS. Proc. Nat. Acad. Sci. USA 37: 796-802.

2689. Swanson, C.P.; Rupert, C.S.; Yost, H.T., Jr. 1953. INFRARED ABSORPTION AND TEMPERATURE STUDIES ON THE BUDS AND CHROMOSOMES OF *TRADESCANTIA PALUDOSA*. Am. J. Bot. 40: 557-565.

2690. Sweeney, B.M.; Haxo, F.T.; Hastings, J.W. 1959. ACTION SPECTRA FOR TWO EFFECTS OF LIGHT ON LUMINESCENCE IN *GONYAULAX POLYEDRA*. J. Gen. Physiol. 43: 285-299.

2691. Sweet, H.C.; Hillman, W.S. 1968. THE PHYTOCHROME-MEDIATED NYCTINASTIC RESPONSE OF *SAMANEA* AS AFFECTED BY OXYGEN AND INHIBITORS. Plant Physiol. 43: Suppl.-14 (A).

2692. Sweet, H.C.; Hillman, W.S. 1969. PHYTOCHROME CONTROL OF NYCTINASTY IN *SAMANEA* AS MODIFIED BY OXYGEN, SUBMERGENCE, AND CHEMICALS. Physiol. Plant. 22: 776-786.

2693. Sweet, H.C.; Hillman, W.S. 1969. RESPONSE OF PEA STEM TISSUES WITH DIFFERENT PHYTOCHROME CONTENTS TO RED LIGHT DOSAGE. Plant Physiol. 44: 458-460.

2694. Syperda, G.; McClure, J. 1970. RAPID PHOTOCONTROLLED FLAVONOID CHANGES IN ETIOLATED BARLEY PLUMULES. Am. J. Bot. 57: 763 (A).

2695. Szász, K.; Horváth, I.; Sz.-Barsi, E.; Garay, A.S. 1969. ON THE ACCUMU-LATION OF STARCH IN RED LIGHT AND THE POSSIBLE ROLE OF CHLOROPHYLL-B IN THIS PROCESS. Acta Bot. Acad. Sci. Hung. 15: 167-170.

2696. Szász, K.; Sz.-Barsi, E. 1971. STIMULATORY EFFECT OF BLUE LIGHT ON PROTEIN ACCUMULATION IN THE LEAVES OF *SINAPIS ALBA* L. Bot. Kozl. 58: 95-98 (HUNG) (ENG Summary).

2697. Szweykowska, A. 1957. ANTHOCYANIN PIGMENT AND THE INFLUENCE OF LIGHT ON THE DEVELOPMENT OF CABBAGE SEEDLINGS. Acta Soc. Bot. Pol. 26: 349-359.

2698. Takahashi, N. 1964. PHOTOMORPHOGENESIS IN RICE PLANTS, *ORYZA SATIVA* L. I. FORMATIVE RESPONSE TO MONOCHROMATIC LIGHT IN LEAVES. Tohoku Daigaku Nogaku KenKyusho Hokoku 15: 185-197 (JAP) (ENG Summary).

2699. Takimoto, A.; Ikeda, K. 1959. STUDIES ON THE LIGHT CONTROLLING FLOWER INITIATION OF *PHARBITIS NIL*. I. INTENSITY AND QUALITY OF THE LIGHT PRECEDING THE INDUCTIVE DARK PERIOD. Bot. Mag. 72: 137-145.

2700. Takimoto, A.; Ikeda, K. 1969. STUDIES ON THE LIGHT CONTROLLING PHOTO-PERIODIC INDUCTION OF *PHARBITIS NIL*. II. EFFECT OF FAR-RED LIGHT PRECEDING THE INDUCTIVE DARK PERIOD. Bot. Mag. 72: 181-189.

2701. Takimoto, A.; Ikeda, K. 1959. STUDIES ON THE LIGHT CONTROLLING FLOWER INITIATION OF *PHARBITIS NIL*. III. LIGHT-SENSITIVITY OF THE FIRST PROCESS OF INDUCTIVE DARK PERIOD. Bot. Mag. 72: 388-396.

2702.   Takimoto, A.; Ikeda, K.   1960.   STUDIES ON THE LIGHT CONTROLLING FLOWER
        INITIATION OF *PHARBITIS NIL*. IV. FURTHER STUDIES ON THE LIGHT PRE-
        CEDING THE INDUCTIVE DARK PERIOD.   Bot. Mag. 73: 37-43.

2703.   Takimoto, A.; Ikeda, K.   1960.   STUDIES ON THE LIGHT CONTROLLING FLOWER
        INITIATION OF *PHARBITIS NIL*. V. ON THE LIGHT FOLLOWING THE INDUCTIVE
        DARK PERIOD.   Bot. Mag. 73: 91-97.

2704.   Takimoto, A.; Ikeda, K.   1960.   STUDIES ON THE LIGHT CONTROLLING FLOWER
        INITIATION OF *PHARBITIS NIL*. VII. LIGHT-BREAK.   Bot. Mag. 73:
        341-348.

2705.   Takimoto, A.; Ikeda, K.   1960.   STUDIES ON THE LIGHT CONTROLLING FLOWER
        INITIATION OF *PHARBITIS NIL*. VIII. LIGHT-SENSITIVITY OF THE INDUCTIVE
        DARK PROCESS.   Bot. Mag. 73: 468-473.

2706.   Takimoto, A.   1961.   ON THE LIGHT CONTROLLING FLOWER INITIATION OF *SILENE
        ARMERIA*.   Plant Cell Physiol. 2: 71-75.

2707.   Takimoto, A.; Naito, Y.   1962.   STUDIES ON THE LIGHT CONTROLLING FLOWER
        INITIATION OF *PHARBITIS NIL*. IX. FURTHER STUDIES ON THE EFFECT OF
        FAR-RED PRECEDING THE INDUCTIVE DARK PERIOD.   Bot. Mag. 75: 205-211.

2708.   Takimoto, A.; Naito, Y.   1962.   STUDIES ON THE LIGHT CONTROLLING FLOWER
        INITIATION OF *PHARBITIS NIL*. X. PHOTOPERIODIC RESPONSES OF THE SEED-
        LINGS GROWN UNDER VARIOUS LIGHT CONDITIONS.   Bot. Mag. 75: 255-263.

2709.   Takimoto, A.; Hamner, K.C.   1964.   EFFECT OF TEMPERATURE AND PRECONDI-
        TIONING ON PHOTOPERIODIC RESPONSE OF *PHARBITIS NIL*.   Plant Physiol.
        39: 1024-1030.

2710.   Takimoto, A.; Hamner, K.C.   1965.   STUDIES ON RED LIGHT INTERRUPTION IN
        RELATION TO TIMING MECHANISMS INVOLVED IN THE PHOTOPERIODIC RESPONSE
        OF *PHARBITIS NIL*.   Plant Physiol. 40: 852-854.

2711.   Takimoto, A.; Hamner, K.C.   1965.   EFFECT OF DOUBLE RED LIGHT INTERRUP-
        TIONS ON THE PHOTOPERIODIC RESPONSE OF *PHARBITIS NIL*.   Plant Physiol.
        40: 855-858.

2712.   Takimoto, A.; Hamner, K.C.   1965.   EFFECT OF FAR-RED LIGHT AND ITS INTER-
        ACTION WITH RED LIGHT IN THE PHOTOPERIODIC RESPONSE OF *PHARBITIS NIL*.
        Plant Physiol. 40: 859-864.

2713.   Takimoto, A.; Hamner, K.C.   1965.   KINETIC STUDIES ON PIGMENT SYSTEMS
        CONCERNED WITH THE PHOTOPERIODIC RESPONSE IN *PHARBITIS NIL*.   Plant
        Physiol. 40: 865-872.

2714. Takimoto, A. 1967. SPECTRAL DEPENDENCE OF DIFFERENT LIGHT REACTIONS ASSOCIATED WITH PHOTOPERIODIC RESPONSE IN *PHARBITIS NIL*. Bot. Mag. 80: 213-220.

2715. Takimoto, A. 1967. STUDIES ON THE LIGHT AFFECTING THE INITIATION OF ENDOGENOUS RHYTHMS CONCERNED WITH PHOTOPERIODIC RESPONSES IN *PHARBITIS NIL*. Bot. Mag. 80: 241-247.

2716. Takimoto, A. 1967. EFFECTS OF LOW-INTENSITY LIGHT ON THE PHOTOPERIODIC RESPONSE. *Physiology of Flowering in Pharbitis nil*, Ed. S. Imamura, Japan. Soc. Plant Physiol., Tokyo, pp. 37-51 (R).

2717. Takimoto, A. 1967. TIMING MECHANISMS IN PHOTOPERIODISM. *Physiology of Flowering in Pharbitis nil*, Ed. S. Imamura, Japan. Soc. Plant Physiol., Tokyo, pp. 53-72 (R).

2718. Takimoto, A. 1967. THE SPECTRAL DEPENDENCE OF PHOTOPERIODIC RESPONSES. *Physiology of Flowering in Pharbitis nil*, Ed. S. Imamura, Japan. Soc. Plant Physiol., Tokyo, pp. 73-93 (R).

2719. Takimoto, A. 1973. FLOWER INITIATION OF *LEMNA PERPUSILLA* UNDER CONTINUOUS LOW-INTENSITY LIGHT. Plant Cell Physiol. 14: 1217-1219.

2720. Tan, K.K. 1974. RED-FAR-RED REVERSIBLE PHOTOREACTION IN THE RECOVERY FROM BLUE-LIGHT INHIBITION OF SPORULATION IN *BOTRYTIS CINEREA*. J. Gen. Microbiol. 82: 201-202.

2721. Tanada, T. 1965. EFFECTS OF RED AND FAR-RED LIGHT ON RB ABSORPTION BY MUNG BEAN SEEDLINGS. Plant Physiol. 40: Suppl.-54 (A).

2722. Tanada, T. 1968. A RAPIDLY PHOTOREVERSIBLE ELECTROSTATIC CHARGE CHANGE IN MUNG BEAN AND BARLEY TOPS. Plant Physiol. 43: Suppl.-14 (A).

2723. Tanada, T. 1968. A RAPID PHOTOREVERSIBLE RESPONSE OF BARLEY ROOT TIPS IN THE PRESENCE OF 3-INDOLEACETIC ACID. Proc. Nat. Acad. Sci. USA 59: 376-380.

2724. Tanada, T. 1968. SUBSTANCES ESSENTIAL FOR A RED, FAR-RED LIGHT REVERSIBLE ATTACHMENT OF MUNG BEAN ROOT TIPS TO GLASS. Plant Physiol. 43: 2070-2071.

2725. Tanada, T. 1969. AN EARLY LESION FROM LOW DOSES OF X-IRRADIATION IN PLANT CELLS. Radiat. Res. 37: 103-107.

2726. Tanada, T. 1972. ANTAGONISTIC EFFECTS OF IAA AND ABA ON THE PHYTOCHROME-MEDIATED ATTACHMENT OF MUNG BEAN ROOT TIPS ON GLASS. Plant Physiol. 49: Suppl.-54, Abstr. No. 302 (A).

2727. Tanada, T. 1972. PHYTOCHROME CONTROL OF ANOTHER PHYTOCHROME-MEDIATED PROCESS. Plant Physiol. 49: 560-562.

2728. Tanada, T. 1972. ON THE INVOLVEMENT OF ACETYLCHOLINE IN PHYTOCHROME ACTION. Plant Physiol. 49: 860-861.

2729. Tanada, T. 1972. ANTAGONISM BETWEEN INDOLEACETIC ACID AND ABSCISIC ACID ON A RAPID PHYTOCHROME-MEDIATED PROCESS. Nature (London) 236: 460-461.

2729.5 Tanada, T. 1973. NECESSITY FOR BORON IN THE PHYTOCHROME-MEDIATED BIO-ELECTRIC POTENTIAL CHANGES. Proc. I Annu. Meet. Am. Soc. Photobiol., p. 181, Abstr. No. ThPM-E2 (A).

2730. Tanada, T. 1973. INDOLEACETIC ACID AND ABSCISIC ACID ANTAGONISM. I. ON THE PHYTOCHROME-MEDIATED ATTACHMENT OF MUNG BEAN ROOT TIPS ON GLASS. Plant Physiol. 51: 150-153.

2731. Tanada, T. 1973. INDOLEACETIC ACID AND ABSCISIC ACID ANTAGONISM II. ON THE PHYTOCHROME-MEDIATED ATTACHMENT OF BARLEY ROOT TIPS ON GLASS. Plant Physiol. 51: 154-157.

2732. Tanada, T. 1974. BORON-INDUCED BIOELECTRIC FIELD CHANGE IN MUNG BEAN HYPOCOTYL. Plant Physiol. 53: 775-776.

2733. Taylor, A.O.; Bonner, B.A. 1967. ISOLATION OF PHYTOCHROME FROM THE ALGA *MESOTAENIUM* AND LIVERWORT *SPHAEROCARPUS*. Plant Physiol. 42: 762-766.

2734. Taylor, A.O. 1968. *IN VITRO* PHYTOCHROME DARK REVERSION PROCESS. Plant Physiol. 43: 767-774.

2735. Taylorson, R.B. 1969. PHOTOCONTROL OF ROUGH CINQUEFOIL SEED GERMINA-TION AND ITS ENHANCEMENT BY TEMPERATURE MANIPULATION AND KNO_3. Weed Sci. 17: 144-148.

2736. Taylorson, R.B.; Borthwick, H.A. 1969. LIGHT FILTRATION BY FOLIAR CANOPIES: SIGNIFICANCE FOR LIGHT-CONTROLLED WEED SEED GERMINATION. Weed Sci. 17: 48-51.

2737. Taylorson, R.B.; Hendricks, S.B. 1969. ACTION OF PHYTOCHROME DURING PRECHILLING OF *AMARANTHUS RETROFLEXUS* L. SEEDS. Plant Physiol. 44: 821-825.

2738. Taylorson, R.B. 1970. CHANGES IN DORMANCY AND VIABILITY OF WEED SEEDS IN SOILS. Weed Sci. 18: 265-269.

2739. Taylorson, R.B.; Hendricks, S.B. 1971. CHANGES IN PHYTOCHROME EXPRESSED BY GERMINATION OF *AMARANTHUS RETROFLEXUS* L. SEEDS. Plant Physiol. 47: 619-622.

2740. Taylorson, R.B.; Hendricks, S.B. 1972. INTERACTIONS OF LIGHT AND A TEMPERATURE SHIFT ON SEED GERMINATION. Plant Physiol. 49: 127-130.

2741. Taylorson, R.B.; Hendricks, S.B. 1972. REHYDRATION OF PHYTOCHROME IN IMBIBING SEEDS OF *AMARANTHUS RETROFLEXUS* L. Plant Physiol. 49: 663-665.

2742. Taylorson, R.B.; Hendricks, S.B. 1972. PHYTOCHROME CONTROL OF GERMINA-TION OF *RUMEX CRISPUS* L. SEEDS INDUCED BY TEMPERATURE SHIFTS. Plant Physiol. 50: 645-648.

2743. Taylorson, R.B.; Hendricks, S.B. 1973. PROMOTION OF SEED GERMINATION BY CYANIDE. Plant Physiol. 52: 23-27.

2744. Taylorson, R.B.; Hendricks, S.B. 1973. PHYTOCHROME TRANSFORMATION AND ACTION IN SEEDS OF *RUMEX CRISPUS* L. DURING SECONDARY DORMANCY. Plant Physiol. 52: 475-479.

2745. Teodoresco, E. 1899. INFLUENCE DES DIFFERENTES RADIATIONS LUMINEUSES SUR LA FORME ET LA STRUCTURE DES PLANTES. Ann. Sci. Nat. Bot. Ser. 8, 10: 141-262.

2746. Teodoresco, E.-C. 1929. OBSERVATIONS SUR LA CROISSANCE DES PLANTES AUX LUMIÈRES DE DIVERSES LONGUEURS D'ONDE. Ann. Sci. Nat. Bot. Ser. 10, 11: 201-336.

2747. Tepfer, D.A.; Bonnett, H.T. 1972. THE ROLE OF PHYTOCHROME IN THE GEO-TROPIC BEHAVIOR OF ROOTS OF *CONVOLVULUS ARVENSIS*. Planta 106: 311-324.

2748. Tezuka, T.; Yamamoto, Y. 1969. NAD KINASE AND PHYTOCHROME. Bot. Mag. 82: 130-133.

2749. Tezuka, T.; Tsudzuki, T.; Yamamoto, Y. 1971. PHYTOCHROME ACTIVITY IN THE DEVELOPMENTAL PROCESS OF PLANTS. Proc. 36th Annu. Meet. Bot. Soc. Japan (not obtained).

2750. Tezuka, T.; Tsudzuki, T.; Yamamoto, Y. 1971. PHYTOCHROME AND NAD KINASE. Proc. 36th Annu. Meet. Bot. Soc. Japan (not obtained).

2751. Tezuka, T.; Yamamoto, Y. 1972. PHOTOREGULATION OF NICOTINAMIDE ADENINE DINUCLEOTIDE KINASE ACTIVITY IN CELL-FREE EXTRACTS. Plant Physiol. 50: 458-462.

2752. Tezuka, T.; Yamamoto, Y. 1974. KINETICS OF ACTIVATION OF NICOTINAMIDE ADENINE DINUCLEOTIDE KINASE BY PHYTOCHROME-FAR RED-ABSORBING FORM. Plant Physiol. 53: 717-722.

2753. Thelan, O. 1910. NATÜRLICHES KÜNSTLICHES UND MONOCHROMATISCHES LICHT IN SEINER BEDEUTUNG FÜR ENTWICKLUNG UND DIE STOFFPRODUKTION EINIGER KULTURPFLANZEN. Ph.D. Thesis, Univ. Rostock.

2754. Thibault, P.; André, M.; Guérin de Moutgareuil, P. 1968. CINÉTIQUE D'ACTION DU ROUGE LOINTAIN SUR LA CAPACITÉ EN OXYGÈNE PHOTOSYNTHÉTI-QUE STABLE. C.R. Acad. Sci. Ser. D. 267: 2140-2143.

2755. Thibault, P. 1969. ACTIVATION PAR LE ROUGE LOINTAIN DE LA CAPACITÉ STABLE EN OXYGÈNE PHOTOSYNTHÉTIQUE: SPECTRE D'ACTION DU PHÉNOMÈNE. C.R. Acad. Sci. Ser. D. 269: 1758-1761.

2756. Thibault, P. 1970. ACTIVATION DE LA CAPACITÉ STABLE EN OXYGÈNE PHOTO-SYNTHÉTIQUE: EFFET ANTAGONISTE ROUGE-ROUGE LOINTAIN. C.R. Acad. Sci. Ser. D. 270: 1980-1983.

2757. Thibault, P.; Michel, J.P. 1971. POSSIBLE ROLE OF PHYTOCHROME IN PHOSPHORYLATIONS AND PHOTOSYNTHETIC OXYGEN EVOLUTION IN CORN LEAVES (ZEA MAYS). Proc. Eur. Annu. Sump. Plant Photomorphogenesis, (Athens), pp. 52-53 (A).

2758. Thibault, P.; Michel, J.P. 1972. POSSIBLE ROLE OF PHYTOCHROME IN PHOSPHORYLATIONS AND PHOTOSYNTHETIC OXYGEN EVOLUTION IN CORN LEAVES (ZEA MAYS). Proc. Int. Congr. Photosynth. Res. 2nd, pp. 599-609.

2759. Thien, W.; Schopfer, P. 1974. CONTROL BY PHYTOCHROME OF CYTOPLASMIC AND PLASTID RIBOSOMAL RNA IN MUSTARD COTYLEDONS. Proc. Eur. Annu. Symp. Plant Photomorphogenesis, (Antwerpen), pp. 44-45.

2760. Thimann, K.V. 1964. STUDIES ON THE MOVEMENT OF AUXIN IN TISSUES AND ITS MODIFICATION BY GRAVITY AND LIGHT. Colloq. Int. C.N.R.S. 123: 575-585 (R).

2761. Thimann, K.V. 1965. BEDEUTUNG DES LICHTES FÜR WACHSTUM, PIGMENTIERUNG UND BEWEGUNGSPHÄNOMENE BEI PFLANZEN. Nova Acta Leopold. 31: 153-167 (R).

2762. Thimann, K.V. 1967. PHOTOTROPISM. Comp. Biochem. 27: 1-29 (R).

2763. Thomas, J.B. 1965. PRIMARY PHOTOPROCESSES IN BIOLOGY. North-Holland Publishing Co., Amsterdam, John Wiley and Sons, Inc., New York (R).

2764. Thomas, J.P.; Butler, G.L.; O'Kelley, J.C. 1972. ISOLATION AND CHARACTERIZATION OF PROTEIN PIGMENTS ABSORBING AT WAVELENGTHS WHICH REGULATE CELL DIVISION IN A PHOTOSYNTHESIZING ORGANISM, *PROTOSIPHON BOTRYOIDES*. ASB Bull. 19: 105 (A).

2765. Thomas, J.P.; O'Kelley, J.C. 1973. THE PHOTOREVERSIBLE NATURE OF A PIGMENT SYSTEM IN THE GREEN ALGA *PROTOSIPHON BOTRYOIDES* KLEBS. Photochem. Photobiol. 17: 469-472.

2766. Thomas, T.H.; Pavlevitch, D.; Austin, R.B. 1974. HORMONAL INVOLVEMENT IN THE PHYTOCHROME-CONTROLLED DORMANCY-RELEASE OF CELERY SEEDS (*APIUM GRAVEOLENS*). Plant Physiol. 53: Suppl.-7, Abstr. No. 31 (A).

2767. Thompson, P.A. 1968. THE EFFECT OF SOME PROMOTERS AND INHIBITORS ON THE LIGHT CONTROLLED GERMINATION OF STRAWBERRY SEEDS; *FRAGARIA VESCA SEMPERFLORENS* EHR. Physiol. Plant. 21: 833-841.

2768. Thomson, B.F. 1959. FAR RED REVERSAL OF INTERNODE-STIMULATING EFFECT OF RED LIGHT ON PEAS. Am. J. Bot. 46: 740-742.

2769. Thomson, B.F.; Miller, P.M. 1961. GROWTH PATTERNS OF PEA SEEDLINGS IN DARKNESS AND IN RED AND WHITE LIGHT. Am. J. Bot. 48: 256-261.

2770. Thomson, B.F.; Miller, P.M. 1962. THE ROLE OF LIGHT IN HISTOGENESIS AND DIFFERENTIATION IN THE SHOOT OF *PISUM SATIVUM*. I. THE APICAL REGION. Am. J. Bot. 49: 303-310.

2771. Thomson, B.F.; Miller, P.M. 1962. THE ROLE OF LIGHT IN HISTOGENESIS AND DIFFERENTIATION IN THE SHOOT OF *PISUM SATIVUM*. II. THE LEAF. Am. J. Bot. 49: 383-387.

2772. Thomson, B.F.; Miller, P.M. 1963. THE ROLE OF LIGHT IN THE HISTOGENESIS AND DIFFERENTIATION IN THE SHOOT OF *PISUM SATIVUM*. III. THE INTERNODE. Am. J. Bot. 50: 219-227.

2773. Thorning, I. 1955. UNTERSUCHUNGEN ÜBER DIE LICHTWACHSTUMREAKTIONEN DEKAPITIERTER AVENAKOLEOPTILEN. Z. Bot. 43: 175-179.

2774. Thornton, R.M.; Thimann, K.V. 1967. TRANSIENT EFFECTS OF LIGHT ON AUXIN TRANSPORT IN THE *AVENA* COLEOPTILE. Plant Physiol. 42: 247-257.

2775. Tilly, F. 1935. ÜBER SENSIBILISIERUNG UND DESENSIBILISIERUNG LICHTEMPFINDLICHER SAMEN (*LYTHRUM SALICARIA* L.). Z. Bot. 28: 401-445.

2776. Tobin, E.M.; Briggs, W.R. 1969. PHYTOCHROME IN EMBRYOS OF *PINUS PALUSTRIS*. Plant Physiol. 44: 148-150.

2777. Tobin, E.M. 1972. PHYTOCHROME: STUDIES OF PROTEIN CONFORMATION AND OF THE ROLE OF HYDRATION IN PHOTOTRANSFORMATION. Ph.D. Thesis, Harvard Univ., Cambridge.

2778. Tobin, E.M.; Briggs, W.R. 1973. STUDIES ON THE PROTEIN CONFORMATION OF PHYTOCHROME. Photochem. Photobiol. 18: 487-495.

2779. Tobin, E.M.; Briggs, W.R.; Brown, P.K. 1973. THE ROLE OF HYDRATION IN THE PHOTOTRANSFORMATION OF PHYTOCHROME. Photochem. Photobiol. 18: 497-503.

2780. Tokhver, A.K. 1970. DEPENDENCE OF THE DARK FORMATION OF ANTHOCYANINS IN BUCKWHEAT SEEDLINGS ON THE DURATION OF PRELIMINARY ILLUMINATION. Fiziol. Rast. 17: 54-57 (RUS) Consultants Bureau English Translation, pp. 44-46.

2781. Tokhver, A.K.; Voskresenskaya, N.P. 1971. EFFECT OF LIGHT SPECTRAL COMPOSITION ON LIGHT CURVES OF ANTHOCYANIN ACCUMULATION IN BUCKWHEAT SEEDLINGS. Fiziol. Rast. 18: 904-910 (RUS) (ENG Summary).

2782. Tokhver, A.K. 1972. EFFECT OF PERIODIC INTERRUPTION OF ILLUMINATION ON ANTHOCYANIN ACCUMULATION IN BUCKWHEAT SEEDLINGS. Fiziol. Rast. 19: 819-823 (RUS) (ENG Summary).

2783. Toole, E.H.; Borthwick, H.A.; Hendricks, S.B.; Toole, V.K. 1953. PHYSIOLOGICAL STUDIES OF THE EFFECTS OF LIGHT AND TEMPERATURE ON SEED GERMINATION. Proc. Int. Seed Test. Assoc. 18: 267-276.

2784. Toole, E.H.; Toole, V.K.; Borthwick, H.A.; Hendricks, S.B. 1955. PHOTOCONTROL OF *LEPIDIUM* SEED GERMINATION. Plant Physiol. 30: 15-21.

2785. Toole, E.H.; Toole, V.K.; Borthwick, H.A.; Hendricks, S.B. 1955. INTERACTION OF TEMPERATURE AND LIGHT IN GERMINATION OF SEEDS. Plant Physiol. 30: 473-478.

2786. Toole, E.H.; Hendricks, S.B.; Borthwick, H.A.; Toole, V.K. 1956. PHYSIOLOGY OF SEED GERMINATION. Annu. Rev. Plant Physiol. 7: 299-324 (R).

2787. Toole, E.H.; Snow, A.G., Jr.; Toole, V.K.; Borthwick, H.A. 1956. EFFECTS OF LIGHT AND TEMPERATURE ON GERMINATION OF VIRGINIA PINE SEEDS. Plant Physiol. 31: Suppl.-36 (A).

2788. Toole, E.H.; Toole, V.K.; Borthwick, H.A.; Hendricks, S.B. 1957. CHANGING SENSITIVITY OF SEEDS TO LIGHT. Plant Physiol. 32: Suppl.-11 (A).

2789. Toole, E.H.; Toole, V.K.; Hendricks, S.B.; Borthwick, H.A. 1957. EFFECT OF TEMPERATURE ON GERMINATION OF LIGHT-SENSITIVE SEEDS. Proc. Int. Seed Test. Assoc. 22: 196-204.

2790. Toole, E.H. 1958. SEED PHYSIOLOGY AND DORMANCY-HISTORICAL HIGHLIGHTS. *Fifty Years of Seed Testing Association Official Seed Analyst of North America*, pp. 41-45 (R).

2791. Toole, E.H.; Toole, V.K.; Borthwick, H.A.; Hendricks, S.B.; Downs, R.J. 1958. ACTION OF LIGHT ON GERMINATION OF SEEDS OF *PAULOWNIA TOMEN-TOSA*. Plant Physiol. 33: Suppl.-23 (A).

2792. Toole, E.H. 1959. MECHANISMS OF DORMANCY IN SEEDS. Proc. IX Int. Bot. Congr. 2: 401 (A).

2793. Toole, E.H. 1959. EFFECT OF LIGHT ON THE GERMINATION OF SEEDS. *Photoperiodism and Related Phenemona in Plants and Animals*, Ed. R.B. Withrow, A.A.A.S., Washington, D.C., pp. 89-99 (R).

2794. Toole, E.H. 1961. THE EFFECT OF LIGHT AND OTHER VARIABLES ON THE CONTROL OF SEED GERMINATION. Proc. Int. Seed Test. Assoc. 26: 659-673 (R).

2795. Toole, E.H. 1961. MECHANISM OF DORMANCY OF SEEDS AND TUBERS. *Recent Advances in Botany 9th International Botanical Congress*, Montreal 2: 1208-1210 (R).

2796. Toole, E.H.; Toole, V.K. 1961. UNTIL TIME AND PLACE ARE SUITABLE. *Yearbook of Agriculture*, pp. 99-105 (R).

2797. Toole, V.K.; Toole, E.H.; Borthwick, H.A.; Hendricks. S.B. 1957. PHYSIOLOGY OF SEED DORMANCY. Proc. Int. Seed Test. Assoc. 22: 1-15.

2798. Toole, V.K.; Borthwick, H.A.; Toole, E.H.; Snow, A.G., Jr. 1958. THE GERMINATION RESPONSE OF SEEDS OF *PINUS TAEDA* TO LIGHT. Plant Physiol. 33: Suppl.-23 (A).

2799. Toole, V.K.; Cathey, H.M. 1961. RESPONSES TO GIBBERELLIN OF LIGHT-REQUIRING SEEDS OF LETTUCE AND *LEPIDIUM VIRGINICUM*. Plant Physiol. 36: 663-671.

2800. Toole, V.K.; Toole, E.H.; Hendricks, S.B.; Borthwick, H.A.; Snow, A.G., Jr. 1961. RESPONSES OF SEEDS OF *PINUS VIRGINIANA* TO LIGHT. Plant Physiol. 36: 285-290.

2801. Toole, V.K.; Toole, E.H.; Borthwick, H.A.; Snow, A.G., Jr. 1962. RESPONSES OF SEEDS OF *PINUS TAEDA* AND *P. STROBUS* TO LIGHT. Plant Physiol. 37: 228-233.

2802. Toole, V.K. 1963. LIGHT CONTROL OF SEED GERMINATION. Proc. Assoc. Off. Seed Anal. 53: 124-143 (R).

2803. Toole, V.K.; Borthwick, H.A. 1966. LIGHT RESPONSES OF *ERAGROSTIS CURVULA* SEEDS. Plant Physiol. 41: Suppl.-17 (A).

2804. Toole, V.K.; Borthwick, H.A. 1968. LIGHT RESPONSES OF *ERAGROSTIS CURVULA* SEED. Proc. Int. Seed Test. Assoc. 33: 515-530.

2805. Toole, V.K.; Borthwick, H.A. 1968. THE PHOTOREACTION CONTROLLING SEED GERMINATION IN *ERAGROSTIS CURVULA*. Plant Cell Physiol. 9: 125-136.

2806. Toole, V.K.; Borthwick, H.A. 1971. EFFECT OF LIGHT, TEMPERATURE, AND THEIR INTERACTIONS ON GERMINATION OF SEEDS OF KENTUCKY BLUEGRASS (*POA PRATENSIS* L.). Am. Soc. Hortic. Sci. 96: 301-304.

2807. Toole, V.K. 1973. EFFECTS OF LIGHT, TEMPERATURE, AND THEIR INTERACTIONS ON THE GERMINATION OF SEEDS. Seed. Sci. Technol. 1: 339-396 (R).

2808. Toriyama, H. 1973. EFFECTS OF RED AND FAR-RED LIGHT UPON THE PRIMARY ROOT OF MUNG BEAN SEEDLINGS. Plant Physiol. 51: Suppl.-51, Abstr. No. 278 (A).

2809. Toriyama, H.; Jaffe, M.J. 1973. EFFECTS OF RED AND FAR-RED LIGHT UPON THE YELLOW PIGMENT OF EXCISED SECONDARY ROOT APICES OF *PHASEOLUS AUREUS*. Proc. Jpn. Acad. 49: 748-753.

2810. Torrey, J.G. 1951. EFFECTS OF LIGHT ON ROOT GROWTH. Proc. Am. Soc. Plant Physiol. Meeting, Sept. 9-12, Minneapolis, Minn., p. 11 (A).

2811. Torrey, J.G. 1952. EFFECTS OF LIGHT ON ELONGATION AND BRANCHING IN PEA ROOTS. Plant Physiol. 27: 591-602.

2812. Towill, L.R.; Ikuma, H. 1972. PHOTOCONTROL OF THE GERMINATION OF *ONOCLEA* SPORES. Plant Physiol. 49: Suppl.-63, Abstr. No. 356 (A).

2813. Towill, L.R.; Ikuma, H. 1973. PHOTOCONTROL OF THE GERMINATION OF *ONOCLEA* SPORES I. ACTION SPECTRUM. Plant Physiol. 51: 973-978.

2814. Travis, R.L.; Key, J.L.; Ross, C.W. 1974. ACTIVATION OF 80 S MAIZE RIBOSOMES BY RED LIGHT TREATMENT OF DARK-GROWN SEEDLINGS. Plant Physiol. 53: 28-31.

2815. Tregunna, E.B.; Krotkov, G.; Nelson, C.D. 1962. EFFECT OF WHITE, RED, AND BLUE LIGHT ON THE NATURE OF THE PRODUCTS OF PHOTOSYNTHESIS IN TOBACCO LEAVES. Can. J. Bot. 40: 317-326.

2816. Tremmel, B.C. 1970. A MODEL FOR PHYTOCHROME MEDIATED CONTROL OF GROWTH IN *AVENA*. Published by B.C. Tremmel, 2421-B San Antonio St., Austin, Texas 78705.

2817. Tremmel, B.C.; Yem, A. 1974. ENZYME MEDIATED DIFFERENTIATION DURING
EARLY CORN PHOTOMORPHOGENESIS. Plant Physiol. 53: Suppl.-1, Abstr.
No. 1 (A).

2818. Trémolières, A.; Jacques, R.; Mazliak, P. 1973. RÉGULATION PAR LA
LUMIÈRE DE L'ACCUMULATION DE L'ACIDE LINOLÉNIQUE DANS LA JEUNE
FEUILLE DE POIS. SPECTRE D'ACTION, INFLUENCE DE L'INTENSITÉ DE
L'ÉCLAIREMENT ET RÔLE DU PHYTOCHROME. Physiol. Veg. 11: 239-251
(ENG Summary).

2818.5 Trillmich, F. 1971. LOKALISATION VON PHYTOCHROM UND FLAVIN IN PARTI-
KULÄREM MATERIAL AUS KOLEOPTILEN VON MAIS (*ZEA MAYS* L.). M.S. Thesis
Univ. Freiburg, Germany.

2819. Trumpf, C. 1924. UEBER DEN EINFLUSS INTERMITTIERENDER BELICHTUNG AUF
DAS ETIOLEMENT DER PFLANZEN. Bot. Arch. 5: 381-410.

2820. Tso, T.C.; Kasperbauer, M.J.; Sorokin, T.P. 1970. EFFECT OF PHOTOPERIOD
AND END-OF-DAY LIGHT QUALITY ON ALKALOIDS AND PHENOLIC COMPOUNDS OF
TOBACCO. Plant Physiol. 45: 330-333.

2821. Tucker, D.J.; Mansfield, T.A. 1972. EFFECTS OF LIGHT QUALITY ON APICAL
DOMINANCE IN *XANTHIUM STRUMARIUM* AND THE ASSOCIATED CHANGES IN ENDO-
GENOUS LEVELS OF ABSCISIC ACID AND CYTOKININS. Planta 102: 140-151.

2822. Tureckaja, R. Ch. 1951. THE INFLUENCE OF LIGHT ON THE PROCESS OF ROOT
FORMATION ON CUTTINGS OF SOME PLANTS. Dokl. Akad. Nauk SSSR 76:
137-140 (RUS).

2823. Turner, M.R. 1969. PHOTOMORPHOGENETIC RESPONSES OF THE LETTUCE SEEDLING
(C.V. GREAT LAKES). Abstr. British Photobiol. Group Bull., Reading
Univ., p. 21 (A).

2824. Turner, M.R.; Vince, D. 1969. PHOTOSENSORY MECHANISMS IN THE LETTUCE
SEEDLING HYPOCOTYL. Planta 84: 368-382.

2825. Ullrich, H.; Canel, M. 1939. ÜBER DAS PHOTOPERIODISCHE WIRKUNGSSPEK-
TRUM BEI ISARIA-SOMMERGERSTE. Naturwissenschaften 27: 367.

2826. Ullrich, H. 1939. PHOTOPERIODISMUS UND BLÜHHORMONE. Ber. Dtsch. Bot.
Ges. 57: 40-52.

2827. Unser, G.; Mohr, H. 1970. PHYTOCHROME-MEDIATED INCREASE OF GALACTO-
LIPIDS IN MUSTARD SEEDLINGS. Naturwissenschaften 57: 358-359.

2828. Unser, G.; Masoner, M. 1972. KINETICS OF MONOGALACTOSYLTRANSFERASE IN
MUSTARD SEEDLINGS. Naturwissenschaften 59: 39.

2829. Unser, I. 1972. UNTERSUCHUNG DER PHYTOCHROMPHOTOKONVERSION IN SAMEN UND
JUNGEN KEIMLINGEN VON *SINAPIS ALBA* L. MIT HILFE DER ANTHOCYANAKUMULA-
TION. Ph.D. Thesis, Univ. Freiburg, Germany.

2830. Valanne, N. 1966. THE GERMINATION PHASES OF MOSS SPORES AND THEIR CON-
TROL BY LIGHT. Ann. Bot. Fenn. 3: 1-60.

2831. Valanne, N. 1971. THE EFFECTS OF PROLONGED DARKNESS AND LIGHT ON THE
FINE STRUCTURE OF *CERATODON PURPUREUS*. Can. J. Bot. 49: 547-554.

2832. Valio, I.F.M.; Schwabe, W.W. 1969. GROWTH AND DORMANCY IN *LUNULARIA
CRUCIATA* (L.) DUM. IV. LIGHT AND TEMPERATURE CONTROL OF RHIZOID
FORMATION IN GEMMAE. J. Exp. Bot. 20: 615-628.

2833. Van den Driessche, R. 1970. INFLUENCE OF LIGHT INTENSITY AND PHOTO-
PERIOD ON FROST-HARDINESS DEVELOPMENT IN DOUGLAS-FIR SEEDLINGS. Can.
J. Bot. 48: 2129-2134.

2834. Van den Muijzenberg, E.W.B. 1948. ENIGE PROEVEN MET VERSCHILLENDE LICHT
EN STRALINGSBRONNEN BIJ KASPLANTEN. Meded. Dir. Tuinbouw Neth. 11:
495-502 (ENG Summary).

2835. Van der Veen, R. 1948. STORING SEED POTATOES IN ARTIFICALLY-LIGHTED
CELLARS. Philips Tech. Rev. 10: 318-322.

2836. Van der Veen, R. 1949. INFLUENCE OF LIGHT UPON PLANTS. Philips Tech.
Rev. 11: 43-49 (R).

2837. Van der Veen, R. 1957. PLANT GROWTH IN COLOURED LIGHT. Sci. Hortic.
13: 33-37 (R).

2838. Van der Veen, R.; Meijer, G. 1959. *LIGHT AND PLANT GROWTH*. N.V.
Philips Gloeilampfabriek, Eindhoven, Holland, pp. 83-118 (R).

2839. Van der Veen, R.; Meijer, G. 1961. CRITICAL DAYLENGTH OF THE SHORT-DAY
PLANT *SALVIA OCCIDENTALIS* IN RED AND FAR-RED RADIATION. Proc. III
Int. Congr. Photobiol., Copenhagen, pp. 389-390.

2840. Van der Veen, R. 1970. THE IMPORTANCE OF THE RED-FAR RED ANTAGONISM IN
PHOTOBLASTIC SEEDS. Acta Bot. Neerl. 19: 809-812.

2841. Van Overbeek, J. 1936. GROWTH HORMONE AND MESOCOTYL GROWTH. Recl.
Trav. Bot. Neerl. 33: 333-340.

2842. Van Poucke, M.; Barthe, F.; Mohr, H. 1969. PHYTOCHROME-MEDIATED INDUC-
TION OF ASCORBIC ACID OXIDASE IN MUSTARD SEEDLINGS. Naturwissenschaften 56: 417.

2843. Van Poucke, M.; Barthe, F. 1970. INDUCTION OF GLYCOLLATE OXIDASE ACTI-
VITY IN MUSTARD SEEDLINGS UNDER THE INFLUENCE OF CONTINUOUS IRRADIA-
TION WITH RED AND FAR-RED LIGHT. Planta 94: 308-318.

2844. Van Poucke, M.; Cerff, R.; Barthe, F.; Mohr, H. 1970. SIMULTANEOUS
INDUCTION OF GLYCOLATE ODIDASE AND GLYOXYLATE REDUCTASE IN WHITE
MUSTARD SEEDLINGS BY PHYTOCHROME. Naturwissenschaften 56: 132-133.

2845. Van Poucke, M.; Rethy, R. 1972. PHYTOCHROME-CONTROLLED FORMATION OF
ANTHOCYANIN-LIKE SUBSTANCES IN *MARCHANTIA POLYMORPHA* L. Proc. VI
Int. Congr. Photobiol., Abstr. No. 200 (A).

2846. Van Rooden, J.; Akkermans, L.M.A.; Van der Veen, R. 1970. A STUDY ON
PHOTOBLASTISM IN SEEDS OF SOME TROPICAL WEEDS. Acta Bot. Neerl. 19:
257-264.

2847. Van Schoor, G.H.J. 1942. L'AUGMENTATION DE POIDS DE *TRADESCANTIA*
FLUMINENSIS KTH EN FONCTION DE L'ÉCLAIREMENT. Bull. Soc. R. Bot.
Belg. 74: 184-200.

2848. Van Schoor, G.H.J. 1950. LE COMPARTEMENT D'*ELODEA CANADENSIS* RICH. EN
FONCTION DE LA QUALITÉ ET DE LA QUANTITÉ DE L'ÉCLAIREMENT. Soc. R.
Bot. Belg. 83: 77-103.

2849. Van Staden, J.; Wareing, P.F. 1972. THE EFFECT OF LIGHT ON ENDOGENOUS
CYTOKININ LEVELS IN SEEDS OF *RUMEX OBTUSIFOLIUS*. Planta 104:
126-133.

2850. Van Staden, J. 1973. CHANGES IN ENDOGENOUS CYTOKININS OF LETTUCE SEED
DURING GERMINATION. Physiol. Plant. 28: 222-227.

2851. Varshney, C.K. 1968. GERMINATION OF THE LIGHT-SENSITIVE SEEDS OF
OCIMUM AMERICANUM LINN. New Phytol. 67: 125-129.

2852. Veleminský, J. 1965. PROMOTION OF *ARABIDOPSIS* SEED GERMINATION BY BLUE,
RED AND FAR-RED LIGHT. Arabidopsis Inf. Ser. 3: 5-6.

2853. Velikanov, L.P.; Pumpianskaya, S.L. 1970. ON THE PARTICIPATION OF
PHYTOCHROME IN THE PHOTOPERIODIC REACTION OF *ARABIDOPSIS THALIANA*
(L.) HENYH. Arabidopsis Inf. Ser. 7: 12-13.

2854. Venkataraman, R.; Seth, P.N.; Maheshwari, S.C. 1970. STUDIES ON THE
GROWTH AND FLOWERING OF A SHORT-DAY PLANT, *WOLFFIA MICROSCOPICA*. I.
GENERAL ASPECTS AND INDUCTION OF FLOWERING BY CYTOKININS. Z.
Pflanzenphysiol. 62: 316-327.

2855. Vicente, M.; Engelhardt, M.; Silberschmidt, K. 1962. THE INFLUENCE OF
TEMPERATURE ON THE GERMINATION RESPONSE TO LIGHT OF SEEDS OF *RUMEX
OBTUSIFOLIUS* L. Phyton (Buenos Aires) 19: 163-167.

2856. Vicente, M.; Noronha, A.B.; Silberschmidt, K.; Meneghini, M. 1968.
SUCCESSIVE REVERSION OF THE EFFECT OF TEMPERATURE ON GERMINATION OF
RUMEX OBTUSIFOLIUS L. BY FAR-RED LIGHT. Phyton (Buenos Aires) 25:
11-13.

2857. Vidaver, W.; Hsiao, A.I.-H. 1972. PHYTOCHROME TRANSFORMATION IN LETTUCE
SEED IRRADIATED AT VARIOUS TEMPERATURES. Plant Physiol. 50: 249-251.

2858. Vidaver, W.; Hsiao, A.I.-H. 1972. PERSISTENCE OF PHYTOCHROME-MEDIATED
GERMINATION CONTROL IN LETTUCE SEEDS FOR 1 YEAR FOLLOWING A SINGLE
MONOCHROMATIC LIGHT FLASH. Can. J. Bot. 50: 687-689.

2859. Vidaver, W.; Hsiao, A.I.-H. 1974. ACTIONS OF GIBBERELLIC ACID AND
PHYTOCHROME ON THE GERMINATION OF GRAND RAPIDS LETTUCE SEEDS. Plant
Physiol. 53: 266-268.

2860. Vince, D. 1956. STUDIES ON THE EFFECTS OF LIGHT QUALITY ON THE GROWTH
AND DEVELOPMENT OF PLANTS. II. FORMATIVE EFFECTS IN *LYCOPERSICON
ESCULENTUM* AND *PISUM SATIVUM*. J. Hortic. Sci. 31: 16-24.

2861. Vince, D. 1957. PHOTOPERIODISM AND FLOWERING, WITH SPECIAL REFERENCE
TO CHRYSANTHEUM. Sci. Hortic. 13: 7-14 (R).

2862. Vince, D. 1964. PHOTOMORPHOGENESIS IN PLANT STEMS. Biol. Rev.
Cambridge Philos. Soc. 39: 506-536 (R).

2863. Vince, D. 1963. THE PLANT'S LIGHT REQUIREMENTS. *Engineering Aspects
of Environmental Control for Plant Growth*. Aust. C.S.I.R.O.,
Melbourne, pp. 135-158 (R).

2864. Vince, D. 1964. THE PROMOTING EFFECT OF FAR-RED LIGHT ON FLOWERING IN
THE LONG DAY PLANT *LOLIUM TEMULENTUM*. Proc. IV Int. Congr. Photobiol., p. 110 (A).

2865. Vince, D.; Blake, J.; Spencer, R. 1964. SOME EFFECTS OF WAVELENGTH OF
THE SUPPLEMENTARY LIGHT ON THE PHOTOPERIODIC BEHAVIOR OF LONG-DAY
PLANTS, CARNATION AND LETTUCE. Physiol. Plant. 17: 119-125.

2866. Vince, D. 1965. THE PROMOTING EFFECT OF FAR-RED LIGHT ON FLOWERING IN
THE LONG DAY PLANT *LOLIUM TEMULENTUM*. Physiol. Plant. 18: 474-482.

2867. Vince, D. 1966. SPECTRAL DISTRIBUTION OF LIGHT AFFECTING GROWTH AND DEVELOPMENT: ANGIOSPERMS. *Environmental Biology*, Ed. P.L. Altman and D.S. Dittmer, Fed. Am. Soc. Exp. Biol. Bethesda, pp. 147-154 (R).

2868. Vince, D. 1966. AN INTERPRETATION ON THE PROMOTING EFFECT OF FAR-RED LIGHT ON THE FLOWERING OF LONG-DAY PLANTS. Photochem. Photobiol. 5: 449-450 (R-D).

2869. Vince, D. 1966. THE ROLE OF PHYTOCHROME IN THE REGULATION OF PLANT DEVELOPMENT BY LIGHT. Sci. Hortic. 18: 77-83 (R).

2870. Vince, D.; Grill, R. 1966. THE PHOTORECEPTORS INVOLVED IN ANTHOCYANIN SYNTHESIS. Photochem. Photobiol. 5: 407-411.

2871. Vince, D. 1967. GIBBERELLIC ACID AND THE LIGHT INHIBITION OF STEM ELONGATION. Planta 75: 291-308.

2872. Vince, D. 1968. GROWTH AND ANTHOCYANIN SYNTHESIS IN EXCISED *SORGHUM* INTERNODES. I. EFFECTS OF GROWTH REGULATING SUBSTANCES. Planta 82: 261-279.

2873. Vince, D. 1969. RESPONSES OF SOME LONG DAY PLANTS TO RED AND FAR-RED LIGHT. Brit. Photobiol. Group Bull.: 21, Reading Univ., March 27-28, p. 4 (A).

2874. Vince, D. 1970. THE CONTROL OF FLOWERING AND OTHER RESPONSES TO DAY-LENGTH: PARTS I, II. R. Hortic. Soc. 95: 214-275 (R).

2875. Vince, D. 1971. INTERACTIONS OF LIGHT AND ETHYLENE IN THE CONTROL OF PLUMULAR HOOK MOVEMENTS. Proc. Eur. Annu. Symp. Plant Photomorpho-genesis, (Athens), pp. 54-55 (A).

2876. Vince, D. 1972. PHYTOCHROME AND FLOWERING. *Phytochrome*, Ed. K. Mitrakos and W. Shropshire, Jr., Academic Press: London and New York, pp. 257-291 (R).

2877. Vince-Prue, D. 1973. PHYTOCHROME AND THE NATURAL LIGHT ENVIRONMENT. Ann. Acad. Bras. Cienc. 45: 93-101 (R).

2877.5 Vince-Prue, D.; Guttridge, C.G. 1973. FLORAL INITIATION IN STRAWBERRY: SPECTRAL EVIDENCE FOR THE REGULATION OF FLOWERING BY LONG-DAY INHIBI-TION. Planta 110: 165-172.

2878. Virgin, H. 1958. VÄXTENS KÄNSLIGHET FÖR RÖTT OCH INFRARÖTT LJUS. EN EXPOSÉ ÖVER ETT GAMMALT PROBLEM MED NYA ASPEKTER. Saertr. Bot. Not. Lund. 111: 257-273 (R).

2879. Virgin, H.I. 1958. STUDIES ON THE FORMATION OF PROTOCHLOROPHYLL AND CHLOROPHYLL A UNDER VARYING LIGHT TREATMENT. Physiol. Plant. 11: 347-362.

2880. Virgin, H.I. 1961. PLANT CELL RESPONSE TO VISIBLE LIGHT EXCLUDING PHOTOSYNTHESIS. Proc. III Int. Congr. Photobiol., pp. 15-26 (R).

2881. Virgin, H.I. 1961. ACTION SPECTRUM FOR THE ELIMINATION OF THE LAG PHASE IN CHLOROPHYLL FORMATION IN PREVIOUSLY DARK GROWN LEAVES OF WHEAT. Physiol. Plant. 14: 439-452.

2882. Virgin, H.I. 1962. LIGHT-INDUCED UNFOLDING OF THE GRASS LEAF. Physiol. Plant. 15: 380-389.

2883. Virgin, H.I. 1966. CAROTENOID SYNTHESIS IN LEAVES OF WHEAT AFTER IRRADIATION BY RED LIGHT. Physiol. Plant. 19: 40-46.

2884. Virgin, H.I. 1967. CAROTENOID SYNTHESIS IN LEAVES OF ETIOLATED WHEAT SEEDLINGS AFTER VARYING LIGHT AND DARK TREATMENTS. Physiol. Plant. 20: 314-320.

2885. Virgin, H.I.; Arvidsson, L.G. 1968. ON THE DELIMITATION OF CHLOROPHYLL FORMATION AFTER AN IRRADIATION WITH A SHARPLY DEFINED LIGHT AREA. Physiol. Plant. 21: 1177-1184.

2886. Virgin, H.I. 1968. LIGHT AND CHLOROPLAST MOVEMENTS. *Aspects of Cell Motility*. Symp. Soc. Exp. Biol. 22, Cambridge Univ. Press, pp. 329-352 (R).

2887. Virgin, H.I. 1972. CHLOROPHYLL BIOSYNTHESIS AND PHYTOCHROME ACTION. *Phytochrome*, Ed. K. Mitrakos and W. Shropshire, Jr., Academic Press: London and New York, pp. 371-404 (R).

2888. Vlasenok, L.I.; Yarimovich, Z.V. 1970. EFFECT OF PHYTOCHROME ON THE HYDROLYTIC ACTIVITY OF CHLOROPHYLLASE. *Metab. Str. Fotosin. App.*, Ed. A.A. Shlyk, Nauk. i Tekhnika, Minsk, pp. 77-81 (RUS).

2889. Vlitos, A.J.; Meudt, W. 1957. THE EFFECT OF LIGHT AND OF THE SHOOT APEX ON THE ACTION OF GIBBERELLIC ACID. Contrib. Boyce Thompson Inst. 19: 55-62.

2890. Voerkel, S.H. 1933. UNTERSUCHUNGEN ÜBER DIE PHOTOTAXIS DER CHLOROPLAS-TEN. Planta 21: 156-205.

2891. Vogt, E. 1915. ÜBER DEN EINFLUSS DES LICHTS AUF DAS WACHSTUM DER KOLEOPTILE VON *AVENA SATIVA*. Z. Bot. 7: 193-270.

2892. Voskresenskaja, N.P.   1950.   THE EFFECT OF THE LIGHT WAVELENGTH ON THE
       SYNTHESIS OF CARBOHYDRATES AND PROTEINS IN A LEAF.   Dokl. Akad.
       Nauk. SSSR 72: 173-176 (RUS).

2893. Voskresenskaja, N.P.   1952.   CONCERNING THE INFLUENCE OF THE SPECTRAL
       COMPOSITION OF THE LIGHTS ON THE COMPOSITION OF THE PHOTOSYNTHESIS
       PRODUCTS.   Dokl. Akad. Nauk. SSSR 86: 429-432 (RUS).

2894. Voskresenkaja, N.P.   1953.   THE EFFECTS OF THE CONDITIONS OF ILLUMINATION
       ON THE COMPOSITION OF THE PRODUCTS OF PHOTOSYNTHESIS.   Trudy Inst.
       Fiziol. Rast. Akad. Nauk. SSSR 8: 42-56 (RUS).

2895. Voskresenskaja, N.P.   1953.   THE SIGNIFICANCE OF THE SPECTRAL QUALITY OF
       LIGHT FOR THE PHOTOSYNTHETIC PRODUCTION OF ORGANIC SUBSTANCES.   Dokl.
       Akad. Nauk. SSSR 93: 911-914 (RUS).

2896. Voskresenskaja, N.P.   1956.   CONCERNING THE FORMATION OF ORGANIC ACIDS
       AND AMINO ACIDS BY PHOTOSYNTHESIS IN DIFFERENT CONDITIONS OF LIGHT-
       ING.   Fiziol. Rast. 3: 49-57 (RUS).

2897. Voskresenskaja, N.P.; Grisshina, G.S.   1956.   METABOLISM OF $^{14}CO_2$ IN
       PLANTS UNDER VARIOUS LIGHTING CONDITIONS.   Dokl. Akad. Nauk. SSSR
       106: 565-568 (RUS).

2898. Voskresenskaja, N.P.; Grisshina, G.S.   1958.   THE PROLONGED ACTION OF
       LIGHT OF DIFFERENT SPECTRAL COMPOSITION ON PLANTS.   Fiziol. Rast.
       (RUS) Consultants Bureau English Translation 5: 139-148.

2899. Voskresenskaja, N.P.; Grisshina, G.S.   1959.   THE EFFECTS OF INTENSITY
       AND SPECTRAL COMPOSITION OF IRRADIATION ON THE METABOLIC PRODUCTS.
       Dokl. Akad. Nauk. SSSR 124: 469-472 (RUS).

2900. Voskresenskaja, N.P.   1965.   *PHOTOSYNTHESIS AND THE SPECTRAL COMPOSITION
       OF LIGHT*.   Nayka, pp. 216-309 (RUS) (R).

2901. Voskresenskaja, N.P.; Wiel, YU.A.   1966.   THE EFFECT OF LIGHT QUALITY ON
       SYNTHESIS OF TRYPTOPHANE IN BARLEY SEEDLINGS.   Fiziol. Rast. 13:
       762-768 (RUS) (ENG Summary).

2902. Voskresenskaja, N.P.; Nechaeva, E.P.   1967.   EFFECT OF BLUE, RED AND
       GREEN LIGHT ON THE PROTEIN, NUCLEIC ACID, AND CHLOROPHYLL CONTENT IN
       YOUNG BARLEY PLANTS.   Fiziol. Rast. 14: 299-308 (RUS) Consultants
       Bureau English Translation, pp. 254-261.

2903. Voskresenskaja, N.P.   1972.   BLUE LIGHT AND CARBON METABOLISM.   Annu.
       Rev. Plant Physiol. 23: 219-234 (R).

2904. Voskresenskaja, N.P.; Khodzhiev, A. 1972. ACTIVITY OF GLYCOLATE PATH-
WAY REACTIONS IN PLANTS GROWN IN RED AND BLUE LIGHT. Dokl. Akad.
Nauk. Tadzh. SSSR 15: 60-63 (RUS).

2905. Voss, J. 1936. ÜBER DEN EINFLUSS VERSCHIEDENER LICHT- UND STRAHLENARTEN
AUF DIE ENTWICKLUNG LANDWIRTSCHAFTLICHER KULTURPFLANZEN. Angew. Bot.
18: 43-75.

2906. Vyas, L.N.; Garg, R.K. 1971. RESPONSES TO GIBBERELLIN OF LIGHT-
REQUIRING SEEDS OF *VERBENA BIPINNATIFIDA* NUTT. Z. Pflanzenphysiol.
65: 189-194.

2907. Vyas, L.N.; Garg, R.K. 1973. A REVERSIBLE PHOTOREACTION CONTROLLING
GERMINATION OF *VERBENA BIPINNATIFIDA* NUTT. SEEDS. Biochem. Physiol.
Pflanz. 164: 636-638.

2908. Wada, M.; Furuya, M. 1970. PHOTOCONTROL OF THE ORIENTATION OF CELL
DIVISION IN *ADIANTUM*. I. EFFECTS OF THE DARK AND RED PERIODS IN THE
APICAL CELLS OF GAMETOPHYTES. Dev. Growth Differ. 12: 109-118.

2909. Wada, M.; Furuya, M. 1971. PHOTOCONTROL OF THE ORIENTATION OF CELL
DIVISION IN *ADIANTUM*. II. EFFECTS OF THE DIRECTION OF WHITE LIGHT ON
THE APICAL CELL OF GAMETOPHYTES. Planta 98: 177-185.

2910. Wada, M.; Furuya, M. 1972. PHYTOCHROME ACTION OF THE TIMING OF CELL
DIVISION IN *ADIANTUM* GAMETOPHYTES. Plant Physiol. 49: 110-113.

2911. Wada, M.; Furuya, M. 1973. PHOTOCONTROL OF THE ORIENTATION OF CELL
DIVISION IN *ADIANTUM*. III. EFFECTS OF METABOLIC INHIBITORS. Dev.
Growth Differ. 15: 73-80.

2912. Wada, M.; Furuya, M. 1974. ACTION SPECTRUM FOR THE TIMING OF PHOTO-
INDUCED CELL DIVISION IN *ADIANTUM* GAMETOPHYTES. Physiol. Plant. 32:
377-381.

2913. Wagné, C. 1964. THE DISTRIBUTION OF THE LIGHT-EFFECT IN PARTLY IRRADIA-
TED GRASS LEAVES. Physiol. Plant. 17: 751-756.

2914. Wagné, C. 1965. THE DISTRIBUTION OF THE LIGHT EFFECT FROM IRRADIATED
TO NON-IRRADIATED PARTS OF GRASS LEAVES. Physiol. Plant. 18: 1001-
1006.

2915. Wagner, E.; Mohr, H. 1966. KINETIC STUDIES TO INTERPRET 'HIGH ENERGY
PHENOMENA' OF PHOTOMORPHOGENESIS ON THE BASIS OF PHYTOCHROME.
Photochem. Photobiol. 5: 397-406.

2916. Wagner, E.; Mohr, H. 1966. KINETISCHE STUDIEN ZUR INTERPRETATION DER WIRKUNG VON SUKZEDANBESTRAHLUNGEN MIT HELLROT UND DUNKELROT BEI DER PHOTOMORPHOGENESE (ANTHOCYANSYNTHESE BEI *SINAPIS ALBA* L.). Planta 70: 34-41 (ENG Summary).

2917. Wagner, E.; Mohr, H. 1966. "PRIMÄRE" UND "SEKUNDÄRE" DIFFERENZIERUNG IM ZUSAMMENHANG MIT DER PHOTOMORPHOGENESE VON KEIMPFLANZEN (*SINAPIS ALBA* L.). Planta 71: 204-221 (ENG Summary).

2918. Wagner, E. 1967. EIN BEITRAG ZUR PHYTOCHROMINDUZIERTEN PHOTOMORPHO-GENESE DES SENFKEIMLINGS (*SINAPIS ALBA*). Ph.D. Thesis, Univ. Frei-burg, Germany.

2919. Wagner, E.; Bienger, I.; Mohr, H. 1967. DIE STEIGERUNG DER DURCH PHYTO-CHROM BEWIRKTEN ANTHOCYANSYNTHESE DES SENFKEIMLINGS (*SINAPIS ALBA* L.) DURCH CHLORAMPHENICOL. Planta 75: 1-9 (ENG Summary).

2920. Wagner, E.; Cumming, B.G. 1970. BETACYANIN ACCUMULATION, CHLOROPHYLL CONTENT, AND FLOWER INITIATION IN *CHENOPODIUM RUBRUM* AS RELATED TO ENDOGENOUS RHYTHMICITY AND PHYTOCHROME ACTION. Can. J. Bot. 48: 1-18.

2921. Wagner, E. 1971. CONDITIONING OF ENDOGENOUS RHYTHMICITY IN BETACYANIN ACCUMULATION AND TURNOVER IN *CHENOPODIUM RUBRUM* SEEDLINGS BY LIGHT AND TEMPERATURE CYCLES. Proc. Eur. Annu. Symp. Plant Photomorpho-genesis, (Athens), p. 56 (A).

2922. Wagner, E.; Frosch, S.; Deitzer, G.F. 1974. MEMBRANE OSCILLATOR HYPOTH-ESIS OF PHOTOPERIODIC CONTROL. Proc. Eur. Annu. Symp. Plant Photo-morphogenesis, (Antwerpen), pp. 15-19 (R-D).

2923. Wagner, E.; Frosch, S.; Kempf, O. 1974. ENDOGENOUS RHYTHMICITY AND ENERGY TRANSDUCTION. VII. PHYTOCHROME-MODULATED RHYTHMS IN PYRIDINE NUCLEOTIDE LEVELS IN SEEDLINGS OF *CHENOPODIUM RUBRUM*. Plant Sci. Lett. 3: 43-48.

2924. Wagner, G.; Haupt, W.; Laux, A. 1972. REVERSIBLE INHIBITION OF CHLORO-PLAST MOVEMENT BY CYTOCHALASIN B IN THE GREEN ALGA *MOUGEOTIA*. Science 176: 808-809.

2925. Wagner, G.; Bentrup, F.W. 1973. LICHTABHÄNGIGE K^+-UND Cl^--FLÜSSE BEI *MOUGEOTIA*. Ber. Dtsch. Bot. Ges. 86: 365-369 (ENG Summary).

2926. Wagner, G. 1974. IONENFLÜSSE UND PHYTOCHROMABHÄNGIGE CHLOROPLASTENBE-WEGUNG BEI *MOUGEOTIA* SPEC. Ph.D. Thesis, Univ. Tübingen, Germany.

2927. Wagner, G. 1974. SOME PHYSIOLOGICAL PROPERTIES OF PHYTOCHROME IN THE ALGA *MOUGEOTIA*, AS STUDIED BY CYTOCHALASIN B AND AMINOPHYLLINE. Proc. Eur. Annu. Symp. Plant Photomorphogenesis, (Antwerpen), pp. 22-25.

2928. Wagner, G. 1974. LIGHT DEPENDENT ION FLUXES IN *MOUGEOTIA*: CONTROL BY PHOTOSYNTHESIS, NOT BY PHYTOCHROME. *Membrane Transport in Plants*, Springer-Verlag, Berlin, Heidelberg, New York, pp. 186-191 (R).

2929. Walker, T.S.; Bailey, J.L. 1968. TWO SPECTRALLY DIFFERENT FORMS OF THE PHYTOCHROME CHROMOPHORE EXTRACTED FROM ETIOLATED OAT SEEDLINGS. Biochem. J. 107: 603-605.

2930. Walker, T.S.; Bailey, J.L. 1970. STUDIES ON PHYTOCHROME. TWO PHOTO-REVERSIBLE CHROMOPROTEINS FROM ETIOLATED OAT SEEDLINGS. Biochem. J. 120: 607-612.

2931. Walker, T.S.; Bailey, J.L. 1970. STUDIES ON PHYTOCHROME. SOME PROPER-TIES OF ELECTROPHORETICALLY PURE PHYTOCHROME. Biochem. J. 120: 613-622.

2932. Wallrabe, E. 1944. ÜBER DIE WIRKUNG VON LICHT VERSCHIEDENER WELLEN-LÄNGE AUF DIE BLÜTENBILDUNG UND DIE SUKKULENZ DER BLÄTTER BEI DER KURZTAGSPFLANZE *KALANCHOË BLOSSFELDIANA*. Bot. Arch. 45: 281-316.

2933. Wareing, P.F. 1956. PHOTOPERIODISM IN WOODY PLANTS. Annu. Rev. Plant Physiol. 7: 191-214 (R).

2934. Wareing, P.F. 1957. PHOTOPERIODISM IN RELATION TO DORMANCY. Sci. Hortic. 13: 15-20 (R).

2935. Wareing, P.F.; Black, M. 1957. SENSITIVITY OF LIGHT-INHIBITED SEEDS TO CERTAIN SPECTRAL REGIONS. Nature (London) 180: 395.

2936. Wareing, P.F. 1958. PHOTOPERIODISM IN PLANTS AND ANIMALS. Nature (London) 181: 535-536 (R).

2937. Wareing, P.F.; Black, M. 1958. PHOTOPERIODISM IN SEEDS AND SEEDLINGS OF WOODY SPECIES. *The Physiology of Forest Trees*, Ed. K.V. Thimann, Ronald Press, New York, pp. 539-556 (R).

2938. Wareing, P.F.; Black, M. 1958. SIMILAR EFFECTS OF BLUE AND INFRA-RED RADIATION ON LIGHT SENSITIVE SEEDS. Nature (London) 181: 1420-1421.

2939. Wareing, P.F. 1959. PHOTOPERIODISM IN SEEDS AND BUDS. *Photoperiodism and Related Phenomena in Plants and Animals*, Ed. R.B. Withrow, AAAS, Washington, D.C., pp. 73-87.

2940. Wareing, P.F.; Black, M. 1961. THE INHIBITION OF GERMINATION OF SEEDS
       BY RADIATION. Recent Adv. Bot. 2: 1031-1033 (R).

2941. Wareing, P.F. 1969. GERMINATION AND DORMANCY. *Physiology of Plant
       Growth and Development*, Ed. M.B. Wilkins, McGraw-Hill, New York,
       pp. 604-644 (R).

2941.2 Wareing, P.F. 1971. THE CONTROL OF SEED DORMANCY. Biochem. J. 124:
       1P-2P (R).

2941.5 Wareing, P.F.; Phillips, I.D.J. 1970. *The Control of Growth and
       Differentiation in Plants*. Pergamon Press, New York, pp. 164-195;
       240-242 (R).

2942. Wareing, P.F.; Van Staden, J.; Webb, D.P. 1973. ENDOGENOUS HORMONES IN
       THE CONTROL OF SEED DORMANCY. Proc. Easter Sch. Agric. Sci., Univ.
       Nottingham 19: 145-155 (R).

2943. Wassink, E.C.; Krijthe, N.; Van der Scheer, C. 1950. ON THE EFFECT OF
       LIGHT OF VARIOUS SPECTRAL REGIONS ON THE SPROUTING OF POTATO-TUBERS.
       Proc. K. Ned. Akad. Wet. Ser. C. 53: 1228-1239.

2944. Wassink, E.C.; Sluijsmans, C.M.J.; Stolwijk, J.A.J. 1950. ON SOME
       PHOTOPERIODIC AND FORMATIVE EFFECTS OF COLOURED LIGHT IN *BRASSICA
       RAPA, F. OLEIFERA, SUBF. ANNUA*. Proc. K. Ned. Akad. Wet. Ser. C.
       53: 1466-1475.

2945. Wassink, E.C.; Stolwijk, J.A.J.; Beemster, A.B.R. 1951. DEPENDENCE OF
       FORMATIVE AND PHOTOPERIODIC REACTIONS IN *BRASSICA RAPA* VAR., *COSMOS*
       AND *LACTUCA* ON WAVELENGTH AND TIME OF IRRADIATION. Proc. K. Ned.
       Akad. Wet. Ser. C. 54: 421-432.

2946. Wassink, E.C.; Stolwijk, J.A.J. 1952. EFFECTS OF LIGHT OF NARROW SPEC-
       TRAL REGIONS ON GROWTH AND DEVELOPMENT OF PLANTS I, II. Proc. K.
       Ned. Akad. Wet. Ser. C. 55: 471-488.

2947. Wassink, E.C. 1954. ON PLANTS GROWN EXCLUSIVELY IN LIGHT OF RESTRICTED
       SPECTRAL REGIONS. Proc. VIII Int. Bot. Congr., pp. 316-317 (R).

2948. Wassink, E.C.; Stolwijk, J.A.J. 1956. EFFECTS OF LIGHT QUALITY ON
       PLANT GROWTH. Annu. Rev. Plant Physiol. 7: 373-400 (R).

2949. Wassink, E.C. 1957. INTERACTION OF LIGHT, OTHER EXTERNAL FACTORS, AND
       GENETIC DIFFERENCES IN FORMATIVE EFFECTS IN PLANTS. Colloq. Int.
       Photo-thermo periodisme, Parma, Italy, pp. 75-88 (R).

2950. Wassink, E.C. 1957. THE STUDY OF PLANT GROWTH IN CONTROLLED ENVIRON-
MENTS. Proc. Easter Sch. Agric. Sci., Univ. Nottingham, 4: 36-57
(R).

2951. Wassink, E.C.; Bensink, J.; DeLint, P.J.A.L. 1957. FORMATIVE EFFECTS
OF LIGHT QUALITY AND INTENSITY ON PLANTS. Proc. II Int. Congr.
Photobiol., pp. 343-360 (R-D).

2952. Wassink, E.C.; Sytsema, W. 1958. PETIOLE LENGTH REACTION IN *HYOSCYAMUS
NIGER* UPON DAYLENGTH EXTENSION WITH LIGHT OF NARROW SPECTRAL REGIONS
AS CORRELATED WITH THE LENGTH OF THE BASIC LIGHT PERIOD, AND UPON
NIGHT INTERRUPTION WITH RED AND INFRARED RADIATIONS. Meded.
Landbouwhogesch. Wageningen 58-7: 1-6.

2953. Wassink, E.C.; DeLint, P.J.A.L.; Bensink, J. 1959. SOME EFFECTS OF
HIGH-INTENSITY IRRADIATION OF NARROW SPECTRAL REGIONS. *Photoperiod-
ism and Related Phenomenon in Plants and Animals*, Ed. R.B. Withrow,
A.A.A.S. Washington, D.C., pp. 111-127.

2954. Wassink, E.C. 1961. SOME ASPECTS OF PHOTOCONTROL OF PLANT GROWTH AND
DEVELOPMENT. Recent Adv. Bot. 1: 41-47 (R).

2955. Wassink, E.C. 1974. MEMBRANES AND PHYTOCHROME ACTION. Meded. Landbouwhogesch. Wageningen 74-22: 1-5 (R).

2956. Waterman, T.H. 1966. RESPONSES TO POLARIZED LIGHT: PLANTS. *Environmental Biology*, Ed. P.L. Altman and D.S. Dittman, Fed. Am. Soc. Exp.
Biol., pp. 164-165 (R).

2957. Waxman, S. 1957. THE DEVELOPMENT OF WOODY PLANTS AS AFFECTED BY PHOTO-
PERIODIC TREATMENTS. Ph.D. Thesis, Cornell Univ., Ithaca.

2958. Weidner, M.; Jakobs, M.; Mohr, H. 1965. ÜBER DEN EINFLUSS DES PHYTO-
CHROMS AUF DEN GEHALT AN RIBONUCLEINSÄURE UND PROTEIN IN SENFKEIM-
LINGEN (*SINAPIS ALBA* L.). Z. Naturforsch. Teil B 20: 689-693 (ENG
Summary).

2959. Weidner, M. 1967. UNTERSUCHUNGEN ZUR REGULATION DES RNS-STOFFWECHSELS
DURCH PHYTOCHROM BEIM SENFKEIMLING (*SINAPIS ALBA* L.). Ph.D. Thesis,
Univ. Freiburg, Germany.

2960. Weidner, M. 1967. DER DNS-GEHALT VON KOTYLEDONEN UND HYPOKOTYL DES
SENFKEIMLINGS (*SINAPIS ALBA* L.) BEI DER PHYTOCHROMGESTEUERTEN
PHOTOMORPHOGENESE. Planta 75: 94-98 (ENG Summary).

2961. Weidner, M. 1967. REGULATION OF RNA SYNTHESIS OF PHYTOCHROME IN THE MUSTARD SEEDLING (*SINAPIS ALBA* L.). Proc. Eur. Annu. Symp. Plant Photomorphogenesis, (Hvar), pp. 117-119.

2962. Weidner, M.; Mohr, H. 1967. ZUR REGULATION DER RNS-SYNTHESE DURCH PHYTOCHROM BEI DER PHOTOMORPHOGENESE DES SENFKEIMLINGS (*SINAPIS ALBA* L.). Planta 75: 99-108 (ENG Summary).

2963. Weidner, M.; Mohr, H. 1967. DIE WIRKUNG VON ACTINOMYCIN D AUF DIE PHYTOCHROM-ABHÄNGIGEN VERÄNDERUNGEN DES RNS-GEHALTES IM SENFKEIMLING (*SINAPIS ALBA* L.). Planta 75: 109-113 (ENG Summary).

2964. Weidner, M.; Rissland, I.; Mohr, H. 1968. PHOTOINDUCTION OF PHENYLALA-NINE AMMONIA-LYASE IN MUSTARD SEEDLINGS: INVOLVEMENT OF PHYTOCHROME. Naturwissenschaften 55: 452.

2965. Weidner, M.; Rissland, I.; Lohmann, L.; Huault, C.; Mohr, H. 1969. DIE REGULATION DER PAL*-AKTIVITÄT DURCH PHYTOCHROM IN SENFKEIMLINGEN (*SINAPIS ALBA* L.). Planta 86: 33-41 (ENG Summary).

2966. Weidner, M.; Rissland, I.; Dittes, L.; Mohr, H. 1970. PHYTOCHROME IN-DUCED PHENYLALANINE AMMONIA-LYASE (PAL; EC 4.3.1.5) SYNTHESIS IN *SINAPIS ALBA* L.; THE INFLUENCE OF THE AGE OF SEEDLINGS. Plant Physiol. 46: Suppl.-36, Abstr. No. 195 (A).

2967. Weinert, H. 1909. UNTERSUCHUNGEN ÜBER WACHSTUM UND TROPISTISCHE BEWEGUNGSERSCHEINUNGEN DER RHIZOIDEN THALLÖSER LEBERMOOSE. Bot. Ztg. 67: 201-230.

2968. Weintraub, R.L. 1940. INHIBITION OF FIRST INTERNODE OF *AVENA SATIVA* BY RADIATION. Abstr. 17th Annu. Mtg. Am. Soc. Plant Physiol., p. 4, Philadelphia, Pa. (not obtained) (A).

2969. Weintraub, R.L.; McAlister, E.D. 1942. DEVELOPMENTAL PHYSIOLOGY OF THE GRASS SEEDLING. I. INHIBITION OF THE MESOCOTYL OF *AVENA SATIVA* BY CONTINUOUS EXPOSURE TO LIGHT OF LOW INTENSITIES. Smithson. Misc. Collect. 101: 1-10.

2970. Weintraub, R.L.; Price, L. 1947. DEVELOPMENTAL PHYSIOLOGY OF THE GRASS SEEDLING II. INHIBITION OF MESOCOTYL ELONGATION IN VARIOUS GRASSES BY RED AND BY VIOLET LIGHT. Smithson. Misc. Collect. 106: 1-15.

2971. Weintraub, R.L. 1948. INFLUENCE OF LIGHT ON CHEMICAL INHIBITION OF LETTUCE SEED GERMINATION. Smithson. Misc. Collect. 107: 1-8.

2972. Weintraub, R.L.; Robinson, C. 1968. STUDY OF THE PHYTOCHROME SYSTEM IN THE COLEOPTILE OF *ZEA MAYS*. Proc. V Int. Congr. Photobiol., p. 157 (A).

2973. Weintraub, R.L.; Morton, J.S. 1969. GROWTH OF ORGANS OF GRASS SEEDLING. Proc. XI Int. Bot. Congr., p. 234 (A).

2974. Weintraub, R.L.; Lawson, V.R. 1972. MECHANISM OF PHYTOCHROME-MEDIATED EFFECTS OF LIGHT ON CELL GROWTH. Proc. VI Int. Congr. Photobiol. Abstr. No. 161 (A).

2975. Weis, J.S.; Jaffee, M.J. 1969. PHOTOENHANCEMENT BY BLUE LIGHT OF ORGANOGENESIS IN TOBACCO PITH CULTURES. Proc. XI Int. Bot. Congr., p. 234 (A).

2976. Weisenseel, M.; Haupt, W. 1957. DIE TEMPERATURABHÄNGIGKEIT DER CHLOROPLASTENBEWEGUNG BEI *MOUGEOTIA* SPEC. Naturwissenschaften 54: 145.

2977. Weisenseel, M. 1968. VERGLEICHENDE UNTERSUCHUNGEN ZUM EINFLUSS DER TEMPERATUR AUF LICHTINDUZIERTE CHLOROPLASTENVERLAGERUNGEN. I. DIE WIRKUNG VERSCHIEDENER LICHTINTENSITÄTEN AUF DIE CHLOROPLASTENANORD-NUNG UND IHRE ABHÄNGIGKEIT VON DER TEMPERATUR. Z. Pflanzenphysiol. 59: 56-69 (ENG Summary).

2978. Weisenseel, M. 1968. VERGLEICHENDE UNTERSUCHUNGEN ZUM EINFLUSS DER TEMPERATUR AUF LICHTINDUZIERTE CHLOROPLASTENVERLAGERUNGEN. II. DIE STATISTISCHE BEWEGUNGSGESCHWINDIGKEIT DER CHLOROPLASTEN UND IHRE ABHÄNGIGKEIT VON DER TEMPERATUR. Z. Pflanzenphysiol. 59: 153-171 (ENG Summary).

2979. Weisenseel, M.H.; Smeibidl, E. 1973. PHYTOCHROME CONTROLS THE WATER PERMEABILITY IN *MOUGEOTIA*. Z. Pflanzenphysiol. 70: 420-431 (GR Summary).

2979.5 Weisenseel, M.; Haupt, W. 1974. THE PHOTOMORPHOGENIC PIGMENT PHYTO-CHROME: A MEMBRANE EFFECTOR? *Membrane Transport in Plants*, Ed. U. Zimmerman and J. Dainty. Springer-Verlag; Berlin, Heidelberg, New York, pp. 427-434 (R).

2980. Weisz, J. 1960. ACTION DES TEMPÉRATURES RELATIVEMENT BASSES SUR LA GERMINATION DANS LA KINÉTINE, DANS SEMENCES DE LAITUE, VARIÉTÉ 'GRAND RAPIDS'. C.R. Acad. Sci. Ser. D: 125-127.

2981. Weisz-Leff, J. 1961. ÉTUDE DES INTERACTIONS ENTRE LA KINETINE ET LA LUMIÈRE SUR LA GERMINATION DES AKÉNES DE LAITUE, VARIÉTÉ 'GRAND RAPIDS'. Ph.D. Thesis, Sorbonne (not obtained) (Referred to by Evenari, M. 1961. Proc. Int. Seed Test. Assoc. 26: 597-658).

2982. Wellburn, F.A.M.; Wellburn, A.R. 1973. RESPONSE OF ETIOPLASTS *IN SITU* AND IN ISOLATED SUSPENSIONS TO PRE-ILLUMINATION WITH VARIOUS COMBINATIONS OF RED, FAR-RED AND BLUE LIGHT. New Phytol. 72: 55-60.

2983. Wellensiek, S.J.; Doorenbos, J.; De Zeeuw, D. 1954. THE MECHANISM OF PHOTOPERIODISM. Proc. VIII Int. Bot. Congr., pp. 307-315 (R).

2984. Wellensiek, S.J. 1959. THE INHIBITORY ACTION OF LIGHT ON THE FLORAL INDUCTION OF *PERILLA CRISPA*. Proc. K. Ned. Akad. Wet. Ser. C. 62: 195-203.

2985. Wellmann, E. 1971. PHYTOCHROME CONTROL OF FLAVONE GLYCOSIDE SYNTHESIS IN CELL SUSPENSION CULTURES OF PARSLEY. Proc. Eur. Annu. Symp. Plant Photomorphogenesis, (Athens), p. 57 (A).

2986. Wellmann, E. 1971. PHYTOCHROME-MEDIATED FLAVONE GLYCOSIDE SYNTHESIS IN CELL SUSPENSION CULTURES OF *PETROSELINUM HORTENSE* AFTER PREIRRADIATION WITH ULTRAVIOLET LIGHT. Planta 101: 283-286.

2987. Wellmann, E. 1972. ULTRAVIOLET LIGHT-DEPENDENT FLAVONOID SYNTHESIS IN PARSLEY. Proc. VI Int. Congr. Photobiol., Abstr. No. 167 (A).

2988. Wellmann, E. 1973. ZUSAMMENWIRKEN VON ULTRAVIOLETTEM LICHT UND PHYTOCHROM WÄHREND WACHSTUMS- UND DIFFERENZIERUNGSTORGÄNGEN IN PETERSILIE (*PETROSELINUM HORTENSE*). Hoppe-Seyler's Z. Physiol. Chem. 354: 1256-1257 (A).

2989. Wellmann, E. 1974. DIFFERENTIAL RESPONSE OF ENZYMES OF FLAVONOID BIOSYNTHESIS TO PHYTOCHROME IN MUSTARD COTYLEDONS (*SINAPIS ALBA* L.). Proc. Eur. Annu. Symp. Plant Photomorphogenesis, (Antwerpen), p. 125.

2990. Wellmann, E. 1974. REGULATION DER FLAVONOIDBIOSYNTHESE DURCH ULTRAVIOLETTES LICHT UND PHYTOCHROM IN ZELLKULTUREN UND KEIMLINGEN VON PETERSILIE (*PETROSELINUM HORTENSE* HOFFM.). Ber. Dtsch. Bot. Ges. 87: 267-273 (ENG Summary).

2991. Wellmann, E. 1974. GEWEBESPEZIFISCHE KONTROLLE VON ENZYMEN DES FLAVONOIDSTOFFWECHSELS DURCH PHYTOCHROM IN KOTYLEDONEN DES SENFKEIMLINGS (*SINAPIS ALBA* L.). Ber. Dtsch. Bot. Ges. 87: 275-279 (ENG Summary).

2992. Wellmann, E.; Baron, D. 1974. DURCH PHYTOCHROM KONTROLLIERTE ENZYME DER FLAVONOIDSYNTHESE IN ZELLSUSPENSIONSKULTUREN VON PETERSILIE (*PETROSELINUM HORTENSE* HOFFM.). Planta 119: 161-164 (ENG Summary).

2993. Wellmann, E.; Schopfer, P. 1974. PHYTOCHROME-MEDIATED ENZYME *DE NOVO* SYNTHESIS (PAL) IN CELL SUSPENSION CULTURES OF PARSLEY (*PETROSELINUM HORTENSE*). Proc. Eur. Annu. Symp. Plant Photomorphogenesis, (Antwerpen), p. 66.

2994. Went, F.W. 1935. HORMONES, INVOLVED IN ROOT FORMATION. THE PHENOMENON OF INHIBITION. Proc. Int. Bot. Congr., Amsterdam 2: 267-269 (A).

2995. Went, F.W.; Thimann, K.V. 1937. EFFECT OF LIGHT ON ROOT FORMATION. *Phytohormones*, The Macmillan Co., New York, pp. 192-194 (R).

2996. Went, F.W. 1941. EFFECTS OF LIGHT ON STEM AND LEAF GROWTH. Am. J. Bot. 28: 83-95.

2997. Went, F.W. 1958. PLANT GROWTH IN RESPONSE TO LIGHT. Proc. Annu. Biol. Colloq. (Oreg. State Univ.) 19: 2-9 (R).

2998. Went, F.W. 1961. EFFECT OF LIGHT AND TEMPERATURE ON PLANT GROWTH. *Growth in Living Systems*, Ed. M.X. Zarrow, Proc. Int. Symp. Growth, Purdue Univ., Basic Books, Inc., New York, pp. 557-566.

2999. Wetherell, D.F.; Koukkari, W.L. 1967. HIGH PHYTOCHROME LEVELS IN CULTURED TISSUE OF THE WILD CARROT, *DAUCUS CAROTA*. Plant Physiol. 42: 302-303.

3000. Wetherell, D.F. 1969. PHYTOCHROME IN CULTURED WILD CARROT TISSUE. I. SYNTHESIS. Plant Physiol. 44: 1734-1737.

3001. Wetherell, D.F.; Koukkari, W.L. 1970. PHYTOCHROME IN CULTURED WILD CARROT TISSUE. II. DARK TRANSFORMATIONS. Plant Physiol. 46: 350-351.

3002. White, J.M.; Pike, C.S. 1974. RAPID PHYTOCHROME-MEDIATED CHANGES IN ADENOSINE 5'-TRIPHOSPHATE CONTENT OF ETIOLATED BEAN BUDS. Plant Physiol. 53: 76-79.

3003. Whitmore, R.A. 1944. LIGHT AND PIGMENT DEVELOPMENT IN THE KIDNEY BEAN. Plant Physiol. 19: 569-578.

3004. Whitrow, G.J. 1961. INDIVIDUAL TIME. *The Natural Philosophy of Time*, Published by G.J. Whitrow, Thomas Nelson and Sons, New York (R).

3005. Wiegand, O.F.; Schrank, A.R. 1956. RED LIGHT AND ELONGATION INTERRELATIONSHIPS IN *AVENA* COLEOPTILE SECTIONS. Plant Physiol. 31: Suppl.-12 (A).

3006. Wiegand, O.F.; Schrank, A.R. 1959. REGIMEN FOR GROWING UNIFORM *AVENA* COLEOPTILES. Bot. Gaz. (Chicago) 121: 106-110.

3007. Wiegand, O.F.; Schrank, A.R. 1961. EFFECTS OF RED LIGHT ON *AVENA* COLEOPTILE GROWTH. Plant Physiol. 36: Suppl.-41 (A).

3008. Wiegand, O.F. 1963. EFFECT OF RED LIGHT ON THE RESPONSES OF *AVENA SATIVA* SEEDLINGS. Plant Physiol. 38: Suppl.-23-24 (A).

3009. Wiegand, O.F. 1968. RED LIGHT RESPONSES OF INTACT *AVENA* COLEOPTILES. Plant Physiol. 43: Suppl.-22 (A).

3010. Wiegand, O.F. 1970. DIRECT AND INDIRECT RESPONSES OF *AVENA SATIVA* TO RED LIGHT. Plant Physiol. 46: Suppl.-1, Abstr. No. 4 (A).

3011. Wiegand, O.F.; Stewart, S.L. 1974. INHIBITION AND THE COURSE OF COLEOP- TILE PHOTOMORPHOGENESIS. Plant Physiol. 53: Suppl.-1, Abstr. No. 2.

3012. Wiesner, J. 1876. UNTERSUCHUNGEN ÜBER DER EINFLUSS DES LICHTES UND DER STRAHLENDEN WÄRME AUF DIE TRANSSPIRATION DER PFLANZE. Sitzungsber. Akad. Wiss. Wien, Math. Naturwiss. Kl., Abt. 1, 74: 477-531. Also published in French (Ann. Sci. Nat. Bot. Ser. 6, iv, 145-176).

3013. Wiesner, J. 1882. DIE HELIOTROPISCHEN ERSCHEINUNGEN IM PFLANZENREICHE. EINE PHYSIOLOGISCHE MONOGRAPHIE II. THEIL. Denkschr. Akad. Wiss. Wien, Math. Naturwiss. Kl. Abt. 1, 43: 1-92.

3014. Wiesner, J. 1893. PHOTOMETRISCHE UNTERSUCHUNGEN AUF PFLANZENPHYSIOLO- GISCHEN GEBIETE. ERSTE ABHANDLUNG ORIENTIERENDE VERSUCHE ÜBER DEN EINFLUSS DER SOGENANNTEN CHEMISCHEN LICHTINTENSITÄT AUF DEN GESTALTUNGSPROCESS DER PFLANZENORGANE. Sitzungsber. Akad. Wiss. Wien, Math. Naturwiss. Kl. Abt. 1, C, 11: 291-350.

3015. Wilkins, H.F.; Roh, S.M. 1972. THE EFFECT OF BULB PRE-EMERGENCE TEMPER- ATURE TREATMENT AND SUBSEQUENT SHOOT POST-EMERGENCE LIGHT TREATMENT ON THE GROWTH AND FLOWERING OF *LILIUM LONGIFLORUM* THUNB, 'NELLIE WHITE'. Plant Physiol. 49: Suppl.-54, Abstr. No. 304 (A).

3016. Wilkins, M.B. 1963. RED LIGHT AND THE GEOTROPIC RESPONSE OF THE *AVENA* COLEOPTILE. Plant Physiol. 38: Suppl.-24 (A).

3017. Wilkins, M.B.; Goldsmith, M.H.M. 1964. THE EFFECTS OF RED, FAR-RED, AND BLUE LIGHT ON THE GEOTROPIC RESPONSE OF COLEOPTILES OF *ZEA MAYS*. J. Exp. Bot. 15: 600-616.

3018. Wilkins, M.B. 1965. RED LIGHT AND THE GEOTROPIC RESPONSE OF THE *AVENA* COLEOPTILE. Plant Physiol. 40: 24-34.

3019. Wilkins, M.B. 1966. GEOTROPISM. Annu. Rev. Plant Physiol. 17: 379-408 (R).

3020. Wilkins, M.B. 1969. CIRCADIAN RHYTHMS IN PLANTS. *Physiology of Plant Growth and Development*, Ed. M.B. Wilkins, McGraw-Hill, New York, pp. 647-671 (R).

3021. Wilkins, M.B. 1973. AN ENDOGENOUS CIRCADIAN RHYTHM IN THE RATE OF CARBON DIOXIDE OUTPUT OF *BRYOPHYLLUM*. VI. ACTION SPECTRUM FOR THE INDUCTION OF PHASE SHIFTS BY VISIBLE RADIATION. J. Exp. Bot. 24: 488-496.

3021.5 Wilkins, M.B. 1973. CIRCADIAN RHYTHMS IN PLANTS. *Biological Aspects of Circadian Rhythms*, Ed. J.N. Mills, Plenum Press, London and New York, pp. 235-279.

3022. Williams, B.J., Jr.; Pellett, N.E.; Klein, R.M. 1972. PHYTOCHROME CONTROL OF GROWTH CESSATION AND INITIATION OF COLD ACCLIMATION IN SELECTED WOODY PLANTS. Plant Physiol. 50: 262-265.

3023. Williams, C.N.; Raghavan, V. 1966. EFFECTS OF LIGHT AND GROWTH SUBSTANCES ON THE DIURNAL MOVEMENTS OF THE LEAFLETS OF *MIMOSA PUDICA*. J. Exp. Bot. 17: 742-749.

3024. Williams, G.R.; Novelli, G.D. 1964. EFFECT OF PREILLUMINATION IN AN AMINO ACID INCORPORATING SYSTEM FROM ETIOLATED PLANTS. Plant Physiol. 39: Suppl.-51 (A).

3025. Williams, G.R.; Novelli, G.D. 1968. RIBOSOME CHANGES FOLLOWING ILLUMINATION OF DARK-GROWN PLANTS. Biochim. Biophys. Acta 155: 183-192.

3026. Williams, S. 1938. EXPERIMENTAL MORPHOLOGY. *Manual of Pteridology*, Ed. F. Verdoorn, Martinus Nijhoff, The Hague, Netherlands, pp. 105-140.

3027. Williams, W.T. 1956. ETIOLATION PHENOMENA AND LEAF EXPANSION. *The Growth of Leaves*, Ed. F.L. Milthorpe, Butterworths Scientific, London, pp. 127-138 (R).

3028. Williamson, F.A.; Morré, D.J. 1974. ROUGH ENDOPLASMIC RETICULUM: ISOLATION AND PHYTOCHROME CONTENT. Plant Physiol. 53: Suppl.-46, Abstr. No. 255 (A).

3029. Wilson, J.R.; Schwabe, W.W. 1964. GROWTH AND DORMANCY IN *LUNULARIA CRUCIATA* (L.) DUM. III. THE WAVELENGTHS OF LIGHT EFFECTIVE IN PHOTOPERIODIC CONTROL. J. Exp. Bot. 15: 368-380.

3030. Wilson, W.P. 1897. PRELIMINARY OBSERVATIONS ON THE MOVEMENTS OF THE LEAVES OF *MELILOTUS ALBA* L. AND OTHER PLANTS. Contrib. Bot. Lab. Univ. Pennsylvania 1: 67-73.

3031. Witham, F.H.; Miller, C.O. 1965. BIOLOGICAL PROPERTIES OF A KINETIN-LIKE SUBSTANCE OCCURRING IN *ZEA MAYS*. Physiol. Plant. 18: 1007-1017.

3032. Withrow, R.B. 1934. INTENSITY AND WAVELENGTH OF ARTIFICIAL SUPPLEMEN-TAL RADIATION AS FACTORS IN THE FLOWERING RESPONSE OF PANSY, ASTER, AND STOCK. Abstr. 11th Annu. Meet. Am. Soc. Plant Physiol., Pittsburgh, Pa. (not obtained) (A) (Referred by Burkholder, P.R. (1936) Bot. Rev. 2: 97-168).

3033. Withrow, R.B. 1934. THE RESPONSE OF GREENHOUSE CROPS TO ELECTRIC LIGHT SUPPLEMENTING DAYLIGHT. Trans. Illum. Eng. Soc. 29: 65-77.

3034. Withrow, R.B.; Benedict, H.M. 1936. PHOTOPERIODIC RESPONSES OF CERTAIN GREENHOUSE ANNUALS AS INFLUENCED BY INTENSITY AND WAVELENGTH OF ARTIFICIAL LIGHT USED TO LENGTHEN THE DAYLIGHT PERIOD. Plant Physiol. 11: 225-249.

3035. Withrow, R.B.; Biebel, J.P. 1936. PHOTOPERIODIC RESPONSE OF CERTAIN LONG AND SHORT DAY PLANTS TO FILTERED RADIATION APPLIED AS A SUPPLEMENT TO DAYLIGHT. Plant Physiol. 11: 807-819.

3036. Withrow, R.B.; Withrow, A.P. 1939. EFFECT OF VARIOUS WAVEBANDS OF VISIBLE RADIATION ON THE MORPHOLOGY OF RED KIDNEY BEAN SEEDLINGS. Abstr. 16th Annu. Meet. Amer. Soc. Plant Physiol., p. 4 (not obtained) (A).

3037. Withrow, R.B.; Withrow, A.P. 1940. THE EFFECT OF VARIOUS WAVEBANDS OF SUPPLEMENTARY RADIATION ON THE PHOTOPERIODIC RESPONSE OF CERTAIN PLANTS. Plant Physiol. 15: 609-624.

3038. Withrow, R.B. 1941. RESPONSE OF SEEDLINGS TO VARIOUS WAVEBANDS OF LOW INTENSITY IRRADIATIONS. Plant Physiol. 16: 241-256.

3039. Withrow, R.B. 1951. REPORT OF THE DIVISION OF RADIATION AND ORGANISMS. Smithson. Inst. Annu. Rep., pp. 120-122.

3040. Withrow, R.B.; Price, L.; Schocken, V.; Elstad, V. 1951. PIGMENT SYN-THESIS ASSOCIATED WITH PHOTOMORPHOGENESIS IN BEAN, CORN AND OAT SEEDLINGS. Abstr. Am. Soc. Plant Physiol. Meet., Sept. 9-12, Minneapolis, Minnesota, p. 30 (A).

3041. Withrow, R.B. 1952. REPORT OF THE DIVISION OF RADIATION AND ORGANISMS. Smithson. Inst. Annu. Rep., pp. 134-135.

3042. Withrow, R.B. 1953. REPORT OF THE DIVISION OF RADIATION AND ORGANISMS. Smithson. Inst. Annu. Rep., pp. 123-125.

3043. Withrow, R.B.; Klein, W.H.; Price, L.; Elstad, V. 1953. INFLUENCE OF VISIBLE AND NEAR INFRARED RADIANT ENERGY ON ORGAN DEVELOPMENT AND PIGMENT SYNTHESIS IN BEAN AND CORN. Plant Physiol. 28: 1-14.

3044. Withrow, R.B. 1954. REPORT OF THE DIVISION OF RADIATION AND ORGANISMS. Smithson. Inst. Annu. Rep., pp. 48-50.

3045. Withrow, R.B.; Klein, W.H.; Elstad, V. 1955. THE ACTION SPECTRUM OF THE REVERSAL OF THE PHOTOINDUCTION OF HOOK OPENING IN THE HYPOCOTYL OF BEAN. Plant Physiol. 30: Suppl.-9 (A).

3046. Withrow, R.B.; Wolff, J.B.; Price, L. 1956. ELIMINATION OF THE LAG PHASE OF CHLOROPHYLL SYNTHESIS IN DARK-GROWN BEAN LEAVES BY A PRE-TREATMENT WITH LOW IRRADIANCES OF MONOCHROMATIC ENERGY. Plant Physiol. 31: Suppl.-13-14 (A).

3047. Withrow, R.B. 1957. KINETIC ANALYSIS OF PHOTOPERIODISM. Colloq. Int. Photo-thermo periodism, Parma, Italy, pp. 111-113.

3048. Withrow, R.B.; Klein, W.H. 1957. ACTION SPECTRA AND KINETICS OF PHOTO-MORPHOGENESIS. Proc. II Int. Congr. Photobiol., pp. 444-452.

3049. Withrow, R.B.; Klein, W.H.; Elstad, V. 1957. ACTION SPECTRA OF PHOTO-MORPHOGENIC INDUCTION AND ITS PHOTOINACTIVATION. Plant Physiol. 32: 453-462.

3050. Withrow, R.B.; Moh, C.C. 1957. NONIONIZING RADIANT ENERGY AS AN AGENT IN ALTERING THE INCIDENCE OF X-RAY-INDUCED CHROMATID ABERRATIONS. I. EFFECTS OF FAR-RED AND INFRARED RADIANT ENERGY ON *TRADESCANTIA* AND *VICIA*. Radiat. Res. 6: 491-500.

3051. Withrow, R.B. 1959. A KINETIC ANALYSIS OF PHOTOPERIODISM. *Photoperiodism and Related Phenomena in Plants and Animals*, Ed. R.B. Withrow, A.A.A.S., Washington, D.C., pp. 439-471 (R-D).

3052. Wojciechowski, Z. 1965. FITOCHROM. Postepy Biochem. 11: 285-294 (R).

3053. Wolf, F.T. 1971. EFFECTS OF LIGHT ON THE ENZYMATIC ACTIVITIES OF GREEN PLANTS. Adv. Front. Plant Sci. 29: 19-96 (R).

3054. Wolff, J.B.; Price, L.; Withrow, R.B. 1957. STIMULATION OF PROTOCHLORO-PHYLL SYNTHESIS IN DARK-GROWN BEAN LEAVES BY IRRADIATION WITH LOW ENERGY. Plant Physiol. 32: Suppl.-9 (A).

3055. Wolff, J.B.; Price, L. 1960. THE EFFECT OF SUGARS ON CHLOROPHYLL BIO-SYNTHESIS IN HIGHER PLANTS. J. Biol. Chem. 235: 1603-1608.

3056. Wolff, S. 1960. PROBLEMS OF ENERGY TRANSFER IN RADIATION-INDUCED CHROMOSOME DAMAGE. Radiat. Res. Suppl. 2: 122-132 (R).

3057. Wolff, S.; Luippold, H.E. 1961. ON THE APPARENT SYNERGISTIC EFFECT OF FAR-RED AND X-RAYS IN THE PRODUCTION OF CHROMATID ABERRATIONS. *Progress in Photobiology*, Ed. B. Chr. Christensen and B. Buchman. Elsevier Publ. Co. Amsterdam, pp. 457-460.

3058. Wolff, S.; Luippold, H.E. 1965. MITOTIC DELAY AND THE APPARENT SYNERGISM OF FAR-RED RADIATION AND X-RAYS IN THE PRODUCTION OF CHROMOSOMAL ABBERATIONS. Photochem. Photobiol. 4: 439-445.

3059. Wollny, E. 1894. UNTERSUCHUNGEN ÜBER DEN EINFLUSS DER LICHTFARBE AUF DAS PRODUKTIONSVERMÖGEN UND DIE TRANSPIRATION DER PFLANZEN. Forsch. Geb. Agrikulturphysik 17: 317-333.

3060. Wong, P.P.; Zucker, M.; Creasy, L.L. 1974. INDUCTION OF PHENYLALANINE AMMONIA-LYASE IN STRAWBERRY LEAF DISKS. ACTION SPECTRA AND EFFECTS OF WOUNDING, SUCROSE, AND LIGHT. Plant Physiol. 54: 659-665.

3061. Woodhead, S.; Swain, T. 1974. EFFECT OF LIGHT ON BETALAIN AND CINNAMIC ACID BIOSYNTHESIS IN *AMARANTHUS CAUDATUS*. Phytochemistry 13: 953-956.

3062. Wulff, R.; Medina, E. 1969. GERMINATION OF SEEDS IN *JUSSIAEA SUFFRUTICOSA*. Plant Cell Physiol. 10: 503-511.

3063. Wulff, R.; Medina, E. 1971. GERMINATION OF SEEDS IN *HYPTIS SUAVEOLENS* POIT. Plant Cell Physiol. 12: 567-579.

3064. Wulff, R.; Muñoz, V. 1973. DESTRUCCION EN LUZ CONTINUA Y TRANSFORMACIONES EN OSCURIDAD DEL FITOCROMO EN PLANTULAS ETIOLADAS DE *JUSSIAEA SUFFRUTICOSA*. Acta Cient. Ven. 24: 34-35 (A).

3065. Wurf, H.K. 1971. PHYTOCHROME, GERMINATION AND RNA SYNTHESIS IN SEEDS OF *CUCUMIS SATIVUS*. Ph.D. Thesis, Columbia Univ., New York.

3066. Yamaki, T. 1958. PHYSIOLOGICAL FUNCTIONS OF GIBBERELLIN. Nogyo Oyobi Engei 33: 1165-1168 (JAP).

3067. Yamaki, T.; Hashimoto, T.; Ishii, T.; Yamada, M. 1968. SOME PHYSIOLOGICAL EFFECTS OF GIBBERELLIN ON SEED GERMINATION, LEAF EXPANSION, DEHYDRATION OF MITOCHRONDRIA AND PROBABLE FORMATION OF GIBBERELLIN IN LEAF. Abs. II Meet. Jap. Gibberellin Res. Assoc., pp. 51-52 (not obtained) (A) (Referred to by Toole, V.K.; Cathey, H.M. (1961). Plant Physiol. 36: 663-671).

3068. Yamaki, T.; Fujii, T. 1968. EFFECT OF LIGHT ON AUXIN TRANSPORT THROUGH THE NODE TISSUE OF *AVENA* SEEDLING. Biochem. Physiol. Plant Growth Subst. Proc. Int. Conf. Plant Growth Subst. 6th 1967, pp. 1025-1036.

3069. Yamamoto, N.; Sasaki, S.; Asakawa, S. 1974. POLYSOME FORMATION INDUCED BY LIGHT IN *PINUS THUNBERGII* SEED EMBRYOS. Plant Cell Physiol. 15: 1143-1146.

3070. Yamamoto, Y.; Tezuka, T. 1969. NAD KINASE ACTIVITY REGULATED WITH PHYTOCHROME ACTION. Proc. XI Int. Bot Congr., p. 245 (A).

3071. Yamamoto, Y. 1970. ROLE OF NICOTINAMIDE ADENINE DINUCLEOTIDE PHOSPHATE IN THE REGULATION OF METABOLISM IN HIGHER PLANTS. Seikagaku 42: 1-18 (JAP).

3072. Yamamoto, Y.; Tezuka, T. 1972. REGULATION OF NAD KINASE BY PHYTOCHROME AND CONTROL OF METABOLISM BY VARIATION OF NADP LEVEL. *Phytochrome*, Ed. K. Mitrakos and W. Shropshire, Jr., Academic Press: London and New York, pp. 407-429 (R).

3073. Yamamoto, Y.; Tezuka, T. 1974. LEVELS OF NICOTINAMIDE NUCLEOTIDE CO-ENZYMES IN PLANT TISSUES VARYING WITH ENVIRONMENTAL CONDITIONS. *Plant Growth Substances 1973*, Proc. VIII Int. Conf. Plant Growth Subst. Tokyo, pp. 683-690.

3074. Yang, B.Y. 1970. EFFECT OF LIGHT AND CHEMICALS ON THE GROWTH AND DE-VELOPMENT OF GAMETOPHYTE OF *HAPLOMITRIUM ROTUNDIFOLIUM*. Taiwania 15: 301-318.

3075. Yang, C.P.; Mancinelli, A.L. 1974. ACTION OF STREPTOMYCIN UPON ANTHO-CYANIN AND CHLOROPHYLL SYNTHESIS. Plant Physiol. 53: Suppl.-2, Abstr. No. 7 (A).

3076. Yaniv, Z.; Mancinelli, A.L. 1966. PHYTOCHROME CONTROL OF GERMINATION IN DARK-GERMINATING TOMATO SEEDS. Plant Physiol. 41: Suppl.-17 (A).

3077. Yaniv, Z. 1967. PHYTOCHROME AND SEED GERMINATION. Ph.D. Thesis, Columbia Univ., New York.

3078. Yaniv, Z.; Mancinelli, A.L. 1967. PHYTOCHROME AND SEED GERMINATION. II. CHANGES OF P_{fr} REQUIREMENT FOR GERMINATION IN TOMATO SEEDS. Plant Physiol. 42: 1147-1148.

3079. Yaniv, Z.; Mancinelli, A.L.; Smith, P. 1967. PHYTOCHROME AND SEED GER-MINATION. III. ACTION OF PROLONGED FAR-RED IRRADIATION ON THE GERMI-NATION OF TOMATO AND CUCUMBER SEEDS. Plant Physiol. 42: 1479-1482.

3080. Yaniv, Z.; Mancinelli, A.L. 1968. PHYTOCHROME AND SEED GERMINATION. IV. ACTION OF LIGHT SOURCES WITH DIFFERENT SPECTRAL ENERGY DISTRIBUTION ON THE GERMINATION OF TOMATO SEEDS. Plant Physiol. 43: 117-120.

3081. Yopp, J.H. 1973. THE ROLE OF LIGHT AND GROWTH REGULATORS IN THE OPENING OF THE *DENTARIA* PETIOLAR HOOK. Plant Physiol. 51: 714-717.

3082. Yost, H.T., Jr. 1951. THE FREQUENCY OF X-RAY INDUCED CHROMOSOME ABERRATIONS IN *TRADESCANTIA* AS MODIFIED BY NEAR INFRARED RADIATION. Genetics 36: 176-184.

3083. Yost, H.T., Jr. 1952. THE EFFECT OF INTENSITY OF INFRARED ON X-RAY IN-DUCED CHROMOSOME ABERRATIONS IN *TRADESCANTIA*. Genetics 37: 457-468.

3084. Yuldashev, A. Kh.; Tuichev, A.J.; Ikremov, K.I.; Ganiev, B.Z. 1974. ISOLATION AND INVESTIGATION OF THE PHYSIOCHEMICAL PROPERTIES OF PHYTOCHROME OF COTTON. Nauch. Soobshch. 2: 74 (RUS) (not obtained).

3085. Yunghans, H.O.; Jaffe, M.J. 1970. UNCOUPLING OF OXIDATIVE PHOSPHORYLA-TION BY RED LIGHT OR ACETYLCHOLINE DURING THE EARLY EVENTS OF PHYTO-CHROME MEDIATED PHOTOMORPHOGENESIS. Plant Physiol. 46: Suppl.-2, Abstr. No. 10 (A).

3086. Yunghans, H.; Jaffe, M.J. 1970. PHYTOCHROME CONTROLLED ADHESION OF MUNG BEAN ROOT TIPS TO GLASS: A DETAILED CHARACTERIZATION OF THE PHENOME-NON. Physiol. Plant. 23: 1004-1016.

3087. Yunghans, H.; Jaffe, M.J. 1972. RAPID RESPIRATORY CHANGES DUE TO RED LIGHT OR ACETYLCHOLINE DURING THE EARLY EVENTS OF PHYTOCHROME-MEDIATED PHOTOMORPHOGENESIS. Plant Physiol. 49: 1-7.

3088. Zacharewicz, E. 1902. ÉTUDE COMPARATIVE DES DIFFÉRENTS VERRES DE COULEUR APPLIQUÉS AU VITRAGE DES SERRES. J. Soc. Nat. Hort. France 4 Ser. 3: 265-268 (same as ÜBER DEN EINFLUSS DER FARBIGEN LICHT-RAHLEN AUF DIE KULTUR DER ERDBEERE, Biedermann's Zentralb. 24: 495).

3089. Zak, E.G. 1965. EFFECT OF MOLECULAR OXYGEN ON THE FORMATION OF AMINO ACIDS IN PHOTOSYNTHESIZING CHLORELLA UNDER VARIOUS CONDITIONS OF ILLUMINATION. Fiziol. Rast. 12: 263-269 (RUS) (ENG Summary).

3090. Zantedeschi, F. 1843. DELL' INFLUENZA DEI RAGGI SOLARI RIFRATTI DAI VETRI COLORATI SULLA VEGETAZIONE DELLE PIANTE E GERMINAZIONE DE' SEMI. Memorie Dell I.R. Instituto Veneto di Scienze, Lettere et arti Vol. I: 269-294.

3091. Zantedeschi, F. 1843. DE L'INFLUENCE QU'EXERCENT SUR LA VÉGÉTATION DES
PLANTES ET LA GERMINATION DES GRAINES LES RAYONS SOLAIRES TRANSMIS À
TRAVERS DES VERRES COLORÉS. C.R. Acad. Sci. Paris, 1843, Vol. XVI,
pp. 747-749.

3092. Zantedeschi, F. 1844. DE L'INFLUENCE DES RAYONS SOLAIRES TRANSMIS PAR
DES VERRES COLORÉS SUR LA VÉGÉTATION DES PLANTES ET LA GERMINATION
DES GRAINES. C.R. Acad. Sci. Paris 18: 849-854.

3093. Zeevaart, J.A.D. 1962. PHYSIOLOGY OF FLOWERING. Science 137: 723-731
(R).

3094. Zeevaart, J.A.D. 1963. CLIMATIC CONTROL OF REPRODUCTION DEVELOPMENT.
B. PHYTOCHROME AND ITS CONTROL OF FLOWERING. *Environmental Control
of Plant Growth*, Ed. L.T. Evans, Academic Press: New York and London,
pp. 297-299 (R).

3095. Zeevaart, J.A.D.; Marushige, K. 1967. BIOCHEMICAL APPROACHES.
Physiology of Flowering in Pharbitis nil, Ed. S. Imamura, Japan. Soc.
Plant Physiol., Tokyo, pp. 121-138 (R).

3096. Zelitch, I. 1963. THE CONTROL AND MECHANISMS OF STOMATAL MOVEMENT.
Stomata and Water Relations in Plants, Ed. I. Zelitch, Bull. 664,
Conn. Agric. Exp. Sta., New Haven, pp. 18-42 (R-D).

3097. Ziegler, H.; Ziegler, I.; Schmidt-Clausen, H.J. 1965. DER EINFLUSS DER
INTENSITÄT UND QUALITÄT DES LICHTES AUF DIE AKTIVITÄTSSTEIGERUNG DER
NADP$^+$-ABHÄNGIGEN GLYCERIN-ALDEHYD-3-PHOSPHAT-DEHYDROGENASE. Planta
67: 344-356 (ENG Summary).

3098. Zimmerman, B.K. 1962. AN ANALYSIS OF PHOTOTROPIC CURVATURE IN OAT
COLEOPTILES. Ph.D. Thesis, Stanford Univ. (available as Biophys.
Lab. Rep. No. 69, W.W. Hansen Lab. Phys., Stanford).

3099. Zimmerman, B.K.; Briggs, W.R. 1963. PHOTOTROPIC DOSAGE-RESPONSE CURVES
FOR OAT COLEOPTILES. Plant Physiol. 38: 248-253.

3100. Zimmerman, B.K.; Briggs, W.R. 1963. A KINETIC MODEL FOR PHOTOTROPIC
RESPONSES OF OAT COLEOPTILES. Plant Physiol. 38: 253-361.

3101. Zimmerman, C.E. 1962. AUTOTROPHIC DEVELOPMENT OF DODDER (*CUSCUTA
PENTAGONA* ENGLM.) *IN VITRO*. Crop Sci. 2: 449-450.

3102. Ziv, M.; Halevy, A.H.; Ashri, A. 1973. PHYTOHORMONES AND LIGHT REGULA-
TION OF THE GROWTH HABIT IN PEANUTS (*ARACHIS HYPOGAEA* L.). Plant
Cell Physiol. 14: 727-735.

3103. Zollikofer, C. 1920. UEBER DIE TROPISTISCHE WIRKUNG VON ROTEM LICHT AUF DUNKELPFLANZEN VON *AVENA SATIVA*. Proc. Acad. Sci. Amst. 23: 577-584.

3104. Zouaghi, M.; Malcoste, R.; Rollin, P. 1972. ETUDE DU PHYTOCHROME DE-TECTABLE, *IN VIVO* DANS LES GRAINES DE *CUCURBITA PEPO* L. AU COURS DES DIFFERENTES PHASES DE LA GERMINATION. Planta 106: 30-43 (ENG Summary).

3105. Zouaghi, M. 1973. CONTRIBUTION A L'ETUDE DU PHYTOCHROME DETECTABLE *IN VIVO* DANS LES GRAINES DE *CUCURBITA PEPO* L. AU COURS DES DIFFERENTES PHASES DE LA GERMINATION. Ph.D. Thesis, Univ. Rouen, France.

3106. Zucker, M. 1972. LIGHT AND ENZYMES. Annu. Rev. Plant Physiol. 23: 133-156 (R).

3107. Zurzycka, A. 1951. THE INFLUENCE OF THE WAVE LENGTH OF LIGHT ON THE MOVEMENTS OF CHLOROPLASTS IN *LEMNA TRISULCA* 1. Acta Soc. Bot. Pol. 21: 17-37.

3108. Zurzycki, J.; Zurzycka, A. 1951. INVESTIGATION ONTO PHOTOTACTIC MOVE-MENTS OF CHLOROPLASTS IN *SELAGINELLA MARTENSII* SPRING. Bull. Acad. Pol. Sci. Lett. Cracovie, Ser. B, pp. 235-251.

3109. Zurzycki, J. 1957. FORMATIVE EFFECTS OF VARIOUS SPECTRAL REGIONS OF LIGHT ON *LEMNA TRISULCA* L. Meded. Landbouwhogesch. Wageningen 57-11: 1-14.

3110. Zurzycki, J. 1962. THE MECHANISM OF THE MOVEMENTS OF PLASTIDS. *Hand-buch der Pflanzenphysiologie*, Ed. W. Ruhland, Berlin-Göttingen Heidelberg, Springer 17/2: 940-978 (R).

3111. Zurzycki, J. 1962. THE ACTION SPECTRUM FOR THE LIGHT DEPENDED MOVEMENTS OF CHLOROPLASTS IN *LEMNA TRISULCA* L. Acta Soc. Bot. Pol. 31: 489-538.

3112. Zurzycki, J. 1964. INVESTIGATIONS ON THE CONTRACTION OF CHLOROPLASTS IN *MNIUM UNDULATUM* (L.) WEIS. Protoplasma 58: 458-482.

3113. Zurzycki, J. 1964. THE EFFECTS OF SIMULTANEOUS ACTION OF THE SHORT AND LONG WAVE PARTS OF SPECTRUM OF THE MOVEMENTS OF CHLOROPLASTS. Acta Soc. Bot. Pol. 33: 133-139.

3114. Zurzycki, J. 1965. THE ENERGY OF CHLOROPLAST MOVEMENTS IN *LEMNA TRI-SULCA* L. Acta Soc. Bot. Pol. 34: 637-666.

3115. Zurzycki, J. 1966. INVESTIGATIONS ON THE CONTRACTION OF CHLOROPLASTS IN *MNIUM UNDULATUM* (L.) WEIS. II. STUDIES ON ISOLATED CHLOROPLASTS. Acta Soc. Bot. Pol. 35: 281-291.

3116. Zurzycki, J. 1966. THE POSSIBLE ROLE OF PHOTOPHOSPHORYLATION IN THE MOVEMENTS OF PLASTIDS. *Currents of Photosynthesis*, Ed. J.B. Thomas and J.C. Goodbeer, Rotterdam, pp. 235-242 (R-D).

3117. Zurzycki, J. 1967. PROPERTIES AND LOCALIZATION OF THE PHOTORECEPTOR ACTIVE IN DISPLACEMENTS OF CHLOROPLASTS IN *FUNARIA HYGROMETRICA*. I. ACTION SPECTRUM. Acta Soc. Bot. Pol. 36: 133-142.

3118. Zurzycki, J. 1967. PROPERTIES AND LOCALIZATION OF THE PHOTORECEPTOR ACTIVE IN DISPLACEMENTS OF CHLOROPLASTS IN *FUNARIA HYGROMETRICA* II. STUDIES WITH POLARIZED LIGHT. Acta Soc. Bot. Pol. 36: 143-152.

3119. Zurzycki, J. 1967. PROPERTIES AND LOCALIZATION OF THE PHOTORECEPTOR ACTIVE IN DISPLACEMENTS OF CHLOROPLASTS IN *FUNARIA HYGRAMETRICA*. III. CYTOCHEMICAL STUDIES. Acta Soc. Bot. Pol. 36: 617-625.

3120. Zurzycki, J. 1967. ORIENTATION AND LOCALIZATION OF THE MOLECULES OF PHOTORECEPTOR ACTIVE IN DISPLACEMENTS OF CHLOROPLASTS IN *FUNARIA HYGROMETRICA*. Proc. Eur. Annu. Symp. Plant Photomorphogenesis, (Hvar), pp. 131-134.

3121. Zurzycki, J. 1968. PROPERTIES AND LOCALIZATION OF THE PHOTORECEPTOR ACTIVE IN DISPLACEMENTS OF CHLOROPLASTS IN *FUNARIA HYGROMETRICA*. V. STUDIES ON PLASMOLIZED CELLS. Acta Soc. Bot. Pol. 37: 11-17.

3122. Zurzycki, J. 1969. EXPERIMENTAL MODIFICATION OF THE REACTION PATTERN OF *LEMNA* LEAF CELLS TO POLARIZED LIGHT. Protoplasma 68: 193-207.

3123. Zurzycki, J.; Lelatko, Z. 1969. ACTION DICHROISM IN THE CHLOROPLASTS REARRANGEMENTS IN VARIOUS PLANT SPECIES. Acta Soc. Bot. Pol. 38: 493-506.

AUTHOR INDEX

Blondel, Jean-Didien 1163

Blondon, Francois 181

Blumenthal-Goldschmidt, Shulamith
641

Bocchi, Ada 1622, 1624

Bock, Gudrun 182, 987

Bogorad, Lawrence 183, 184, 185, 1422

Böhm, J. A. 186

Boisard, Jean 187, 188, 189, 190,
191, 192, 193, 194, 195, 196, 197,
198, 1652, 1653, 1693, 1707, 1710,
2588

Bokura, Takeharu 199

Bonatti, Piera 1550

Bonnell, Karen F. 1147

Bonner, Bruce A. 200, 201, 202, 203,
204, 205, 206, 851, 2202, 2733

Bonner, James 207, 208, 1585, 1586,
2334

Bonner, Walter D., Jr. 1185

Bonnett, Howard T. 209, 2747

Boresch, Karl 210

Borodin, J. 211, 212

Borthwick, Harry A. 213, 214, 215,
216, 217, 218, 219, 220, 221, 222,
223, 224, 225, 226, 227, 228, 229,
230, 231, 232, 233, 234, 235, 236,
237, 238, 239, 240, 241, 242, 243,
244, 245, 246, 247, 364, 366, 369,
370, 441, 527, 528, 529, 626, 627,
686, 687, 927, 1046, 1047, 1048,
1049, 1051, 1056, 1057, 1058, 1066,
1068, 1070, 1073, 1326, 1327, 1329,
1330, 1664, 1665, 1667, 1963, 2054,
2055, 2056, 2057, 2058, 2059, 2089,
2094, 2408, 2409, 2410, 2411, 2736,

2783, 2784, 2785, 2786, 2787, 2788,
2789, 2791, 2797, 2798, 2800, 2801,
2803, 2804, 2805, 2806

Bose, Jagadis C. 248

Bottomley, W. 249, 250, 251

Boutin, Michael E. 252

Bradbeer, J. W. 253, 254, 255

Bradley, Matthews O. 256

Brandt, A. B. 257

Brauner, L. 258, 259

Brauner, M. 258

Bregeaut, J. 260

Brett, D. W. 261

Brian, Percy W. 262, 263

Briggs, Winslow R. 198, 264, 265, 266,
267, 268, 269, 270, 271, 272, 273,
274, 275, 276, 277, 278, 279, 280,
281, 282, 283, 284, 285, 388, 405,
646, 647, 695, 818, 819, 821, 822,
1138, 1521, 1522, 1707, 1710, 1731,
1733, 1735, 1977, 1988, 1989, 2082,
2083, 2084, 2127, 2152, 2153, 2220,
2221, 2222, 2571, 2776, 2778, 2779,
3099, 3100

Brook, P. J. 286

Brooker, John D. 287

Brown, F. 2110, 2111

Brown, John A. M. 288, 289, 290, 291

Brown, Paul K. 2779

Brown, T. J. 292

Brulfert, Jeanne 293, 1188

Brüning, K. 550

Brunner, H. 2311

Bryan, G. 1422

Buchholz, J. T. 294

Buck, John 295

255

Devay, M.   508

DeZeeuw, D.   2983

Dickson, M. H.   393

Diekmann, H.   509

Dierickx, P. J.   510

Dimitrova-Rousseva, E.   511

Dinus, Ronald J.   512

Diskin, T.   1459

Dittes, Hermann   512.5, 513

Dittes, L.   514, 2966

Dixon, P. F.   1781

Dmitrieva, V. I.   515

Dnyansagar, V. R.   1377

Domash, V. I.   25, 849, 850

Doorenbos, J.   516, 2983

Dooskin, Ruth H.   517, 518

Dörffling, K.   519

Dorofeeva, E. V.   2289

Dorscheid, Trude   520, 521, 522, 523

Dow, D.   490

Downs, Robert J.   241, 335, 340, 524,
   525, 526, 527, 528, 529, 530, 531,
   532, 533, 534, 535, 536, 537, 538,
   539, 540, 1051, 1669, 1793, 2089,
   2091, 2094, 2791

Dring, Matthew J.   541, 542

Drumm, Helga   9, 543, 544, 545, 546,
   547, 548, 549, 550, 551, 552, 553,
   554, 1241, 1905

Drury, K. Susan   2297

Dubois, Jean   555

DuBuy, H. G.   556, 557, 558, 559, 560,
   561, 562

Duda, Michal   563

Duke, Stephen O.   564, 565

Dunaway, Charles   362

Dunn, Stuart   142, 566, 1810

Durandin, A. I.   567

Durant, Jennie P.   568, 2035

Duranton, Henri   572, 573

Durley, R. C.   2207

Durst, Francis   569, 570, 571, 572, 573

Dyke, Inga J.   82

E

Edge, H. J. W.   255

Edsall, Pamela C.   1419

Edwards, John L.   415, 416, 418, 419,
   420, 423, 501, 574, 575, 576, 1432,
   2501

Egles, Dominique   577

Eisenstadt, Frone Anna   578, 579, 1675,
   1676

Elchinger, I.   547, 573

El Dabh, R.   580, 581

El Hattab, Ahmed H.   582

Eliason, E. J.   583

Elliott, Ruth F.   584

Elliott, William M.   585, 586, 587, 588

Elstad, V.   1424, 1425, 1426, 1427,
   1428, 2500, 3040, 3043, 3045, 3049

Eltinge, Ethel Taber   589

Engelhardt, Miriam   2855

Engelmann, Wolfgang   311, 590, 1318

Engelsma, Gerrit   591, 592, 593, 594,
   595, 596, 597, 598, 599, 600, 601,
   602, 603, 604, 605, 606, 607, 608,
   609, 1767, 1768

Enloe, A.   610

Ephrat, Ephraim   1277, 1278, 1279, 1280

Eremeyeva, O. V.   2290, 2291, 2293

Erez, Amnon   611, 612, 613

Erner, Y.   614

Ernst, A. 615
Esashi, Yoji 616, 617, 618, 619, 620, 621, 622, 874, 875, 876
Etherton, B. 2173, 2176
Etzold, Helmut 307, 623, 1222, 1223
Eude, Dominique (see Klein-Eude, Dominique) 2260
Evans, L. T. 624, 625, 626, 627, 628, 629, 630, 1159, 1533
Evenari, Michael 631, 632, 633, 634, 635, 636, 637, 638, 639, 640, 641, 642, 643, 644, 645, 905, 1721, 2107
Everett, Marylee S. 646, 647, 648

F

Faivre, E. 649
Falk, Heinz 546, 650
Famintzin, A. 651
Feirabend, Jürgen 652, 653, 654, 949
Felippe, G. M. 655, 656
Fellows, M. P. 2189
Feltner, Kurt C. 657
Fernqvist, I. B. 658
Fetzer, Jörg 659, 992
Filner, Barbara 660, 1414
Fioretti, Laura 1629
Firer, E. L. 1527
Firer, E. M. 1530, 2524, 2525, 2529
Firn, Richard D. 315, 660.5
Fischer, Walter 661
Fischer-Arnold, Gertrud 662
Fisher, Robert W. 663
Flammarion, Camille 664, 665, 666, 667, 668
Flemion, Florence 669
Fletcher, L. A. 670
Fletcher, R. A. 671, 672, 673

Flint, Lewis H. 674, 675, 676, 677, 678, 679, 680, 681, 682, 683, 684
Flohrs, Heide 685
Fluck, R. 1237
Fondeville, Jean-Claude 686, 687, 688, 2411
Fork, David C. 269, 270, 274, 277, 278
Förster, Karl 689
Fortanier, E. J. 690
Forward, Richard B., Jr. 691, 692, 693, 693.5, 694
Fosket, Elizabeth B. 695
Foster, William I. 2490
Fountain, D. 178
Fox, L. Raymond 696, 697, 698, 699
Fraikin, G. Ya. 700, 2290, 2291, 2293, 2294
Frank, B. 701
Frank, Sylvia 702
Frankland, Barry 703, 704, 705, 706, 707, 1358, 1359, 1360, 1361, 2555
Fredericq, H. 468, 469, 470, 472, 473, 484, 580, 581, 708, 709, 710, 711, 712, 713, 714, 715, 716, 717, 718, 719, 720, 721, 722, 723
Freeman, J. 807
French, Christopher J. 724, 725
French, C. Stacy 584
Frenyó, V. 838
Freyre, Ruben H. 1192
Frey-Wyssling, Albert F. 726
Frick, Hugh 727, 728
Friederich, Karl-Ernst 729, 730
Friend, Douglas J. C. 731, 732, 733, 734, 735, 736, 737, 738

Gladen, A. A.   844, 1285, 1774, 1775, 1777

Glass, Bentley   845, 846

Glessner, L.   1753

Globerson, D.   847, 848

Godnev, T. N.   25, 849, 850

Goeschl, John D.   851, 852, 853

Goethe, J. W. von   854

Goldacre, P. L.   855

Goldsmith, Mary Helen M.   3017

Goodwin, Richard H.   856, 857, 858, 859

Goodwin, T. W.   407, 1076, 1077, 1124, 1125

Gorda, M. V.   1775

Gordon, Solon A.   384, 389, 390, 860, 861, 862, 863, 864, 865, 866, 867, 1965, 1991, 1992, 2674

Gordon, W. R.   868

Goren, Raphael   614, 869, 870, 871

Gorter, Christine J.   872

Gortikova, N.   873

Gortner, Willis A.   1376

Goss, James A.   1281, 1282

Gotô, Nobuharu   874, 875, 876

Gottschall, Virginia   1600, 1603

Graham, D.   877, 878, 879, 880, 2465

Grahl, Adolf   881

Grant Lipp, A. E.   882

Greany, Robin H.   1807

Green, G. H.   292

Green, J. Reynolds   883

Gregor, H.-D.   884

Gregory-Southworth, A.   885

Greppin, Hubert   886, 2068, 2069

Greuell, E. H. M.   1500

Grieve, A. M.   877, 878, 880

Griffith, Mildred M.   887, 2121, 2122, 2124

Grill, Renate E. M.   888, 889, 890, 891, 892, 893, 894, 895, 896, 897, 898, 899, 900, 901, 2870

Grishina, G. S.   2897, 2898, 2899

Grodzinsky, Dnitrii M.   296, 297, 298, 902

Guérin de Montgareuil, Pierre   1987, 2754

Guernsey, Frances S.   1564

Guerrier, Daniele   293

Gugliada, M. L.   903

Guminetsky, S. G.   296, 298

Gupta, Subhashni   904

Gutterman, Yitzchak   905, 906, 907, 908

Guttridge, C. G.   2877.5

Gvozdikovskaya, A. T.   2602

Gwynn, Dennis   909

Gyldenholm, A. O.   254, 255

H

Haack, O. H. A.   910, 911

Haagen-Smit, A. J.   1442

Haber, Alan H.   912, 913, 914, 915, 916, 917, 918, 919, 2232

Habermann, Helen M.   920, 921, 921.2, 921.5

Hachtel, Wolfgang   922

Häcker, Manfred   923, 924, 925

Hadwiger, Lee A.   926

Hagen, C. E.   927

Hahn, Lamont W.   928

Haid, Heidi   1680, 1681

Haight, Thomas H.   929

2058, 2059, 2089, 2393, 2408, 2409,
2410, 2411, 2519, 2520, 2521, 2522,
2524, 2525, 2530, 2532, 2533, 2534,
2737, 2739, 2740, 2741, 2742, 2743,
2744, 2783, 2784, 2785, 2786, 2788,
2789, 2791, 2797, 2800

Henshall, J. D. 1076, 1077

Henslow, George 1078

Herm, K. 1079

Hertel, R. 1705

Hewett, E. W. 1080

Heydecker, W. 905

Heytler, P. G. 1944

Hiatt, A. J. 1331

Hibben, Samuel G. 1081

Higgins, George M. 1082, 2489, 2490

Hillman, William S. 100, 127, 256,
398, 399, 400, 401, 402, 696, 697,
698, 699, 773, 774, 778, 782, 931,
932, 933, 934, 1083, 1084, 1085,
1086, 1087, 1088, 1089, 1090, 1091,
1092, 1093, 1094, 1095, 1096, 1097,
1098, 1099, 1100, 1101, 1102, 1103,
1104, 1105, 1106, 1107, 1108, 1109,
1110, 1111, 1112, 1113, 1114, 1115,
1116, 1117, 1118, 1140, 1142, 1143,
1144, 1145, 1362, 1363, 1364, 1365,
1367, 1480, 1481, 1482, 1483, 2280,
2281, 2282, 2691, 2692, 2693

Hiron, R. W. P. 315

Hobson, David J. 1119

Hock, Bertold 1120, 1120.5, 1121,
1122, 2444

Hodson, H. Kent 1123

Hogetsu, Daisuke 1828

Holderied, Ch. 1888

Holdgate, D. P. 1124, 1125

Holdsworth, M. 1126, 1127

Holl, G. 1873

Hollaender, Alexander 1341, 1343,
1345, 2684

Holland, R. W. K. 1128, 1129, 1130

Holm, R. E. 1

Holmes, M. G. 1131

Holowinsky, Andrew W. 1132, 1133, 1134

Hopkins, David W. 282, 1135, 1136,
1137, 1138, 1734, 2571

Hopkins, T. R. 1139

Hopkins, William G. 38, 778, 1140,
1141, 1142, 1143, 1144, 1145, 1146,
1147, 1148, 1149

Horváth, I. 1150, 2695

Horwitz, B. A. 886

Horwitz, L. P. 886

Hösel, W. 89

Hoshizaki, Takashi 1151

Howland, Gary P. 1152

Hsiao, Andrew I-Hsiung 1153, 1154,
1155, 1156, 1157, 1158, 2577, 2857,
2858, 2859

Hsiao, Theodore C. 1159

Huault, Claude 1160, 1161, 1162, 1163,
1164, 1165, 1433, 1434, 1546, 1655,
1656, 1891, 2259, 2965

Hubert, B. 762

Hughes, A. P. 406, 1166, 1167, 1168,
1169

Huisinga, B. 1170, 1171, 1172

Humphries, E. C. 1173

Hunt, Robert 1174

Hunter, Norvell W. 1175

Hunter, Roy Jr. 1175

262

K

Kadman-Zahavi, Avishag 612, 613, 847, 848, 1258, 1259, 1260, 1261, 1262, 1263, 1264, 1265, 1266, 1267, 1268, 1269, 1270, 1271, 1272, 1273, 1274, 1275, 1276, 1277, 1278, 1279, 1280, 1914, 1915

Kahn, Albert 1281, 1282, 1283, 1284

Kalinin, F. L. 1285, 1774, 1775, 1777

Kandeler, Riklef 1208, 1286, 1287, 1288, 1289, 1290, 1291, 1292, 1293, 1294, 1295, 1296, 1297, 1298

Kang, Bin G. 1299, 1300, 1301, 1302, 1303, 1304, 1305, 1306, 1307, 1307.5, 1308, 1309

Kar, Monoranjan 1813

Karow, Heidemarie (see Oelze-Karow, Heidemarie) 1310, 1311

Karssen, Cornelis M. 1312, 1313, 1314, 1315, 1316

Karvé, Anand D. 1317, 1318, 1319, 1320

Kasche, Volker 433, 1577, 1578

Kasemir, Helga (see Harraschain, (Helga) 1206, 1207, 1321, 1322, 1323, 1324, 1325, 1905

Kasperbauer, Michael J. 1326, 1327, 1328, 1329, 1330, 1331, 1332, 1333, 1334, 1335, 1336, 1337, 1534, 2212, 2820

Kass, Lee B. 1338

Kato, Yukio 1339

Katunskij, V. M. 1340

Katz, Joseph J. 430

Katz, J. M. 1352

Kaufman, Berwind P. 1341, 1342, 1343, 1344, 1345, 1346, 1347, 1348, 1349, 1350, 1351

Kaufman, P. B. 1352

Kaul, K. N. 1816

Kauss, H. 314

Keerberg, Hille 1353, 1354

Keerberg, Olav 1353, 1354

Kefford, N. P. 1355

Keirns, J. J. 807

Keister, Donald L. 1356

Kempf, O. 2923

Kende, Hans 1357

Kendrick, Richard E. 704, 1358, 1359, 1360, 1361, 1362, 1363, 1364, 1365, 1366, 1367, 1368, 1369, 1370, 1371, 1372, 1373, 1374, 1375, 2596, 2598

Kent, Martha 1376

Key, Joe L. 2814

Khalatkar, A. S. 1377

Khan, A. A. 1378, 1379, 1380, 1381

Khavkin, E. E. 1382

Khodzhiev, A. 2904

Khudairi, A. Karim 1245, 1383, 1384, 1385, 1386, 1387, 1388, 1389

Kidd, George H. 1390, 2138, 2140

Kimura, Kazuyoshi 1177, 1391, 1392, 1393

Kincaid, Randall R. 1394

King, John W. 1175

King, Roderick W. 628, 1395, 1396, 1397, 1398

Kinnersley, A. M. 1399

Kinzel, Wilhelm 1400, 1401, 1402, 1403, 1404

Kiplinger, D. C. 2213

Kirk, J. T. O. 1405
Kirkland, Linda 1406
Kirschner, R. L. 2085
Kirschstein, M. J. 2226
Kitano, Hiroshi 2497
Klebs, Georg 1407, 1408, 1409, 1410
Kleiber, Helga 1411, 1412, 1413
Klein, Attila O. 660, 885, 1414,
1415, 2088
Klein, Deana T. 1416
Klein, Richard M. 252, 834, 1416,
1417, 1418, 1419, 2454, 2455, 3022
Klein, Shimon 636, 1420, 1421, 1422,
1458
Klein, William H. 288, 290, 291, 420,
501, 574, 1034, 1423, 1424, 1425,
1426, 1427, 1428, 1429, 1430, 1431,
1432, 1820, 1821, 1822, 2142, 2143,
2144, 2145, 2146, 2500, 2501, 2545,
2546, 2547, 2548, 2612, 2619, 3043,
3045, 3048, 3049
Klein-Eude, Dominique (see Eude, Domi-
nique) 1163, 1433, 1434
Kleshnin, A. F. 1435, 1436, 1437
Kleudgen, H. K. 1437.5
Kline, M. G. 1438
Koehler, Karl-Hermann (see Köhler,
Karl-Hermann) 1454, 1455
Koeppe, O. J. 2046
Koevenig, James L. 1439
Kofranek, Anton M. 1440, 1441
Kögl, Fritz 1442
Kohl, Friedrich G. 1443, 1444
Kohlbecker, Ruth 1445
Köhler, Diethard 1446, 1447, 1448,
1449, 1450, 1451, 1452, 1453

Köhler, Günther 980
Köhler, Karl-Hermann (see Koehler, Karl-
Hermann) 1456
Koller, Barbara 1457, 2556
Koller, Dov 1458, 1459, 1460, 1461,
1462, 1463, 1464, 1975, 2277, 2278
Kolli, S. 1465
Kommerell, Elisabeth 1466
Kondo, Noriaki 754, 1467, 1468
Kondurushkin, I. A. 1469
Koningsberger, V. J. 1470, 1471
Konishi, Michio 1472, 1473, 1474,
1474.5
Könitz, Walter 305, 1475
Konjević, R. 1981, 1982
Konstantinova, T. N. 1476, 1477
Kopcewicz, J. 1478, 1479
Kotani, Shûzô 1203
Kotlyarova, G. M. 2038
Koukkari, Willard L. 868, 1104, 1480,
1481, 1482, 1483, 1484, 1748, 2999,
3001
Kowallik, Wolfgang 1485, 1486, 1487,
1488, 2095, 2096
Kraml, Manfred 1001, 1489, 1490
Kranz, A. R. 509, 1038, 1039, 1491,
1492, 1493
Kraus, G. 1494
Kreis, David J., Jr. 2366
Krijthe, N. 2943
Krinsky, Norman I. 1495
Kritsky, M. S. 1496
Kroes, Hanno H. 1497, 1498, 1499, 1500,
1501, 1502
Kröger, Birgit 1014, 1020

Krotkov, G. 1028, 1029, 1030, 1032, 1033, 1503, 2815

Krug, H. 1504

Ku (Tai), Ping-Kaung 1505, 1506, 1674, 1677

Kuehnert, Charles C. 929

Kugrens, Paul 1956

Kühnert, E. 1122

Kuiper, Pieter J. C. 1507

Kujawski, Ronald F. 1508, 1509

Kumamoto, Junji 1979

Kuperman, F. M. 1510, 1511, 1512, 1513, 2511

Kurtz, Edwin B., Jr. 26, 1514

Küstner, Heinz 1515

Kuzmenko, A. A. 1516

Kuznetsov, E. D. 1517, 1518, 2487

Kuznetsova, G. K. 2603

Kvasnyuk, A. K. 76, 77

L

Laber, L. J. 2344

Lackmann, I. 1519

LaCroix, L. J. 1520

Laetsch, W. M. 1521, 1522, 1523

Lakshmi, S. 1644

Laloraya, M. M. 1524

Lambert, Claude 573, 1525

Landgraf, John E. 1526

Lane, Harry C. 342, 350, 1328, 1527, 1528, 1529, 1530, 1531, 1532, 1533, 1534

Lane, R. D. 1535

Lang, Anton 1357, 1536, 1537, 1954, 1955, 2390, 2392, 2394

Lange, Herbert 1538, 1539, 1540, 1541, 1879, 1880, 1891, 1900, 2503, 2618

Lange, Siegfried 1542

Langewellpott-Kunze, D. 1543

Langston, R. 1544

Larcher, Ghislain 1164, 1545, 1546, 1655, 1656

Larpent, Jean-Paul 1547, 1549, 1549.5

Larpent, Monique (see Larpent-Gourgaud, Monique) 1548

Larpent-Gourgaud, Monique (see Larpent, Monique) 1548.5, 1549, 1549.5

Laudi, Giannino 1550

Laux, Anneliese 1014, 2924

Lavee, S. 611

Lawson, Verna R. 1551, 2974

Lebedev, S. I. 2496

Lecharny, Alain 1552, 1553

LeDeunff, Yvon 1554, 1555, 1556, 1557

Lee, O. Y. 1558

Leff, Judith (see Weisz-Leff, Judith; Weisz, Judith) 1559

Leggatt, C. W. 1560

Leitgeb, H. 1561

Lelatko, Z. 3123

LeNoir, William C., Jr. 1562

Leopold, A. Carl 658, 1544, 1563, 1564

Letouzé, Robert 96, 1565, 1566

Lewak, Stanislaw 1567, 2567, 2568

Lewis, Lowell N. 2037

Lhoste, J. M. 1568

Lichtenthaler, H. K. 1437.5, 1569, 1570

Lie, T. A. 1571

Liebig, Margarete 1572

Lighter, David A. 2571

Liljenberg, Conny 1573

Lindner, Hermann 1010, 1020, 1574

Link, Wolfgang 1575, 1888, 1892, 2276

Linsbauer, K. 1576

Linschitz, Henry 351, 433, 1577, 1578

Lion, J. 1579

Lips, S. H. 1579.5

Lisansky, Stephen G. 1580, 1581, 1582, 1583

Listowski, A. 1584

Litse, R. A. 2496

Liverman, James L. 936, 1247, 1248, 1585, 1586, 1587, 1588, 1589, 1590, 1591, 1592, 1593, 2466, 2468

Lloyd, F. E. 1594

Lockhart, James A. 1595, 1596, 1597, 1598, 1599, 1600, 1601, 1602, 1603, 1604, 1605, 1606, 1607, 1608, 1609, 1610, 1611, 1612, 1613, 1614, 1960, 2008

Loercher, Lars (see Lörcher, Lars) 1617, 1618, 1619, 1620

Lohmann, L. 1891, 2965

Lona, Fausto 1621, 1622, 1623, 1624, 1625, 1626, 1627, 1628, 1629

Lonski, J. 2

Lörcher, Lars (see Loercher, Lars) 306, 1615, 1616

Lourtioux, Andrée 14, 15, 16, 1630

Loveys, B. R. 98, 1631, 1632

Lucas, N. M. C. 656

Ludwig, Fritz 1633, 1634

Luippold, H. E. 3057, 3058

Luippold, Helen J. 917

Lünenschloss, A. 1839

Lüttge, Ulrich 1450

Lutz, J. 1785

Lyon, Jessye L. 11.5

M

Ma, Te Hsiu 1635, 1636

Macfarlane, J. M. 1637

Machlis, Leonard 1638, 1794, 1795, 1796, 1797

Mackenzie, John M., Jr. 1639, 1710

Madsen, Axel 69

Maeda, Eizo 1640

Maeda, Mineko 1641

Maeng, Jueson 1389

Magness, J. R. 1642, 1643

Magomedov, I. M. 2325

Maheshwari, Satish C. 29, 904, 1644, 2854

Maignan, Gérard 2253, 2256

Makhlina, A. M. 2326

Malcolm, A. A. 1646

Malcoste, Roger 190, 191, 192, 193, 1164, 1546, 1647, 1648, 1649, 1650, 1651, 1652, 1653, 1654, 1655, 1656, 1657, 1658, 2043, 2260, 3104

Maltzahn, K. E. von 835, 836

Manabe, Katsushi 785, 1659, 1660, 1661, 1662

Mancinelli, Alberto L. 13, 74, 518, 579, 1505, 1663, 1664, 1665, 1666, 1667, 1668, 1669, 1670, 1671, 1672, 1673, 1674, 1675, 1676, 1677, 2589, 3075, 3076, 3078, 3079, 3080

Manetas, J. 1678

Mani, Jean-Claude 1939.5

Mann, Jay D. 1679, 1680, 1681

Manning, Howard E. 1682

Mansfield, T. A. 1683, 1684, 1685, 1686, 1687, 2821

Mantouvalos, G. 1688, 1689, 1823, 1825

Mapson, L. W. 1690, 1691, 1692

Marchal, B. (see Marchal-Gabriac, B.) 1703, 1704, 2375, 2376, 2377, 2378

Marchal-Gabriac, B. (see Marchal, B.) 1693

Marcus, Abraham 1694, 1695, 1696

Margaris, N. 1697, 1823, 1826

Margulies, Maurice M. 1698, 1699

Marinoff, Philip 2357, 2365

Marmé, Dieter 194, 195, 198, 1700, 1701, 1702, 1703, 1704, 1705, 1706, 1707, 1708, 1709, 1710, 2155, 2156, 2157, 2158, 2375, 2376, 2377, 2378, 2379, 2399

Maróti, M. 838

Marsh, Paul B. 1711

Martelli, Maurizio 102

Martin, John H. 1712

Martin, Marie 2239

Marushige, Keiji 1713, 1714, 3095

Marushige, Yasuko 1713

Marziani, Giovanna 2044

Masoner, M. 1207, 1715, 2828

Masuda, Yoshio 788, 1716

Masulli, Ottaviano 1717, 1718

Mathon, C.-Ch. 1719, 2662

Maton, J. 581

Matsuo, Eisuke 1720

Maximov, G. B. 2324

Mayer, A. M. 90, 634, 641, 1458, 1721, 1722, 1723

Mayer, Frank 1724, 1725

Mazliak, Paul 2818

Mazzolani, Gaspare 1726, 1727, 1728, 1729, 1730

McAlister, Edward D. 677, 679, 2969

McArthur, James A. 1731, 1732, 1733, 1734, 1735

McClure, Jerry W. 356, 1736, 1737, 1738, 1739, 2370, 2694

McCullough, James M. 1740, 1741

McDonald, M. R. 1351

McDonough, Walter T. 1742, 1743, 1744, 1745, 1746

McElroy, W. D. 1747

McEvoy, Robert C. 1484, 1748

McIlrath, Wayne J. 183

McIlvaine, H. R. C. 1749, 2112, 2113

McKenzie, J. S. 1750

Mclemore, B. F. 1751, 1752

McNitt, R. E. 1753

Medina, Ernesto 3062, 3063

Medina, Vicente J. 418

Mego, John L. 1754

Meidner, Hans 1686, 1755

Meijer, Gerard 592, 593, 1756, 1757, 1758, 1759, 1760, 1761, 1762, 1763, 1764, 1765, 1766, 1767, 1768, 1769, 1770, 1771, 2838, 2839

Meischke, Dieter 1772

Melnichuk, Yu. P. 844, 1285, 1773, 1774, 1775, 1776, 1777

Meneghini, M. 1919, 2856

Menhenett, Roger 360.5, 1778, 1779

Menzel, H. 959, 970

Mer, C. L. 1780, 1781, 1782, 1783, 2317

Mertz, Dan 1784, 1785

Merzalow, S. M. 2511

Meudt, W. 2889

Meyer, Fritz J. 1786

Meyer, U. 1874

Michanol, d'Yvette 1912

Michel, Jean-Pierre 1787, 1788, 1789,
2757, 2758

Mikhailov, A. P. 1929

Miller, Carlos O. 348, 1790, 1791,
1792, 1793, 3031

Miller, David H. 1794, 1795, 1796,
1797

Miller, John H. 585, 586, 588, 663,
928, 1798, 1799, 1800, 1801, 1802,
1803, 1804, 1805, 1806, 1807, 1808,
1811

Miller, Joyce M. 1809

Miller, Ken 2174

Miller, Nancy R. 1810

Miller, Pauline Monz 1799, 1801,
1802, 1803, 1804, 1805, 1808, 1811,
2769, 2770, 2771, 2772

Mirande, Marcel 1812

Mishra, Dinabandhu 1813, 1814

Misra, L. P. 1816, 1817

Mitchell, W. D. 1947

Mitra, G. C. 1815, 1816, 1817

Mitrakos, Konstantinos 789, 1431,
1678, 1689, 1818, 1819, 1820, 1821,
1822, 1823, 1824, 1825, 1826, 2144,
2145, 2146, 2612, 2619

Miyachi, Shigetoh 1827, 1828, 2024,
2025, 2026

Miyata, Hisao 1829

Miyoshi, Yasuhiro 1830

Moereels, E. 492

Moh, C. C. 1423, 1831, 1832, 1833,
1834, 3050

Mohr, Hans 9, 93, 130, 131, 304, 494,
513, 514, 544, 545, 546, 547, 548,
549, 550, 551, 552, 553, 569, 570,
727, 728, 742, 923, 944, 952, 959,
1120, 1121, 1122, 1207, 1240, 1310,
1311, 1322, 1323, 1324, 1325, 1412,
1413, 1538, 1539, 1541, 1715, 1835,
1836, 1837, 1838, 1839, 1840, 1841,
1842, 1843, 1844, 1845, 1846, 1847
1848, 1849, 1850, 1851, 1852, 1853
1854, 1855, 1856, 1857, 1858, 1859,
1860, 1861, 1862, 1863, 1864, 1865,
1866, 1867, 1868, 1869, 1870, 1871,
1872, 1873, 1874, 1875, 1876, 1877,
1878, 1879, 1880, 1881, 1882, 1883,
1884, 1885, 1886, 1887, 1888, 1889,
1890, 1891, 1892, 1893, 1894, 1895,
1896, 1897, 1898, 1899, 1900, 1901,
1902, 1903, 1904, 1905, 1906, 2017,
2018, 2019, 2020, 2021, 2022, 2023,
2032, 2033, 2063, 2064, 2071, 2228,
2276, 2380, 2382, 2402, 2403, 2405,
2406, 2434, 2437, 2449, 2502, 2503,
2827, 2842, 2844, 2915, 2916, 2917,
2919, 2958, 2962, 2963, 2964, 2965,
2966

Molina, C. 840

Möller, Jürgen 546, 547, 548, 1907

Molteni, E. 103

Mondain-Monval, Odile D. 1908

Monéger, René 1909, 1910, 1911, 1912

Monselise, S. P. 614, 1913, 1914, 1915

Montaldi, Edgardo R. 133

Montemartini, Luigi 1916

Moore, E. C. 1351
Moore, Paul H. 1917, 1918, 2210
Moore, Peter B. 1132
Moraes, Walkyria B. C. 1919
Morel, Claudine 2169, 2172
Moreland, Charles F. 682, 683
Morgan, Page W. 1920, 1921, 1922, 2125
Morré, D. J. 3028
Morren, Charles 1923
Mörtel, Gertraud 1015
Morton, Jean S. 1924, 2973
Moscowitz, Albert 323, 324
Moser, Ilse 313
Moshkov, B. S. 1925, 1926, 1927, 1928, 1929, 1930, 1931, 1932, 1933, 1934, 1935, 1936
Mouravieff, Igor 1937, 1938, 1939
Mousseron-Canet, Magdeleine 1939.5
Mugele, Fritz 977, 994, 1940, 1941
Muir, Robert M. 1942, 1943
Müller, Dieter 977, 980
Mumford, Franklin E. 34, 35, 36, 37, 743, 744, 1244, 1944, 1945, 1946, 1947, 1948, 1949, 1950, 1951, 2554, 2605
Munns, Rana 2465
Muñoz, V. 3064
Murneek, A. E. 1952
Murray, Diane 457, 458
Murray, D. R. 254
Murray, P. B. 10

N

Nabors, Murray W. 1953, 1954, 1955, 1956
Nagao, Akinori 55

Nagata, Yoko 1957
Nair, Helen 2464
Naito, Yoshiyuki 2707, 2708
Nakachi, Kei 2681
Nakagawa, Atsushi 747
Nakamura, S. 1958, 1959
Nakata, Shigeru 1960
Nakayama, Shidai 234, 1961, 1962, 1963, 1964
Naqvi, S. M. 1965
Nast, Charlotte 1810
Naundorf, Gerhard 1966
Naylor, Aubrey W. 565, 1967, 1968, 1969
Nebel, Bernard J. 1969, 1970, 1971, 1972, 1973, 1974
Nechaeva, E. P. 2902
Neeman, Melita 1265
Negbi, Moshé 134, 135, 1461, 1462, 1975, 1976, 1977, 2277, 2278
Negm, Fayek B. 1978, 1979
Nelson, C. D. 1028, 1029, 1030, 1032, 1033, 2815
Nešković, Mirjana 1980, 1981, 1982, 1983
Neumann, Gert 631, 632, 635, 636, 640, 641, 1721, 2107
Neuscheler-Wirth, Hannelore (see Wirth, Hannelore) 1984, 1985
Newman, D. W. 1986, 1987
Newman, Ian A. 1988, 1989, 1990
Nezgovorova, L. A. 1994
Ng, Mavis Y. L. (see Ng, Yuk Lin) 1991
Ng, Yuk Lin (see Ng, Mavis Y. L.) 1992
Nichiporovich, A. A. 1993, 1994, 1995
Niemann, G. J. 1996
Nilsson, J. 149

Purves, William K.   647, 1101, 2151, 2152, 2153
Pyfrom, H. T.   43
Pyrkosch, Gerhard   2154

Q

Quail, P. H.   377, 378, 2155, 2156, 2157, 2158, 2159, 2160, 2161, 2162, 2379, 2399
Quantz, Ludwig   947
Queiroz, Orlando   293, 2163, 2164, 2165, 2166, 2167, 2168, 2169, 2170, 2171, 2172

R

Racusen, Richard   2173, 2174, 2175, 2176, 2177
Ragahavan, V.   2178, 2179, 2180, 2181, 2182, 2183, 2184, 2185, 3023
Railton, I. D.   2186, 2187, 2207, 2208
Raju, P. V.   460
Rane, B. V.   1377
Raschke, K.   2188, 2189
Rasmussen, Ole   507
Rast, Dora   2190, 2191
Rasumov, V. I.   2192, 2193
Rauwenhoff, N. W. P.   2194
Raven, C. W.   2195, 2196, 2197, 2198, 2199, 2200, 2201, 2591
Ray, Peter M.   1299, 1300, 1301, 1302
Reed, Walfred A.   206, 2202, 2203
Reid, Brian R.   2037
Reid, D. M.   360, 2204, 2205, 2206, 2207, 2208
Reid, Hay B.   1918, 2209, 2210, 2516
Reinert, J.   884, 2211
Reinert, R. A.   1332, 1333, 2212
Reisch, K. W.   2213

Remer, W.   2214
Rentschler, Hans-Günther   2215
Rest, J.   255
Resühr, Bruno   2216
Rethy, R.   2217, 2845
Rezk, Malak R.   2218
Rice, Harbert V.   283, 284, 819, 2219, 2220, 2221, 2222
Richardson, M.   174
Richardson, Norman   2223
Richardson, S. D.   2224
Richter, Gerhard   2225, 2226
Richter, Richard   2609
Ries, E.   17, 2227
Ries, Julius v.   1633, 1634
Ripetsky, R. T.   503
Rissland, Inge   514, 1891, 2228, 2964, 2965, 2966
Ritter, J. W.   2229
Röbbelen, Gerhard   2230
Robertson, James   118
Robinson, Curtis   2231, 2972
Roesel, Hilde A.   2232
Roh, Seung M.   2233, 2234, 2235, 3015
Rohrbaugh, Lawrence M.   2236
Rollin, Paul   79, 188, 197, 260, 577, 1163, 1433, 1434, 1653, 1656, 1657, 1693, 2237, 2238, 2239, 2240, 2241, 2242, 2243, 2244, 2245, 2246, 2247, 2248, 2249, 2250, 2251, 2252, 2253, 2254, 2255, 2256, 2257, 2258, 2259, 2260, 2261, 2262, 2588, 3104
Rombach, J.   2263, 2264, 2265, 2266, 2267, 2268, 2269, 2270
Romberger, J. A.   2271
Ronzhina, O. A.   2039

Schiff, Jerome A. 1133

Schlickewei, Inge 1880

Schmidt, P. 2398

Schmidt, Werner 2379, 2380, 2383,
 2399, 2400, 2401

Schmidt-Clausen, H. J. 3097

Schnarrenberger, Claus 2402, 2403,
 2404, 2405, 2406

Schneider, Charles L. 2407

Schneider, Michael J. 245, 687, 2408,
 2409, 2410, 2411, 2412, 2413, 2414,
 2415, 2416

Schocken, V. 3040

Scholz, Alfred 2417

Schönbohm, Ekkehard 988, 994, 1021,
 2418, 2419, 2420, 2421, 2422, 2423,
 2424, 2425, 2426, 2427, 2428, 2429,
 2430, 2431, 2432, 2433

Schönfeld, Ingrid 989, 991

Schopfer, J. F. 2661

Schopfer, Peter 11, 145, 554, 2018,
 2073, 2434, 2435, 2436, 2437, 2438,
 2439, 2440, 2441, 2442, 2443, 2444,
 2445, 2446, 2447, 2448, 2449, 2450,
 2451, 2452, 2453, 2759, 2993

Schoser, Gustav 1318

Schrank, A. R. 3005, 3006, 3007

Schulz, M. Richardis 2454, 2455

Schulz, N. 2456

Schulz, R. 2457

Schulze, G. 2570

Schwabe, W. W. 2458, 2459, 2460, 2461,
 2832, 3029

Schwemmle, Berthold 2462

Schwochau, Martin E. 926

Scott, E. G. 2463

Scott, N. Steele 2464, 2465, 2553

Scott, Ralph A. Jr. 1590, 2466, 2467,
 2468

Scott, Tom K. 2469

Scully, N. J. 2054, 2055

Segal, N. 1462

Seitz, Konrad 1004, 2470, 2471, 2472,
 2473, 2474, 2475, 2476, 2477, 2478,
 2479

Selman, I. W. 2480

Sen, D. N. 136, 382, 383

Sen, N. 2481

Sen, S. P. 2482

Senebier, Jean 2483

Senf, R. 1885

Senn, G. 2484

Seth, P. N. 2854

Setty, Shantha L. 2485, 2486

Shakhov, A. A. 1469, 1517, 1518, 2487

Shapiro, Seymour 2488

Sharma, K. D. 382

Shaw, Michael 2373

Shaw, Stanley 823

Sheard, Charles 1082, 2489, 2490

Sheard, R. W. 1254, 1255

Sheehan, Thomas J. 2491

Shen-Miller, Jane 1753, 2492, 2493

Sherwin, John E. 2494

Shevchuk, S. N. 2498, 2499

Shibasaki, S. 20

Shibata, Kazuo 1468

Shihira, Ikuko 974

Shinohara, Toshikiyo 2497

Shirley, Hardy L. 2495

Shive, William 2550

Shiyan, P. N. 2496

2583, 2584, 2585, 2586, 2587, 2588, 2589, 2590, 2591, 2592, 2593, 2594, 2595, 2596, 2597, 2598

Spruit, H. C. 2597

Srivastava, H. N. 1524

Stabenau, Helmut 2599

Stadelmann, E. 1558

Stafford, Helen A. 2600

Stahl, Ernst 2601

Stanishevenkaya, E. M. 2498

Stanko, S. A. 2602, 2603

Stanley, R. G. 2604

Starr, Lawrence 1587

Stasny, J. T. 2605

Steer, B. T. 2606, 2607

Steers, Edward Jr. 415, 416, 422

Stein, Gabriel 632, 633, 635, 640, 2608, 2609

Steiner, Adolf M. 650, 1540, 1821, 2610, 2611, 2612, 2613, 2614, 2615, 2616, 2617, 2618, 2619, 2620, 2621, 2622, 2623, 2624, 2625, 2626, 2627, 2628, 2629, 2630, 2631, 2632, 2633, 2634

Stelzner, G. 2635

Stephan, Johannes 2636, 2637, 2638, 2639

Stephani, Marilyn C. 1806

Stern, K. 300

Stewart, Seldon L. 2640, 2641, 3011

Stewart, W. D. 49, 50

Stickland, R. G. 2642

Stift, A. 2659

Stimson, William R. 2412, 2413, 2414, 2415, 2416, 2643

Stockdale, Dennis L. 2035

Stöhr, H. 924

Stoklasa, Julius 2644, 2645

Stolwijk, J. A. J. 2646, 2647, 2648, 2649, 2650, 2651, 2652, 2944, 2945, 2946, 2948

Stone, Benjamin P. 2653

Stoppel, R. 2654

Storey, W. B. 1680

Stoutjesdijk, Ph. 2655, 2656

Stowe, Bruce B. 2656.5

Strain, Harold H. 2657

Street, H. E. 2463, 2658

Steeter, L. R. 2065

Strohmer, Friedrick 2659

Stroud, A. N. 867

Stroun, M. 1719, 2660, 2661, 2662

Sudakov, V. L. 2663, 2664

Sugai, Michizo 782.5, 2665, 2666, 2667, 2668

Sugawara, Tomota 2669

Sugimoto, Tohru 2681

Sugiura, Masahiro 2670

Sugiura, Tsuguo 1640

Sunderland, N. 2642

Suriano, J. R. 415, 416

Surrey, Kenneth 860, 861, 863, 865, 2671, 2672, 2673, 2674, 2675, 2676, 2677, 2678

Susinno, R. 1677

Suzuki, Hideo 787, 2679, 2680, 2681

Suzuki, Shōhō 753

Suzuki, Yoshihiro 149, 2682, 2683

Swain, T. 19, 425, 1690, 1692, 3061

Swanson, C. P. 1747, 2684, 2685, 2686, 2687, 2688, 2689

Sweeney, B. M. 2690

Sweet, Haven C. 2691, 2692, 2693
Syperda, Glenn 2694
Sytsema, W. 2952
Szász, Kálmán 1150, 2695, 2696
Szász-Barsi, Eszter 2695, 2696
Szweykowska, A. 2697

T

Takahashi, Norindo 2683, 2698
Takimoto, Atsushi 940, 1714, 1830,
    2699, 2700, 2701, 2702, 2703, 2704,
    2705, 2706, 2707, 2708, 2709, 2710,
    2711, 2712, 2713, 2714, 2715, 2716,
    2717, 2718, 2719
Tan, K. K. 2720
Tanada, Takuma 2721, 2722, 2723,
    2724, 2725, 2726, 2727, 2728, 2729,
    2729.5, 2730, 2731, 2732
Taylor, A. O. 2733, 2734
Taylor, Eldon E. 1711
Taylor, H. F. 315
Taylorson, R. B. 245, 2735, 2736,
    2737, 2738, 2739, 2740, 2741, 2742,
    2743, 2744
Teas, Howard J. 2491
Tenenbaum, Joseph 433
Teodoresco, E.-C. 2745, 2746
Tepfer, David A. 2747
Tevini, M. 1079
Tezuka, Takafumi 2748, 2749, 2750,
    2751, 2752, 3070, 3072, 3073
Thelan, Otto 2753
Thengane, R. J. 1377
Thibault, Pierre 1788, 1789, 2754,
    2755, 2756, 2757, 2758
Thiele, D. 2570
Thiele, Rosmarie 983

Thielebein, Martin 881
Thielmann, M. 1204
Thien, W. 2759
Thimann, Kenneth V. 385, 1178, 1179,
    1180, 1181, 1182, 1183, 1186, 1991,
    1992, 2760, 2761, 2762, 2774, 2995
Thoma, Linda 1235, 1238
Thomas, J. B. 2763
Thomas, Jerry P. 362, 2764, 2765
Thomas, Roderick G. 772, 775
Thomas, T. H. 2766
Thompson, P. A. 2767
Thompson, Paula J. 919
Thompson, William F. 822
Thomson, Betty F. 2768, 2769, 2770,
    2771, 2772
Thorning, Irmtraut 2773
Thornton, Robert M. 2774
Tilly, Fritz 2775
Tilney-Bassett, R. A. F. 1405
Tobin, Elaine M. 279, 2776, 2777, 2778,
    2779
Tobita, H. 1964
Tokhver, A. K. 2780, 2781, 2782
Tolbert, N. E. 913, 915, 916, 1378,
    1379
Tolkowsky, Abby 1670, 1672
Toole, Eben H. 220, 223, 242, 1058,
    2783, 2784, 2785, 2786, 2787, 2788,
    2789, 2790, 2791, 2792, 2793, 2794,
    2795, 2796, 2797, 2798, 2800, 2801
Toole, Vivian K. 220, 223, 242, 245,
    1058, 1073, 2783, 2784, 2785, 2786,
    2787, 2788, 2789, 2791, 2796, 2797,
    2798, 2799, 2800, 2801, 2802, 2803,
    2804, 2805, 2806, 2807

Vince-Prue, Daphne 888, 890, 891,
  897, 898, 899, 1037, 1128, 1130,
  2328, 2329, 2330, 2331, 2332, 2824,
  2860, 2861, 2862, 2863, 2864, 2865,
  2866, 2867, 2868, 2869, 2870, 2871,
  2872, 2873, 2874, 2875, 2876, 2877,
  2877.5

Virgin, Hemming I. 148, 2878, 2879,
  2880, 2881, 2882, 2883, 2884, 2885,
  2886, 2887

Vlasenok, L. I. 2888

Vlitos, A. J. 177, 2076, 2889

Voerkel, S. Heinz 2890

Vogt, Ernst 2891

Voskresenskaja, N. P. 1994, 1995,
  2781, 2892, 2893, 2894, 2895, 2896,
  2897, 2898, 2899, 2900, 2901, 2902,
  2903, 2904

Voss, J. 2905

Vrettou, S. 1823

Vyas, L. N. 2906, 2907

W

Wada, Masamitsu 2908, 2909, 2910,
  2911, 2912

Wagné, Claes 2913, 2914

Wagner, Edgar 444, 740, 741, 742,
  1881, 2915, 2916, 2917, 2918, 2919,
  2920, 2921, 2022, 2923

Wagner, Gottfried 2924, 2925, 2926,
  2927, 2928

Wain, R. L. 2542

Walker, T. S. 2929, 2930, 2931

Wallrabe, Elisabeth 947, 2932

Walne, Patricia L. 919

Wansor, Julia 1417

Wareing, P. F. 98, 168, 169, 170, 171,
  172, 173, 1080, 1631, 1632, 1815,
  2186, 2187, 2849, 2933, 2934, 2935,
  2936, 2937, 2938, 2939, 2940, 2941,
  2941.2, 2941.5, 2942

Wartenberg, Arnold 521

Wassink, E. C. 449, 2943, 2944, 2945,
  2946, 2947, 2948, 2949, 2950, 2951,
  2952, 2953, 2954, 2955

Waterman, Talbot H. 2956

Waxman, S. 2957

Webb, D. P. 2942

Wehrung, M. 1849

Weidner, Manfred 1891, 2958, 2959,
  2960, 2961, 2962, 2963, 2964, 2965,
  2966

Weinert, Hans 2967

Weintraub, Robert L. 855, 2968, 2969,
  2970, 2971, 2972, 2973, 2974

Weis, J. S. 2975

Weisenseel, Manfred 1002, 2976, 2977,
  2978, 2979, 2979.5

Weiser, C. J. 1750

Weisz, Judith (see Weisz-Leff, Judith;
  Leff, Judith) 2980

Weisz-Leff, Judith (see Leff, Judith;
  Weisz, Judith) 2981

Wellburn, A. R. 2982

Wellburn, Florence A. M. 2982

Wellensiek, S. J. 516, 2983, 2984

Wellmann, Eckard 2985, 2986, 2987,
  2988, 2989, 2990, 2991, 2992, 2993

Went, F. W. 2056, 2549, 2994, 2995,
  2996, 2997, 2998

West, H. R. 119

Yeoman, M. M.   464

Yguerabide, Juan   2286, 2287

Yocum, Conrad S.   1299

Yokohama, Yasutsugu   1199

Yopp, John H.   3081

Yost, Henry T. Jr.   2687, 2688, 2689,
  3082, 3083

Yulanovskaya, M. V.   1928

Yuldashev, A. Kh.   3084

Yunghans, H. O.   3085, 3086, 3087

Z

Zacharewicz, E.   3088

Zak, E. G.   3089

Zalik, Saul   671, 672, 673

Zantedeschi, Francesco   3090, 3091,
  3092

Zeevaart, Jan A. D.   2652, 3093, 3094,
  3095

Zelitch, I.   3096

Zenk, M. H.   2396, 2397

Ziegler, Hubert   3097

Ziegler, Irmgard   3097

Zimmerman, Burke K.   3098, 3099, 3100

Zimmermann, Charles E.   3101

Ziv, Meira   3102

Zollikofer, Clara   3103

Zollinger, Wendell D.   275

Zouaghi, Mongi   3104, 3105

Zucker, Milton   3060, 3106

Zurzycka, Alicja   3107, 3108

Zurzycki, Jan   3108, 3109, 3110, 3111,
  3112, 3113, 3114, 3115, 3116, 3117,
  3118, 3119, 3120, 3121, 3122, 3123

BIOLOGICAL MATERIALS INDEX

Abelia grandiflora Rehd. (*Caprifoliaceae*) 2957

Abultilon Theophrasti, Medic. (*Malvaceae*) (Velvet Leaf) 657

Acer platanoides, L. (*Aceraceae*) (Norway Maple) 2645

Acer Pseudo-Platanus, L. (*Aceraceae*) (Sycamore Maple) 2745

Acer rubrum, L. (*Aceraceae*) (Red, Scarlet or Swamp Maple) 529, 2645

Acetabularia crenulata, Lamouroux (*Dasycladaceae*) (Green Algae) 2225, 2226

Acetabularia mediterranea (*Dasycladaceae*) (Green Algae) 404, 2225, 2226

Achillea (*Asteraceae*) 1404

Achillea Millefolium, L. (*Asteraceae*) (Common Yarrow) 765

Achimenes longiflora, DC. (*Gesneriaceae*) 504, 507

Achyrantha spp. (*Amaranthaceae*) 666

Adiantum spp. L. (*Polypodiaceae*) (Fern) 760, 1078

Adiantum Capillus-Veneris L. (*Polypodiaceae*) (Venushair, True or Black Maiden-
hair Fern) 321, 2908, 2909, 2910, 2911, 2912

Adiantum scutum, Hort. (*Polypodiaceae*) (Fern) 321

Adiantum Weigandii, Moore (*Polypodiaceae*) (Fern) 1916

Aechmea fasciata, Baker (*Bromeliaceae*) 538

Aechmea nudicaulis, Griseb. (*Bromeliaceae*) 538

Aegilops ovata, L. (*Poaceae*) 906

Aegopodium podograria, L. (*Apiaceae*) (Goutweed or Bishops-weed) 104

Aesculus Hippocastanum L. (*Hippocastanaceae*) (Common Horse-Chestnut) 900,
2645, 2745

Aethionema cappadocicum, Spreng. (*Brassicaceae*) 769

Aethionema diastrophis, Fisch. (*Brassicaceae*) 769

Aethionema grandiflorum, Boiss. & Hohen. (*Brassicaceae*) 765, 769

Aethusa cynapium, L. (*Apiaceae*) (Fool's parsley) 1625

Ageratum conyzoides, L. (*Asteraceae*) 2840, 2846

Agrostemma githago, L. (*Caryophyllaceae*) (Corn-cockle) 1445

Agrostis stolonifera, L. (*Poaceae*) 12, 395, 1253

Aira caespitosa (*Poaceae*) 1256

Aira flexuosa (*Poaceae*) 395

Ajuga reptans, L. (*Lamiaceae*) 756, 757

Albizia julibrissin, Durazz. (*Fabaceae*) (Silk Tree) 44, 630, 802, 805,
868, 1104, 1226, 1230, 1483, 1484, 1748, 2355, 2356, 2357, 2358, 2359, 2360,
2361, 2362, 2363, 2364, 2365, 2366, 2368

Albizzia lophantha, Benth. (*Fabaceae*) (Lebbeck Tree) 1104, 2006

Alicularia scalaris 211

Alisma Plantago, L. (*Alismaceae*) 756, 757

Allium cepa, L. (*Liliaceae*) (Common onion) 353, 1096, 1755, 1959

Allium neapolitanum, Cyr. (*Liliaceae*) 1481

Allium suaveolens (*Liliaceae*) 1402

Allosorus falcatus 321

Allosorus sagittatus 211

Alnus firma var. yasha Winkl. (*Betulaceae*) 974

Alnus Inokumai (*Betulaceae*) 55

Alnus tinctoria, Sarg. (*Betulaceae*) 974

Alopecurus pratensis, L. (*Poaceae*) (Meadow Foxtail) 1256

Alsophila australis, R. Br. (*Cyatheaceae*) 321, 1040, 1860, 2045

Alternanthera sessilis (L.) R. Br. (*Amaranthaceae*) 461

Alyssum calycinum (*Brassicaceae*) 763, 769

Alyssum maritimum, Lam. (*Brassicaceae*) (Sweet Alyssum) 769

Amaranthus albus L. (*Amaranthaceae*) (Tumbleweed) 2738, 2743

Amaranthus arenicola, I. M. Johnston (*Amaranthaceae*) 1073

Amaranthus blitoides, S. Wats. (*Amaranthaceae*) 1258

Amaranthus caudatus L. (*Amaranthaceae*) (Pigweed) 526, 529, 704, 706, 724,
    843, 1277, 1280, 1358, 1359, 1360, 1361, 1366, 1369, 1370, 1371, 1454, 1455,
    1456, 1693, 1772, 2216, 2596, 3061

Amaranthus dubins, Mart. (*Amaranthaceae*) 2846

Amaranthus fimbriatus (*Amaranthaceae*) 2573

Amaranthus paniculatus L. (*Amaranthaceae*) 2190, 2191

Amaranthus retroflexus, L. (*Amaranthaceae*) (Pigweed or Wild beet) 75, 638,
    657, 1259, 1260, 1269, 1277, 1279, 1280, 1437, 1772, 2114, 2736, 2737, 2738,
    2739, 2741

Amaranthus tricolor, L. (*Amaranthaceae*) 839, 840, 842, 843, 2077, 2078, 2079

Amicia zygomeris, DC (*Fabaceae*) 2006

Amphicarpa monoica, (L.) Ell. (*Fabaceae*) (Hog peanut) 2495

Amygdalus communis, L. (*Rosaceae*) (Almond) 2645

Anagallis arvensis L. (*Primulaceae*) (Poor Mans Weatherglass) 882, 1188, 2051,
    2052

Anagallis caerulea, Schreber. (*Primulaceae*) 1408

Anemia Phyllitidis, Swartz. (*Schizaeaceae*) 2126

Anethum graveolens, L. (*Apiaceae*) (Dill) 529, 1532, 1533, 1967

Anthemis tinctoria, L. (*Asteraceae*) (Golden Marguerite) 765, 766, 767

Apium graveolens, L. (*Apiaceae*) (Celery) 1096, 2766

Apium graveolens var. rapaceum, DC. (*Apiaceae*) (Celeriac) 1096

Aponogeton distachyus L. (*Aponogetonaceae*) (Water Hawthron) 1938

Apple (*Roseaceae*) 540, 665, 670, 1567, 1642, 1643, 2065, 2148, 2522

Arabidopsis thaliana (L.) Heynh. (*Brassicaceae*) (Mouse-ear Cress) 29, 288, 289, 290, 291, 509, 1034, 1038, 1039, 1491, 1492, 1493, 1740, 1741, 2230, 2500, 2506, 2852, 2853

Arachis hypogea L. (*Fabaceae*) (Peanut) 690, 1273, 1276, 2006, 2745, 3102

Arctium lappa L. (*Asteraceae*) (Great Burdock) 1958

Aristolochia clematitis, L. (*Aristolochiaceae*) 459

Artemisia monosperma, Del. (*Asteraceae*) 1461

Asparagus officinalis, L. (*Liliaceae*) (Garden Asparagus) 1096

Asparagus Sprengeri, Regel. (*Liliaceae*) 3123

Aspergillus 2291

Asphodelus ramosus, L. (*Liliaceae*) 1400

Aspidistra elatior, Blume (*Liliaceae*) 1353, 2154

Aspidium elongatum (*Polypodiaceae*) 321

Aspidium Filix-mas Swartz. (*Polypodiaceae*) 1916, 2045, 2126

Aspidium molle, Swartz (*Polypodiaceae*) 211

Aspidium spinulosum, Swartz. (*Polypodiaceae*) 211

Asplenium spp. L. (*Polypodiaceae*) 1078

Asplenium alatum, HBK (*Polypodiaceae*) 211

Asplenium australe, Br. (*Polypodiaceae*) 1916

Asplenium diversifolium (*Polypodiaceae*) 321

Asplenium lasiopteris (*Polypodiaceae*) 211

Asplenium Nidus, L. (*Polypodiaceae*) (Bird's-Nest Fern) 2180, 2181, 2183

Asplenium ruta muraria, L. (*Polypodiaceae*) 2045

Asplenium trichomanes, L. (*Polypodiaceae*) 2045

Asteracantha longifolia (*Acanthaceae*) 382

Aster spp. L. (*Asteraceae*) 2384, 2388, 3032, 3033, 3034

Aster ericöides, L. (*Asteraceae*) (Heath Aster) 759

Aster linosyris (*Asteraceae*) 759

Aster multiflorus, Ait. (*Asteraceae*) (Heath Aster) 759

Asystasia gangetica, T. Anders. (*Acanthaceae*) 81

Athyrium filix femina, Roth. (*Polypodiaceae*) (Lady fern) 2045

Atrichum undulatum 2351

Atriplex dimorphostegia, Kar. & Kir. (*Chenopodiaceae*) 1462, 1463

Aucuba japonica, Thunb. (*Cornaceae*) 1078

Avena elatior, L. (*Poaceae*) (Tall Oat-grass) 1256

Avena fatua L. (*Poaceae*) (Wild Oat) 434

Avena sativa, L. (*Poaceae*) (Oat) 12, 14, 15, 36, 37, 58, 72, 73, 79, 80, 82,
 105, 156, 157, 158, 159, 160, 161, 162, 163, 164, 165, 166, 256, 265, 271,
 274, 275, 277, 278, 324, 330, 390, 403, 408, 409, 410, 411, 423, 431, 433,
 446, 447, 448, 450, 501, 517, 518, 556, 557, 558, 560, 561, 563, 574, 647,
 648, 702, 743, 744, 754, 778, 782, 819, 820, 823, 834, 856, 857, 858, 859,
 861, 863, 879, 1136, 1137, 1142, 1144, 1145, 1146, 1147, 1148, 1149, 1170,
 1171, 1172, 1216, 1244, 1251, 1352, 1366, 1373, 1383, 1390, 1442, 1457, 1467,
 1468, 1470, 1490, 1497, 1498, 1499, 1500, 1502, 1542, 1564, 1577, 1578, 1579,
 1580, 1581, 1583, 1585, 1586, 1617, 1660, 1666, 1738, 1780, 1781, 1783, 1942,
 1943, 1945, 1946, 1947, 1948, 1950, 1988, 1989, 1990, 2049, 2081, 2082, 2084,
 2128, 2129, 2132, 2133, 2134, 2135, 2137, 2138, 2139, 2140, 2141, 2152, 2153,
 2192, 2219, 2220, 2221, 2222, 2280, 2281, 2282, 2283, 2284, 2285, 2286, 2287,
 2295, 2297, 2317, 2345, 2346, 2347, 2349, 2350, 2381, 2389, 2407, 2529, 2534,
 2537, 2545, 2547, 2556, 2566, 2575, 2598, 2605, 2640, 2641, 2645, 2734, 2751,
 2752, 2773, 2774, 2777, 2816, 2841, 2891, 2905, 2929, 2930, 2931, 2968, 2970,
 2982, 3005, 3006, 3007, 3008, 3009, 3010, 3011, 3016, 3018, 3068, 3073, 3098,
 3099, 3100, 3103

Azalea spp. L. (*Ericaceae*) 760, 900

Azalea indica, L. (*Ericaceae*) 763

Bacillus (Bacteria) 2291

Baeria chrysostoma, Fisch. & Mey. (*Asteraceae*) 2549

Balantium antarcticum (*Dicksoniaceae*) 1040, 2636

Balsum pear (Momordica Charantia, L.) (*Cucurbitaceae*) 1959

Bangia fuscopurpurea 2223

Barbarea verna, Aschers. (*Brassicaceae*) (Winter-Cress) 2740

Barbarea vulgaris, R. Br. (*Brassicaceae*) (Yellow rocket) 2736, 2738, 2740,
 2789

Barley (Hordeum vulgare, L.) (*Poaceae*) 25, 43, 57, 59, 76, 214, 215, 218, 219, 267, 319, 348, 360.5, 505, 532, 567, 1140, 1263, 1269, 1515, 1520, 1544, 1551, 1564, 1778, 2039, 2119, 2204, 2205, 2206, 2384, 2498, 2514, 2524, 2556, 2657, 2669, 2694, 2722, 2825, 2826, 2901, 2902, 2904, 3059

Basella alba, L. (*Basellaceae*) (Malabar-Nightshade) 1365

Bauhinia monandra, Kurz. (*Fabaceae*) (Butterfly-Flower or Jerusalem Date) 1126

Bean (Phaseolus spp. L.) (*Fabaceae*) 21, 267, 666, 854, 887, 936, 1051, 1081, 1086, 1134, 1185, 1340, 1419, 1587, 1591, 1592, 1682, 1694, 1695, 1698, 1761, 1762, 1790, 1919, 1920, 1921, 2043, 2085, 2120, 2123, 2195, 2296, 2384, 2386, 2466, 2467, 2468, 2483, 2545, 3025, 3040, 3041, 3042, 3043, 3044, 3045, 3046, 3048, 3054

Beef heart mitochondria 1809

Beet (Beta spp. L.) (*Chenopodiaceae*) 854

Begonia spp. L. (*Begoniaceae*) 900, 1081, 2386

Begonia Evansiana Andr. (*Begoniaceae*) 616, 618, 619, 621, 622

Begonia hiemalis (*Begoniaceae*) 2273

Bellis perennis, L. (*Asteraceae*) (True or English Daisy) 900

Berteroa incana, (L.) DC. (*Brassicaceae*) (Hoary Alyssum) 765, 769, 2789

Beta vulgaris, L. (*Chenopodiaceae*) (Sugar beet) (red beet) 1096, 1530, 1532, 1533, 1967, 2080, 2409, 2644

Betula alba, L. (*Betulaceae*) (White Birch) 2645

Betula lutea, Michx. (*Betulaceae*) (Yellow Birch) 2002

Betula pubescens, Erhr. (*Betulaceae*) (Birch) 168, 169, 171, 172, 2002, 2655

Betula verrucosa, Ehrh. (*Betulaceae*) (Birch) 172

Bidens spp., L. (*Asteraceae*) (Bur Marigold) 2846

Bidens radiala, Thuill. (*Asteraceae*) 2238, 2240, 2245

Billbergia elegans (*Bromeliaceae*) 538

Billbergia pyramidalis, Lindl. (*Bromeliaceae*) 538

Biloxi soybean (*Fabaceae*) 2054

Biophytum sensitivum, DC. (*Oxalidaceae*) 2601

Biota orientalis, Endl. (*Cupressaceae*) (Oriental Arbor-Vitae) 2050

Blasia pusilla, L. (*Blasiaceae*) (Liverwort) 211

Blechnum brasiliense, Desv. (*Polypodiaceae*) 321

Blechnum spicant, With. (*Polypodiaceae*) 2045

Blechnum triangulare (*Polypodiaceae*) 1916

Blitum capitatum, L. (*Chenopodiaceae*) (Strawberry Blite) 1212

Blitum virgatum (*Chenopodiaceae*) 1212

Botrytis cinerea (fungi) 2720

Boussingaultia baselloides, Hook. (*Basellaceae*) 2746

Box (*Buxaceae*) 1078

Brachythecium rutabubum, (Hedw.) Bry. (*Hypnaceae*) 1035

Brachythecium velutinum, (Hedw.) Bry. (*Hypnaceae*) 1584

Brassica alba, Rabenh. (*Brassicaceae*) (White Mustard) 2114

Brassica campestris, L. (*Brassicaceae*) (Field Mustard) 734, 735, 736, 737,
  2944

Brassica hibern (*Brassicaceae*) 1256

Brassica juncea, Coss. (*Brassicaceae*) (Leaf Mustard) 1288, 1289, 1290

Brassica napobrassica, Mill. (*Brassicaceae*) (Rutabaga) 1096

Brassica napus, L. (*Brassicaceae*) (Rape) 12, 395, 1174, 1256, 1445, 1625

Brassica nigra, Koch. (*Brassicaceae*) (Black Mustard) 1288, 1289, 1290

Brassica oleracea L. (*Brassicaceae*) (Cabbage) 604, 1256, 1288, 1305, 1308,
  1505, 1506, 1530, 1677, 2066, 2067, 2521, 2523, 2552, 2697

Brassica oleracea var. capitata L. (*Brassicaceae*) (Cabbage) 1096

Brassica oleracea var. botrytis, L. (*Brassicaceae*) (Cauliflower) 1096, 1480,
  1482, 1530, 2152, 2153

Brassica oleracea var. gemmifera, Zenker. (*Brassicaceae*) (Brussels sprouts)
  1096

Brassica oleracea var. italica, Plenck. (*Brassicaceae*) (Sprouting Broccoli)
  1096

Brassica pekinensis, Rupn. (*Brassicaceae*) (Chinese cabbage) 1096, 2669

Brassica rapa L. (*Brassicaceae*) (turnip) 334, 395, 500, 888, 889, 890, 891,
  892, 893, 896, 898, 899, 900, 1305, 1505, 1506, 1749, 2075, 2113, 2114, 2414,
  2415, 2416, 2521, 2523, 2643, 2649, 2944, 2945

Brassica rapa var. lorifolia, Bailey (*Brassicaceae*) (turnip) 1096

Bromus inermis, Leyss. (*Poaceae*) (Awnless or Hungarian Brome) 1204

Bromus tectorum L. (*Poaceae*) 2655

Brunella vulgaris (*Brunelliaceae*) 763

Bryophyllum, spp. Salisb. (*Crassulaceae*) 1927

Bryophyllum fedtschenkoi, R. Hamet & Perrier (*Crassulaceae*) 3021

Bryophyllum pinnatum, Kurz. (*Crassulaceae*) 589

Bryum capillare, Hedw. (*Bryaceae*) (Moss) 2398

Bryum cirrhetum (*Bryaceae*) (Moss) 2398

Bryum lacuste (*Bryaceae*) (Moss) 2398

Bryum pendulum, (Hornsch.) Schimp. (*Bryaceae*) (Moss) 1035

Bryum roseum (*Bryaceae*) (Moss) 2398

Bucegia romanica 2746

Buckwheat (*Polygonaceae*) 46, 47, 2753, 3059

Bulb 1812

Bulbocodium vernum, L. (*Lilaceae*) 1481

Bush beans 3059

Cabbage (*Brassicaceae*) 667, 816, 850, 1052, 1437, 1674, 1927, 2519

Cactus (*Cactaceae*) 1078

Calabash gourd 1959

Calendula spp. L. (*Asteraceae*) (marigold) 1269, 2838

Calla aethiopica, L. (*Araceae*) (Common Calla) 760, 948

Calliandra inequilatera (*Fabaceae*) 1104

Callistephus chinensis, Nees. (*Asteraceae*) (China Aster) 406, 763, 1166,
    1167, 2273, 3034, 3035, 3037

Callitriche verna, L. (*Callitrichaceae*) 212, 459

Calotropis procera, Dry. (*Asclepiadaceae*) 2481, 2840, 2846

Camassia esculenta, Rob. (*Liliaceae*) (Bear grass) 1481

Camelia spp. L. (*Theaceae*) 760, 762

Camelia japonica, L. (*Theaceae*) 763

Camelina microcarpa, Andrz. (*Brassicaceae*) 2789

Camelina sativa, (L.) Crantz. (*Brassicaceae*) (False Flax) 12, 395

Campanula pyramidalis, L. (*Campanulaceae*) (Chimney Bellflower) 459

Campanula rotundifolia, L. (*Campanulaceae*) (Bluebell or Harebell) 756, 758

Candida guilliermondii (yeast) 700, 2294

Canistrum Lindenii, Mez. (*Bromeliaceae*) 538

Cannabis sativa, L. (*Cannabidaceae*) (Hemp) 12, 395, 1256, 1717, 1718, 2745

Capsella bursa-pastoris, (L.) Medic. (*Brassicaceae*) (Shepherds-pouch) 2789

Cardamine pratensis, L. (*Brassicaceae*) (Cuckoo-Flower) 900

Carnegiea gigantea, Britt & Rose (*Cactaceae*) (Saquaro Giant Cactus) 26, 1514

Carrichtera annua, (L.) Asch. (*Brassicaceae*) 906

Carrot (*Apiaceae*) 555, 849, 1959, 2103, 2104

Carthamus tinctorius L. (*Asteraceae*) (Safflower or False Saffron) 1319

Caryopteris x clandonensis (*Verbenaceae*) 2091

Caryopteris incana, Miq. (*Verbenaceae*) 2094

Cassia Chamaecrista, L. (*Fabaceae*) (Partridge Pea) 1637

Cassia floribunda, Hort. (*Fabaceae*) 2006

Cassia nictitans, L. (*Fabaceae*) (Wild sensitive Plant) 1637

Cassia Tora, L. (*Fabaceae*) (Sicklepod) 1637

Castanea vesea, Gaertn. (*Fagaceae*) (Spanish or Eurasian Chestnut) 2080

Castor bean (*Euphorbiaceae*) 2904

Catalpa bignonioides, Walt. (*Bignoniaceae*) (Common Catalpa or Indian bean)
    529, 1530

Catalpa speciosa, Warder. (*Bignoniaceae*) (Western Catalpa) 695, 2050

Catharinaea undulata 2636

Cauliflower (*Brassicaceae*) 342, 350

Celery (*Apiaceae*) 1959

Celosia spp. L. (*Amaranthaceae*) 1524

Celosia cristata, (L.) Ktze. (*Amaranthaceae*) (Cockscomb) 843

Celosia plumosa, Hort. (*Amaranthaceae*) 841, 842, 843

Centaurea Cyanus, L. (*Asteraceae*) (Corn Flower or Bachelors-Button) 765, 1625

Centaurea montana, L. (*Asteraceae*) (Mountain Bluet) 765

Cerastium arvense, L. (*Caryophyllaceae*) (Starry Grasswort) 900

Ceratodon purpureus, (L.) Brid. (*Ditrichaceae*) (Moss) 2830, 2831

Ceratophyllum demersum, L. (*Ceratophyllaceae*) 756, 757

Ceratopteris thalictroides (*Parkeriaceae*) 1561, 2639

Cereus pentalophus (*Cactaceae*) 3092

Ceterach officinarum 321

Chamaecyparis Lawsoniana, (Murr.) Parl. (*Cupressaceae*) (Lawson Cypress) 2050

Chamaecyparis obtusa, Sieb. & Zucc. (*Cupressaceae*) (Hinoki Cypress) 974

Chamaecyparis pisifera, Sieb. & Zucc. (*Cupressaceae*) (Sawara Cypress) 974

Chara (*Characeae*) 1494, 2217

Chara zeylanica (*Characeae*) 1641

Cheilanthes farinosa (*Polypodiaceae*) (fern) 2185

Cheiranthus Allionii, Hort. (*Brassicaceae*) 769

Chenopodium album L. (*Chenopodiaceae*) (lambsquartens) 4, 435, 436, 440, 1131,
    1312, 1313, 1314, 1315, 1316, 2736, 2738

Chenopodium amaranticolor, Coste & Reyn. (*Chenopodiaceae*) 305, 308, 1440,
    1441, 1475

Chenopodium aristatum L. (*Chenopodiaceae*) 440

Chenopodium botrys, L. (*Chenopodiaceae*) 4, 438, 440

Chenopodium foetidum, L. (*Chenopodiaceae*) 440

Chenopodium glaucum, L. (*Chenopodiaceae*) 4, 435, 436, 440

Chenopodium polyspermum, L. (*Chenopodiaceae*) 1213, 1214, 1215, 1217, 1218, 1219, 1220, 1552, 1553

Chenopodium rubrum L. (*Chenopodiaceae*) 38, 435, 436, 437, 439, 440, 441, 445, 739, 740, 741, 1326, 1327, 1330, 1395, 1396, 1397, 1398, 1663, 2371, 2920, 2921, 2923

Chenopodium salinum, Standl. (*Chenopodiaceae*) 436

Chlamydomonas eugametos (*Chlorophyceae*) (green algae) 958

Chlamydomonas gymnogama (*Chlorophyceae*) (green algae) 362

Chlamydomonas moeivusii (*Chlorophyceae*) (green algae) 958

Chlamydomonas reinhardtii (*Chlorophyceae*) (green algae) 292

Chlorella spp. (*Chlorellaceae*) 1828, 2096, 3089

Chlorella ellipsoidea (*Chlorellaceae*) (green algae) 1827, 2024, 2025, 2026

Chlorella fusca (*Chlorellaceae*) (green algae) 2570

Chlorella pyrenoidosa (*Chlorellaceae*) (green algae) 17, 362, 1485, 1486, 1487, 1488, 2095, 3039

Chlorella vulgaris (*Chlorellaceae*) (green algae) 397, 1028, 1029, 1030, 1032, 1033, 1503

Chloris ciliata (*Poaceae*) 828

Chloris verticillata, Nutt. (*Poaceae*) (windmill grass) 657

Chlorogonium elongatum, Dang. (*Chlorophyceae*) (green algae) 2599

Chryptotaenia japonica 1959

Chrysanthemum spp. L. (*Asteraceae*) 900, 1269, 2386, 2388

Chrysanthemum coronarium L. (*Asteraceae*) (Garland Chrysanthemum or Crown Daisy) 1959

Chrysanthemum indicium, L. (*Asteraceae*) 759

Chrysanthemum Leucanthemum, L. (*Asteraceae*) (Ox-Eye Daisy or Whiteweed) 765

Chrysanthemum morifolium, Ramat. (*Asteraceae*) (Florists Chrysanthemum) 232, 238, 364, 366, 368, 369, 370, 371, 1272, 1275, 1278, 1279, 1280, 1530, 2213, 2491

Cicer arietinum L. (*Fabaceae*) (Chick Pea) 88, 89, 1717, 1718, 2745

Cichorium Intybus, L. (*Asteraceae*) (Chicory) 1096

Cirriphyllum piliferum (*Hypnaceae*) (Moss) 3123

Cirsium palustre, (L.) Scop. (*Asteraceae*) 2655

Citrullus colocynthis (L.) Schrad. (*Cucurbitaceae*) (Colocynth or Bitterapple) 192, 1459, 1653, 1658

Citrullus lanatus (*Cucurbitaceae*) 136

Citrus aurantium (L.) Swingle (*Rutaceae*) (Sour Orange or Lime) 614, 1913, 1914, 1915

Citrus sinensis, Osbeck (*Rutaceae*) (Orange) 1096

Cladonia cristatella (Lichen) 837

Cleome Burmanii W. & A (*Capparidaceae*) 81

Clianthus Dampiere, Cunn. (*Fabaceae*) (Glory Pea) 2006

Clostridium (Bacteria) 2291

Clusia mexicana (*Cluslaceae*) 2154

Cobaea macrostoma, Pav. (*Polemoniaceae*) 459

Cobaea scandens, Cav. (*Polemoniaceae*) 665

Cocklebur (*Asteraceae*) 1544

Cocos nucifera, L. (*Palmaceae*) (Coconut) 1096

Coleus spp. Lour. (*Lamiaceae*) 666, 667, 1078

Coleus blumei, Benth. (*Lamiaceae*) 589, 1439, 2109

Coleus blumei x C. frederici (*Lamiaceae*) 930, 932

Coleus rehneltianus, hybridus (*Lamiaceae*) 2273

Colutea arborescens, L. (*Fabaceae*) 2006

Commelina nudiflora, L. (*Commelinaceae*) (Day Flower) 81

Conocephalum conicum, (L.) Wiggers (*Marchantiaceae*) (Liverwort) 2746

Convalloria spp. L. (*Liliaceae*) (lilly of the valley) 2272

Convolvulus arvensis, L. (*Convolvulaceae*) (field bindweed) 209, 2747

Convolvulus minor, Hort. (*Convolvulaceae*) (Dwarf Morning-Glory) 1174

Corn (*Poaceae*) 76, 146, 267, 337, 342, 350, 387, 665, 684, 1081, 1317, 1639, 1753, 1787, 1788, 2039, 2144, 2145, 2146, 2493, 2612, 2756, 2892, 2893, 2894, 2904, 3040, 3043

Cornus alba, L. (*Cornaceae*) 900, 2590

Cornus stolonifera, Michx. (*Cornaceae*) (red osier dogwood) 1750, 3022

Corylus Avellana, L. (*Corylaceae*) (Common or European Filbert) 2645

Cosmos spp. Cav. (*Asteraceae*) 667, 2388

Cosmos bipinnatus, Cav. (*Asteraceae*) 500, 759, 1280, 1623, 2647, 2648, 2649, 2945, 2946, 3035

Cotton (*Malvaceae*) 3084

Crambe hispanica (*Brassicaceae*) 769

Crataegus oxyacantha, L. (*Rosaceae*) (Hawthorn) 2645

Crepis spp., L. (*Asteraceae*) 2388

Crepis capillaris, (L.) Wallr. (*Asteraceae*) 1176

Crepis leontodontoides (*Asteraceae*) 1625

Cress (*Brassicaceae*) 854, 1174

Crocus ancyrensis, Maw. (*Iridaceae*) 1481

Crytostegia grandiflora, R. Br. (*Asclepiadaceae*) 2481

Cucumber (*Cucurbitaceae*) 13, 25, 257, 1082, 1437, 1670, 1675, 1927, 1959,
    2231, 2272, 2489, 2834, 3079

Cucumis melo, L. (*Cucurbitaceae*) (Melon or Muskmelon) 1649, 1959

Cucumis prophetarum, L. (*Cucurbitaceae*) 907

Cucumis sativus, L. (*Cucurbitaceae*) (cucumber) 62, 66, 179, 180, 192, 578,
    579, 589, 591, 592, 593, 594, 596, 597, 598, 600, 601, 603, 604, 605, 606,
    607, 608, 907, 1101, 1598, 1607, 1649, 1652, 1653, 1658, 1672, 1758, 1759,
    1768, 1771, 2273, 2589, 2590, 2683, 3065, 3077

Cucurbita spp., L. (*Cucurbitaceae*) 248

Cucurbita maxima, Duchesne. (*Cucurbitaceae*) (Autumn, Winter or acorn squash)
    190, 192, 459, 1096, 1530, 1653, 1658, 2322, 2374, 2746

Cucurbita moseata, Duchesne. (*Cucurbitaceae*) (squash) 2675, 2677, 2678

Cucurbita pepo, L. (*Cucurbitaceae*) (Zucchini yellow squash) 190, 192, 193,
    195, 196, 197, 198, 1096, 1545, 1598, 1607, 1653, 1658, 1693, 1707, 1708,
    1709, 1710, 1772, 2156, 2157, 2158, 2159, 2160, 2322, 2374, 2383, 2399, 2400,
    2401, 2745, 3077, 3104, 3105

Currant (Black) (*Saxifragaceae*) 1469

Cuscuta gronovii, Willd. (*Convolvulaceae*) (dodder) 1508, 1509

Cuscuta indecora, Choisy (*Convolvulaceae*) (dodder) 1328, 1531, 1534

Cuscuta pentagona, Engelm. (*Convolvulaceae*) (dodder) 2098, 3101

Cydonia vulgaris, Pers. (*Rosaceae*) (Quince) 2645

Cydonium falcatum 321

Cynara Scolymus, L. (*Asteraceae*) (globe artichoke) 1096

Cynosurus cristatus, L. (*Poaceae*) (Crested Dogs-Tail) 395, 2655

Cyperus alterniflora, L. (*Cyperaceae*) (Umbrella-Plant) 1204

Cyperus rotundus, L. (*Cyperaceae*) (Nutgrass, Purple Nutsedge) 133, 386

Cypripedium harbor x Cyp. merlin (*Orchidaceae*) (Lady's Slipper) 408

Cystopteris fragilis 321

Dactylis glomerata, L. (*Poaceae*) (Orchard-Grass) 1256

Datura ferox, L. (*Solanaceae*) 322, 903, 2574

Daucus carota, L. (*Apiaceae*) (carrot) 27, 1096, 1256, 2109, 2999, 3000, 3001

Davallia chinensis, Smith var. stricta, Hort. (*Polypodiaceae*) (Fern) 321

Dawsonia longiseta (*Polytrichaceae*) (Moss) 2351

Dawsonia polytrichoides (*Polytrichaceae*) (Moss) 2351

Dawsonia superba (*Polytrichaceae*) (Moss) 2351

Delphinium elatum, L. (*Ranunculaceae*) (Candle Larkspur) 1404

Dendroligotrichum dendroides (*Polytrichaceae*) (Moss) 2351

Dentaria diphylla, Michx. (*Brassicaceae*) (Pepper-Root) 3081

Deutzia gracilis, Sieb. & Zucc. (*Saxifragaceae*) 760, 761

Dianthus alpinus, L. (*Caryophyllaceae*) 1403

Dianthus barbatus, L. (*Caryophyllaceae*) (Sweet William) 761

Dianthus carthusianorum, L. (*Caryophyllaceae*) 1403

Dianthus caryophyllus, L. (*Caryophyllaceae*) (Carnation) 2865

Dianthus chinensis, L. (*Caryophyllaceae*) (Annual pinks) 1365

Dianthus microlepis, Boiss. (*Caryophyllaceae*) 1403

Dianthus superbus, L. (*Caryophyllaceae*) 1403

Dicranella heteromalla, (Hedw.) Schimp. (*Dicranaceae*) (Moss) 1584

Dicranum scoparium, Hedw. (*Dicranaceae*) 2830

Digitalis spp., L. (*Scrophulariaceae*) 2840

Digitalis purpurea, L. (*Scrophulariaceae*) (Common Foxglove) 1772, 2041

Digitaria sanguinalis, (L.) Scop. (*Poaceae*) 1916

Digitaria spp., Heist. (*Poaceae*) (Crabgrass) 657, 1408

Dill (*Apiaceae*) 527

Dodder (*Convolvulaceae*) 3059

Doodia caudata, R. Br. (*Polypodiaceae*) 1040

Doodia lunulata (*Polypodiaceae*) 1916

Draparnaldia mutabilis, (Roth) Cederq. 1547

Drosera spathulata (*Droseraceae*) (Sundew) 1402, 1404

Drosophila melanogaster 845, 846, 1341, 1342, 1343, 1344, 1345, 1346, 1347, 1348, 1349, 1350, 1351

Dryopteris erythrosora (*Polypodiaceae*) 1152

Dryopteris Filix-mas (L.) Schott (*Polypodiaceae*) (Male Fern) 107, 108, 109, 110, 111, 112, 113, 114, 115, 304, 307, 493.5, 494, 543, 544, 545, 623, 650, 959, 1152, 1322, 1835, 1836, 1860, 1862, 1878, 2031, 2032, 2033, 2061, 2062, 2063, 2064, 2402, 2613, 2614, 2615, 2620, 2628, 2629, 2630, 2655

Dwarf pea (*Fabaceae*) 315

Echeveria spp., DC. (*Crassulaceae*) 1078

Echeveria metallica, Lem. (*Crassulaceae*) 1078

Echinocactus ottonis, Link & Otto (*Cactaceae*) 3090, 3091, 3092

Echinochloa colora, (L.) Link (*Poaceae*) 2846

Echinochloa crusgalli, L. (*Poaceae*) (barnyard grass) 2738

Echinodorus ranunculoides, L. (*Alismaceae*) 1939

Ectothiorhodospira shaposhnikovii 2291, 2292

Egg-plant (*Solanaceae*) 1959

Elodea spp. Michx. (*Hydrocharitaceae*) (Waterweed) 826

Elodea canadensis, Michx. (*Hydrocharitaceae*) 1494, 2470, 2477, 2848

Elsholtzia argyi, Lev. (*Lamiaceae*) 1197

Epilobium angustifolium, L. (*Onagraceae*) (Fireweed or Great Willow-Herb.)
    1403

Epilobium cephalostigma, Hausk. (*Onagraceae*) 1200

Epilobium hirsutum, L. (*Onagraceae*) 1772, 2655

Epilobium roseum (*Onagraceae*) 1403

Eragrostis cilianensis, Vignolo-Lutati (*Poaceae*) (stink grass) 657

Eragrostis curvula, (Schrad.) Nees (*Poaceae*) (Weeping Lovegrass) 2803,
    2804, 2805

Eragrostis ferruginea, Beauv. (*Poaceae*) 749, 750, 751, 753, 1199

Erigeron spp., L. (*Asteraceae*) 1404

Erigeron canadensis (*Asteraceae*) 1403

Erysimum cheiranthoides, L. (*Brassicaceae*) (Wormseed Mustard) 395

Erythrina indica, Lam. (*Fabaceae*) 248

Escholtzia californica, Cham. (*Papaveraceae*) (California Poppy) 765

Euglena gracilis, Klebs (*Euglenaceae*) (Alge) 252, 1133

Euonymus japonicus, L. (*Celastraceae*) (Spindle Tree) 1078, 1523

Euphorbia spp. L. (*Euphorbiaceae*) (Spurge) 1078

Euphorbia suprina (*Euphorbiaceae*) (Milk-purslane) 657

Faba vulgaris, Moench (*Fabaceae*) (Broad Bean) 2745

Fagopyrum esculentum, Moench. (*Polygonaceae*) (common buckwheat) 50, 952,
    1321, 1870, 2114, 2396, 2397, 2495, 2502, 2780, 2781, 2782

Fagopyrum vulgare (*Polygonaceae*) 2109

Fegatetla conica (Moss) 2967

Fern 107, 108, 109, 110, 111, 112, 113, 114, 115, 701, 1078, 2456, 2656

Festuca duriuscula, L. (*Poaceae*) (Hard Fescue) 1256

Festuca ovina, L. (*Poaceae*) (Sheeps Fescue) 395

Ficus elastica, Roxb. (*Moraceae*) (Rubber Plant) 948

Field beans (*Fabaceae*) 3059

Fig tree 666

Fir (*Pinaceae*) 850

Flax (*Linaceae*) 666

Four O'clock (*Nyctaginaceae*) 46

Fragaria spp., L. (*Rosaceae*) (Strawberry) 2273

Fragaria ananassa, Duchesne. (*Rosaceae*) (Strawberry) 1280, 2877.5

Fragaria vesca, L. (*Rosaceae*) (Strawberry) 425, 1692, 2393, 2767, 3060

Fragaria virginiana, Duchesne. (*Rosaceae*) (Virginian Strawberry) 2785, 2789

Fraxinus excelsior, L. (*Oleaceae*) (European Ash) 756, 2745

Fuchsia spp., L. (*Onagraceae*) 1128, 1129, 2386, 2873

Fuchsia hybrida, Voss (*Onagraceae*) (Common garden fuchsia) 761

Funaria (*Funariaceae*) (Moss) 1222, 2484

Funaria hygrometrica, Hedw. (*Funariaceae*) (Moss) 93, 211, 307, 503, 955, 956,
   1035, 1223, 1548, 1549.5, 2147, 2398, 2830, 2890, 3117, 3118, 3119, 3120, 3121

Fungi 1496

Galinsoga parviflora, Cav. (*Asteraceae*) 2495, 2846

Geranium spp. L. (*Geraniaceae*) (Cranesbill) 665, 666, 668, 1081

Gerbera spp., Cass. (*Asteraceae*) 1265

Geum canadense, Jacq. (*Rosaceae*) 2495

Gherkin (*Cucurbitaceae*) 602, 609, 725, 1246, 1761, 1767

Ginkgo biloba, L. (*Ginkgoaceae*) (Ginkgo) 901, 1246.5

Gladiolus spp., L. (*Iridaceae*) 1263, 1480

Glechoma hederacea, L. (*Lamiaceae*) (Ground Ivy) 756, 757

Gleditsia triacanthos, L. (*Fabaceae*) (Honey or Sweet Locust) 2746

Gloxinia hybrida (*Gesneriaceae*) 760

Glycine hispida, Maxim. (*Fabaceae*) 767, 2006

Glycine max, Merr. (*Fabaceae*) (Soybean) 357, 358, 526, 529, 1143, 1530,
   2482, 2515, 2516, 2877.5

Glycine soja, Sieb. & Zucc. (*Fabaceae*) (Soybean) 767, 2075

Gnaphalium lanceolatum (*Asteraceae*) 761

Gnaphalium silvaticum (*Asteraceae*) 1772

Gonyaulax polyedra (*Gonyaulaceae*) 2690

Gossypium herbaceum, L. (*Malvaceae*) (Levant Cotton) 381

Gossypium hirsutum, L. (*Malvaceae*) (Upland Cotton) 935, 936, 2125, 2543

Grapes (*Vitaceae*) 666, 667, 2102

Gymnogramma massoni (*Polypodiaceae*) (Fern) 1916

Gymnogramma sulfurea, Desv. (*Polypodiaceae*) (Fern) 321

Gyrodinium dorsum, Kofoid (*Gymnodiniaceae*) 691, 692, 693, 693.5, 694

Haplomitrium rotundifolium (*Haplomitriaceae*) (Liverwort) 3074

Haplopappus gracilis, (Nutt) Gray (*Asteraceae*) 884, 1519, 2211, 2642

Hedera amurensis, Hort. (*Araliaceae*) (Colchis Ivy) 767

Hedera colchica, Koch. var. arborea (*Araliaceae*) 767

Hedera Helix, L. (*Araliaceae*) (English Ivy) 2645, 2746

Helianthus annuus, L. (*Asteraceae*) (Common Sunflower) 143, 271, 528, 706,
    900, 920, 921, 921.2, 921.5, 948, 1572, 1598, 1966, 2538, 2745, 2746

Helianthus cucumerifolius, Torr. & Gray. (*Asteraceae*) (Cucumber-leaf Sun-
    flower) 2075, 2109, 2495, 3035

Helianthus tuberosus L. (*Asteraceae*) (Jerusalem artichoke) 464, 571, 572,
    573, 1481, 1525, 1999, 2000, 2746

Helichrysum bracteatum, Andr. (*Asteraceae*) (Strawflower) 763

Heliotropium peruvianum, L. (*Boraginaceae*) (Common Heliotrope) 761

Hemp (*Cannabinaceae*) 1340

Hibiscus spp. L. (*Malvaceae*) (Rose-Mallow) 529

Hibiscus Rosa-sinensis L. (*Malvaceae*) (Chinese Hibiscus) 81, 762

Hieracium Pilosella, L. (*Asteraceae*) (Mouse-ear Hawkweed) 756

Hippeastrum spp. (*Amaryllidaceae*) (Amaryllis) 1481

Holcus lanatus, L. (*Poaceae*) (Velvet-grass) 12, 395

Holcus sorghum var. sudanensis, Hitche. (*Poaceae*) (Sudan-Grass) 2109

Hordeum distichum, L. (*Poaceae*) (Barley) 68, 69, 70, 2645

Hordeum sativium, Pers. (*Poaceae*) (Barley) 1277

Hordeum vulgare, L. (*Poaceae*) (barley) 58, 120, 271, 356, 360, 408, 411,
    506, 507, 526, 529, 1079, 1143, 1303, 1377, 1437.5, 1530, 1532, 1533, 1569,
    1579.5, 1737, 1738, 1739, 1779, 1986, 1987, 2049, 2137, 2139, 2207, 2208,
    2295, 2370, 2482, 2723, 2725, 2727, 2731

Hormidium flaccidum (*Ulotrichaceae*) (green algae) 2417, 2484

Hortensia spp. (*Saxifragaceae*) (Hydrangea) 760

Hottonia palustris, L. (*Primulaceae*) (Featherfoil) 3123

Hyacinthus spp., L. (*Liliaceae*) (Hyacinth) 412, 1481

Hydrocharis morsus-ranae, L. (*Hydrocharitaceae*) (frog's-Bit) 1494, 2539, 2540, 2541

Hydrophyllum virginicum, L. (*Hydrophyllaceae*) (John's cabbage) 1628

Hyoscyamus desertorum, Asch. (*Solanaceae*) 2278

Hyoscyamus niger, L. (*Solanaceae*) (Henbane) 449, 497, 498, 499, 500, 526, 527, 582, 900, 1257, 1277, 1530, 1532, 1533, 1757, 1761, 1762, 1765, 2058, 2408, 2409, 2410, 2652, 2951, 2952, 2953

Hypericum japonicum, Thunb. (*Cluslaceae*) (St. Johnswort) 1200

Hypochoeris radicata, L. (*Asteraceae*) (Cat's ear) 765

Hyptis atrorubens (*Lamiaceae*) 2840

Hyptis suaveolens, Poit. (*Lamiaceae*) 3063

Iberis amara, L. (*Brassicaceae*) (Rocket candytuft) 763, 767, 769, 3090, 3091

Iberis Coronaria, Hort. (*Brassicaceae*) (Rocket candytuft) 2649, 2946

Iberis intermedia (*Brassicaceae*) 769

Iberis umbellata, L. (*Brassicaceae*) (Globe candytuft) 769

Impatiens Balsamina, L. (*Balsaminaceae*) (Garden balsam) 765, 1627, 1629, 3090, 3091, 3092

Impatiens tricornis (*Balsaminaceae*) 2194

Ipomoea Batatas, Lam. (*Convolvulaceae*) (Sweet potato) 1096, 1481

Ipomoea cairica, Sweet (*Convolvulaceae*) 81

Ipomoea coccinea, L. (*Convolvulaceae*) (Red Morning Glory) 590

Ipomoea Hederacea, (L.) Jacq. (*Convolvulaceae*) 507, 528

Ipomoea purpurea, (L.) Lam. (*Convolvulaceae*) (Common Morning Glory) 459, 900, 2746

Ipomoea Quamoclit, L. (*Convolvulaceae*) 81

Iris spp., L. (*Iridaceae*) 1481

Jussiaea peruviana (*Onagraceae*) 2108

Jussiaea suffruticosa, L. (*Onagraceae*) 45, 3062, 3064

Kalanchoë spp., Adans. (*Crassulaceae*) 2388

Kalanchoë blossfeldiana, v. Poellnitz. (*Crssulaceae*) 293, 311, 580, 581, 590, 708, 709, 712, 714, 723, 947, 1318, 1757, 2163, 2164, 2165, 2166, 2167, 2168, 2169, 2172, 2459, 2877.5, 2932

Kalanchoë coccinea, Welw. (*Crassulaceae*) 765

Kalanchoë laciniata, DC. (*Crassulaceae*) 765

Kalanchoë rotundifolia, Haw. (*Crassulaceae*) 363

Kalanchoë thyrsiflora (*Crassulaceae*) 765

Kidney bean   (*Fabaceae*)   1354, 1927, 2039, 2822, 2892, 2894, 2899, 2904

Kochia scoparia, Schrad. (*Chenopodiaceae*) (Summer-Cypress) 657

Kochia trichophylla, Voss. (*Chenopodiaceae*) 2190

Lactobacterium (Bacteria) 2291

Lactuca sativa, L. (*Asteraceae*) (Lettuce) 1, 2, 4, 118, 119, 134, 135, 174,
178, 188, 189, 220, 222, 316, 317, 318, 322, 434, 500, 501, 507, 578, 584,
589, 627, 682, 703, 765, 905, 906, 909, 914, 915, 916, 917, 923, 960, 961,
962, 963, 964, 965, 966, 967, 968, 970, 994, 1051, 1096, 1153, 1154, 1155,
1156, 1157, 1158, 1178, 1179, 1180, 1181, 1184, 1186, 1208, 1282, 1283, 1284,
1379, 1381, 1420, 1445, 1449, 1530, 1559, 1560, 1618, 1620, 1649, 1665, 1679,
1681, 1726, 1727, 1728, 1729, 1730, 1745, 1746, 1826, 1846, 1849, 1861, 1869,
1881, 1954, 1955, 1956, 1970, 1978, 1979, 2049, 2241, 2252, 2253, 2255, 2277,
2390, 2391, 2392, 2394, 2420, 2438, 2479, 2517, 2518, 2555, 2576, 2577, 2588,
2649, 2653, 2672, 2673, 2674, 2676, 2743, 2783, 2789, 2799, 2824, 2850, 2857,
2858, 2859, 2938, 2939, 2940, 2945, 3031

Lactuca scariola, L. (*Asteraceae*) (Prickly Lettuce) 906, 1621, 1624

Lamium album, L. (*Lamiaceae*) (Snowflake) 900

Lamium amplexicaule, L. (*Lamiaceae*) (henbit) 1253

Larch (*Pinaceae*) 910

Larix decidua, Mill. (*Pinaceae*) (European Larch) 1550

Larix europea, DC. (*Pinaceae*) (European Larch) 2645

Larix leptolepis, Gord. (*Pinaceae*) (Japanese Larch) 1757

Lathyrus spp. L. (*Fabaceae*) 900

Laurel (*Lauraceae*) 1078

Lemna spp. L. (*Lemnaceae*) 1576

Lemna gibba (*Lemnaceae*) 405, 620, 1092, 1115, 1194, 1195, 1286, 1292, 1294,
1296, 1297, 1829, 2042, 2267

Lemna minor, L. (*Lemnaceae*) 393, 408, 727, 728, 1084, 1087, 1088, 1098, 1115,
2263, 2264, 2265, 2266, 2267, 2268, 2269, 2270

Lemna paucicostato (*Lemnaceae*) 904, 1115

Lemna perpusilla, Torr. (*Lemnaceae*) 620, 931, 933, 934, 1089, 1092, 1094,
1095, 1100, 1102, 1108, 1109, 1110, 1111, 1112, 1113, 1115, 1118, 1297, 1389,
1406, 2015, 2151, 2266, 2267, 2719

Lemna trisulca, L. (*Lemnaceae*) 212, 1002, 2977, 2978, 3107, 3109, 3111, 3113,
3114, 3116, 3122, 3123

Lemon (*Rutaceae*) 1925

Lens culinaris, Medic. (*Fabaceae*) (Lentil) 2086

Lepidium campestre, (L.) R. Br. (*Brassicaceae*) (field pepperweed) 2738, 2789

Lepidium densiflorum, Schrad. (*Brassicaceae*) 2784

Lepidium Draba (*Brassicaceae*) 763, 769

Lepidium sativum, L. (*Brassicaceae*) (Garden-Cress) 395, 1174, 1818, 1923, 2745, 2746

Lepidium virinicum, L. (*Brassicaceae*) (Virginia pepperweed) 245, 1051, 2736, 2740, 2743, 2783, 2784, 2785, 2788, 2789, 2799

Leptadenia pyrotechnica (*Asclepiadaceae*) 2481

Lettuce (*Asteraceae*) 3, 46, 90, 92, 117, 171, 257, 296, 299, 631, 632, 633, 634, 635, 636, 640, 641, 644, 666, 668, 674, 675, 676, 677, 678, 679, 680, 830, 831, 832, 847, 848, 850, 865, 912, 913, 927, 1078, 1182, 1183, 1209, 1281, 1378, 1383, 1384, 1421, 1437, 1461, 1564, 1666, 1667, 1680, 1712, 1721, 1791, 1920, 1921, 1953, 2106, 2107, 2272, 2388, 2483, 2489, 2509, 2550, 2608, 2609, 2671, 2797, 2823, 2865, 2875, 2971, 2980, 2981

Leucaena glauca Benth. (*Fabaceae*) (White Popinae) 1104

Libertia formosa, Graham (*Iridaceae*) 1204

Lilac (*Oleaceae*) 1469

Lilium longiflorim, Thunb. (*Liliaceae*) (Easter lily) 1720, 2233, 2234, 2235, 3015

Lilium superbum, L. (*Liliaceae*) (Turk's-cap-lily) 1481

Linum usitatissimum, L. (*Linaceae*) (flax) 261, 395, 2320

Lobelia spp., L. (*Campanulaceae*) 2384, 2386

Lobelia Dortmanna, L. (*Campanulaceae*) 3

Lobelia Erinus, L. (*Campanulaceae*) 466, 765, 1408

Loblolly pine (*Pinaceae*) 1535

Loiseleuria procumbens, Desv. (*Ericaeae*) (Alpine-Azalea) 139

Lolium spp., L. (*Poaceae*) (Rye Grass) 2864, 2868, 2873

Lolium italicum, A. Br. (*Poaceae*) (Italian Rye-Grass) 12

Lolium perenne, L. (*Poaceae*) (Perennial Rye-Grass) 1256

Lolium temulentum, L. (*Poaceae*) (darnel) 181, 624, 626, 1129, 1130, 1533, 2866

Lomaria Spicant (*Polypodiaceae*) 321

Lombardy poplar (*Salicaceae*) 2488

Lunularia cruciata L. (*Marchantiaceae*) 713, 2461, 2832, 3029

Lunularia Vulgaris (*Marchantiaceae*) 2967

Lupine (*Fabaceae*) 3059

Lupinus alba L. (*Fabaceae*) (White Lupine) 5, 6, 7, 8, 10, 11, 1086, 1717, 1718, 2745, 3059

Lychnis alba, Mill. (*Caryophyllaceae*) (White cockle) 2738

Lycopersicon esculentum, Mill. (*Solanaceae*) (Tomato) 367, 507, 529, 578, 1096, 1385, 1530, 1908, 2109, 2495, 2658, 2860, 3038, 3077

Lycopus Europaeus, L. (*Lamiaceae*) 762, 767

Lygodium japonicum, Swartz. (*Schizaeaceae*) 1040

Lysimachia mauritiana, Lam. (*Primulaceae*) 1200

Lythrum Salicaria, L. (*Lythraceae*) (Spike or Purple Loosestrite) 1466, 1772, 2240, 2242, 2245, 2775

Maize (*Poaceae*) 257, 334, 407, 666, 1059, 1140, 1431, 2161, 2195, 2381.5, 2669

Malcolmia maritima, R. Br. (*Brassicaceae*) (Virginian stock) 763, 769

Malus spp., Mill. (*Rosaceae*) (Apple) 1096

Marchantia polymorpha, L. (*Marchantiaceae*) (Liverwort) 211, 469, 470, 472, 473, 484, 689, 710, 713, 714, 715, 716, 717, 718, 719, 720, 721, 723, 1191, 1997, 1998, 2637, 2746, 2845, 2967

Marchantia polyrhiza 2387, 2388, 2457

Marigold (*Asteraceae*) 1081

Marsilea quadrifolia, L. (*Marsileaceae*) 1123, 2006

Marsilea vestita (*Marsileaceae*) 829, 1521, 1522

Matricaria Chamomilla, L. (*Asteraceae*) (Sweet False Chamomile) 765, 900, 2333

Matricaria inodora, L. (*Asteraceae*) (Scentless False Chamomile) 765

Matteuccia struthiopteris, (L.) Todaro (*Polypodiaceae*) (Fern) 1242

Matthiola annua, Sweet (*Brassicaceae*) (Ten Weeks or Intermediate Stock) 761

Matthiola incana, R. Br. (*Brassicaceae*) (Stock) 769, 1174, 3034

Medinilla magnifica, Lindl. (*Melastomataceae*) 762

Melianthus major, L. (*Melianthaceae*) 459

Melilotus spp., Mill. (*Fabaceae*) 1530

Melilotus alba, Desr. (*Fabaceae*) (Sweet clover) 1329, 3030

Melinis minutiflora, Beauv. (*Poaceae*) (Molasses Grass) 2846

Menispermum cocculus, L. (*Memispermaceae*) (Moonseed) 2746

Mentha silvestris, L. (*Lamiaceae*) (Mint) 763

Mentha piperita, L. (*Lamiaceae*) (Peppermint) 511

Mentha rotundifolia, Huds. (*Lamiaceae*) (Round-leaved Mint) 762

Mentzelia aspera, L. (*Loasaceae*) 2846

Mesocarpus, Hassall (*Chlorophyceae*) (Algae) 2484

Mesotaenium caldariorum (*Mesotaeniaceae*) (green algae) 520, 521, 522, 523, 824, 825, 983, 1000, 2733

Mespilus germanica, L. (*Rosaceae*) 2645

Microcystis aeruginosa (*Chroococcaceae*) (Blue-green Algae) 1030

Mice 866

Millet (*Poaceae*) 527, 1340, 2513, 2661

Milo (*Poaceae*) 534, 539, 1528

Mimosa spp., L. (*Fabaceae*) 665

Mimosa invisa (*Fabaceae*) 756

Mimosa pudica, L. (*Fabaceae*) (Sensitive plant) 20, 121, 248, 325, 329, 686, 687, 688, 1230, 1280, 1717, 1718, 2006, 2229, 2362, 2363, 2364, 2411, 2485, 2486, 3023

Mimulus luteus, L. (*Scrophulariaceae*) 765, 1625

Mirabilis jalapa, L. (*Nyctaginaceae*) (Four-o-clocks) 1365, 1366, 1761, 1762, 2075, 2109, 2836

Mnium sp. (*Mniaceae*) (Moss) 651

Mnium affine, Bland. (*Mniaceae*) (Moss) 835

Mnium cuspidatum, Hedw. (*Mniaceae*) 3123

Mnium hornum, Hedw. (*Mniaceae*) (Moss) 836

Mnium medium, Bry. Eur. (*Mniaceae*) (Moss) 3123

Mnium undulatum, (L.) Weis (*Mniaceae*) (Moss) 836, 3112, 3115

Moss 93, 953, 954, 955, 2456, 2656

Mougeotia, spp. (*Zygnemataceae*) (green alga) 182, 659, 661, 685, 976, 977, 978, 980, 981, 984, 987, 988, 991, 992, 999, 1004, 1006, 1007, 1008, 1011, 1014, 1015, 1016, 1017, 1019, 1022, 1023, 1024, 1026.5, 1027, 1221, 1940, 1941, 1984, 1985, 2418, 2419, 2421, 2422, 2423, 2424, 2425, 2426, 2427, 2428, 2430, 2432, 2433, 2484, 2924, 2925, 2926, 2927, 2928, 2976, 2977, 2978, 2979, 2979.5

Mung bean (*Fabaceae*) 314, 957, 1230, 2173, 2175, 2176, 2324, 2721, 2722

Musa sapientium, L. (*Musaceae*) (banana) 1096

Mustard (*Brassicaceae*) 816, 1209, 1674, 2753

Myosotis hispida (*Boraginaceae*) 1916

Myosotis palustris, Lam. (*Boraginaceae*) (True Forget-Me-Not) 1630

Myricaria germanica, Desy. (*Tamaricaceae*) (false tamarisk) 1402

Myrthus moschata (*Myrtaceae*) 3091, 3092

Narcissus spp., L. (*Amaryllidaceae*) 459, 1481

Nasturtium spp., L. (*Tropaeolaceae*) 1081

Nasturtium silvestre (*Brassicaceae*) 765, 769

Nemophila insignis, Dougl. (*Hydrophyllaceae*) 170, 171, 173, 188, 1545, 1649,
    1650, 1651, 1657, 1658, 1676, 2240, 2245, 2255, 2256, 2260, 2588, 2935, 2939,
    2940

Nephrolepis exaltata, Schott. (*Polypodiaceae*) (Sword fern) 321

Neslea paniculata, (L.) Desv. (*Brassicaceae*) (Ball Mustard) 763, 769

Neurospora crassa 1416

Nicotiana spp., L. (*Solanaceae*) 1400

Nicotiana rustica, L. (*Solanaceae*) (Wild Tobacco) 85, 838, 1408, 1516, 1579.5

Nicotiana silvestris, Spegazzini & Comes (*Solanaceae*) 2896, 2897

Nicotiana tabacum, L. (*Solanaceae*) (Tobacco) 49, 71, 116, 589, 838, 921,
    921.5, 1331, 1332, 1333, 1334, 1335, 1336, 1337, 1466, 1516, 1523, 1530, 1772,
    2109, 2212, 2495, 2497, 2670, 2783, 2785, 2789, 2815, 2820, 2896, 2897

Nicotiana Tabacum var. macrophylla, Shrank (*Solanaceae*) 395

Nidularium fulgens, Lem. (*Bromeliaceae*) 538

Nigella, spp., L. (*Ranunculaceae*) (Fennel-Flower) 1196, 1404

Nigella damascena, L. (*Ranunculaceae*) (Love-in-a-Mist) 1200, 1400, 1648,
    1649, 1772

Nigella sativa (*Ranunculaceae*) 1400, 1402, 1772

Nitella pulchella (*Characeae*) (Algae) 1641

Oats (*Poaceae*) 16, 34, 35, 36, 37, 57, 267, 270, 347, 348, 389, 496, 799, 817,
    967, 1099, 1436, 1551, 1639, 1782, 1793, 2003, 2348, 2384, 2635, 2669, 2753,
    2968, 2969, 3040, 3059

Ocimum americanum, L. (*Lamiaceae*) 2851

Ocimum Basilicum, L. (*Lamiaceae*) (Common Basil) 763

Ocymum viride (*Lamiaceae*) 3091, 3092

Oenothera berteriana (*Onagraceae*) 922

Oenothera biennis, L. (*Onagraceae*) (Common Evening Primrose) 2745, 2789

Oenothera lamarckiana, De Vries (*Onagraceae*) 748

Oenothera odorata, Jacq. (*Onagraceae*) 922

Oil perilla 1925

Onoclea sensibilis, L.　(*Polypodiaceae*)　(Sensitive-fern)　663, 1798, 1799, 1800, 1801, 1802, 1803, 1804, 1805, 1806, 1807, 1811, 2812, 2813

Ononis sicula, Guss.　(*Fabaceae*)　904

Opuntia cochenillifera, (L.) Mill.　(*Cactaceae*)　2047

Oryza sativa, L.　(*Poaceae*)　(Rice)　199, 408, 411, 460, 783, 786, 788, 1178, 1189, 1190, 1355, 1716, 1808, 1813, 1814, 2034, 2060, 2099, 2100, 2101, 2139, 2482, 2494, 2698

Oryzopsis miliacea, Benth. & Hook　(*Poaceae*)　(Mountain Rice)　1975

Osmunda cinnamomea, L.　(*Osmundaceae*)　(Cinnamon-fern)　929, 1152, 1874

Osmunda Claytoniana, L.　(*Osmundaceae*)　(Interrupted fern)　321, 380, 1874

Osmunda regalis, Tryon　(*Osmundaceae*)　1409, 2045, 2126, 2639

Oxalis spp., L.　(*Oxalidaceae*)　(Wood-Sorrel)　2318

Oxalis Acetosella, L.　(*Oxalidaceae*)　103

Oxalis corniculata, L.　(*Oxalidaceae*)　2006

Oxalis esculenta　(*Oxalidaceae*)　2386

Oxalis lasiandra, Zucc.　(*Oxalidaceae*)　2047

Oxalis multiflora, Jacq.　(*Oxalidaceae*)　3091, 3092

Oxalis stricta, L.　(*Oxalidaceae*)　1637, 2006

Paeonia officinalis, L.　(*Ranunculaceae*)　(Peony)　2745

Palms spp.　(*Arecaceae*)　1078

Panicum dichotomiflorum, Michx.　(*Poaceae*)　(Fall panicum)　2738

Pansy　(*Violaceae*)　3032, 3033

Papaver somniferum, L.　(*Papaveraceae*)　(Opium Poppy)　395

Pastinaca sativa, L.　(*Apiaceae*)　(Parsnip)　1096, 1480, 1481, 1482, 2734

Paulownia spp., Sieb. & Zucc.　(*Scrophulariaceae*)　242

Paulownia tomentosa, Steud.　(*Scrophulariaceae*)　974, 2791

Pea　(*Fabaceae*)　3, 30, 31, 123, 124, 126, 128, 154, 200, 201, 202, 203, 205, 519, 660.5, 665, 666, 771, 772, 773, 776, 793, 794, 795, 796, 797, 799, 803, 816, 855, 869, 872, 877, 880, 1076, 1077, 1083, 1084, 1086, 1090, 1097, 1099, 1140, 1224, 1304, 1340, 1446, 1448, 1564, 1595, 1626, 1731, 1775, 1981, 1982, 2195, 2542, 2554, 2556, 2580, 2582, 2594, 2669, 2753, 2768, 2994, 2996

Peach　(*Rosaceae*)　1269

Peanut　(*Fabaceae*)　873

Pear　(*Rosaceae*)　665

Pelargonium spp., L'Her.　(*Geraniaceae*)　(Storksbill)　1078, 2384

Pelargonium zonale, Ait.　(*Geraniaceae*)　(Horseshoe Geranium)　948

Pellia epiphylla (*Urticaceae*) 211, 2746, 2967

Pennisetum setosum, (Sw.) (L.) Rioh. (*Poaceae*) 2846

Peperomia clusiaefolia (*Piperaceae*) 2154

Pepper 1959

Perilla spp., L. (*Lamiaceae*) 137, 666, 1927, 1928, 1929, 1959

Perilla crispa (Benth.) Deane (*Lamiaceae*) 2984

Perilla frutescens, (L.) Britt. (*Lamiaceae*) 1530

Perilla nankinensis, Bailey (*Lamiaceae*) 765, 886, 2877.5

Perilla ocymoides, L. (*Lamiaceae*) 297, 767, 1435, 1622

Perilla ocymoides var. nankinensis, Voss (*Lamiaceae*) 767

Persea americana, Mill. (*Lauraceae*) (Avocado) 1096

Petroselinum hortense, Hoffm. (*Apiaceae*) (Parsley) 2985, 2986, 2987,
    2988, 2990, 2992, 2993

Petunia sp., Juss. (*Solanaceae*) (Petunia) 46, 47, 367, 900, 1129, 1762,
    2386, 2631, 2838

Petunia grandiflora (*Solanaceae*) (Petunia) 627

Petunia hybrida, Vilm. (*Solanaceae*) (Common Garden Petunia) 1532, 1533, 2029,
    2109, 2623, 2632, 2633

Petunia multiflora (*Solanaceae*) (Petunia) 627

Phacelia tanacetifolia, Benth. (*Hydrophyllaceae*) 260, 385, 578, 1042, 1043,
    1649, 1676, 1772, 2214, 2216, 2237, 2238, 2239, 2240, 2243, 2244, 2245, 2252,
    2256, 2454, 2455, 2638

Phalaris canariensis, L. (*Poaceae*) (Canary-grass) 395, 1717, 1718

Pharbitis nil, Roth. (*Convolvulaceae*) (Japanese Morning Glory) 234, 628, 708,
    711, 714, 738, 1139, 1177, 1261, 1262, 1263, 1264, 1267, 1272, 1277, 1279,
    1280, 1391, 1392, 1398, 1472, 1473, 1474, 1474.5, 1713, 1714, 1830, 1961,
    1962, 1963, 1964, 2027, 2049, 2053, 2340, 2699, 2700, 2701, 2702, 2703, 2704,
    2705, 2707, 2708, 2709, 2710, 2711, 2712, 2713, 2714, 2715, 2748, 2751, 3095

Phaseolus spp., L. (*Fabaceae*) (Bean) 2318

Phaseolus acutifoluis, Gray (*Fabaceae*) (Butter pea) 1562

Phaseolus aureus, Roxb. (*Fabaceae*) (Mung bean) 399, 507, 1129, 1130, 1228,
    1232, 1234, 1235, 1236, 1237, 1238, 2008, 2148, 2174, 2323, 2324, 2325, 2326,
    2723, 2724, 2726, 2727, 2728, 2729, 2729.5, 2730, 2732, 2808, 2809, 3085,
    3086, 3087

Phaseolus coccineus, L. (*Fabaceae*) (Scarlet Runner Bean) 1143

Phaseolus multiflorus, (Willd) Lam. (*Fabaceae*) (Scarlet Runner Bean) 259, 300, 301, 306, 313, 1572, 1615, 1616, 1717, 1718, 2362, 2364, 2654, 2745, 2819

Phaseolus mungo, L. (*Fabaceae*) (Black Gram) 19

Phaseolus vulgaris, L. (*Fabaceae*) (Common Bean, Kidney Bean) 22, 23, 143, 253, 254, 255, 271, 373, 457, 458, 471, 474, 475, 476, 477, 478, 479, 480, 481, 482, 485, 486, 487, 488, 489, 490, 491, 492, 501, 507, 524, 525, 527, 528, 531, 533, 535, 574, 589, 655, 658, 660, 671, 672, 673, 683, 874, 875, 876, 883, 885, 975, 1045, 1119, 1131, 1132, 1140, 1141, 1143, 1299, 1300, 1301, 1302, 1353, 1356, 1370, 1414, 1415, 1417, 1418, 1422, 1423, 1424, 1425, 1426, 1427, 1428, 1429, 1430, 1432, 1441, 1447, 1597, 1598, 1599, 1608, 1609, 1610, 1612, 1614, 1619, 1646, 1661, 1699, 1754, 1810, 1922, 1960, 2006, 2072, 2087, 2088, 2121, 2124, 2125, 2142, 2143, 2197, 2198, 2199, 2236, 2252, 2298, 2299, 2300, 2301, 2362, 2364, 2501, 2546, 2547, 2548, 2563, 2591, 2606, 2607, 2669, 2898, 3002, 3003, 3036, 3038, 3039, 3049, 3055

Phegopteris effusa (*Polypodiaceae*) 211

Philadelphus coronarius, L. (*Saxifragaceae*) (Mock-orange) 2645

Phleum pratense, L. (*Poaceae*) (Timothy) 1256, 2600

Physalis alkekengi, (L.) Pers. (*Solanaceae*) (Chinese Lantern-Plant) 2682

Physalis Franchetti, Hort. (*Solanaceae*) 75

Physcomitrium pyriforme, Brid. (*Funariaceae*) (Moss) 956, 1969, 1970

Physcomitrium turbinatum, (Mx.) Brid. (*Funariaceae*) (Moss) 1971, 1972, 1973, 1974

Phycomyces 2507

Phyteuma Scheuchzeri, All. (*Campanulaceae*) 756, 758

Phytolacca decandra, L. (*Phytolaccaceae*) (Pokeweed) 2080

Picea abies (L.) Karst. (*Pinaceae*) (Norway Spruce) 84, 1129, 2252, 2389

Picea excelsa, Link. (*Pinaceae*) (Norway Spruce) 1550, 2645

Picea glehnii, Mast. (*Pinaceae*) (Saghalin Spruce) 54

Pig Kidney 384, 867

Pine (*Pinaceae*) 850

Pinguicula vulgaris, L. (*Lentibulariaceae*) (Common Butterwort) 1402, 1404

Pinus densiflora, Sieb. & Zucc. (*Pinaceae*) (Japanese Red Pine) 974, 1203

Pinus merkussii, Jungh. & de Vries (*Pinaceae*) 901

Pinus mughus, Scop. (*Pinaceae*) 2050

Pinus nigra, Arnold (*Pinaceae*) (Austrian Pine) 901, 2043

Pinus nigra var. austriaca, Aschers. & Graebn. (*Pinaceae*) 1545

Pinus palustris, Mill. (*Pinaceae*) (Long-leaf pine) 1751, 2776, 2777

Pinus ponderosa, Dougl. (*Pinaceae*) (Western Yellow Pine, Arizona Pine) 529

Pinus strobus, L. (*Pinaceae*) (White Pine) 2801

Pinus sylvestris L. (*Pinaceae*) (Scotch Pine) 583, 901, 910, 911, 1478, 1479,
  2009, 2010, 2011, 2012, 2655

Pinus Taeda L. (*Pinaceae*) (Loblolly Pine) 529, 1752, 2495, 2798, 2801

Pinus Thunbergii, Parl. (*Pinaceae*) (Japanese Black Pine) 54, 56, 974, 1203,
  3069

Pinus virginiana, Mill. (*Pinaceae*) (Scrub Pine) 2800

Pirus aucuparia, Gaertner (*Rosaceae*) (European Mountain-Ash) 900

Pirus malus L. (*Rosaceae*) (Apple) 2567

Pisum arvense, L. (*Fabaceae*) (Field Pea) 1254, 1255

Pisum sativum, L. (*Fabaceae*) (pea) 19, 32, 33, 60, 125, 127, 129, 143, 148,
  249, 250, 251, 271, 287, 398, 399, 400, 401, 402, 403, 408, 585, 586, 587,
  588, 646, 647, 696, 697, 698, 699, 706, 774, 775, 777, 778, 782, 785, 851,
  852, 853, 870, 871, 878, 900, 926, 950, 951, 1001, 1010, 1013, 1020, 1106,
  1138, 1143, 1149, 1175, 1225, 1227, 1229, 1233, 1245, 1306, 1307, 1307.5,
  1309, 1357, 1364, 1366, 1367, 1368, 1369, 1370, 1371, 1372, 1374, 1375,
  1376, 1387, 1447, 1450, 1451, 1452, 1453, 1457, 1489, 1558, 1571, 1574, 1581,
  1596, 1598, 1600, 1601, 1602, 1603, 1606, 1609, 1659, 1662, 1732, 1733, 1735,
  1775, 1784, 1785, 1826, 1942, 1944, 1980, 1983, 1996, 2036, 2037, 2046, 2056,
  2076, 2117, 2137, 2152, 2153, 2196, 2197, 2198, 2199, 2201, 2219, 2221, 2252,
  2280, 2281, 2283, 2284, 2312, 2313, 2314, 2315, 2316, 2327, 2328, 2329, 2330,
  2331, 2332, 2364, 2464, 2465, 2542, 2558, 2559, 2578, 2579, 2581, 2583, 2584,
  2585, 2586, 2590, 2591, 2597, 2598, 2644, 2645, 2647, 2648, 2656.5, 2663,
  2664, 2693, 2734, 2748, 2751, 2769, 2770, 2771, 2772, 2777, 2810, 2811, 2818,
  2860, 2871, 2889, 2905, 2931, 3038

Plantago hirtella (*Plantaginaceae*) (Plantain) 1127

Plantago major L. (*Plantaginaceae*) (Common Plantain) 816, 2218, 2840

Plantago minor (*Plantaginaceae*) 816

Platycerium alcicorne, Desw. (*Polypodiaceae*) 2045

Plum (*Rosaceae*) 665

Poa, annua, L. (*Poaceae*) (Annual Bluegrass) 1408

Poa nemoralis, L. (*Poaceae*) (Wood Meadow-Grass) 395, 1256

Poa Pratensis, L. (*Poaceae*) (Kentucky Bluegrass) 91, 1073, 1256, 1400, 1401, 1402, 1403, 2806

Poa trivialis, L. (*Poaceae*) (Rough-Stalked Meadow Grass) 1256

Podophyllum peltatum, L. (*Berberidaceae*) (May Apple) 1481

Pohlia nutans, (Hedev.) Lindb. (*Bryaceae*) (Moss) 1815, 1816, 1817

Poinciana Gilliesi, Hook. (*Fabaceae*) 1104

Polygonatum odoratum (*Liliaceae*) 3123

Polygonum fagopydum, L. (*Polygonaceae*) 2745

Polygonum sieboldii, de Vriese. (*Polygonaceae*) (Japanese Knotweed or Mexican-Bamboo) 2080

Polypodium Reinwardtii (*Polypodiaceae*) 321

Polypodium repens (*Polypodiaceae*) 211

Polypodium rubrium (*Polypodiaceae*) 321

Polypodium vulgare L. (*Polypodiaceae*) (Wall fern) 2045, 2126, 2655

Polytricadelphus magellanicus (*Polytrichaceae*) 2351

Polytrichum commune, Hedw. (*Polytrichaceae*) 928, 1338, 2351

Polytrichum formosum, Hedw. (*Polytrichaceae*) 2351

Populus grandifolia (*Salicaceae*) 2080

Populus nigra, L. (*Salicaceae*) (Black poplar) 756, 757

Populus x robusta 1080

Porophyllum lanceolatum, DC (*Asteraceae*) 656

Porphyra tenera (*Bangiaceae*) (Red alga) 541, 2215

Portulaca grandiflora, Hook. (*Portulacaceae*) (Rose moss) 1320, 1365

Portulaca oleracea L. (*Portulacaceae*) (Common purslane) 566, 904, 908, 2738, 2840, 2846

Potamogeton natans, L. (*Potamogetonaceae*) 756, 757

Potamogeton crispus, L. (*Potamogetonaceae*) (Pondweed) 493, 3123

Potatoes (*Solanaceae*) 25, 2384, 2386, 2835, 2943, 3059

Potentilla norvegica, L. (*Rosaceae*) 2735, 2736

Preissia commutata (*Marchantiaceae*) (Liverwort) 2746

Prenanthes purpurea (*Asteraceae*) 1772

Primrose (*Primulaceae*) 760

Primula obconica, Hance. (*Primulaceae*) 760, 762

Protosiphon botryoides, Klebs (*Protosiphonaceae*) (green algae) 361, 362, 568, 2035, 2764, 2765

Prunus spp., L. (*Rosaceae*) (plum) 1096

Prunus cerasus, L. (*Rosaceae*) (Sour cherry) 2645

Prunus laurocerasus, L. (*Rosaceae*) (Common Cherry-Laurel) 948

Prunus padus, L. (*Rosaceae*) (European bird cherry) 2645

Prunus persica (L.) Stokes. (*Rosaceae*) (Peach) 611, 612, 613, 669, 1096

Prunus triloba, Lindl. (*Rosaceae*) (Flowering Almond) 762

Pseudomonas 2291

Pseudomonas fluorescens (Bacterium) 2290

Pseudotsuga menziesii, (Mirb.) Franco (*Pinaceae*) (Douglas fir) 512, 2224, 2833

Pteridium aquilinum, (L.) Kuhn (*Polypodiaceae*) 465, 2045, 2178, 2179, 2180, 2182, 2184, 2568, 2746

Pteris argyrea, Moore (*Polypodiaceae*) 321

Pteris cretica, L. (*Polypodiaceae*) 321

Pteris flabellata (*Polypodiaceae*) 321

Pteris longifolia, L. (*Polypodiaceae*) 380, 1409, 2636, 2746

Pteris serrulata, L. (*Polypodiaceae*) 211, 321

Pteris tremula, R. Br. (*Polypodiaceae*) 321

Pteris vespertilionis (*Polypodiaceae*) 211

Pteris vittata, L. (*Polypodiaceae*) (fern) 211, 782.5, 1201, 1202, 1339, 2665, 2666, 2667, 2668

Pumpkin (*Cucurbitaceae*) 194, 2155, 2379

Pyracantha coccinea, Roem. (*Rosaceae*) (fiery thorn) 3022

Pyrus spp., L. (*Rosaceae*) (Pear) 1096

Pyrus malus, L. (*Rosaceae*) (Apple) 48, 2568

Quercus peduncalata, Ehrh. (*Fagaceae*) (English Oak) 2080, 2745

Quesnelia lateralis (*Brumeliaceae*) 538

Radish (*Brassicaceae*) 257, 854, 1078, 1140, 1162, 1209, 1437, 1654, 1959, 2272, 2489, 2669

Raimannia Oenotheren (*Onagraceae*) 1543

Ranunculus bulbosus, L. (*Ranunculaceae*) (Bulbous Buttercup) 900

Raphanus praecox minor (*Brassicaceae*) 1209

Raphanus sativus, L. (*Brassicaceae*) (radish) 99, 100, 101, 102, 395, 589, 648, 1096, 1143, 1161, 1163, 1164, 1165, 1200, 1433, 1434, 1545, 1546, 1569, 1649, 1655, 1656, 1658, 2114, 2388, 2512

Rat 860, 861, 863, 1185

Reboulia hemisphasrica, (L.) Raddi (*Marchantiaceae*) 2746

Red cabbage (*Brassicaceae*) 539, 1287

Reseda odorata, L. (*Resedaceae*) (Common Mignionette) 1174, 1916

Rhododendron ferrugineum L. (*Ericaceae*) 141

Rhododendron luteum, Sweet (*Ericaceae*) 2050

Rhodotypos Kerriodes, Seib. & Zucc. (*Rosaceae*) (Jetbead) 669

Rice (*Poaceae*) 1263, 1639, 1640, 2544

Ricinus communis, L. (*Euphorbiaceae*) (Castor-Bean) 948

Ricinus communis L. var. sanquineus (*Euphorbiaceae*) (Castor Bean) 2745

Robinia Pseudoacacia, L. (*Fabaceae*) (Black Locust) 258, 2006

Rosa canina, L. (*Rosaceae*) (Dog Rose) 900

Rose (*Rosaceae*) 1269

Roupala corcovadensia, Hort. (*Proteaceae*) 762

Rubus fructicosus, Hort. (*Rosaceae*) 2745

Rudbeckia bicolor, Nutt. (*Asteraceae*) 24

Rudbeckia speciosa, Wenderoth (*Asteraceae*) 761

Ruellia tuberosa, L. (*Acanthaceae*) 382, 2840, 2846

Rumex Acetosa, L. (*Polygonaceae*) (Garden sorrel) 811

Rumex alpinus, L. (*Polygonaceae*) 138, 140, 1545

Rumex conglomeratus, Murr. (*Polygonaceae*) 811

Rumex crispus, L. (*Polygonaceae*) (Curly dock or yellow dock) 811, 1554, 1555, 1556, 1557, 2742, 2744

Rumex hydrolapathum, Huds. (*Polygonaceae*) 811

Rumex obtusifolius L. (*Polygonaceae*) (Broadleaf dock) 1198, 2736, 2740, 2849, 2855, 2856

Rumex patientia, L. (*Polygonaceae*) (Patience Dock) 2372

Rye (*Poaceae*) 652, 653, 654, 733, 817, 1124, 1551, 1639, 1977, 2384, 2779, 2888

Rye grass (*Poaceae*) 665

Saccharomyces (yeast) 2291

Saccharum officinarum, L. (*Poaceae*) (Sugar Cane) 1530

Sagina maritima (*Caryophyllaceae*) 2655

Sagina nodosa, (L.) Fenzl. (*Caryophyllaceae*) 2655

Sagina procumbens, L. (*Caryophyllaceae*) 2655

Sagittaria sagittifolia, L. (*Alismaceae*) (Old-World Arrowhead) 756, 757

Sagittaria subulata, Buchenau. (*Alismaceae*) 756, 757

Saguaro cactus (*Cactaceae*) (Carnegiea gigantea, Britt. & Rose Saguaro or Giant cactus) 26, 1514

Salix babylonica, L. (*Salicaceae*) (weeping willow) 1565, 1566

Salix cinerea, L. (*Salicaceae*) (Gray willow) 2655

Salix repens, L. (*Salicaceae*) (Creeping willow) 2655

Salvia spp., L. (*Lamiaceae*) (Sage) 46, 667, 2388

Salvia occidentalis (*Lamiaceae*) 1756, 1757, 1760, 1762, 1763, 1764, 1765, 2838, 2839

Salvia runcinata (*Lamiaceae*) 761

Salvia splendens, Sello (*Lamiaceae*) (Scarlet Sage) 1530, 3035, 3037

Samanea saman, Merr. (*Fabaceae*) (Rain-Tree) 807, 810, 2177, 2362, 2363, 2364, 2369, 2691, 2692

Sambucus nigra, L. (*Caprifoliaceae*) (European Elder) 3123

Sanseviera laurenti, Wildem. (*Agavaceae*) (Bowstring Hemp) 762

Saxifrage spp., L. (*Saxifragaceae*) 2384

Scabiosa atropurpurea, L. (*Dipsacaceae*) (Sweet Scabious) 3035, 3037

Scenedesmus acuminatus (*Scenedesmaceae*) (green algae) 1030

Scolopendrium officinarum (*Polypodiaceae*) 2746

Scolopendrium vulgare, Smith (*Polypodiaceae*) 321

Secale cerale, L. (*Poaceae*) (rye) 80, 279, 281, 297, 408, 410, 411, 415, 416, 418, 419, 420, 421, 422, 423, 446, 575, 576, 819, 820, 821, 822, 1125, 1138, 2081, 2083, 2084, 2137, 2139, 2219, 2220, 2221, 2222, 2302, 2566, 2571, 2777, 2778

Sedum Aizoon, L. (*Crassulaceae*) 767

Sedum dasyphyllum, L. (*Crassulaceae*) 186

Sedum kamtschaticum, Fisch. (*Crassulaceae*) 747, 767

Sedum lydium, Boiss. (*Crassulaceae*) 767

Sedum maximum, Suter. (*Crassulaceae*) 3123

Sedum selskianum, Regel. & Maack. (*Crassulaceae*) 767

Sedum sexangulare, L. (*Crassulaceae*) 186

Sedum spectabile, Boreau. (*Crassulaceae*) 767, 1408

Sedum telephium, L. (*Crassulaceae*) 767, 2746

Selaginella Kraussiana, Braun. (*Selaginellaceae*) 713

Selaginella martensii, Spring. (*Selaginellaceae*) 1724, 1725, 2977, 2978, 3108

Sempervivum spp., L. (*Crassulaceae*) (Houseleek) 2746

Sempervivum acuminatum, Schott. (*Crassulaceae*) 1408

Sempervivum albidum, Schnittsp. & Lehm. (*Crassulaceae*) 1408, 1410

Sempervivum blandum, Schott. (*Crassulaceae*) 1408

Sempervivum Funkii, Lej. (*Crassulaceae*) 756, 757, 1408, 1410

Sempervivum moggridgei, Hook. De Smet. (*Crassulaceae*) 1408

Sempervivum Reginae - Amaliae, Heldr. & Sart. (*Crassulaceae*) 1408

Sempervivum tectorum, L. (*Crassulaceae*) 756, 757, 1408, 2745, 2746

Sempervivum tomentosum, Schittsp. & Lehm. (*Crassulaceae*) 1408

Sempervivum webbianum, Hort. (*Crassulaceae*) 1408

Senecio formosus, H.B.K. (*Asteraceae*) 2846

Senecio odoris, Defl. (*Asteraceae*) 1507

Sensitive plant (*Fabaceae*) 462, 664, 666, 667, 668

Sequoia sempervirens, Endl. (*Taxodiaceae*) (Redwood) 2495

Sesamum radiatum, Schum. (*Pedaliaceae*) 81

Setaria italica, Beauv. (*Poaceae*) (Common Millet) 529, 531, 1277, 1279, 1280

Setaria lutescens, Weigel (*Poaceae*) (yellow foxtail) 657

Setaria viridis, (L.) Beauv. (*Poaceae*) (green foxtail) 657, 2738

Sicyos angulatus, L. (*Cucurbitaceae*) (Bur-Cucumber) 2746

Sida grewioides (*Malvaceae*) 383

Sida spinosa, L. (*Malvaceae*) (Prickly Mallow) 383

Silene Armeria, L. (*Caryophyllaceae*) (Sweet William Catchfly) 2706

Silene pendula, L. (*Caryophyllaceae*) 1408

Scilla sibirica, Haw. (*Liliaceae*) 1481

Sinapis alba, L. (*Brassicaceae*) (White Mustard) 9, 63, 64, 65, 87, 100, 130,
131, 132, 144, 145, 167, 188, 302, 372, 373, 374, 375, 376, 377, 378, 395,
399, 507, 510, 512.5, 513, 514, 546, 547, 548, 549, 550, 551, 552, 553, 554,
563, 569, 570, 729, 730, 742, 761, 769, 813, 924, 925, 943, 944, 967, 991,
994, 1001, 1120, 1120.5, 1121, 1122, 1160, 1161, 1205, 1206, 1207, 1239, 1240,
1241, 1266, 1269, 1277, 1288, 1289, 1310, 1311, 1323, 1324, 1325, 1362, 1363,
1399, 1411, 1412, 1413, 1445, 1489, 1505, 1506, 1526, 1538, 1539, 1540, 1541,
1575, 1649, 1677, 1700, 1701, 1702, 1703, 1704, 1715, 1762, 1837, 1838, 1839,
1840, 1841, 1842, 1847, 1848, 1851, 1855, 1859, 1863, 1879, 1880, 1882, 1884,
1885, 1887, 1888, 1891, 1892, 1893, 1895, 1897, 1898, 1900, 1905, 1906, 1907,
2008, 2014, 2016, 2017, 2018, 2019, 2020, 2021, 2022, 2023, 2071, 2073, 2228,
2259, 2272, 2276, 2320, 2374, 2375, 2376, 2377, 2378, 2379, 2381, 2382, 2401,
2403, 2404, 2405, 2406, 2416, 2434, 2435, 2436, 2437, 2438, 2439, 2440, 2441,
2442, 2443, 2444, 2445, 2449, 2451, 2452, 2453, 2478, 2502, 2503, 2513, 2514,

2597, 2616, 2617, 2618, 2621, 2622, 2624, 2634, 2647, 2648, 2649, 2696, 2759, 2827, 2828, 2829, 2842, 2843, 2844, 2915, 2916, 2917, 2918, 2919, 2958, 2959, 2960, 2961, 2962, 2963, 2964, 2965, 2966, 2989, 2991

Sinapis arvensis, L. (*Brassicaceae*) (Charlock) 705

Sinningia speciosa, Benth. & Hook. (*Gesneriaceae*) (Gloxinia) 2353, 2354

Sisymbrium altissimum, L. (*Brassicaceae*) (Tumble-Mustard) 2789

Sisymbrium sophia (*Brassicaceae*) 769

Sisymbrium officinale, (L.) Scop. (*Brassicaceae*) (Hedge-Mustard) 2789

Sium latifolium, L. (*Apiaceae*) 758

Snapbeans (*Fabaceae*) 816

Soja max, L. (*Fabaceae*) (Soybean) 2055, 2109, 3037, 3038

Solanum andigena, L. (*Solanaceae*) 2186, 2187

Solanum aviculare, Forst. (*Solanaceae*) 2603

Solanum lacciniatum, Ait. (*Solanaceae*) 2603

Solanum lycopersicum, L. (*Solanaceae*) (Tomato) 500, 2273, 2649, 2946

Solanum melongena, L. (*Solanaceae*) (eggplant) 1096

Solanum nigrum, L. (*Solanaceae*) 816, 1916

Solanum tuberosum, L. (*Solanaceae*) (Potato) 106, 941, 942, 1096, 1481, 2745, 3038

Solanum virginianum (*Solanaceae*) 816

Solidago vigaurea, L. (*Asteraceae*) (European Goldenrod) 759

Sophora japonica, L. (*Fabaceae*) (Japanese Pagoda Tree, Chinese Scholar Tree) 2006, 2746

Sorghum vulgare, Pers. (*Poaceae*) (Sorghum) 367, 424, 537, 879, 1140, 1143, 1263, 1528, 1530, 2872

Soya (*Fabaceae*) 1340

Soybean (*Fabaceae*) 359, 610, 939, 1140, 1150, 1544, 1564, 2669, 3028

Sparaxis spp., Ker. (*Iridaceae*) (Wand-Flower) 1481

Specularia Speculum, A. DC. (*Campanulaceae*) 1408

Spergula arvensis, L. (*Caryophyllaceae*) 2040

Spergula maxima (*Caryophyllaceae*) 1256

Sphaerocarpus spp. (*Sphaerocarpaceae*) (Liverwort) 2733

Sphaerocarpus donnellii, Aust. (*Sphaerocarpaceae*) (Liverwort) 1638, 1794, 1795, 1796, 1797, 2610, 2611, 2613, 2614, 2615, 2620, 2625, 2626, 2627, 2630

Spinach (*Chenopodiaceae*) 3, 25, 2118, 2272, 2388, 2483

Spinacia oleracea, L. (*Chenopodiaceae*) (Spinach) 886, 1365, 1530, 2068, 2069, 2647, 2648, 2649, 3037

Spiraea spp. L. (*Rosaceae*) 667

Spirodela intermedia (*Lemnaceae*) 1736, 2267

Spirodela oligorrhiza, (Kurtz.) Hegelm. (*Lemnaceae*) 1991, 1992, 2115, 2116

Spirodela polyrrhiza (L.) Schleid (*Lemnaceae*) (duckweed) 453, 455, 456, 507, 1115, 1909, 1910, 1911, 2115, 2116

Spirogyra sp. (*Zygnemataceae*) (Algae) 1957

Spirogyra porticalis (*Zygnemataceae*) (Algae) 1916

Spruce (*Pinaceae*) 910, 911

Squash (*Cucurbitaceae*) 1959

Stellaria holostea, L. (*Caryophyllaceae*) (Easter Bells) 900

Stellaria media, (L.) Cyrillo (*Caryophyllaceae*) (Common Chickweed) 2738

Stinging nettle (*Urticaceae*) 2386

Stock (*Brassicaceae*) 3032, 3033

Strawberry (*Rosaceae*) 413, 665, 666, 1269, 1270, 1690, 1691, 2272, 3088

Strobilanthes, spp., Blume (*Acanthaceae*) 666, 667, 668

Struthiopteris filicastrum, All. (*Polypodiaceae*) 959, 1873

Struthiopteris fragilis (*Polypodiaceae*) 321

Sugar beet (*Chenopodiaceae*) 2659, 2897

Sugar cane (*Poaceae*) 973

Summer rape (*Brassicaceae*) 3059

Summer rye (*Poaceae*) 3059

Summer wheat (*Poaceae*) 3059

Sunflower (*Asteraceae*) 2892, 2893, 2894, 2895, 2897

Sweet pea (*Fabaceae*) 2272

Symphytum cordatum, Willd. (*Boraginaceae*) 3123

Synedrella nodiflora (L.) Gaertn. (*Asteraceae*) 615, 2846

Syringa vulgaris, L. (*Oleaceae*) (Common lilac) 900, 2645

Taraxacum officinale, Weber (*Asteraceae*) (Common Dandelion) 355, 900, 2342, 2343

Taxus baccata, L. (*Taxaceae*) (English Yew) 901, 3012

Teosinte (*Poaceae*) 2388

Tetraphis pellucida, (L.) Rabenh. (*Tetraphidaceae*) (Moss) 1548.5, 1549, 1549.5

Tibouchina longifolia (*Melastomataceae*) 2840

Tilia parvifolia, Ehrh. (*Tiliaceae*) (Small-Leaved Linden) 2645

Tithonia speciosa, Hook. (*Asteraceae*) 3035, 3037

Tobacco (*Solanaceae*) 78, 95, 96, 726, 920, 1127, 1394, 1469, 1503, 2028, 2030, 2120, 2388, 2975, 3066

Tofieldia calyculata, (L.) Wahlenb. (*Liliaceae*) 141, 1403, 1404

Tomato (*Solanaceae*) 3, 18, 46, 47, 74, 147, 414, 577, 790, 791, 1243, 1247, 1248, 1249, 1252, 1386, 1388, 1589, 1591, 1664, 1668, 1671, 1759, 1761, 1762, 1908, 1959, 2090, 2272, 2386, 2480, 2834, 3076, 3078, 3079, 3080

Torenia crustaceae Cham. (*Scrophulariaceae*) 81

Torenia fournieri, Lind. (*Scrophulariaceae*) 1408

Tortella inclinata, Hedw. (*Pottiaceae*) (Moss) 1584

Tradescantia, spp., L. (*Commelinaceae*) (Spiderwort) 666, 2306, 2307, 2310, 3050

Tradescantia albiflora, Kunth. (*Commelinaceae*) 948, 2308, 2311

Tradescantia fluminensis, Vell. (*Commelinaceae*) (Wandering Jew) 2047, 2495, 2847 (Kth.)

Tradescantia paludosa, Anders. (*Commelinaceae*) 1635, 1636, 2684, 2685, 2686, 2687, 2688, 2689, 3082, 3083

Tradescantia undata (*Commelinaceae*) 765

Tradescantia viridis (*Commelinaceae*) 1572

Tragopogon porrifolius, L. (*Asteraceae*) (Oyster Plant) 649

Trianea bogotensis, Karst. (*Hydrocharitaceae*) (American Frogsbit) 1494

Trifolium fragiferum, L. (*Fabaceae*) (Strawberry Clover) 946

Trifolium pratense, L. (*Fabaceae*) (Red Clover) 761, 900, 1256

Trifolium repens, L. (*Fabaceae*) (White Clover) 2006

Trillium grandiflorum, Salisb. (*Liliaceae*) 1481

Tripleurospermum maritimum (*Asteraceae*) 1131

Triticum spp., L. (*Poaceae*) 82, 994

Triticum aestivum, L. (*Poaceae*) (Common Wheat) 506, 737, 1277, 1303, 1393, 1631, 1632

Triticum compactum, Host. (*Poaceae*) (Wheat) 529

Triticum sativum, Lam. (*Poaceae*) (Wheat) 408, 879, 1256

Triticum vulgare, Vill. (*Poaceae*) (Wheat) 919, 1210, 1211, 2232, 2305, 2420, 2661

Tritonia crocosmaeflora, Lemoine (*Iridaceae*) 2645

Tolypothrix tenuis (*Scytonemataceae*) (Blue-green alga) 2395

Tropaeolum spp., L. (*Tropaeolaceae*) (Nasturtium) 459

Tropaeolum majus, L. (*Tropaeolaceae*) (Garden Nasturtium) 206, 466, 495, 1916, 2202, 2203, 2320, 2328, 2329, 2331, 2332

Tulipa spp., L. (*Liliaceae*) (Tulip) 1481

Turnera ulmifolia, L. (*Meliaceae*) 81

Turnip (*Brassicaceae*) 854, 894, 895, 897, 1052, 2112, 2272, 2412, 2413, 2489, 2519, 2870

Turritis glabra (*Brassicaceae*) 763, 769

Ullucus tuberosus, Caldas. (*Basellaceae*) 2192

Ulmus americana, L. (*Ulmaceae*) (American Elm) 2789

Urtica dioica, L. (*Urticaceae*) (Stinging Nettle) 1494

Urtica pilulifera, L. (*Urticaceae*) 1623

Utricularia vulgaris, L. (*Lentibulariaceae*) 3123

Vallisneria spiralis, L. (*Hydrocharitaceae*) (Wild Celery) 756, 757, 1494, 2471, 2472, 2474, 2475, 2476, 2477

Vanilla dilloniana, Correl (*Orchidaceae*) 1192

Vanilla phaeantha, Reichb. (*Orchidaceae*) 1192

Vanilla planifolia, Andr. (*Orchidaceae*) (Common Vanilla) 1192

Vaucheria sessilis (*Vaucheriaceae*) 662, 989, 1026.5, 3123

Venturia inaequalis, (Cke.) Wint. (Fungi) 286

Veratrum spp., L. (*Liliaceae*) (False Hellebore) 1404

Verbascum thapsus, L. (*Scrophulariaceae*) (Common Mullein) 1742, 1743, 1744, 2785, 2789

Verbena bipinnatifida, Nutt. (*Verbenaceae*) 2906, 2907

Verbena ciliata (*Verbenaceae*) 1594

Veronica Beccabunga, L. (*Scrophulariaceae*) 1937

Veronica Chamaedrys, L. (*Scrophulariaceae*) 1408

Veronica imperialis, Hort. (*Scrophulariaceae*) 459

Veronica peregrina, L. (*Scrophulariaceae*) 1041, 1042, 1401, 1404

Veronica Tournefortii, C.C. Gmel. (*Scrophulariaceae*) 1772

Vicia commuis (*Fabaceae*) (Vetch) 666

Vicia faba, L. (*Fabaceae*) (Broad bean) 143, 257, 332, 630, 948, 1159, 1571, 1680, 1717, 1718, 1831, 1832, 1833, 1834, 2695, 3050, 3054, 3058, 3097

Vicia sativa, L. (*Fabaceae*) (Common or Spring Vetch) 2745, 3013, 3014

Vigna sesquipedalis, Fruwirth (*Fabaceae*) (Asparagus Bean) 745, 746, 3071

Vigna sinensis, Savi. (*Fabaceae*) (Cowpea) 789, 1826

Viola spp. L. (*Violaceae*) (Violet) 2594

Viola tricolor, L. (*Violaceae*) (Pansy) 900, 2593, 3034

Virginia pine (*Pinaceae*) 1535, 2787

Viscum album, L. (*Loranthaceae*) (Mistletoe) 1044

Vitis vinifera, L. (*Vitaceae*) (Wine Grape) 2551

Vriesia regina, Ant. (*Bromeliaceae*) 538

Wallflower (*Brassicaceae*) 1078

Watermelon (*Cucurbitaceae*) 1959

Wax gourd (*Cucurbitaceae*) 1959

Webera commutata, Schimp. (Moss) 1584

Webera mutans Schreb. (Moss) 1584

Weigela spp. Thunb. (*Caprifoliaceae*) 2957

Weigela florida, A. DC. (*Caprifoliaceae*) 3022

Weisia viridula, (L.) Hedw. (*Pottiaceae*) 1584

Wheat (*Poaceae*) 76, 77, 98, 149, 150, 151, 152, 153, 154, 257, 508, 532, 665,
   731, 732, 844, 949, 1285, 1518, 1551, 1573, 1633, 1634, 1775, 1777, 2289,
   2463, 2487, 2513, 2514, 2602, 2879, 2880, 2882, 2883, 2884, 2885, 2905, 2913,
   2914

White pine (*Pinaceae*) 910, 1535

Winter rye (*Poaceae*) 25

Wittrockia superba (*Bromeliaceae*) 538

Wolffia microscopica (*Lemnaceae*) 2854

Xanthium spp., L. (*Asteraceae*) (Cocklebur) 183

Xanthium Commune, Britton (*Asteraceae*) 1544, 1564, 2482

Xanethum itaticum, Moretti (*Asteraceae*) 1625

Xanthium pensylvanicum, Wallr. (*Asteraceae*) (Cocklebur) 1, 24, 92, 143, 241,
   367, 617, 874, 875, 1132, 1143, 1380, 1383, 1384, 1663, 1669, 1683, 1684,
   1685, 1686, 1755, 1917, 1918, 2053, 2209, 2210, 2213, 2334, 2335, 2337, 2340,
   3037, 3038

Xanthium saccharatum, Widder. (*Asteraceae*) (Cocklebur) 221, 524, 2055

Xanthium strumarium, L. (*Asteraceae*) (Cocklebur) 1987, 2877.5

Zea Mays, L. (*Poaceae*) (Corn) 143, 154, 264, 265, 271, 272, 298, 330, 333,
   388, 399, 408, 411, 493, 502, 507, 564, 565, 589, 778, 823, 879, 1096, 1143,
   1280, 1370, 1490, 1530, 1612, 1678, 1689, 1705, 1706, 1709, 1717, 1718, 1789,
   1821, 1822, 1823, 1825, 1826, 1924, 1965, 2047, 2080, 2127, 2139, 2153, 2156,
   2159, 2162, 2188, 2189, 2197, 2198, 2199, 2221, 2280, 2281, 2284, 2344, 2381,

2399, 2469, 2492, 2499, 2579, 2586, 2590, 2591, 2594, 2596, 2619, 2644, 2645, 2754, 2755, 2757, 2758, 2814, 2817, 2818.5, 2970, 2972, 2973, 3012, 3017, 3024, 3025, 3035, 3038, 3039

Zebrina pendula, Schnizl. (*Commelinaceae*) (Wandering Jew) 2495

Zygocactus truncatus, Schum. (*Cactaceae*) (Crab Cactus, Christmas Cactus) 2877.5

TAXONOMIC INDEX

Family 2. *Protosiphonaceae*
 Protosiphon botryoides

Family 3. *Chlorellaceae*
 Chlorella spp.
 Chlorella ellipsoidea
 Chlorella fusca
 Chlorella pyrenoidosa
 Chlorella vulgaris

Family 4. *Scenedesmaceae*
 Scenedesmus acuminatus

Family 5. *Dasycladaceae*
 Acetabularia crenulata
 Acetabularia mediterranea

Family 6. *Ulotrichaceae*
 Hormidium flaccidum

Family 7. *Zygnemataceae*
 Mougeotia spp.
 Spirogyra spp.
 Spirogyra porticalis

Family 8. *Mesotaeniaceae*
 Mesotaenium caldariorum

Family 9. *Characeae*
 Chara spp.
 Chara zeylanica
 Nitella pulchella

Division. MYCOTA (Fungi)

 Class. PHYCOMYCETES

  Family 1. *Mucoraceae*
   Phycomyces

 Class. DEUTEROMYCETES (Fungi Imperfecti)

  Family 1. *Aspergillaceae*
   Aspergillus

 Class. ASCOMYCETES

  Family 1. *Mycosphaerellaceae*
   Venturia inaequalis

Family 2. *Sphaeriaceae*

    Neurospora crassa

Division. BRYOPHYTA

    Class I. HEPATICAE (Liverworts)

        Family 1. *Blasiaceae*

            Blasia pusilla, L.

        Family 2. *Marchantiaceae*

            Conocephalum conicum, (L.) Wiggers

            Fegatella conica

            Lunularia cruciata, (L.) Wiggers

            Lunularia vulgaris

            Marchantia polymorpha, L.

            Marchantia polyrhiza

            Preissia commutata

            Reboulia hemisphaerica, (L.) Raddi

        Family 3. *Sphaerocarpaceae*

            Sphaerocarpus spp.

            Sphaerocarpus donnelli, Aust.

        Family 4. *Haplomitriaceae*

            Haplomitrium rotundifolium

    Class II. MUSCI (Mosses)

        Family 1. *Tetraphidaceae*

            Tetraphis pellucida, (L.) Rabenh

        Family 2. *Polytrichaceae*

            Dawsonia longiseta

            Dawsonia polytrichoides

            Dawsonia superba

            Dendroligotrichum dendroides

            Polytrichadelphus magellanicus

            Polytrichum commune, Hedw.

            Polytrichum formosum, Hedw.

        Family 3. *Ditrichaceae*

            Ceratodon purpureus, (Hedw.) Brid.

        Family 4. *Dicranaceae*

            Dicranum heteromalla, (Hedw.) Schimp

            Dicranum scoparium, Hedw.

Family 5. *Pottiaceae*

        Tortella inclinata, Hedw.

        Weisia viridula (L.) Hedw.

Family 6. *Funariaceae*

        Funaria spp.

        Funaria hygrometrica, Hedw.

        Physcomitrium pyriforme, Brid.

Family 7. *Bryaceae*

        Bryum capillare, Hedw.

        Bryum cirrhetum

        Bryum lacuste

        Bryum pendulum, (Hornsch.) Schimp

        Bryum roseum

        Pohlia nutans, (Hedw.) Lindb.

Family 8. *Mniaceae*

        Mnium affine, Bland

        Mnium cuspidatum, Hedw.

        Mnium hornum, Hedw.

        Mnium medium, Bry. Eur.

        Mnium undulatum, (L.) Weis

Family 9. *Hypnaceae*

        Brachythecium rutabubum, (Hedw.) Bry.

        Brachythecium velutinum, (Hedw.) Bry.

        Cirriphyllum piliferum, (Hedw.) Grout

Division III. PTERIDOPHYTA

    Class I. FILICINAE

        Family 1. *Osmundaceae* (Flowering Fern Family)

                Osmunda cinnamomea, L.

                Osmunda Claytoniana, L.

                Osmunda Regalis, Tryon

        Family 2. *Schizaeaceae* (Schizea-Fern Family)

                Anemia Phyllitidis, Swartz.

                Lygodium japonicum, Swartz.

        Family 3. *Cyatheaceae* (Tree-Fern Family)

                Alsophila australis, R. Br.

Family 4. *Dicksoniaceae* (Dicksonia Family)
Balantium antarcticum

Family 5. *Polypodiaceae* (Common-Fern Family)

Adiantum spp. L.

Adiantum Capillus-Veneris, L.

Adiantum scutum, Hort.

Adiantum Weigandii, Moore

Aspidium elongatum

Aspidium Filix-mas, Swartz.

Aspidium molle, Sw.

Aspidium spinulosum, Swartz.

Asplenium spp. L.

Asplenium alatum, HBK

Asplenium australe, Br.

Asplenium diversifolium

Asplenium lasiopteris

Asplenium Nidus, L.

Asplenium rutamuraria, L.

Asplenium trichomanes, L.

Athyrium Filix-femina, Roth.

Blechnum brasiliense, Desv.

Blechnum spicant, With.

Blechnum triangulare

Cheilanthes farinosa

Davallia chinensis, Smith var. Stricta

Doodia caudata, R. Br.

Doodia lunulata

Dryopteris erythrosora

Dryopteris Filix-mas, (L.) Schott

Gymnogramma massoni

Gymnogramma sulfurea, Desv.

Lomaria Spicant

Matteuccia struthiopteris, (L.) Todaro

Nephrolepis exaltata, Schott.

Onoclea sensibilis, L.

Phegopteris effusa

322

Platycerium alcicorne, Desv.

Polypodium Reinwardtii

Polypodium repens

Polypodium rubrium

Polypodium vulgare, L.

Pteris argyrea, Moore

Pteris cretica, L.

Pteris flabellata

Pteris longifolia, L.

Pteris serrulata, L.

Pteris tremula, R. Br.

Pteris vespertilionis

Pteris vittata, L.

Scolopendrium officinarum

Scolopendrium vulgare, Smith

Struthiopteris filicastrum, All.

Struthiopteris fragilis

Family 6. *Parkeriaceae* (Floating-Fern Family)

Ceratopteris thalictroides, Brongn.

Family 7. *Selaginellaceae* (Selaginella Family)

Selaginella Kraussiana, Braun.

Selaginella martensii, Spring.

Division I. GYMNOSPERMAE

Family 1. *Ginkgoaceae* (Ginkgo Family)

Ginkgo biloba, L.

Family 2. *Taxaceae* (Yew Family)

Taxus baccata, L.

Family 3. *Pinaceae* (Pine Family)

Pinus densiflora, Sieb. & Zucc.

Pinus merkusii, Jungh. & de Vries

Pinus mughus, Scop.

Pinus nigra, Arnold

Pinus nigra var. austriaca, Aschens. & Graebn.

Pinus palustris, Mill.

Pinus ponderosa, Dougl.

Pinus Strobus, L.

Pinus sylvestris, L.

Pinus Taeda, L.

Pinus Thunbergii, Parl.

Pinus virginiana, Mill.

Larix decidua, Mill.

Larix europaea, DC.

Larix leptolepis, Gord.

Picea Abies, (h.) Karst.

Picea excelsa, Link.

Picea Glehnii, Mast.

Pseudotsuga menziesii, (Mirb.) Franco.

Family 4. *Taxodiaceae* (Taxodium Family)

Sequoia sempervirens, Endl.

Family 5. *Cypressaceae* (Cypress Family)

Chamaecyparis Lawsoniana, (Murr.) Parl.

Chamaecyparis obtusa, Sieb. & Zucc.

Chamaecyparis pisitera, Sieb. & Zucc.

Biota orientalis, Endl.

Division II. ANGIOSPERMAE

Class I. MONOCOTYLEDONEAE

Family 1. *Potamogetonaceae*

Potamogeton crispus, L.

Potamogeton natans, L.

Family 2. *Aponogetonaceae* (Aponogeton Family)

Aponogeton distachyus, L.

Family 3. *Alismataceae* (Water-Plantain Family)

Alisma plantago, L.

Echinodorus ranunculoides, L.

Sagittaria sagittifolia, L.

Sagittaria subulata, Buchenau.

Family 4. *Hydrocharitaceae* (Frog's-Bit Family)

Elodea spp., Michx

Elodea, canadensis, Michx.

Hydrocharis Morsus-ranae, L.

Trianea bogotensis, Karst.

Vallisneria spiralis, L.

Family 5. *Poaceae* (Grass Family)

    Aegilops ovata, L.

    Agrostis stolonifera, L.

    Aira caespitosa

    Aira flexuosa, L.

    Alopecurus pratensis, L.

    Avena elatiur, L.

    Avena fatua, L.

    Avena sativa, L.

    Bromus inermis, Leyss.

    Bromus tectorum, L.

    Chloris ciliata

    Chloris verticillata, Nutt.

    Cynosurus cristatus, L.

    Dactylis glomerata, L.

    Digitaria, spp. Heist.

    Digitaria sanguinalis, (L.) scop.

    Echinochloa colora, (L.) Link

    Echinochloa crusgalli, L.

    Eragrostis cilianensis, Vignolo-Lutati

    Eragrostis curvula, (Schrad.) Wees

    Eragrostis ferruginea, Beauv.

    Festuca duriuscula, L.

    Festuca ovina, L.

    Holcus lanatus, L.

    Holcus sorghum var. sudanensis, Hitche.

    Hordeum distichom, L.

    Hordeum sativium, Pers.

    Hordeum vulgare, L.

    Lolium spp., L.

    Lolium italicum, A. Br.

    Lolium perenne, L.

    Lolium temulentum, L.

    Melinis minutiflora, Beauv.

    Oryza sativa, L.

    Oryzopsis miliacea, Benth. & Hook

Panicum dichotomiflorum, Michx.

Pennisetum setosum (sw.) L. Rioh.

Phalaris canariensis, L.

Phleum pratense, L.

Poa annua, L.

Poa nemoralis, L.

Poa pratensis, L.

Poa trivialis, L.

Saccharum officinarum, L.

Secale cereale, L.

Setaria italica, Beauv.

Setaria lutescens, Weigel

Setaria viridis (L.) Beauv.

Sorghum vulgare, Pers.

Triticum spp., L.

Triticum aestivum, L.

Triticum compactum, Host.

Triticum sativum, Lam.

Triticum vulgare, Vill.

Zea Mays, L.

Family 6. *Cyperaceae* (Sedge Family)

Cyperus alterniflora, L.

Cyperus rotundus, L.

Family 7. *Araceae* (Arum Family)

Calla aethiopica, L.

Family 8. *Arecaceae* (Palm Family)

Cocos nucifera, L.

Family 9. *Lemnaceae* (Duckweed Family)

Lemna spp. L.

Lemna gibba

Lemna minor, L.

Lemna paucicostato

Lemna perpusilla, Torr.

Lemna trisulca, L.

Spirodela intermedia

Spirodela oligorrhiza, (Kurtz) Hegelm.

Spirudela polyrrhiza, (L.) Schleid.

Wolffia microscopica

Family 10. *Bromeliaceae* (Pineapple Family)

Aechmea fasciata, Baken

Aechmea nudicaulis, Griseb.

Billbergia elegans

Billbergia pyramidalis, Lindl.

Canistrum Lindenii, Mez.

Nidularium fulgens, Lem.

Quesnelia lateralis

Vriesia regina, Ant.

Wittrockia superba

Family 11. *Commelinaceae* (Spiderwort Family)

Commelina nudiflora, L.

Tradescantia spp. L.

Tradescantia albiflora, Kunth.

Tradescantia fluminensis, Vell.

Tradescantia paludosa, Anders.

Tradescantia undata

Tradescantia viridis

Zebrina pendula, Schnizl.

Family 12. *Liliaceae* (Lily Family)

Allium cepa, L.

Allium neapolitanum, Cyn.

Allium suaveolens

Asparagus officinalis, L.

Asparagus Sprengeri, Regel.

Asphodelus ramosus, L.

Aspidistra elatior, Blume

Bulbocodium vernum, L.

Camassia esculenta, Rob.

Convalloria spp. L.

Hyacinthus spp. L.

Lilium longiflorim, Thunb.

Lilium superbum, L.

Polygonatum odoratum

Scilla sibirica, Haw.

Tofieldia calyculata, (L.) Wahlenb.

Trillium grandiflorum, Salisb.

Tulipa spp. L.

Veratrum spp. L.

Family 13. *Agavaceae* (Agave Family)

Sanseviera laurenti, Wilden.

Family 14. *Amaryllidaceae* (Amaryllis Family)

Hippeastrum spp.

Narcissus spp. L.

Family 15. *Iridaceae* (Iris Family)

Crocus ancyrensis, Maw.

Gladiolus spp., L.

Iris spp., L.

Libertia formosa, Graham

Sparaxis spp., Ker.

Tritonia crocosmaeflora, Lemoine

Family 16. *Musaceae* (Banana Family)

Musa sapientium, L.

Family 17. *Orchidaceae* (Orchid or Orchis Family)

Cypripedium harbor X Cyp. Merlin

Vanilla dilloniana, Cornel

Vanilla phaeantha, Reichb.

Vanilla planifolia, Andr.

Class II. DICOTYLEDONEAE

Family 1.   *Piperaceae* (Pepper Family)

Peperomia clusiaefolia

Family 2.   *Salicaceae* (Willow Family)

Populus grandifolia

Populus nigra, L.

Salix babylonica, L.

Salix cinerea, L.

Salix repens, L.

Family 3. *Betulaceae* (Birch Family)

Alnus firma var. yasha, Winkl.

Alnus inokumai

Alnus tinctoria, Sarg.

Betula alba, L.

Betula lutea, Michx.

Betula pubescens, Ehrh.

Betula verrucosa, Ehrh.

Corylus Avellana, L.

Family 4. *Fagaceae* (Beech Family)

Castanea vesca, Gaertn.

Quercus pedunculata, Ehrh.

Family 5. *Ulmaceae* (Elm Family)

Ulmus americana, L.

Family 6. *Moraceae* (Mulberry Family)

Ficus elastica, Roxb.

Family 7. *Cannabidaceae* (Hemp Family)

Cannabis sativa, L.

Family 8. *Urticaceae* (Nettle Family)

Pellia epiphylla

Urtica dioica, L.

Urtica pilulifera, L.

Family 9. *Proteaceae* (Protea Family)

Roupala corcovadensia, Hort.

Family 10. *Loranthaceae* (Mistletoe Family)

Viscum album, L.

Family 11. *Aristolochiaceae* (Birthwort Family)

Aristolochia Clematitus, L.

Family 12. *Polygonaceae* (Buckwheat or Knotweed Family)

Fagopyrum esculentum, Moench.

Fagopyrum vulgare

Polygonum fagopydum, L.

Polygonum sieboldii, de Vriese.

Rumex Acetosa, L.

Rumex alpinus, L.

Rumex conglomeratus, Murr.

Rumex crispus, L.

Rumex hydrolapathum, Huds.

Rumex obtusifolius, L.

Rumex patientia, L.

Family 13. *Chenopodiaceae* (Goosefoot Family)

Atriplex dimorphostegia, Kar. & Kir.

Beta vulgaris, L.

Blitum capitatum, L.

Blitum virgatum, L.

Chenopodium album, L.

Chenopodium amaranticolor, Coste & Reyn.

Chenopodium aristatum, L.

Chenopodium botrys, L.

Chenopodium foetidum, L.

Chenopodium glaucum, L.

Chenopodium polyspermum, L.

Chenopodium rubrum, L.

Chenopodium salinum, Standl.

Kochia scoparia, (L.) (Schrad.) Roth

Kochia trichophylla, Voss.

Spinacia oleracea, L.

Family 14. *Amaranthaceae* (Amaranth Family)

Achyrantha spp.

Alternanthera sessilis, (L.) R. Br.

Amaranthus albus, L.

Amaranthus arenicola, I.M. Johnston

Amaranthus blitoides, S. Wats.

Amaranthus caudatus, L.

Amaranthus caudatus var. atropurpureus, Hort.

Amaranthus dubins, Mart.

Amaranthus fimbriatus

Amaranthus paniculatus, L.

Amaranthus retroflexus, L.

Amaranthus tricolor, L.

Celosia spp. L.

Celosia cristata, (L.) Ktze.

Celosia plumosa, Hort.

Family 15. *Nyctaginaceae* (Four-O'Clock Family)

Mirabilis Jalapa, L.

330

Family 16. *Phytolaccaceae* (Pokeweed Family)

   Phytolacca decandra, L.

Family 17. *Portulacaceae* (Purslane Family)

   Portulaca grandiflora, Hook.

   Portulaca oleracea, L.

Family 18. *Basellaceae* (Basella Family)

   Basella alba, L.

   Boussingaultia baselloides, Hook.

   Ullucus tuberosus Caldas.

Family 19. *Caryophyllaceae* (Pink Family)

   Agrostemma githago, L.

   Cerastium arvense, L.

   Dianthus alpinus, L.

   Dianthus barbatus, L.

   Dianthus carthusianorum, L.

   Dianthus caryophyllus, L.

   Dianthus chinensis, L.

   Dianthus microlepis, Boiss.

   Dianthus superbus, L.

   Dicranilla heteromalla, Schimp.

   Lychnis alba, Mill.

   Sagina maritima

   Sagina nodosa, (L.) Fenzl.

   Sagina procumbens, L.

   Silene Armeria, L.

   Silene pendula, L.

   Spergula arvensis, L.

   Spergula maxima

   Stellaria holostea, L.

   Stellaria media, (L.) Cyrillo

Family 20. *Ceratophyllaceae* (Hornwort Family)

   Ceratophyllum demersum, L.

Family 21. *Ranunculaceae* (Crowfoot Family)

   Delphinium elatum, L.

   Nigella spp. L.

   Nigella damascena, L.

Nigella sativa

Paeonia officinalis, L.

Ranunculus bulbosus, L.

Family 22. *Berberidaceae* (Barberry Family)

Podophyllum peltatum, L.

Family 23. *Menispermaceae* (Moonseed Family)

Menispermum cocculus, L.

Family 24. *Lauraceae* (Laurel Family)

Persea americana, Mill.

Family 25. *Papaveraceae* (Poppy Family)

Escholtzia californica, cham.

Papaver somniferum, L.

Family 26. *Capparidaceae* (Caper Family)

Cleome burmanii, W. & A.

Family 27. *Brassicaceae* (Mustard Family)

Aethionema cappadocicum, Spreng.

Aethionema diastrophis, Fisch.

Aethionema grandiflorum, Boiss. & Hohen.

Alyssum calycinum

Alyssum maritimum, Lam.

Arabidopsis thaliana, (L.) Heynh.

Barbarea Verna, Aschers.

Barbarea Vulgaris, R. Br.

Berteroa incana, (L.) DC.

Brassica alba, Rabenh.

Brassica campestris, L.

Brassica hibern

Brassica juncea, Coss.

Brassica napobrassica, Mill.

Brassica napus, L.

Brassica nigra, Koch.

Brassica oleracea, L.

Brassica oleracea var. capitata, L.

Brassica oleracea var. botrytis, L.

Brassica oleracea var. gemmifera, Zenker.

Brassica oleracea var. italica, Plenck.

Brassica pekinensis, Rupr.

Brassica rapa, L.

Brassica rapa var. lorifolia, Bailey

Camelina microcarpa, Andrz.

Camelina sativa, (L.) Crantz.

Capsella bursa-pastoris, (L.) Medic.

Cardamine pratensis, L.

Carrichtera annua, (L.) Asch.

Cheiranthus Allionii, Hort.

Crambe hispanica

Erysimum cheiranthoides, L.

Iberis amara, L.

Iberis coronaria, Hort.

Iberis intermedia

Iberis umbellata, L.

Lepidium campestre, (L.) R. Br.

Lepidium densiflorum, Schrad.

Lepidium draba

Lepidium sativum, L.

Lepidium virinicum, L.

Malcolmia maritima, R. Br.

Matthiola annua, Sweet

Matthiola incana, R. Br.

Nasturtium silvestre

Neslea paniculata, (L.) Desv.

Raphanus praecox minor

Raphanus sativus, L.

Sinapis alba, L.

Sinapis arvensis, L.

Sisymbrium altissimum, L.

Sisymbrium sophia

Sisymbrium officinale, (L.) Scop.

Turritis glabra

Family 28. *Resedaceae* (Mignonette Family)

Reseda odorata, L.

Family 29. *Droseraceae* (Sundew Family)

        Drosera spathulata

Family 30. *Crassulaceae* (Orpine Family)

        Bryophyllum, spp. Salisb.

        Bryophyllum fedtschenkoi, R. Hamet & Perrier

        Bryophyllum pinnatum, Kurz.

        Echeveria spp., DC.

        Echeveria metallica, Lem.

        Kalanchoë spp. Adans.

        Kalanchoë blossfeldiana, v. Poellnitz.

        Kalanchoë coccinea, Welw.

        Kalanchoë laciniata, DC.

        Kalanchoë rotundifolia, Haw.

        Kalanchoë thyrsiflora

        Sedum Aizoon, L.

        Sedum dasyphyllum, L.

        Sedum Kamtschaticum, Fisch.

        Sedum lydium, Boiss.

        Sedum maximum, Suter.

        Sedum selskianum, Regel. & Maack.

        Sedum sexangulare, L.

        Sedum spectabile, Boreau.

        Sedum telephium, L.

        Sempervivum spp. L.

        Sempervivum acuminatum, Schott.

        Sempervivum albidum, Schittsp. & Lehm.

        Sempervivum blandum, Schott.

        Sempervivum Funkii, hej.

        Sempervivum Moggridgei, (De Smet.) Hook.

        Sempervivum Reginae-Amaliae, Heldr. & Sart.

        Sempervivum tectorum, L.

        Sempervivum tomentosum, Schittsp. & Lehm.

        Sempervivum Webbianum, Hort.

Family 31. *Saxifragaceae* (Saxifrage Family)

        Deutzia gracilis, Sieb. & Zucc.

        Hortensia spp.

Philadelphus coronarius, L.

Saxifrage spp. L.

Family 32. *Brunelliaceae* (Brunella Family)

Brunella vulgaris

Family 33. *Rosaceae* (Rose Family)

Amygdalus communis, L.

Crataegus oxyacantha, L.

Cydonia vulgaris, Pers.

Fragaria spp. L.

Fragaria ananassa, Duchesne.

Fragaria vesca, L.

Fragaria virginiana, Duchesne.

Geum canadense, Jacq.

Malus spp. Mill.

Mespilus germanica, L.

Pirus aucuparia, Gaertner

Pirus malus, L.

Potentilla norvegica, L.

Prunus spp. L.

Prunus cerasus, L.

Prunus laurocerasus, L.

Prunus padus, L.

Prunus persica, (L.) Stokes.

Prunus triloba, Lindl.

Pyracantha coccinea, Roem.

Pyrus spp. L.

Pyrus malus, L.

Rhodotypos Kerriodes, Seib. & Zucc.

Rosa canina, L.

Rubus fructicosus, Hort.

Spiraea spp. L.

Family 34. *Fabaceae* (Pea or Pulse Family)

Albizzia julibrissin, Durazz.

Albizzia lophantha, Benth.

Amicia zygomeris, DC.

Amphicarpa monoica, (L.) Ell.

Arachis hypogea, L.

Bauhinia monandra, Kurz.

Calliandra inequilatera

Cassia Chamaecrista, L.

Cassia floribunda, Hort.

Cassia nictitans, L.

Cassia Tora, L.

Cicer arietinum, L.

Clianthus Dampiere, Cumm.

Colutea arborescens, L.

Erythrina indica, Lam.

Faba vulgaris, Moench.

Glycine hispida, Maxim.

Glycine max, Merr.

Glycine Soja, Sieb. & Zucc.

Lathyrus spp. L.

Lens culinaris, Medic.

Leucaena glauca, Benth.

Lupinus alba, L.

Melitotus spp. Mill.

Melitotus alba, Desr.

Mimosa spp. L.

Mimosa invisa

Mimosa pudica, L.

Ononis sicula, Guss.

Phaseolus spp. L.

Phaseolus acutifoluis, Gray

Phaseolus aureus, Roxbg.

Phaseolus coccineus, L.

Phaseolus multiflorus, (Willd.) Lam.

Phaseolus mungo, L.

Phaseolus vulgaris, L.

Pisum arvense, L.

Pisum sativum, L.

Poinciana Gilliesi, Hook.

Robinia Pseudoacacia, L.

Samanea Saman, Merr.

Soja max, L.

Sophora japonica, L.

Trifolium fragiferum, L.

Trifolium pratense, L.

Trifolium repens, L.

Vicia commuis

Vicia faba, L.

Vicia sativa, L.

Vigna sesquipedalis, Fruwirth.

Vigna sinensis, Savi.

Family 35. *Geraniaceae* (Geranium Family)

Geranium spp. L.

Pelargonium spp. L. Her.

Pelargonium zonale, Ait.

Family 36. *Oxalidaceae* (Oxalis or Wood-Sorrel Family)

Biophytum sensitivum, DC.

Oxalis spp. L.

Oxalis Acetosella, L.

Oxalis corniculata, L.

Oxalis esculenta

Oxalis lasiandra, Zucc.

Oxalis multiflora, Jacq.

Oxalis stricta, L.

Family 37. *Tropaeolaceae* (Tropaeolum Family)

Tropaeolum spp. L.

Tropaeolum majus, L.

Family 38. *Linaceae* (Flax Family)

Linum usitatissimum, L.

Family 39. *Rutaceae* (Rue Family)

Citrus aurantium, (L.) Swingle

Citrus sinensis, Osbeck

Family 40. *Meliaceae* (Mahogany Family)

Turnera ulmifolia, L.

Family 41. *Euphorbiaceae* (Spurge Family)

Euphorbia spp. L.

337

Euphorbia supina

Ricinus communis, L.

Ricinus communis, L. var. sanguineus

Family 42. *Buxaceae* (Box Family)

Buxus spp., L.

Family 43. *Callitrichaceae* (Water-Starwort Family)

Callitriche verna, L.

Family 44. *Celastraceae* (Staff-Tree Family)

Euonymus japonicus, L.

Family 45. *Aceraceae* (Maple Family)

Acer platanoides, L.

Acer Pseudo-Platanus, L.

Acer rubrum, L.

Family 46. *Hippocastanaceae* (Buckeye or Horse-Chestnut Family)

Aesculus Hippocastanum, L.

Family 47. *Melianthaceae* (Melianthus Family)

Melianthus major, L.

Family 48. *Balsaminaceae* (Balsam Family)

Impatiens Balsamina, L.

Impatiens tricornis

Family 49. *Vitaceae* (Vine or Grape Family)

Vitis vinifera, L.

Family 50. *Tiliaceae* (Linden or Basswood Family)

Tilia parvifolia, Ehrh.

Family 51. *Malvaceae* (Mallow Family)

Abutilon Theophrasti, Medic.

Gossypium herbaceum, L.

Gossypium hirsutum, L.

Hibiscus spp. L.

Hibiscus Rosa-sinensis, L.

Sida grewioides

Sida spinosa, L.

Family 52. *Theaceae* (Tea Family)

Camellia spp. L.

Camellia japonica, L.

Family 53. *Cluslaceae* (Garcinia or St. John's-Wort Family)

        Clusia mexicana

        Hypericum japonicum, Thunb.

Family 54. *Tamaricaceae* (Tamarisk Family)

        Myricaria germanica, Desy.

Family 55. *Violaceae* (Violet Family)

        Viola spp. L.

        Viola tricolor, L.

Family 56. *Loasaceae* (Loasa Family)

        Mentzelia aspera, L.

Family 57. *Begoniaceae* (Begonia Family)

        Begonia spp. L.

        Begonia Evansiana, Andr.

        Begonia hiemalis

Family 58. *Cactaceae* (Cactus Family)

        Carnegiea gigantea, Britt. & Rose

        Cereus pentalophus

        Echinocactus ottonis, Link & Otto

        Opuntia cochenillifera, (L.) Mill.

        Zygocactus truncatus, Schum.

Family 59. *Lythraceae* (Loosestrife Family)

        Lythrum Salicaria, L.

Family 60. *Myrtaceae* (Myrtle Family)

        Myrthus moschata

Family 61. *Melastomataceae* (Melastoma Family)

        Medinilla magnifica, Lindl.

        Tibouchina lungifolia

Family 62. *Onagraceae* (Evening-Primose Family)

        Epilobium augustifolium, L.

        Epilobium cephalostigma, Hausk.

        Epilobium hirsutum, L.

        Epilobium roseum

        Fuchsia spp. L.

        Fuchsia hybrida, Voss

        Jussiaea peruviana

        Jussiaea suffruticosa, L.

Oenothera berteriana

Oenothera biennis, L.

Oenothera lamarckiana, DeVries

Oenothera odorata, Jacq.

Raimannia Oenotheren

Family 63. *Araliaceae* (Aralia or Ginseng Family)

Hedera amurensis, Hort.

Hedera colchica, Koch. var. arborea

Hedera Helix, L.

Family 64. *Apiaceae* (Parsley Family)

Aegopodium Podograria, L.

Aethusa cynapium, L.

Anethum graveolens, L.

Apium graveolens, L.

Apium gravelolens var. rapaceum, DC.

Daucus carota, L.

Pastinaca sativa, L.

Petroselinum hortense, Hoffm.

Sium latifolium, L.

Family 65. *Cornaceae* (Dogwood Family)

Acuba japenica, Thunb.

Cornus alba, L.

Cornus stolonifera, Michx.

Family 66. *Ericaceae* (Heath Family)

Azalea spp. L.

Azalea indica, L.

Loiseleuria procumbens, Desv.

Rhododendron ferrugineum, L.

Rhododendron Luteum, Sweet

Family 67. *Primulaceae* (Primose Family)

Anagallis arvensis, L.

Anagallis caerulea, Schreber.

Hottonia palustria, L.

Lysimachia mauritiana, Lam.

Primula obconica, Hance.

Family 68. *Oleaceae* (Olive Family)

                Fraxinus excelsior, L.

                Syringa vulgaris, L.

Family 69. *Asclepiadaceae* (Milkweed Family)

                Calotropis procera, Dry

                Crytostegia grandiflora, R. Br.

                Leptadenia pyrotechnica

Family 70. *Convolvulaceae* (Morning-Glory Family)

                Convolvulus arvensis, L.

                Convolvulus minor, Hort.

                Cuscuta gronovii, willd.

                Cuscuta indecora, Choisy

                Cuscuta pentagona, Engelm.

                Ipomoea Batatas, Lam.

                Ipomoea cairica, Sweet

                Ipomoea coccinea, L.

                Ipomoea Hederacea, (L.) Jacq.

                Ipomoea purpurea, (L.) Lam.

                Ipomoea Quamoclit, L.

                Pharbitis nil, Roth

Family 71. *Polemoniaceae* (Phlox Family)

                Cobaea macrostoma, Pav.

                Cobaea scandens, Cav.

Family 72. *Hydrophyllaceae* (Water-Leaf Family)

                Hydrophyllum virginianum, L.

                Nemophila insignis, Dougl.

                Phacelia tanacetifolia, Benth.

Family 73. *Boraginaceae* (Borage Family)

                Heliotropium peruvianum, L.

                Myosotis hispida

                Myosotis palustris, Lam.

                Symphytum cordatum, Willd.

Family 74. *Verbenaceae* (Vervain Family)

                Caryopteris x clandonensis

                Caryopteris incana, Mig.

                Verbena bipinnatifida, Nutt.

Verbena ciliata

Family 75. *Lamiaceae* (Mint Family)

    Ajuga reptans, L.

    Coleus spp. Lour.

    Coleus blumei, Benth.

    Coleus blumei x Coleus frederici

    Coleus rehneltianus hybridus

    Elsholtzia argyi, Lev.

    Glechoma hederacea, L.

    Hyptis atrorubens

    Hyptis suaveolens, Poit.

    Lamium album, L.

    Lamium amplexicaule, L.

    Lycopus Europaeus, L.

    Mentha piperita, L.

    Mentha rotundifolia, Huds.

    Mentha silvestris, L.

    Ocimum americanum, L.

    Ocimum Basilicum, L.

    Ocymum viride

    Perilla spp. L.

    Perilla crispa (Benth.) Deane

    Perilla frutescens, (L.) Britt.

    Perilla nankinensis, Bailey

    Perilla ocymoides, L.

    Perilla ocymoides var. nankinensis, Voss.

    Salvia, spp. L.

    Salvia occidentalis, Swartz

    Salvia runcinata

    Salvia splendens, Sello

Family 76. *Solanaceae* (Nightshade Family)

    Datura ferox, L.

    Hyoscyamus desertorum, Asch.

    Hyoscyamus niger, L.

    Lycopersicun esculentum, Mill.

    Nicotiana spp. L.

Nicotiana rustica, L.

Nicotiana sylvestris, Spegazzini & Comes

Nicotiana Tabacum, L.

Nicotiana Tabacum var. macrophylla, Shrank

Petunia spp. Juss.

Petunia grandiflora

Petunia hybrida, Vilm.

Petunia multiflora

Physalis alkekengi, (L.) Pers.

Physalis Franchetti, Hort.

Solanum andigena, L.

Solanum aviculare, Forst.

Solanum lacciniatum, Ait.

Solanum Lycopersicum, L.

Solanum Melongena, L.

Solanum nigrum, L.

Solantum tuberosum, L.

Solantum virginianum

Family 77. *Scrophulariaceae* (Figwort Family)

Digitalis spp. L.

Digitalis purpurea, L.

Mimulus luteus, L.

Paulowia spp. Sieb. & Zucc.

Paulowia tomentosa, Steud.

Torenia crustacea, Cham.

Torenia fournieri, Lind.

Verbascum Thapsus, L.

Veronica Beccabunga, L.

Veronica Chamaedrys, L.

Veronica imperialis, Hort.

Veronica peregrina, L.

Veronica Tournefortii, C. C. Gmel.

Family 78. *Bignoniaceae* (Bignonia Family)

Catalpa bignonioides, Walt.

Catalpa speciosa, Warder.

Family 79. *Pedaliaceae* (Pedalium Family)
        Sesamum radiatum, Schum.

Family 80. *Gesneriaceae* (Gesneria Family)
        Achimenes longiflora, DC.
        Gloxinia hybrida
        Sinningia speciosa, Benth. & Hook

Family 81. *Lentibulariaceae* (Bladderwort Family)
        Pinguicula vulgaris, L.
        Utricularia vulgaris, L.

Family 82. *Acanthaceae* (Acanthus Family)
        Asteracantha longifolia
        Asystasia gangetica, T. Anders.
        Ruellia tuberosa, L.
        Strobilanthes spp. Blume

Family 83. *Plantaginaceae* (Plaintain Family)
        Plantago hirtella
        Plantago major, L.
        Plantago minor

Family 84. *Caprifoliaceae* (Honeysuckle Family)
        Abelia grandiflora, Rehd.
        Sambucus nigra, L.
        Weigela spp. Thunb.
        Weigela florida, A. DC.

Family 85. *Dipsacaceae* (Teasel Family)
        Scabiosa atropurpurea, L.

Family 86. *Cucurbitaceae* (Gourd Family)
        Citrullus colocynthis, (L.) Schrad.
        Citrullus lanatus
        Cucumis melo, L.
        Cucumis prophetarum, L.
        Cucumis sativus, L.
        Cucurbita spp. L.
        Cucurbita maxima, Duchesne.
        Cucurbita moscata, Duchesne.
        Cucurbita pepo, L.
        Sicyos angulatus, L.

Family 87. *Campanulaceae* (Bluebell or Bellflower Family)

        Campanula pyramidalis, L.

        Campanula rotundifolia, L.

        Lobelia spp. L.

        Phyteuma Scheucheri, All.

        Specularia Speculum, A. DC.

        Lobelia Dortmanna, L.

        Lobelia Erinus, L.

Family 88. *Asteraceae* (Composite Family)

        Achillea Millefolium, L.

        Ageratum conyzoides, L.

        Anthemis tinotoria, L.

        Arctium lappa, L.

        Artemisia monosperma, Del.

        Aster spp. L.

        Aster ericoides, L.

        Aster linosyris

        Aster multiflorus, Ait.

        Baeria chrysostoma, Fisch. & Mey.

        Bellis perennis, L.

        Bidens spp. L.

        Bidens radiala, Thuill.

        Calendula spp. L.

        Callistephus chinensis, Nees.

        Carthamus tinctorius, L.

        Centaurea Cyanus, L.

        Centaurea montana, L.

        Chrysanthemum spp. L.

        Chrysanthemum coronarium, L.

        Chrysanthemum indicium, L.

        Chrysanthemum Leucanthemum, L.

        Chrysanthemum morifolium, Ramat.

        Cichorium Intybus, L.

        Cirsium palustre, (L.) Scop.

        Cosmos spp. Cav.

        Cosmos bipinnatus, Cav.

Crepis spp. L.

Crepis capillaris, (L.) Wallr.

Crepis leontodontoides

Cynara Scolymus, L.

Erigeron spp. L.

Erigeron Canadensis

Galinsoga parviflora, Cav.

Gerbera spp. Cass.

Gnaphalium lanceolatum

Gnaphalium silvaticum

Haplopappus gracilis, (Nutt.) Gray

Helianthus annuus, L.

Helianthus cucumerifolius, Torr. & Gray

Helianthus tuberosus, L.

Helichrysum bracteatum, Andr.

Hieracium Pilosella, L.

Hypochoeris radicata, L.

Lactuca sativa, L.

Lactuca scariola, L.

Matricaria Chamomilla, L.

Matricaria inodora, L.

Porophyllum lanceolatum, DC.

Prenanthes purpurea

Rudbeckia bicolor, Nutt.

Rudbeckia speciosa, Wenderoth

Senecio formosus, H.B.K.

Senecio odoris, Defl.

Solidago vigaurea, L.

Synedrella nodiflora, (L.) Gaertn.

Taraxacum officinale, Weber.

Tithonia speciosa, Hook.

Tragopogon porrifolius, L.

Tripleurospermum maritimum

Xanthium spp. L.

Xanthium commune, Britton.

Xanthium itaticum, Moretti

Xanthium pensylvanicum, Wallr.

Xanthium saccharatum, Widden.

Xanthium strumarium, L.

SUBJECT INDEX

SECTION I: TYPES OF IRRADIANCE

A. Action Spectra

1. *in vitro* 339, 344, 347, 815, 1073, 1958, 2038, 2160, 3043, 3115

2. *in vivo* 3, 12, 16, 58, 71, 73, 75, 78, 81, 84, 105, 116, 131, 132,
137, 149, 150, 151, 153, 159, 163, 173, 181, 189, 214, 215, 218, 219,
220, 221, 223, 234, 245, 248, 259, 288, 289, 290, 291, 295, 302, 304,
306, 319, 325, 329, 332, 337, 356, 361, 362, 380, 387, 388, 389, 390,
397, 424, 462, 499, 500, 503, 520, 521, 524, 525, 537, 541, 553, 557,
560, 561, 568, 572, 573, 577, 582, 586, 588, 592, 593, 623, 627, 662,
666, 671, 672, 673, 676, 677, 678, 679, 686, 687, 691, 692, 694, 709,
724, 731, 737, 756, 815, 816, 825, 826, 854, 858, 859, 872, 873, 883,
886, 899, 901, 909, 910, 911, 919, 943, 944, 952, 958, 961, 963, 964,
970, 974, 976, 978, 988, 989, 1000, 1006, 1008, 1051, 1052, 1058,
1081, 1120.5, 1126, 1159, 1174, 1188, 1189, 1203, 1210, 1211, 1212,
1214, 1217, 1218, 1242, 1251, 1286, 1288, 1317, 1318, 1321, 1327,
1340, 1368, 1371, 1372, 1388, 1393, 1400, 1401, 1402, 1404, 1409,
1411, 1412, 1417, 1424, 1435, 1436, 1445, 1456, 1461, 1466, 1470,
1474.5, 1475, 1487, 1488, 1489, 1494, 1505, 1506, 1507, 1519, 1534,
1552, 1553, 1566, 1567, 1573, 1616, 1637, 1648, 1657, 1658, 1667,
1684, 1685, 1686, 1691, 1692, 1693, 1721, 1724, 1739, 1749, 1753,
1772, 1783, 1804, 1815, 1834, 1835, 1836, 1837, 1838, 1839, 1840,
1841, 1842, 1846, 1849, 1870, 1898, 1908, 1909, 1910, 1911, 1938,
1957, 1959, 1963, 1966, 1970, 1971, 1972, 1991, 1992, 1999, 2006,
2011, 2012, 2015, 2021, 2029, 2030, 2035, 2045, 2047, 2052, 2054,
2055, 2056, 2058, 2065, 2090, 2112, 2113, 2114, 2127, 2147, 2148,
2162, 2196, 2197, 2199, 2215, 2216, 2224, 2229, 2240, 2243, 2253,
2255, 2260, 2273, 2291, 2306, 2307, 2308, 2310, 2322, 2340, 2346,
2348, 2349, 2372, 2387, 2398, 2402, 2408, 2409, 2410, 2411, 2414,
2416, 2418, 2419, 2430, 2454, 2463, 2470, 2471, 2472, 2488, 2489,
2490, 2492, 2493, 2500, 2514, 2521, 2522, 2541, 2549, 2551, 2552,
2582, 2610, 2611, 2613, 2615, 2620, 2626, 2628, 2629, 2636, 2638,
2639, 2643, 2658, 2659, 2662, 2668, 2671, 2672, 2673, 2674, 2676,
2689, 2690, 2694, 2699, 2705, 2706, 2708, 2745, 2755, 2756, 2773,
2784, 2812, 2813, 2818, 2825, 2826, 2830, 2881, 2882, 2890, 2902,
2912, 2932, 2945, 2957, 2969, 2984, 2996, 3013, 3021, 3033, 3039,

3040, 3041, 3044, 3045, 3048, 3049, 3054, 3059, 3060, 3090, 3107,
3109, 3111, 3112, 3113, 3116, 3117, 3118, 3120

B. Dose Response Studies

   1. Duration of irradiation varied 6, 8, 9, 11, 12, 16, 22, 31, 45, 56,
58, 60, 62, 63, 64, 65, 66, 70, 74, 75, 85, 88, 89, 93, 99, 100, 101,
102, 102, 104, 105, 108, 109, 110, 111, 112, 113, 114, 115, 125, 126,
131, 132, 133, 135, 143, 144, 145, 150, 152, 153, 154, 156, 157, 158,
159, 160, 162, 163, 164, 165, 167, 171, 180, 182, 189, 195, 196, 197,
209, 219, 232, 234, 241, 242, 248, 249, 250, 255, 259, 260, 265, 270,
272, 278, 289, 290, 291, 292, 297, 298, 306, 308, 317, 319, 321, 330,
333, 347, 356, 364, 370, 373, 374, 375, 376, 377, 378, 380, 383, 384,
387, 388, 397, 399, 402, 405, 431, 450, 453, 455, 459, 464, 465, 471,
474, 493.5, 494, 498, 499, 502, 505, 506, 510, 512, 514, 517, 518,
520, 525, 528, 537, 538, 539, 541, 543, 544, 545, 546, 547, 550, 552,
553, 554, 556, 557, 560, 569, 570, 578, 579, 580, 582, 583, 585, 586,
588, 591, 592, 593, 594, 596, 597, 598, 600, 601, 602, 603, 604, 605,
607, 609, 612, 613, 616, 617, 618, 619, 620, 622, 623, 626, 627, 630,
631, 652, 654, 656, 659, 661, 662, 674, 685, 686, 687, 692, 700, 704,
719, 720, 724, 726, 728, 729, 730, 734, 741, 742, 746, 749, 773, 774,
775, 777, 789, 791, 794, 811, 815, 816, 820, 821, 823, 824, 825, 826,
830, 835, 842, 847, 852, 854, 858, 863, 867, 870, 872, 874, 875, 884,
888, 889, 890, 894, 895, 896, 897, 898, 900, 903, 904, 909, 910, 911,
921.2, 922, 924, 925, 928, 943, 948, 952, 956, 958, 960, 977, 978,
980, 981, 983, 987, 989, 991, 999, 1007, 1008, 1010, 1013, 1014, 1016,
1017, 1020, 1024, 1029, 1041, 1043, 1044, 1051, 1052, 1058, 1073,
1080, 1081, 1086, 1089, 1097, 1099, 1101, 1120, 1120.5, 1121, 1122,
1127, 1129, 1130, 1152, 1164, 1165, 1171, 1179, 1181, 1186, 1187,
1189, 1195, 1199, 1200, 1202, 1208, 1209, 1210, 1211, 1223, 1234,
1239, 1240, 1241, 1242, 1243, 1246, 1254, 1255, 1256, 1257, 1288,
1290, 1292, 1296, 1300, 1302, 1303, 1311, 1314, 1316, 1320, 1321,
1322, 1323, 1325, 1327, 1329, 1330, 1353, 1354, 1358, 1359, 1360,
1361, 1366, 1367, 1370, 1371, 1372, 1380, 1393, 1394, 1395, 1396,
1398, 1400, 1401, 1402, 1403, 1404, 1408, 1409, 1411, 1417, 1422,
1433, 1434, 1449, 1456 1466, 1474.5, 1475, 1478, 1479, 1488, 1489,
1490, 1505, 1506, 1508, 1509, 1522, 1526, 1528, 1538, 1540, 1541,
1542, 1554, 1559, 1565, 1566, 1569, 1571, 1574, 1575, 1579, 1581,

1584, 1616, 1640, 1655, 1656, 1657, 1658, 1663, 1665, 1666, 1667,
1668, 1671, 1672, 1674, 1677, 1686, 1691, 1692, 1693, 1700, 1701,
1715, 1720, 1724, 1725, 1732, 1737, 1738, 1740, 1741, 1743, 1746,
1751, 1752, 1778, 1787, 1789, 1801, 1802, 1804, 1805, 1806, 1809,
1813, 1814, 1817, 1818, 1830, 1837, 1838, 1839, 1841, 1842, 1846,
1848, 1849, 1855, 1859, 1860, 1862, 1863, 1869, 1870, 1874, 1878,
1879, 1881, 1882, 1884, 1885, 1887, 1888, 1891, 1892, 1893, 1895,
1898, 1900, 1905, 1906, 1922, 1924, 1941, 1942, 1957, 1961, 1963,
1975, 1976, 1982, 1986, 1992, 1998, 1999, 2006, 2008, 2011, 2014,
2016, 2017, 2018, 2020, 2021, 2023, 2024, 2027, 2028, 2031, 2032,
2036, 2037, 2044, 2047, 2049, 2050, 2052, 2053, 2055, 2056, 2058,
2060, 2061, 2062, 2063, 2064, 2068, 2071, 2073, 2076, 2077, 2080,
2090, 2099, 2100, 2103, 2104, 2107, 2116, 2120, 2124, 2127, 2132,
2133, 2146, 2151, 2153, 2154, 2160, 2161, 2162, 2179, 2181, 2183,
2184, 2185, 2188, 2189, 2190, 2196, 2198, 2199, 2203, 2208, 2210,
2211, 2213, 2218, 2226, 2228, 2232, 2235, 2240, 2243, 2244, 2256,
2264, 2276, 2287, 2295, 2305, 2312, 2315, 2327, 2328, 2329, 2330,
2332, 2333, 2335, 2345, 2348, 2349, 2350, 2374, 2377, 2378, 2380,
2390, 2391, 2395, 2397, 2398, 2399, 2402, 2403, 2404, 2405, 2406,
2412, 2416, 2418, 2419, 2420, 2423, 2425, 2427, 2434, 2435, 2436,
2438, 2439, 2440, 2441, 2445, 2449, 2451, 2470, 2474, 2482, 2484,
2489, 2499, 2514, 2521, 2522, 2541, 2543, 2547, 2548, 2558, 2559,
2563, 2574, 2594, 2596, 2599, 2600, 2606, 2610, 2611, 2614, 2616,
2617, 2622, 2625, 2628, 2636, 2637, 2639, 2640, 2641, 2642, 2643,
2644, 2645, 2665, 2666, 2667, 2668, 2670, 2674, 2675, 2676, 2677,
2678, 2683, 2693, 2698, 2699, 2700, 2701, 2704, 2707, 2713, 2714,
2715, 2727, 2728, 2729, 2730, 2731, 2735, 2736, 2739, 2742, 2744,
2747, 2752, 2754, 2759, 2767, 2774, 2781, 2782, 2783, 2784, 2785,
2789, 2797, 2799, 2800, 2801, 2804, 2805, 2806, 2812, 2813, 2816,
2818, 2823, 2824, 2828, 2829, 2830, 2831, 2832, 2842, 2843, 2844,
2846, 2848, 2849, 2852, 2854, 2866, 2879, 2890, 2895, 2906, 2907,
2910, 2912, 2913, 2914, 2915, 2916, 2917, 2918, 2919, 2920, 2926,
2927, 2932, 2938, 2959, 2961, 2962, 2963, 2965, 2966, 2977, 2978,
2981, 2987, 2992, 2993, 2996, 3009, 3013, 3015, 3016, 3017, 3018,
3029, 3061, 3062, 3074, 3077, 3078, 3080, 3083, 3090, 3099, 3100,
3104, 3105, 3107, 3111, 3112, 3113, 3114, 3115, 3116, 3117, 3118,

3120, 3121

2. Intensity of irradiation varied 5, 6, 14, 16, 26, 56, 58, 59, 70, 72, 81, 103, 105, 112, 129, 131, 132, 141, 143, 144, 149, 150, 153, 163, 167, 169, 170, 189, 219, 234, 238, 258, 259, 260, 270, 273, 274, 277, 278, 291, 298, 325, 330, 387, 388, 390, 397, 414, 431, 496, 505, 506, 520, 523, 538, 539, 553, 557, 560, 566, 568, 574, 577, 582, 584, 591, 592, 593, 594, 597, 598, 618, 619, 620, 623, 626, 627, 630, 631, 652, 659, 661, 662, 663, 687, 690, 693, 694, 700, 719, 728, 736, 737, 745, 772, 775, 776, 815, 821, 824, 842, 844, 920, 921.2, 921.5, 922, 943, 944, 952, 958, 960, 961, 963, 978, 983, 988, 989, 1000, 1002, 1004, 1013, 1016, 1017, 1020, 1024, 1034, 1041, 1083, 1086, 1099, 1120.5, 1129, 1130, 1159, 1170, 1181, 1188, 1222, 1223, 1260, 1275, 1317, 1321, 1330, 1353, 1359, 1360, 1371, 1395, 1406, 1409, 1410, 1411, 1417, 1425, 1427, 1432, 1435, 1456, 1461, 1474.5, 1475, 1487, 1488, 1489, 1506, 1507, 1526, 1534, 1541, 1559, 1572, 1584, 1603, 1610, 1616, 1617, 1658, 1665, 1667, 1685, 1686, 1692, 1700, 1701, 1724, 1755, 1756, 1758, 1762, 1763, 1768, 1772, 1796, 1804, 1818, 1836, 1837, 1847, 1849, 1869, 1870, 1873, 1878, 1891, 1895, 1937, 1939, 1941, 1967, 1970, 1971, 1972, 1974, 1976, 1990, 1991, 1998, 2011, 2016, 2031, 2033, 2044, 2047, 2054, 2055, 2061, 2069, 2103, 2109, 2118, 2145, 2161, 2162, 2185, 2189, 2196, 2197, 2198, 2199, 2201, 2203, 2240, 2244, 2245, 2260, 2264, 2265, 2273, 2328, 2329, 2331, 2332, 2345, 2349, 2354, 2371, 2372, 2374, 2381, 2382, 2402, 2418, 2419, 2421, 2422, 2423, 2424, 2425, 2445, 2449, 2454, 2463, 2470, 2471, 2472, 2476, 2478, 2479, 2484, 2486, 2492, 2493, 2500, 2501, 2502, 2511, 2513, 2514, 2521, 2522, 2569, 2593, 2599, 2610, 2611, 2613, 2614, 2625, 2626, 2628, 2629, 2630, 2633, 2636, 2637, 2638, 2641, 2643, 2668, 2690, 2694, 2698, 2700, 2701, 2704, 2707, 2708, 2712, 2714, 2715, 2719, 2722, 2739, 2754, 2781, 2815, 2816, 2818, 2823, 2824, 2829, 2830, 2948, 2881, 2882, 2890, 2910, 2912, 2913, 2914, 2915, 2918, 2935, 2943, 2945, 2969, 2976, 2977, 2978, 2987, 2996, 3017, 3018, 3034, 3041, 3042, 3044, 3048, 3049, 3062, 3083, 3097, 3099, 3100, 3103, 3107, 3111, 3112, 3113, 3114, 3115, 3116, 3117, 3118, 3120, 3122, 3123

C. Effects of various individual spectral bands

1. Near ultra violet 3, 46, 48, 50, 73, 81, 85, 325, 329, 330, 347, 356,

380, 390, 394, 412, 424, 466, 495, 560, 589, 608, 609, 662, 669, 670, 694, 726, 825, 838, 926, 963, 967, 970, 977, 978, 981, 989, 991, 1040, 1082, 1120.5, 1189, 1190, 1209, 1417, 1519, 1598, 1615, 1633, 1634, 1636, 1642, 1643, 1724, 1749, 1772, 1778, 1939, 1972, 1991, 1992, 2006, 2045, 2052, 2065, 2075, 2086, 2100, 2109, 2112, 2113, 2114, 2131, 2133, 2154, 2216, 2224, 2273, 2291, 2292, 2308, 2321, 2372, 2384, 2385, 2386, 2418, 2419, 2430, 2454, 2470, 2471, 2472, 2474, 2475, 2476, 2481, 2490, 2495, 2613, 2615, 2620, 2625, 2626, 2628, 2629, 2630, 2636, 2644, 2645, 2668, 2676, 2720, 2825, 2890, 2912, 2985, 2986, 2987, 2988, 2992, 2993, 3012, 3048, 3060, 3096, 3111, 3112, 3115, 3117, 3118, 3119, 3120

2. Blue 3, 12, 15, 17, 27, 43, 46, 48, 50, 56, 57, 58, 59, 62, 66, 71, 73, 75, 78, 81, 84, 85, 91, 95, 96, 103, 104, 105, 106, 107, 108, 109, 110, 111, 112, 113, 114, 115, 116, 121, 124, 125, 129, 130, 131, 132, 133, 137, 149, 150, 151, 152, 153, 154, 156, 158, 163, 170, 171, 173, 179, 180, 181, 186, 199, 211, 212, 214, 223, 248, 253, 254, 255, 257, 258, 259, 261, 272, 286, 288, 289, 290, 291, 292, 302, 304, 313, 319, 321, 322, 325, 329, 330, 332, 347, 361, 362, 363, 369, 380, 382, 383, 385, 387, 388, 389, 390, 392, 394, 395, 397, 405, 413, 424, 430, 435, 436, 449, 450, 453, 457, 458, 459, 460, 462, 465, 469, 493, 493.5, 494, 495, 497, 499, 500, 507, 511, 520, 521, 522, 525, 528, 532, 534, 537, 540, 541, 543, 544, 545, 555, 557, 558, 560, 561, 563, 566, 567, 568, 572, 573, 578, 582, 583, 586, 587, 588, 591, 592, 593, 594, 596, 597, 598, 601, 602, 603, 604, 605, 607, 608, 609, 612, 613, 614, 615, 618, 619, 620, 621, 622, 623, 627, 630, 631, 636, 638, 640, 649, 651, 652, 654, 658, 659, 662, 663, 664, 665, 666, 667, 668, 669, 671, 672, 673, 674, 675, 676, 677, 678, 679, 680, 684, 686, 687, 689, 690, 691, 692, 693, 694, 701, 704, 709, 724, 725, 731, 732, 737, 756, 757, 758, 759, 761, 763, 765, 766, 767, 769, 777, 782.5, 790, 791, 815, 816, 823, 824, 825, 828, 834, 835, 838, 854, 857, 859, 872, 873, 883, 884, 888, 889, 890, 891, 892, 893, 909, 910, 911, 919, 920, 921, 921.2, 921.5, 926, 929, 930, 931, 933, 934, 941, 943, 944, 948, 949, 952, 955, 957, 958, 960, 963, 967, 970, 973, 974, 975, 976, 978, 988, 989, 1000, 1002, 1014, 1019, 1022, 1024, 1028, 1029, 1030, 1031, 1032, 1033, 1035, 1040, 1041, 1042, 1043, 1044, 1058, 1078, 1081, 1098, 1100, 1102, 1112, 1120.5, 1126, 1133, 1150, 1152, 1159, 1170,

1171, 1174, 1176, 1189, 1190, 1191, 1192, 1199, 1200, 1201, 1202, 1203, 1204, 1210, 1211, 1213, 1214, 1215, 1216, 1217, 1218, 1224, 1225, 1226, 1233, 1242, 1243, 1245, 1251, 1252, 1254, 1255, 1256, 1257, 1258, 1260, 1262, 1263, 1265, 1266, 1269, 1270, 1276, 1277, 1279, 1280, 1286, 1288, 1296, 1297, 1307.5, 1309, 1317, 1318, 1320, 1321, 1322, 1330, 1339, 1340, 1353, 1354, 1358, 1359, 1360, 1361, 1365, 1366, 1376, 1377, 1388, 1391, 1392, 1393, 1400, 1401, 1402, 1403, 1404, 1406, 1408, 1409, 1410, 1411, 1412, 1417, 1427, 1429, 1435, 1436, 1437, 1439, 1445, 1454, 1455, 1456, 1461, 1462, 1463, 1466, 1470, 1474.5, 1475, 1478, 1485, 1486, 1487, 1488, 1489, 1494, 1503, 1507, 1508, 1509, 1515, 1516, 1519, 1534, 1547, 1549, 1549.5, 1560, 1561, 1566, 1572, 1573, 1576, 1584, 1594, 1598, 1603, 1615, 1616, 1630, 1633, 1634, 1637, 1640, 1641, 1648, 1650, 1657, 1658, 1666, 1677, 1684, 1686, 1691, 1692, 1717, 1718, 1720, 1721, 1724, 1725, 1727, 1728, 1729, 1730, 1736, 1737, 1739, 1749, 1753, 1755, 1756, 1757, 1758, 1759, 1760, 1761, 1762, 1763, 1764, 1765, 1767, 1768, 1771, 1772, 1778, 1783, 1787, 1788, 1796, 1802, 1803, 1804, 1806, 1807, 1810, 1811, 1812, 1815, 1816, 1817, 1827, 1828, 1835, 1836, 1837, 1838, 1839, 1840, 1841, 1842, 1846, 1847, 1849, 1859, 1860, 1862, 1870, 1873, 1874, 1878, 1908, 1909, 1910, 1911, 1923, 1925, 1927, 1928, 1933, 1937, 1938, 1941, 1957, 1958, 1959, 1966, 1970, 1972, 1975, 1984, 1988, 1991, 1992, 1993, 1994, 1995, 1998, 1999, 2001, 2005, 2006, 2011, 2015, 2024, 2025, 2026, 2029, 2030, 2031, 2032, 2033, 2034, 2035, 2038, 2045, 2047, 2051, 2052, 2054, 2055, 2060, 2061, 2062, 2063, 2064, 2065, 2070, 2075, 2080, 2095, 2096, 2097, 2098, 2099, 2100, 2102, 2103, 2104, 2106, 2109, 2112, 2113, 2114, 2116, 2118, 2123, 2126, 2127, 2143, 2147, 2148, 2154, 2161, 2178, 2179, 2180, 2181, 2182, 2184, 2185, 2188, 2189, 2192, 2196, 2197, 2199, 2211, 2214, 2216, 2223, 2224, 2225, 2226, 2229, 2230, 2232, 2236, 2237, 2238, 2239, 2240, 2245, 2251, 2252, 2255, 2272, 2273, 2278, 2289, 2291, 2292, 2295, 2305, 2306, 2307, 2308, 2310, 2318, 2320, 2322, 2327, 2328, 2329, 2330, 2331, 2332, 2333, 2342, 2347, 2348, 2349, 2351, 2371, 2372, 2385, 2386, 2387, 2388, 2395, 2397, 2398, 2402, 2411, 2417, 2418, 2419, 2421, 2422, 2423, 2424, 2425, 2426, 2427, 2428, 2430, 2432, 2441, 2454, 2455, 2456, 2459, 2461, 2463, 2469, 2470, 2471, 2472, 2474, 2475, 2476, 2481,

2482, 2483, 2484, 2488, 2490, 2492, 2493, 2495, 2500, 2501, 2509,
2511, 2512, 2513, 2514, 2521, 2522, 2523, 2538, 2539, 2541, 2544,
2549, 2550, 2551, 2552, 2558, 2559, 2569, 2571, 2573, 2574, 2599,
2600, 2601, 2602, 2606, 2607, 2610, 2611, 2613, 2614, 2615, 2620,
2623, 2625, 2626, 2628, 2629, 2631, 2632, 2633, 2634, 2635, 2636,
2637, 2638, 2639, 2642, 2644, 2646, 2647, 2648, 2649, 2652, 2654,
2658, 2659, 2660, 2661, 2662, 2665, 2666, 2667, 2668, 2669, 2671,
2672, 2673, 2674, 2676, 2690, 2695, 2696, 2697, 2698, 2699, 2705,
2708, 2714, 2715, 2719, 2745, 2746, 2753, 2754, 2755, 2756, 2757,
2764, 2765, 2773, 2774, 2781, 2782, 2812, 2813, 2814, 2815, 2819,
2822, 2823, 2824, 2825, 2826, 2830, 2831, 2832, 2834, 2835, 2847,
2848, 2852, 2860, 2865, 2870, 2871, 2872, 2875, 2879, 2881, 2889,
2890, 2892, 2893, 2894, 2895, 2896, 2897, 2898, 2899, 2901, 2902,
2904, 2905, 2910, 2912, 2915, 2918, 2932, 2935, 2938, 2939, 2943,
2944, 2945, 2946, 2951, 2952, 2953, 2957, 2967, 2969, 2970, 2975,
2976, 2977, 2978, 2982, 2984, 2987, 2996, 3003, 3012, 3013, 3014,
3017, 3021, 3023, 3024, 3025, 3029, 3030, 3033, 3034, 3035, 3037,
3038, 3039, 3041, 3043, 3048, 3049, 3054, 3059, 3060, 3077, 3080,
3088, 3089, 3090, 3096, 3097, 3099, 3100, 3102, 3107, 3108, 3109,
3111, 3112, 3113, 3114, 3115, 3116, 3117, 3118, 3119, 3120, 3121,
3122, 3123

3. Red 1, 2, 3, 4, 5, 6, 10, 12, 13, 14, 15, 16, 17, 19, 20, 21, 22, 23,
24, 25, 26, 27, 29, 30, 31, 32, 33, 34, 35, 36, 37, 38, 43, 44, 45,
46, 48, 50, 54, 55, 56, 57, 58, 59, 60, 68, 69, 70, 71, 72, 73, 74,
75, 76, 77, 78, 79, 80, 81, 82, 84, 85, 87, 88, 89, 90, 91, 92, 93,
95, 96, 98, 100, 101, 102, 103, 104, 105, 106, 107, 108, 109, 110,
111, 112, 113, 114, 115, 116, 117, 118, 119, 120, 121, 123, 125, 126,
127, 128, 129, 130, 131, 132, 133, 134, 135, 136, 137, 138, 139, 140,
141, 143, 144, 146, 147, 148, 149, 150, 151, 152, 153, 154, 156, 157,
158, 159, 160, 161, 162, 163, 164, 165, 166, 167, 168, 169, 170, 171,
172, 173, 174, 178, 179, 180, 181, 182, 186, 188, 189, 190, 191, 192,
193, 194, 195, 196, 197, 198, 199, 200, 201, 205, 206, 209, 211, 212,
214, 232, 234, 241, 242, 245, 248, 249, 250, 251, 252, 253, 254, 255,
256, 257, 258, 259, 260, 261, 262, 264, 265, 267, 269, 270, 271, 272,
273, 274, 275, 277, 278, 279, 281, 286, 287, 288, 289, 290, 291, 292,
293, 295, 296, 297, 298, 299, 300, 301, 302, 304, 305, 306, 307, 308,

311, 313, 314, 315, 316, 317, 318, 319, 321, 322, 323, 324, 325, 329,
332, 333, 334, 337, 342, 347, 348, 350, 351, 353, 355, 356, 357, 358,
359, 360, 360.5, 361, 362, 363, 367, 368, 369, 370, 371, 372, 373,
374, 375, 380, 381, 382, 383, 385, 386, 387, 388, 389, 390, 392, 393,
395, 397, 398, 400, 401, 402, 403, 405, 406, 407, 408, 413, 415, 417,
418, 419, 420, 421, 422, 423, 425, 431, 433, 434, 435, 436, 437, 438,
439, 440, 441, 445, 446, 447, 448, 449, 450, 453, 455, 457, 458, 459,
461, 462, 464, 465, 469, 470, 471, 472, 473, 475, 477, 478, 479, 480,
481, 484, 485, 486, 487, 488, 489, 490, 491, 492, 493, 493.5, 494,
495, 496, 497, 498, 499, 500, 501, 502, 503, 504, 505, 506, 507, 509,
511, 512, 517, 518, 519, 520, 521, 522, 523, 524, 525, 526, 527, 528,
529, 530, 532, 533, 534, 537, 538, 539, 540, 541, 543, 544, 545, 550,
552, 553, 554, 555, 556, 557, 558, 560, 561, 563, 564, 566, 567, 568,
571, 572, 573, 574, 575, 576, 577, 578, 579, 580, 581, 582, 583, 584,
585, 586, 587, 588, 590, 591, 592, 593, 594, 598, 604, 610, 611, 612,
613, 614, 615, 616, 617, 618, 619, 620, 621, 622, 623, 624, 626, 627,
628, 630, 631, 632, 634, 635, 636, 638, 641, 644, 646, 647, 649, 650,
651, 652, 654, 655, 656, 657, 658, 659, 660.5, 661, 662, 663, 664,
665, 666, 667, 668, 669, 670, 671, 672, 673, 674, 675, 676, 677, 678,
679, 680, 682, 683, 684, 685, 686, 687, 689, 690, 691, 692, 693,
693.5, 694, 695, 696, 698, 700, 701, 702, 703, 704, 705, 706, 708,
709, 710, 711, 712, 713, 714, 715, 716, 717, 718, 719, 720, 723, 724,
727, 728, 731, 732, 733, 734, 735, 736, 737, 738, 739, 740, 741, 742,
745, 746, 747, 748, 749, 750, 751, 753, 754, 756, 757, 758, 759, 760,
761, 762, 763, 765, 766, 767, 769, 771, 772, 773, 774, 775, 776, 777,
778, 782, 782.5, 783, 786, 788, 790, 791, 793, 794, 795, 796, 797,
803, 805, 810, 811, 815, 816, 819, 820, 821, 822, 823, 825, 826, 828,
830, 831, 832, 833, 834, 835, 836, 837, 838, 842, 843, 844, 847, 848,
849, 850, 851, 852, 853, 854, 855, 856, 857, 859, 860, 861, 863, 864,
865, 869, 870, 871, 872, 873, 874, 875, 876, 877, 878, 879, 880, 882,
883, 884, 885, 886, 887, 889, 890, 891, 892, 893, 894, 895, 896, 898,
899, 900, 901, 903, 904, 905, 907, 908, 909, 910, 911, 914, 916, 917,
919, 920, 921, 921.2, 921.5, 923, 927, 928, 929, 930, 932, 933, 934,
935, 936, 939, 941, 942, 943, 944, 946, 947, 948, 949, 950, 951, 952,
954, 955, 956, 957, 958, 959, 960, 961, 963, 964, 965, 966, 967, 970,
971, 973, 974, 975, 976, 977, 978, 980, 981, 983, 984, 987, 989, 991,

992, 994, 999, 1001, 1004, 1006, 1007, 1008, 1010, 1013, 1015, 1016, 1017, 1019, 1020, 1022, 1024, 1028, 1029, 1030, 1031, 1032, 1033, 1034, 1035, 1038, 1040, 1042, 1043, 1044, 1051, 1052, 1058, 1073, 1076, 1077, 1078, 1079, 1080, 1081, 1083, 1084, 1085, 1086, 1087, 1088, 1089, 1090, 1094, 1095, 1096, 1097, 1098, 1099, 1100, 1101, 1102, 1104, 1106, 1108, 1109, 1110, 1111, 1112, 1113, 1115, 1118, 1119, 1120, 1120.5, 1123, 1124, 1125, 1126, 1127, 1128, 1129, 1130, 1131, 1132, 1133, 1134, 1137, 1138, 1140, 1141, 1142, 1143, 1144, 1145, 1146, 1147, 1148, 1149, 1150, 1152, 1154, 1155, 1156, 1157, 1158, 1159, 1161, 1163, 1166, 1167, 1170, 1171, 1172, 1174, 1175, 1176, 1178, 1179, 1180, 1181, 1182, 1184, 1185, 1186, 1187, 1188, 1189, 1190, 1191, 1193, 1194, 1195, 1196, 1197, 1198, 1199, 1200, 1201, 1202, 1203, 1204, 1205, 1206, 1207, 1208, 1210, 1212, 1213, 1214, 1215, 1216, 1217, 1218, 1219, 1221, 1222, 1223, 1224, 1225, 1226, 1227, 1228, 1229, 1232, 1233, 1234, 1235, 1236, 1237, 1238, 1242, 1243, 1245, 1246.5, 1247, 1251, 1252, 1253, 1254, 1255, 1256, 1257, 1258, 1259, 1260, 1261, 1262, 1263, 1264, 1265, 1266, 1267, 1269, 1271, 1273, 1275, 1276, 1278, 1279, 1280, 1281, 1282, 1283, 1284, 1285, 1286, 1288, 1290, 1292, 1294, 1296, 1297, 1299, 1300, 1301, 1302, 1303, 1304, 1305, 1306, 1307, 1307.5, 1308, 1309, 1311, 1312, 1313, 1314, 1315, 1316, 1317, 1318, 1320, 1321, 1322, 1325, 1326, 1327, 1328, 1329, 1330, 1331, 1332, 1333, 1334, 1335, 1336, 1337, 1338, 1339, 1340, 1352, 1353, 1354, 1355, 1356, 1357, 1358, 1359, 1360, 1361, 1362, 1363, 1364, 1365, 1366, 1367, 1369, 1370, 1371, 1372, 1374, 1375, 1376, 1377, 1378, 1379, 1380, 1381, 1383, 1384, 1385, 1386, 1387, 1388, 1389, 1390, 1391, 1392, 1393, 1394, 1395, 1396, 1397, 1398, 1400, 1401, 1402, 1404, 1406, 1408, 1409, 1410, 1411, 1412, 1413, 1414, 1415, 1416, 1417, 1418, 1419, 1420, 1421, 1422, 1423, 1424, 1425, 1426, 1427, 1428, 1429, 1431, 1432, 1435, 1436, 1437, 1437.5, 1439, 1442, 1445, 1446, 1447, 1448, 1449, 1450, 1451, 1452, 1453, 1454, 1455, 1456, 1459, 1461, 1462, 1463, 1466, 1467, 1468, 1470, 1472, 1473, 1474.5, 1475, 1478, 1479, 1480, 1481, 1482, 1484, 1485, 1486, 1487, 1488, 1489, 1490, 1492, 1493, 1494, 1497, 1498, 1500, 1501, 1502, 1503, 1505, 1506, 1507, 1508, 1509, 1514, 1515, 1516, 1518, 1519, 1520, 1521, 1522, 1524, 1525, 1526, 1528, 1529, 1530, 1531, 1534, 1535, 1538, 1541, 1542, 1544,

1545, 1546, 1547, 1548, 1548.5, 1549, 1549.5, 1550, 1551, 1552, 1553,
1554, 1555, 1558, 1559, 1560, 1561, 1562, 1564, 1565, 1566, 1567,
1571, 1572, 1573, 1574, 1576, 1577, 1578, 1579, 1579.5, 1580, 1581,
1583, 1584, 1585, 1586, 1587, 1589, 1590, 1591, 1592, 1594, 1595,
1596, 1597, 1598, 1599, 1600, 1601, 1602, 1603, 1606, 1607, 1608,
1609, 1610, 1614, 1615, 1616, 1617, 1618, 1619, 1620, 1621, 1622,
1623, 1625, 1628, 1630, 1631, 1632, 1633, 1634, 1637, 1638, 1640,
1641, 1646, 1648, 1649, 1650, 1651, 1652, 1653, 1655, 1656, 1657,
1658, 1659, 1660, 1661, 1662, 1663, 1664, 1665, 1666, 1667, 1668,
1669, 1670, 1671, 1672, 1674, 1675, 1676, 1677, 1678, 1679, 1680,
1681, 1682, 1683, 1684, 1685, 1686, 1688, 1689, 1690, 1691, 1692,
1693, 1694, 1695, 1697, 1699, 1700, 1701, 1702, 1703, 1704, 1706,
1707, 1708, 1709, 1710, 1712, 1713, 1715, 1716, 1717, 1718, 1720,
1721, 1724, 1725, 1726, 1730, 1731, 1732, 1735, 1736, 1737, 1738,
1739, 1740, 1741, 1742, 1743, 1744, 1745, 1746, 1748, 1749, 1750,
1751, 1752, 1753, 1754, 1755, 1756, 1757, 1758, 1759, 1760, 1761,
1762, 1763, 1764, 1765, 1767, 1768, 1771, 1772, 1774, 1776, 1777,
1778, 1779, 1780, 1781, 1782, 1783, 1784, 1785, 1788, 1789, 1790,
1791, 1793, 1794, 1795, 1796, 1797, 1798, 1799, 1800, 1801, 1802,
1803, 1804, 1805, 1806, 1807, 1808, 1809, 1810, 1811, 1812, 1813,
1814, 1815, 1817, 1818, 1820, 1821, 1823, 1825, 1826, 1827, 1828,
1829, 1830, 1832, 1833, 1835, 1836, 1837, 1838, 1839, 1841, 1842,
1846, 1847, 1848, 1849, 1855, 1859, 1860, 1861, 1862, 1863, 1869,
1870, 1873, 1874, 1878, 1881, 1891, 1895, 1900, 1905, 1908, 1909,
1910, 1911, 1913, 1914, 1915, 1917, 1918, 1919, 1920, 1921, 1922,
1924, 1925, 1927, 1928, 1931, 1932, 1933, 1935, 1936, 1937, 1938,
1940, 1941, 1942, 1943, 1944, 1945, 1946, 1948, 1949, 1950, 1951,
1953, 1954, 1955, 1956, 1957, 1958, 1959, 1960, 1961, 1962, 1963,
1964, 1965, 1966, 1967, 1969, 1970, 1971, 1972, 1973, 1974, 1975,
1976, 1977, 1978, 1979, 1980, 1981, 1982, 1983, 1984, 1985, 1986,
1987, 1988, 1989, 1990, 1991, 1992, 1993, 1994, 1995, 1996, 1997,
1998, 1999, 2000, 2001, 2003, 2005, 2006, 2008, 2009, 2010, 2011,
2012, 2014, 2015, 2016, 2018, 2019, 2020, 2021, 2023, 2024, 2025,
2026, 2027, 2028, 2029, 2030, 2031, 2032, 2033, 2034, 2035, 2036,
2037, 2038, 2039, 2040, 2041, 2042, 2043, 2044, 2045, 2047, 2049,
2050, 2051, 2052, 2053, 2054, 2055, 2060, 2061, 2062, 2063, 2064,

2065, 2066, 2067, 2068, 2069, 2070, 2072, 2073, 2075, 2076, 2077,
2080, 2081, 2083, 2084, 2085, 2087, 2088, 2090, 2091, 2094, 2095,
2096, 2097, 2098, 2099, 2100, 2101, 2103, 2104, 2105, 2107, 2108,
2109, 2115, 2116, 2117, 2118, 2119, 2120, 2121, 2122, 2123, 2124,
2125, 2126, 2127, 2128, 2129, 2130, 2131, 2132, 3133, 2137, 2138,
2140, 2141, 2142, 2143, 2144, 2145, 2146, 2147, 2148, 2151, 2152,
2153, 2154, 2155, 2156, 2157, 2158, 2159, 2160, 2161, 2162, 2163,
2164, 2165, 2166, 2167, 2169, 2172, 2173, 2174, 2175, 2176, 2178,
2179, 2180, 2181, 2182, 2183, 2184, 2185, 2186, 2187, 2188, 2189,
2190, 2192, 2194, 2195, 2196, 2197, 2198, 2199, 2200, 2201, 2202,
2203, 2204, 2205, 2206, 2207, 2208, 2209, 2210, 2211, 2212, 2213,
2214, 2215, 2216, 2217, 2218, 2219, 2220, 2221, 2222, 2223, 2224,
2225, 2226, 2229, 2230, 2231, 2232, 2234, 2235, 2236, 2237, 2238,
2239, 2240, 2241, 2242, 2243, 2245, 2251, 2252, 2253, 2255, 2256,
2260, 2264, 2265, 2266, 2267, 2268, 2269, 2270, 2272, 2273, 2277,
2278, 2280, 2281, 2282, 2283, 2284, 2285, 2286, 2287, 2288, 2289,
2291, 2292, 2295, 2296, 2297, 2298, 2299, 2300, 2301, 2302, 2305,
2306, 2307, 2308, 2310, 2311, 2312, 2313, 2314, 2315, 2316, 2317,
2318, 2320, 2322, 2323, 2324, 2325, 2326, 2327, 2328, 2329, 2330,
2331, 2332, 2333, 2334, 2335, 2337, 2340, 2342, 2343, 2344, 2345,
2346, 2347, 2348, 2349, 2350, 2351, 2353, 2354, 2356, 2357, 2359,
2360, 2362, 2363, 2364, 2365, 2366, 2368, 2370, 2371, 2372, 2373,
2374, 2375, 2376, 2377, 2378, 2380, 2381, 2382, 2383, 2386, 2387,
2388, 2389, 2390, 2391, 2392, 2394, 2395, 2396, 2397, 2398, 2399,
2400, 2401, 2402, 2404, 2406, 2407, 2408, 2409, 2410, 2414, 2416,
2417, 2418, 2419, 2420, 2421, 2422, 2423, 2424, 2425, 2426, 2427,
2428, 2430, 2432, 2433, 2434, 2435, 2436, 2438, 2441, 2442, 2445,
2449, 2451, 2453, 2354, 2455, 2456, 2459, 2461, 2463, 2464, 2465,
2466, 2467, 2468, 2469, 2470, 2471, 2472, 2474, 2475, 2476, 2478,
2479, 2480, 2481, 2482, 2483, 2484, 2485, 2486, 2487, 2488, 2490,
2492, 2493, 2494, 2495, 2498, 2499, 2500, 2501, 2502, 2503, 2506,
2509, 2511, 2512, 2513, 2514, 2515, 2516, 2517, 2518, 2521, 2522,
2523, 2537, 2538, 2539, 2540, 2541, 2542, 2543, 2544, 2545, 2546,
2547, 2548, 2549, 2551, 2552, 2554, 2555, 2556, 2558, 2559, 2563,
2566, 2567, 2568, 2569, 2570, 2571, 2573, 2574, 2575, 2576, 2577,
2578, 2579, 2580, 2581, 2582, 2583, 2584, 2585, 2586, 2588, 2589,

2590, 2591, 2593, 2594, 2596, 2597, 2598, 2599, 2600, 2601, 2602, 2603, 2605, 2606, 2607, 2608, 2609, 2610, 2611, 2612, 2613, 2614, 2615, 2619, 2620, 2623, 2625, 2626, 2627, 2628, 2629, 2630, 2632, 2633, 2634, 2635, 2636, 2637, 2638, 2639, 2640, 2641, 2642, 2643, 2646, 2647, 2448, 2649, 2652, 2653, 2654, 2656.5, 2657, 2658, 2659, 2660, 2661, 2662, 2663, 2664, 2665, 2666, 2667, 2668, 2669, 2670, 2671, 2672, 2673, 2674, 2675, 2676, 2677, 2678, 2682, 2683, 2690, 2691, 2692, 2693, 2694, 2695, 2696, 2697, 2698, 2699, 2700, 2702, 2703, 2704, 2705, 2706, 2707, 2708, 2709, 2710, 2711, 2712, 2713, 2714, 2715, 2719, 2720, 2721, 2722, 2723, 2724, 2725, 2726, 2727, 2728, 2729, 2730, 2731, 2732, 2733, 2734, 2735, 2736, 2737, 2738, 2739, 2740, 2741, 2742, 2744, 2745, 2746, 2747, 2751, 2752, 2753, 2756, 2757, 2764, 2765, 2766, 2767, 2768, 2769, 2770, 2771, 2772, 2774, 2775, 2776, 2777, 2778, 2779, 2780, 2781, 2782, 2784, 2785, 2787, 2788, 2789, 2792, 2797, 2798, 2799, 2800, 2801, 2803, 2804, 2805, 2806, 2808, 2809, 2810, 2811, 2812, 2813, 2814, 2815, 2816, 2818, 2818.5, 2819, 2820, 2821, 2822, 2823, 2824, 2825, 2826, 2827, 2829, 2830, 2831, 2832, 2833, 2834, 2835, 2839, 2841, 2842, 2843, 2845, 2846, 2847, 2848, 2849, 2850, 2851, 2852, 2854, 2855, 2857, 2858, 2859, 2860, 2864, 2865, 2866, 2868, 2870, 2871, 2872, 2873, 2875, 2877.5, 2879, 2881, 2882, 2883, 2884, 2885, 2888, 2889, 2890, 2891, 2892, 2893, 2894, 2895, 2896, 2897, 2898, 2899, 2901, 2902, 2904, 2905, 2907, 2908, 2909, 2910, 2911, 2912, 2913, 2914, 2915, 2916, 2917, 2918, 2919, 2920, 2924, 2925, 2926, 2927, 2929, 2930, 2931, 2932, 2935, 2938, 2939, 2943, 2944, 2945, 2946, 2951, 2952, 2953, 2957, 2958, 2959, 2964, 2967, 2968, 2969, 2970, 2972, 2973, 2974, 2975, 2976, 2977, 2978, 2979, 2980, 2981, 2982, 2984, 2985, 2986, 2987, 2989, 2992, 2993, 2994, 2996, 2999, 3000, 3001, 3002, 3003, 3005, 3006, 3007, 3008, 3009, 3010, 3012, 3013, 3016, 3017, 3018, 3021, 3022, 3023, 3024, 3025, 3028, 3029, 3030, 3031, 3033, 3034, 3035, 3038, 3039, 3041, 3042, 3043, 3044, 3045, 3046, 3048, 3049, 3054, 3055, 3059, 3060, 3061, 3062, 3064, 3065, 3066, 3067, 3068, 3069, 3070, 3071, 3073, 3074, 3075, 3076, 3077, 3078, 3079, 3080, 3081, 3085, 3086, 3087, 3088, 3089, 3090, 3096, 3097, 3098, 3099, 3100, 3101, 3103, 3104, 3105, 3107, 3108, 3109, 3111, 3112, 3113, 3114, 3115, 3116, 3117

4. Far red 1, 2, 3, 5, 6, 7, 8, 9, 10, 11, 13, 14, 15, 16, 18, 21, 22, 23, 24, 25, 26, 27, 29, 30, 31, 33, 34, 35, 36, 37, 44, 45, 46, 49, 50, 54, 55, 56, 59, 60, 63, 64, 65, 68, 69, 70, 71, 74, 75, 76, 77, 78, 79, 80, 81, 82, 84, 85, 87, 88, 89, 90, 93, 95, 96, 99, 100, 101, 102, 103, 105, 116, 117, 119, 120, 124, 125, 127, 129, 130, 131, 132, 133, 134, 135, 136, 137, 140, 144, 145, 146, 147, 149, 156, 159, 162, 163, 165, 166, 167, 168, 169, 170, 171, 173, 174, 178, 179, 180, 181, 183, 188, 189, 190, 191, 192, 193, 194, 195, 196, 197, 198, 200, 201, 206, 209, 214, 232, 234, 238, 241, 242, 245, 248, 249, 250, 251, 252, 253, 254, 255, 256, 259, 260, 261, 262, 265, 267, 269, 270, 273, 274, 275, 277, 278, 279, 281, 286, 287, 288, 289, 290, 291, 295, 296, 297, 298, 302, 304, 305, 306, 308, 313, 314, 316, 317, 319, 322, 323, 324, 325, 329, 332, 333, 334, 337, 342, 347, 348, 350, 351, 353, 355, 356, 357, 358, 359, 360.5, 364, 366, 367, 368, 369, 370, 371, 372, 373, 374, 375, 376, 377, 378, 383, 384, 385, 386, 387, 388, 390, 392, 393, 394, 399, 402, 403, 405, 406, 407, 408, 413, 414, 415, 417, 418, 419, 420, 421, 422, 423, 424, 425, 431, 433, 434, 435, 436, 437, 438, 439, 440, 441, 445, 446, 447, 448, 449, 450, 453, 455, 457, 458, 459, 461, 464, 469, 470, 471, 472, 473, 474, 475, 477, 478, 479, 480, 481, 482, 484, 485, 487, 489, 490, 491, 492, 493, 495, 496, 497, 498, 499, 500, 501, 502, 503, 504, 507, 509, 510, 512, 512.5, 513, 514, 517, 518, 519, 520, 521, 524, 525, 527, 529, 530, 532, 533, 534, 537, 538, 539, 541, 546, 548, 550, 551, 552, 553, 554, 556, 557, 561, 564, 565, 568, 569, 570, 571, 572, 573, 574, 575, 576, 577, 578, 579, 580, 581, 582, 584, 585, 587, 590, 591, 592, 593, 594, 598, 600, 604, 610, 611, 616, 617, 618, 619, 620, 621, 622, 623, 624, 626, 627, 628, 630, 631, 632, 634, 635, 636, 638, 640, 641, 644, 646, 647, 652, 654, 655, 656, 657, 659, 660, 660.5, 661, 662, 663, 669, 671, 677, 678, 679, 682, 685, 686, 687, 691, 692, 693, 694, 695, 696, 698, 700, 704, 705, 706, 708, 709, 710, 711, 712, 713, 714, 715, 716, 717, 718, 719, 720, 723, 724, 727, 728, 729, 730, 731, 732, 733, 734, 735, 736, 737, 738, 739, 740, 741, 742, 745, 746, 747, 749, 772, 773, 774, 775, 776, 777, 778, 782, 782.5, 783, 786, 788, 789, 790, 791, 803, 805, 810, 811, 815, 819, 820, 821, 822, 824, 825, 826, 829, 830, 832, 833, 834, 835, 836, 837, 838, 839, 840, 841, 842, 843, 845, 846, 847, 850, 851, 852, 860, 861, 863, 864, 865, 866, 867, 869, 870, 873, 877, 878, 880, 882, 884, 886,

887, 888, 889, 890, 891, 892, 893, 894, 895, 896, 898, 899, 900, 901, 905, 907, 908, 909, 912, 913, 914, 915, 916, 917, 919, 920, 921, 921.2, 921.5, 922, 923, 924, 925, 927, 928, 929, 930, 932, 933, 934, 936, 939, 941, 943, 944, 946, 950, 951, 952, 954, 955, 956, 957, 958, 960, 961, 962, 963, 964, 965, 966, 967, 970, 971, 973, 975, 976, 977, 978, 980, 981, 983, 991, 994, 999, 1001, 1004, 1006, 1007, 1008, 1010, 1013, 1015, 1016, 1017, 1019, 1022, 1024, 1034, 1038, 1045, 1051, 1052, 1058, 1073, 1076, 1077, 1078, 1079, 1080, 1081, 1083, 1084, 1085, 1086, 1087, 1089, 1090, 1096, 1097, 1100, 1101, 1102, 1104, 1106, 1009, 1110, 1112, 1115, 1118, 1120, 1120.5, 1121, 1122, 1123, 1124, 1125, 1126, 1127, 1128, 1129, 1130, 1131, 1132, 1133, 1134, 1137, 1138, 1142, 1143, 1144, 1145, 1148, 1149, 1154, 1155, 1156, 1158, 1161, 1162, 1163, 1164, 1165, 1170, 1178, 1179, 1180, 1181, 1182, 1183, 1184, 1185, 1186, 1187, 1188, 1190, 1191, 1193, 1194, 1195, 1196, 1197, 1198, 1199, 1200, 1205, 1206, 1207, 1208, 1210, 1212, 1213, 1214, 1215, 1216, 1217, 1218, 1219, 1220, 1221, 1226, 1228, 1229, 1232, 1233, 1234, 1235, 1236, 1237, 1238, 1239, 1240, 1241, 1245, 1247, 1248, 1249, 1251, 1253, 1254, 1255, 1257, 1258, 1259, 1260, 1262, 1263, 1264, 1265, 1266, 1267, 1270, 1273, 1275, 1276, 1277, 1278, 1279, 1280, 1281, 1283, 1284, 1286, 1288, 1289, 1290, 1292, 1294, 1296, 1301, 1306, 1310, 1311, 1314, 1315, 1316, 1317, 1318, 1319, 1321, 1323, 1324, 1325, 1326, 1327, 1328, 1329, 1330, 1331, 1332, 1333, 1334, 1335, 1336, 1337, 1338, 1340, 1341, 1342, 1343, 1344, 1345, 1346, 1347, 1348, 1349, 1350, 1351, 1352, 1355, 1356, 1358, 1359, 1360, 1361, 1362, 1363, 1364, 1365, 1366, 1367, 1369, 1370, 1371, 1372, 1374, 1375, 1378, 1379, 1380, 1381, 1384, 1385, 1386, 1387, 1388, 1389, 1390, 1391, 1392, 1395, 1396, 1398, 1406, 1411, 1412, 1413, 1414, 1415, 1416, 1417, 1418, 1419, 1421, 1422, 1424, 1425, 1426, 1427, 1428, 1429, 1431, 1432, 1433, 1434, 1437.5, 1439, 1440, 1441, 1445, 1448, 1450, 1451, 1454, 1455, 1456, 1461, 1462, 1463, 1468, 1470, 1472, 1473, 1474.5, 1475, 1480, 1481, 1483, 1484, 1487, 1489, 1490, 1492, 1493, 1497, 1498, 1500, 1501, 1502, 1505, 1506, 1507, 1508, 1509, 1514, 1518, 1519, 1520, 1521, 1522, 1524, 1525, 1526, 1528, 1530, 1531, 1532, 1533, 1534, 1535, 1538, 1539, 1540, 1541, 1545, 1546, 1547, 1548, 1548.5, 1549, 1549.5, 1550, 1551, 1552, 1553, 1554, 1555, 1556, 1557, 1558,

1562, 1564, 1565, 1566, 1567, 1569, 1571, 1573, 1574, 1575, 1577,
1578, 1579.5, 1580, 1581, 1583, 1585, 1586, 1587, 1591, 1592, 1597,
1598, 1599, 1602, 1603, 1608, 1609, 1610, 1614, 1615, 1616, 1617,
1618, 1619, 1620, 1621, 1622, 1623, 1624, 1625, 1626, 1627, 1628,
1629, 1630, 1635, 1636, 1638, 1640, 1648, 1649, 1650, 1651, 1652,
1653, 1654, 1655, 1656, 1657, 1658, 1659, 1660, 1661, 1662, 1663,
1664, 1665, 1666, 1667, 1668, 1669, 1670, 1671, 1672, 1674, 1675,
1676, 1677, 1678, 1679, 1680, 1681, 1683, 1684, 1685, 1686, 1688,
1689, 1690, 1691, 1692, 1693, 1694, 1965, 1697, 1698, 1699, 1700,
1701, 1702, 1703, 1704, 1706, 1707, 1708, 1709, 1710, 1712, 1713,
1715, 1716, 1717, 1718, 1721, 1726, 1728, 1729, 1730, 1731, 1732,
1735, 1736, 1737, 1738, 1739, 1740, 1741, 1743, 1745, 1748, 1750,
1751, 1753, 1754, 1756, 1759, 1760, 1761, 1762, 1763, 1764, 1765,
1767, 1768, 1771, 1772, 1778, 1783, 1784, 1785, 1787, 1788, 1789,
1790, 1791, 1793, 1795, 1796, 1797, 1799, 1801, 1802, 1803, 1804,
1805, 1806, 1807, 1808, 1809, 1811, 1813, 1814, 1815, 1818, 1823,
1825, 1826, 1829, 1830, 1831, 1832, 1833, 1834, 1835, 1836, 1837,
1838, 1839, 1840, 1841, 1842, 1846, 1847, 1848, 1849, 1855, 1859,
1861, 1863, 1869, 1870, 1873, 1874, 1879, 1880, 1881, 1882, 1884,
1885, 1887, 1888, 1891, 1892, 1898, 1900, 1905, 1906, 1907, 1908,
1913, 1914, 1915, 1917, 1919, 1923, 1929, 1931, 1932, 1935, 1936,
1941, 1942, 1943, 1945, 1946, 1948, 1949, 1950, 1951, 1953, 1954,
1957, 1958, 1959, 1960, 1961, 1962, 1963, 1964, 1969, 1970, 1971,
1972, 1973, 1974, 1976, 1977, 1978, 1979, 1982, 1984, 1986, 1987,
1988, 1989, 1990, 1991, 1992, 1997, 1998, 1999, 2000, 2006, 2008,
2009, 2010, 2011, 2012, 2014, 2015, 2016, 2017, 2018, 2019, 2020,
2021, 2022, 2023, 2025, 2027, 2028, 2029, 2030, 2034, 2036, 2037,
2039, 2040, 2041, 2042, 2043, 2044, 2045, 2046, 2047, 2049, 2050,
2051, 2052, 2054, 2060, 2066, 2067, 2068, 2069, 2071, 2072, 2073,
2077, 2078, 2079, 2081, 2083, 2084, 2087, 2088, 2090, 2091, 2094,
2099, 2100, 2101, 2108, 2115, 2116, 2117, 2118, 2119, 2123, 2127,
2128, 2129, 2130, 2131, 2132, 2133, 2137, 2138, 2140, 2142, 2144,
2145, 2146, 2148, 2152, 2153, 2154, 2156, 2157, 2158, 2159, 2160,
2161, 2162, 2174, 2177, 2182, 2183, 2185, 2189, 2190, 2195, 2196,
2197, 2198, 2199, 2200, 2201, 2202, 2203, 2208, 2209, 2210, 2211,
2212, 2213, 2215, 2216, 2217, 2219, 2220, 2221, 2222, 2223, 2228,

2231, 2232, 2233, 2234, 2235, 2237, 2238, 2239, 2240, 2241, 2242,
2243, 2244, 2245, 2248, 2251, 2252, 2253, 2255, 2256, 2260, 2263,
2264, 2265, 2266, 2267, 2268, 2269, 2270, 2273, 2276, 2277, 2278,
2280, 2281, 2282, 2283, 2284, 2285, 2286, 2287, 2288, 2292, 2295,
2297, 2298, 2302, 2305, 2306, 2307, 2308, 2311, 2312, 2313, 2315,
2316, 2322, 2323, 2324, 2325, 2326, 2327, 2328, 2329, 2330, 2331,
2335, 2340, 2342, 2343, 2344, 2345, 2346, 2347, 2348, 2349, 2351,
2353, 2354, 2356, 2357, 2359, 2360, 2362, 2363, 2364, 2365, 2366,
2368, 2369, 2371, 2372, 2374, 2375, 2376, 2377, 2378, 2380, 2381,
2382, 2383, 2387, 2389, 2390, 2391, 2392, 2394, 2396, 2397, 2399,
2400, 2401, 2402, 2403, 2404, 2405, 2406, 2408, 2409, 2410, 2411,
2412, 2413, 2414, 2415, 2416, 2418, 2419, 2420, 2421, 2432, 2433,
2434, 2435, 2436, 2437, 2438, 2439, 2440, 2441, 2442, 2443, 2444,
2445, 2449, 2451, 2452, 2453, 2454, 2455, 2459, 2461, 2464, 2465,
2466, 2467, 2468, 2472, 2478, 2479, 2480, 2481, 2482, 2485, 2486,
2488, 2490, 2491, 2493, 2494, 2498, 2500, 2502, 2503, 2506, 2512,
2513, 2514, 2515, 2516, 2517, 2518, 2519, 2520, 2521, 2522, 2523,
2538, 2543, 2544, 2545, 2546, 2547, 2548, 2549, 2550, 2551, 2554,
2558, 2563, 2566, 2567, 2568, 2570, 2575, 2576, 2577, 2578, 2579,
2580, 2581, 2582, 2583, 2584, 2585, 2586, 2588, 2589, 2590, 2591,
2593, 2594, 2596, 2597, 2598, 2605, 2606, 2608, 2610, 2611, 2613,
2616, 2617, 2618, 2622, 2624. 2625, 2626, 2627, 2628, 2631, 2632,
2633, 2634, 2636, 2637, 2638, 2642, 2643, 2646, 2647, 2648, 2652,
2653, 2655, 2657, 2658, 2663, 2664, 2665, 2666, 2667, 2670, 2671,
2672, 2673, 2674, 2675, 2676, 2677, 2678, 2682, 2683, 2684, 2685,
2686, 2687, 2688, 2689, 2690, 2691, 2692, 2693, 2697, 2698, 2699,
2700, 2701, 2702, 2703, 2704, 2705, 2706, 2707, 2708, 2712, 2713,
2714, 2715, 2720, 2721, 2722, 2723, 2724, 2725, 2726, 2727, 2728,
2729, 2730, 2731, 2733, 2734, 2735, 2736, 2737, 2738, 2739, 2742,
2743, 2744, 2747, 2751, 2752, 2753, 2754, 2755, 2756, 2757, 2759,
2768, 2774, 2776, 2777, 2778, 2779, 2780, 2781, 2782, 2784, 2785,
2789, 2791, 2792, 2797, 2799, 2800, 2801, 2804, 2805, 2808, 2809,
2812, 2813, 2814, 2818, 2818.5, 2820, 2821, 2823, 2824, 2827, 2828,
2829, 2830, 2831, 2832, 2833, 2839, 2840, 2842, 2843, 2844, 2845,
2846, 2849, 2850, 2851, 2852, 2855, 2856, 2857, 2858, 2859, 2864,
2865, 2866, 2868, 2870, 2871, 2872, 2873, 2875, 2877.5, 2881, 2882,

2888, 2890, 2905, 2906, 2907, 2910, 2912, 2915, 2916, 2917, 2918,
2919, 2920, 2923, 2925, 2926, 2927, 2929, 2930, 2931, 2932, 2935,
2938, 2939, 2943, 2944, 2945, 2946, 2951, 2952, 2953, 2957, 2958,
2959, 2960, 2961, 2962, 2063, 2964, 2965, 2966, 2968, 2972, 2974,
2975, 2979, 2981, 2982, 2984, 2985, 2986, 2987, 2989, 2992, 2993,
2999, 3000, 3001, 3002, 3012, 3013, 3015, 3017, 3018, 3021, 3022,
3028, 3029, 3031, 3033, 3034, 3035, 3038, 3039, 3040, 3041, 3043,
3044, 3045, 3046, 3048. 3049, 3050, 3054, 3057, 3058, 3060, 3062,
3063, 3064, 3065, 3066, 3070, 3071, 3073, 3075, 3076, 3077, 3078,
3079, 3080, 3081, 3082, 3083, 3085, 3086, 3087, 3096, 3098, 3101,
3102, 3104, 3105, 3109, 3112, 3113

D. Effects (synergistic/antagonistic) of various sequences of irradiation with
different spectral bands.

1. Blue-far red antagonism 15, 96, 124, 125, 129, 390, 450, 453, 500,
578, 612, 613, 614, 622, 627, 790, 791, 835, 890, 1112, 1199, 1215,
1269, 1270, 1279, 1280, 1456, 1489, 1509, 1657, 1658, 1753, 1778,
1802, 1836, 1957, 1975, 2052, 2060, 2099, 2189, 2232, 2295, 2327,
2329, 2330, 2331, 2402, 2418, 2419, 2421, 2461, 2538, 2720, 2824,
2890, 2910, 3080

2. Blue-far red synergism 163, 290, 291, 528, 539, 582, 970, 1022, 1024,
1102, 1279, 1280, 1534, 1692, 1787, 1846, 2418, 2419, 2421, 2514,
2754, 2755, 2756, 2757, 2824, 2852, 2901, 2982

3. Blue protection (prevention of red-far-red antagonism) 1001, 1024,
2185, 2666, 2667, 2668

4. Blue-red antagonism 43, 96, 107, 108, 113, 114, 115, 158, 171, 212,
223, 255, 322, 362, 363, 380, 387, 436, 450, 459, 499, 528, 543, 568,
578, 582, 592, 618, 622, 623, 674, 675, 676, 690, 691, 692, 693, 756,
823, 884, 890, 891, 892, 909, 948, 955, 960, 1022, 1024, 1028, 1030,
1031, 1032, 1033, 1041, 1058, 1098, 1100, 1102, 1112, 1200, 1322,
1330, 1409, 1417, 1474.5, 1534, 1549.5, 1566, 1594, 1616, 1633, 1634,
1657, 1658, 1666, 1686, 1692, 1760, 1761, 1762, 1772, 1802, 1817,
1835, 1836, 1878, 1984, 1988, 1993, 1994, 1995, 1998, 2001, 2002,
2031, 2032, 2033, 2035, 2047, 2052, 2060, 2061, 2062, 2063, 2064,
2098, 2116, 2151, 2154, 2185, 2216, 2225, 2226, 2322, 2329, 2331,
2395, 2397, 2402, 2421, 2422, 2424, 2538, 2541, 2610, 2636, 2649,
2660, 2665, 2666, 2667, 2668, 2714, 2715, 2764, 2765, 2774, 2824,

2832, 2902, 2910, 2918, 2938, 2939, 2953, 2982, 3099

5. Blue-red synergism 58, 125, 131, 150, 158, 163, 253, 254, 259, 272, 387, 618, 619, 620, 627, 825, 889, 892, 893, 1269, 1309, 1456, 1508, 1509, 1761, 1768, 2418, 2419, 2421, 2422, 2424, 2426, 2430, 2454, 2630, 2824, 2978, 3100

6. Far red protection (prevention of red response) 999, 1007, 2418, 2419, 2421

7. Ionizing - visible interactions 696, 845, 846, 862, 866, 867, 1158, 1341, 1342, 1343, 1344, 1345, 1346, 1348, 1350, 1351, 1420, 1635, 1636, 1831, 1832, 1833, 1834, 1895, 2117, 2454, 2608, 2609, 2653, 2684, 2685, 2686, 2687, 2688, 2689, 2725, 3044, 3050, 3057, 3058, 3082, 3083

8. Near UV-blue-red interactions 2430, 2472, 2476

9. Near UV protection (prevention of red-far red antagonism) 991, 994, 1001, 1489, 2420, 2608, 2630

10. Near UV-red-far red interactions 991

11. Red-far red antagonism 5, 6, 10, 22, 23, 24, 26, 27, 29, 30, 31, 33, 37, 54, 55, 56, 60, 68, 69, 70, 74, 77, 79, 80, 87, 90, 93, 96, 100, 101, 102, 117, 119, 120, 124, 125, 126, 127, 129, 131, 132, 133, 134, 135, 136, 140, 144, 146, 147, 159, 162, 163, 165, 166, 168, 169, 171, 178, 180, 188, 189, 190, 191, 192, 193, 194, 195, 197, 198, 200, 201, 206, 209, 220, 221 223, 232, 234, 241, 242, 245, 249, 250, 251, 252, 253, 254, 255, 256, 259, 261, 262, 265, 267, 270, 273, 274, 275, 277, 278, 279, 281, 287, 295, 297, 304, 305, 316, 317, 322, 323, 324, 332, 333, 334, 342, 348, 350, 351, 356, 357, 358, 359, 360.5, 364, 366, 367, 368, 369, 370, 373, 386, 387, 388, 390, 392, 402, 403, 405, 406, 407, 408, 415, 417, 418, 419, 420, 421, 422, 423, 431, 433, 436, 438, 441, 446, 447, 448, 453, 455, 458, 464, 469, 470, 472, 473, 475, 477, 478, 479, 480, 481, 484, 485, 487, 489, 490, 491, 492, 499, 500, 501, 502, 503, 504, 509, 512, 517, 518, 519, 524, 525, 526, 527, 528, 533, 534, 537, 538, 539, 541, 550, 552, 554, 564, 571, 572, 574, 575, 576, 577, 578, 579, 580, 581, 582, 584, 585, 587, 592, 604, 610, 611, 617, 618, 622, 627, 628, 630, 631, 632, 635, 638, 641, 644, 646, 647, 652, 655, 657, 659, 660.5, 661, 685, 686, 687, 691, 692, 693, 694, 695, 696, 698, 700, 704, 705, 706, 708, 709, 710, 711, 712, 713, 714, 715, 716, 717, 718, 719, 720, 723, 724, 727, 728, 731, 737, 738, 739, 740,

741, 742, 745, 746, 747, 749, 772, 773, 774, 775, 776, 777, 778, 782,
782.5, 783, 786, 788, 803, 805, 810, 811, 819, 820, 821, 822, 825,
826, 830, 832, 833, 835, 836, 837, 840, 841, 842, 843, 847, 850,
851, 852, 860, 861, 863, 864, 865, 869, 870, 877, 878, 880, 882, 884,
886, 889, 890, 891, 892, 895, 896, 898, 899, 900, 901, 905, 908, 909,
914, 916, 920, 921, 921.2, 921.5, 927, 928, 929, 930, 932, 936, 943,
944, 950, 951, 952, 954, 955, 956, 957, 958, 960, 962, 964, 971, 975,
976, 977, 978, 980, 981, 983, 991, 994, 999, 1001, 1004, 1006, 1007,
1008, 1010, 1013, 1015, 1016, 1017, 1019, 1022, 1024, 1034, 1038,
1051, 1052, 1058, 1073, 1076, 1077, 1078, 1079, 1080, 1083, 1084,
1085, 1086, 1087, 1089, 1090, 1097, 1100, 1101, 1102, 1104, 1109,
1110, 1112, 1120, 1123, 1124, 1125, 1126, 1127, 1128, 1129, 1130,
1132, 1133, 1134, 1137, 1138, 1142, 1143, 1144, 1145, 1148, 1154,
1155, 1156, 1158, 1161, 1163, 1178, 1179, 1180, 1181, 1182, 1186,
1187, 1193, 1194, 1195, 1197, 1199, 1200, 1205, 1206, 1207, 1214,
1215, 1218, 1219, 1221, 1226, 1228, 1229, 1232, 1234, 1235, 1236,
1237, 1238, 1249, 1253, 1254, 1257, 1258, 1259, 1260, 1262, 1264,
1273, 1276, 1281, 1283, 1284, 1286, 1288, 1290, 1292, 1294, 1296,
1301, 1306, 1311, 1315, 1316, 1317, 1318, 1321, 1325, 1326, 1327,
1328, 1329, 1330, 1331, 1332, 1333, 1336, 1338, 1352, 1356, 1359,
1360, 1361, 1362, 1363, 1364, 1365, 1367, 1369, 1370, 1371, 1372,
1374, 1375, 1378, 1379, 1380, 1381, 1385, 1387, 1388, 1390, 1395,
1396, 1398, 1406, 1411, 1412, 1413, 1414, 1415, 1416, 1417, 1421,
1422, 1424, 1425, 1428, 1431, 1432, 1437.5, 1448, 1450, 1451, 1456,
1461, 1468, 1472, 1474.5, 1475, 1480, 1481, 1484, 1489, 1490, 1492,
1493, 1497, 1498, 1500, 1501, 1502, 1505, 1506, 1508, 1509, 1514,
1518, 1521, 1522, 1524, 1525, 1526, 1528, 1530, 1531, 1534, 1541,
1545, 1546, 1548, 1549, 1549.5, 1551, 1552, 1553, 1554, 1555, 1562,
1564, 1565, 1566, 1567, 1571, 1577, 1578, 1579.5, 1580, 1581, 1583,
1585, 1586, 1587, 1592, 1597, 1599, 1615, 1616, 1617, 1618, 1619,
1620, 1635, 1638, 1649, 1650, 1651, 1652, 1653, 1655, 1656, 1657,
1658, 1659, 1660, 1661, 1662, 1664, 1665, 1666, 1667, 1668, 1669,
1670, 1671, 1672, 1674, 1675, 1676, 1677, 1678, 1679, 1680, 1681,
1683, 1684, 1685, 1688, 1689, 1690, 1692, 1693, 1694, 1695, 1697,
1699, 1700, 1701, 1702, 1703, 1704, 1706, 1707, 1708, 1709, 1710,
1712, 1713, 1715, 1716, 1721, 1726, 1731, 1732, 1735, 1736, 1737,

1738, 1740, 1741, 1743, 1750, 1751, 1753, 1754, 1756, 1760, 1761,
1762, 1763, 1772, 1778, 1785, 1788, 1789, 1790, 1791, 1793, 1795,
1796, 1797, 1799, 1801, 1802, 1804, 1805, 1818, 1823, 1825, 1826,
1829, 1830, 1832, 1833, 1835, 1837, 1838, 1839, 1841, 1842, 1846,
1848, 1855, 1859, 1863, 1869, 1870, 1874, 1881, 1891, 1900, 1905,
1908, 1913, 1915, 1917, 1919, 1931, 1932, 1935, 1936, 1941, 1942,
1943, 1945, 1946, 1948, 1949, 1950, 1951, 1953, 1954, 1957, 1961,
1962, 1963, 1964, 1969, 1975, 1976, 1977, 1978, 1979, 1982, 1984,
1986, 1987, 1988, 1989, 1997, 1998, 2008, 2009, 2010, 2011, 2012,
2014, 2016, 2018, 2019, 2020, 2023, 2027, 2028, 2029, 2030, 2036,
2037, 2041, 2042, 2043, 2049, 2050, 2052, 2055, 2060, 2066, 2067,
2068, 2069, 2072, 2073, 2077, 2081, 2083, 2084, 2087, 2088, 2090,
2091, 2094, 2099, 2100, 2101, 2108, 2115, 2116, 2117, 2118, 2119,
2123, 2128, 2129, 2130, 2131, 2132, 2133, 2137, 2138, 2140, 2142,
2144, 2145, 2146, 2148, 2151, 2152, 2153, 2154, 2156, 2157, 2158,
2159, 2160, 2162, 2174, 2183, 2185, 2189, 2190, 2195, 2197, 2198,
2199, 2200, 2201, 2202, 2203, 2208, 2209, 2210, 2212, 2213, 2215,
2216, 2217, 2219, 2220, 2221, 2222, 2232, 2234, 2235, 2237, 2238,
2240, 2241, 2243, 2252, 2253, 2255, 2260, 2264, 2265, 2266, 2267,
2268, 2269, 2270, 2278, 2280, 2281, 2282, 2283, 2284, 2285, 2286,
2287, 2288, 2295, 2297, 2298, 2302, 2305, 2311, 2312, 2313, 2315,
2316, 2322, 2323, 2324, 2425, 2326, 2327, 2328, 2329, 2330, 2331,
2335, 2340, 2343, 2345, 2349, 2353, 2354, 2356, 2357, 2359, 2360,
2362, 2363, 2364, 2365, 2366, 2374, 2375, 2376, 2377, 2378, 2380,
2381, 2382, 2383, 2389, 2390, 2391, 2392, 2394, 2396, 2397, 2399,
2400, 2401, 2402, 2404, 2406, 2408, 2409, 2410, 2414, 2416, 2418,
2419, 2420, 2432, 2433, 2434, 2435, 2436, 2438, 2442, 2445, 2449,
2451, 2453, 2459, 2461, 2464, 2465, 2466, 2467, 2468, 2478, 2479,
2482, 2485, 2486, 2488, 2494, 2498, 2499, 2500, 2501, 2503, 2513,
2514, 2515, 2516, 2517, 2518, 2521, 2543, 2544, 2546, 2548, 2554,
2563, 2566, 2567, 2570, 2574, 2577, 2578, 2579, 2580, 2581, 2582,
2583, 2584, 2585, 2586, 2588, 2589, 2590, 2591, 2593, 2594, 2596,
2597, 2598, 2605, 2606, 2608, 2610, 2611, 2625, 2632, 2637, 2638,
2643, 2649, 2652, 2653, 2663, 2664, 2665, 2666, 2667, 2670, 2671,
2672, 2673, 2674, 2676, 2677, 2678, 2683, 2692, 2693, 2699, 2700,
2704, 2707, 2708, 2712, 2713, 2714, 2715, 2720, 2721, 2722, 2723,

2724, 2725, 2726, 2727, 2728, 2729, 2730, 2731, 2733, 2734, 2735,
2736, 2737, 2738, 2739, 2742, 2744, 2747, 2751, 2752, 2756, 2757,
2768, 2776, 2777, 2778, 2779, 2780, 2783, 2784, 2785, 2789, 2797,
2799, 2800, 2801, 2805, 2808, 2809, 2814, 2818, 2818.5, 2824, 2827,
2829, 2830, 2832, 2842, 2843, 2845, 2846, 2849, 2850, 2851, 2852,
2855, 2857, 2858, 2859, 2870, 2871, 2877.5, 2881, 2882, 2888, 2907,
2910, 2915, 2916, 2918, 2920, 2923, 2925, 2926, 2927, 2929, 2930,
2931, 2952, 2953, 2957, 2958, 2959, 2964, 2968, 2972, 2974, 2979,
2982, 2984, 2985, 2986, 2987, 2992, 2993, 2999, 3000, 3001, 3002,
3017, 3018, 3022, 3028, 3029, 3031, 3044, 3045, 3046, 3048, 3049,
3054, 3064, 3065, 3066, 3070, 3071, 3073, 3075, 3076, 3077, 3078,
3079, 3080, 3086, 3087, 3098, 3104, 3105, 3109

12. Red-far red synergism 14, 131, 132, 181, 260, 618, 619, 620, 623, 624,
626, 627, 661, 890, 892, 893, 896, 899, 960, 961, 964, 965, 966, 970,
1004, 1007, 1008, 1016, 1102, 1194, 1296, 1509, 1768, 1837, 1870,
1914, 1963, 1971, 1973, 1974, 2454, 2472, 2514, 2611, 2712, 2713,
2916, 3018

E. Effects of simultaneous irradiation with two or more defined spectral
bands 14, 15, 48, 50, 116, 131, 137, 156, 181, 215, 232, 269, 270, 277,
393, 397, 440, 445, 499, 577, 619, 620, 646, 672, 687, 690, 731, 732,
735, 812, 813, 814, 815, 821, 886, 943, 944, 960, 961, 962, 964, 965,
966, 970, 1028, 1030, 1031, 1032, 1098, 1102, 1128, 1129, 1145, 1217,
1219, 1252, 1258, 1263, 1288, 1318, 1358, 1360, 1409, 1417, 1422,
1426, 1503, 1534, 1565, 1615, 1651, 1657, 1692, 1713, 1756, 1758,
1759, 1762, 1763, 1772, 1788, 1789, 1832, 1833, 1870, 1881, 1917,
1923, 1970, 1971, 1972, 1973, 1974, 1984, 1998, 2116, 2189, 2199,
2210, 2223, 2255, 2260, 2354, 2388, 2402, 2421, 2422, 2424, 2426,
2454, 2472, 2513, 2514, 2611, 2625, 2630, 2637, 2638, 2643, 2649,
2652, 2656, 2699, 2700, 2702, 2703, 2756, 2865, 2866, 2877.5, 2881,
2916, 2951, 2953, 3036, 3037, 3048, 3102, 3109, 3113

F. Gradient effects (of intensity) 584, 732, 1017

G. High Irradiance Responses (HIR) 5, 6, 7, 8, 9, 10, 22, 23, 27, 59, 62, 63,
64, 65, 66, 74, 88, 89, 99, 100, 101, 102, 112, 131, 132, 133, 144,
145, 150, 159, 180, 189, 196, 197, 245, 258, 260, 269, 270, 277, 289,
290, 291, 297, 316, 317, 322, 329, 360.5, 367, 372, 373, 374, 375,
376, 377, 378, 383, 388, 397, 399, 424, 431, 453, 464, 471, 474, 475,

482, 504, 505, 506, 510, 512, 513, 514, 517, 518, 534, 537, 540, 543,
544, 545, 546, 547, 548, 550, 551, 552, 554, 557, 564, 565, 569, 570,
578, 579, 580, 581, 582, 585, 586, 587, 588, 591, 592, 593, 594, 597,
598, 600, 601, 602, 604, 605, 612, 613, 614, 619, 621, 622, 623, 624,
626, 627, 630, 644, 646, 652, 654, 656, 659, 661, 687, 698, 704, 724,
729, 730, 732, 734, 735, 736, 737, 741, 742, 789, 812, 813, 814, 815,
820, 821, 824, 830, 842, 843, 884, 886, 888, 889, 890, 891, 892, 893,
894, 895, 896, 897, 898, 899, 909, 921, 921.2, 921.5, 922, 923, 924,
928, 944, 952, 958, 959, 960, 961, 962, 963, 964, 965, 966, 967, 970,
972, 989, 992, 1024, 1045, 1052, 1073, 1120, 1120.5, 1121, 1122, 1127,
1130, 1149, 1159, 1161, 1164, 1165, 1188, 1189, 1208, 1212, 1214,
1216, 1220, 1223, 1224, 1225, 1239, 1240, 1241, 1257, 1277, 1279,
1287, 1288, 1290, 1292, 1296, 1311, 1321, 1322, 1358, 1359, 1360,
1361, 1366, 1367, 1368, 1369, 1370, 1371, 1372, 1393, 1395, 1398,
1406, 1411, 1412, 1422, 1433, 1434, 1461, 1463, 1478, 1479, 1505,
1506, 1508, 1509, 1519, 1526, 1534, 1538, 1539, 1540, 1569, 1574,
1575, 1648, 1651, 1655, 1656, 1657, 1658, 1663, 1666, 1667, 1669,
1672, 1674, 1675, 1676, 1677, 1683, 1684, 1685, 1699, 1700, 1701,
1715, 1724, 1732, 1735, 1736, 1737, 1772, 1789, 1802, 1837, 1838,
1839, 1840, 1841, 1846, 1847, 1848, 1849, 1859, 1861, 1863, 1869,
1870, 1871, 1878, 1879, 1882, 1885, 1891, 1892, 1895, 1898, 1900,
1905, 1906, 1907, 1915, 1931, 1932, 1934, 1935, 1936, 1941, 1971,
1972, 1973, 1974, 1975, 1976, 1991, 1992, 1998, 2014, 2016, 2017,
2018, 2020, 2021, 2023, 2024, 2045, 2061, 2062, 2063, 2064, 2071,
2073, 2098, 2103, 2146, 2162, 2189, 2196, 2199, 2203, 2211, 2228,
2235, 2244, 2248, 2251, 2252, 2260, 2276, 2328, 2329, 2331, 2332,
2347, 2348, 2354, 2371, 2374, 2376, 2378, 2380, 2381, 2382, 2389,
2391, 2396, 2397, 2402, 2403, 2404, 2405, 2406, 2408, 2409, 2411,
2412, 2413, 2414, 2415, 2416, 2418, 2419, 2421, 2422, 2424, 2435,
2438, 2439, 2440, 2444, 2445, 2449, 2452, 2453, 2454, 2472, 2500,
2514, 2519, 2520, 2521, 2563, 2611, 2616, 2618, 2622, 2624, 2632,
2634, 2636, 2637, 2641, 2642, 2643, 2666, 2675, 2677, 2678, 2690,
2693, 2694, 2714, 2715, 2719, 2735, 2737, 2739, 2743, 2759, 2781,
2816, 2818, 2823, 2824, 2827, 2829, 2830, 2842, 2843, 2844, 2846,
2852, 2854, 2875, 2913, 2915, 2917, 2918, 2958, 2959, 2961, 2962,
2963, 2964, 2965, 2976, 2977, 2978, 2985, 2986, 2987, 2989, 3015,

3017, 3018, 3029, 3058, 3061, 3062, 3075, 3077, 3080, 3105

H. Periodic Irradiance 3, 15, 23, 24, 26, 59, 68, 84, 95, 104, 120, 138, 140,
148, 150, 168, 254, 265, 301, 302, 305, 306, 308, 315, 360.5, 363,
393, 400, 401, 405, 438, 440, 443, 449, 450, 455, 464, 471, 474, 475,
477, 484, 485, 486, 497, 499, 502, 512, 517, 518, 547, 554, 563, 568,
578, 579, 580, 582, 597, 603, 611, 618, 619, 620, 623, 626, 652, 658,
662, 671, 672, 673, 693, 698, 709, 723, 732, 735, 736, 738, 824, 825,
826, 870, 873, 877, 878, 879, 880, 884, 886, 890, 891, 896, 897, 898,
928, 933, 943, 944, 946, 952, 956, 957, 958, 983, 989, 1010, 1013,
1079, 1092, 1094, 1095, 1098, 1100, 1101, 1102, 1108, 1109, 1110,
1111, 1112, 1113, 1115, 1118, 1127, 1130, 1132, 1149, 1194, 1198,
1200, 1202, 1234, 1247, 1256, 1257, 1260, 1261, 1262, 1264, 1271,
1272, 1275, 1277, 1316, 1320, 1321, 1323, 1325, 1330, 1332, 1338,
1359, 1385, 1387, 1388, 1395, 1396, 1397, 1398, 1410, 1411, 1437,
1437.5, 1440, 1441, 1448, 1475, 1485, 1487, 1505, 1506, 1514, 1522,
1526, 1532, 1533, 1541, 1548.5, 1555, 1565, 1566, 1616, 1638, 1640,
1655, 1664, 1665, 1667, 1668, 1672, 1674, 1676, 1677, 1682, 1683,
1684, 1685, 1695, 1715, 1717, 1718, 1724, 1732, 1752, 1758, 1767,
1788, 1795, 1796, 1797, 1798, 1799, 1801, 1802, 1815, 1829, 1837,
1838, 1839, 1841, 1842, 1846, 1848, 1849, 1869, 1870, 1887, 1891,
1900, 1914, 1915, 1925, 1928, 1931, 1932, 1934, 1935, 1936, 1941,
1967, 1978, 1979, 1982, 1997, 1998, 2008, 2014, 2015, 2028, 2047,
2052, 2060, 2069, 2073, 2087, 2088, 2095, 2096, 2108, 2114, 2115,
2118, 2198, 2199, 2203, 2210, 2228, 2235, 2243, 2263, 2267, 2269,
2270, 2272, 2273, 2278, 2292, 2295, 2306, 2311, 2322, 2327, 2328,
2329, 2330, 2331, 2332, 2353, 2387, 2394, 2418, 2419, 2436, 2451,
2453, 2461, 2464, 2481, 2491, 2511, 2513, 2575, 2578, 2602, 2611,
2636, 2660, 2662, 2666, 2670, 2683, 2685, 2690, 2693, 2699, 2701,
2702, 2703, 2705, 2706, 2709, 2756, 2767, 2769, 2770, 2771, 2772,
2780, 2782, 2801, 2816, 2826, 2839, 2848, 2852, 2870, 2871, 2879,
2883, 2884, 2885, 2902, 2908, 2920, 2926, 2927, 2932, 2939, 2951,
2964, 3000, 3006, 3041, 3046, 3054, 3062, 3065, 3076, 3077, 3078,
3079, 3080, 3081, 3082, 3105, 3109

I. Photoperiodic alteration effects
1. Night breaks 1, 38, 82, 92, 181, 209, 215, 232, 234, 237, 238, 293,
300, 305, 308, 311, 313, 357, 358, 359, 364, 366, 368, 369, 370, 371,

392, 405, 406, 435, 436, 441, 445, 453, 471, 472, 473, 475, 477, 478, 481, 484, 498, 499, 512, 524, 526, 528, 541, 582, 590, 611, 616, 617, 626, 628, 669, 695, 711, 712, 714, 715, 731, 736, 741, 748, 749, 750, 751, 753, 835, 849, 904, 908, 932, 939, 943, 944, 947, 1039, 1080, 1088, 1089, 1094, 1095, 1098, 1100, 1102, 1115, 1123, 1126, 1128, 1129, 1130, 1139, 1166, 1167, 1194, 1195, 1199, 1200, 1213, 1217, 1261, 1264, 1267, 1270, 1275, 1276, 1278, 1279, 1280, 1286, 1292, 1294, 1296, 1313, 1326, 1327, 1329, 1330, 1359, 1385, 1387, 1388, 1389, 1395, 1396, 1397, 1398, 1406, 1411, 1475, 1528, 1532, 1533, 1544, 1553, 1564, 1565, 1625, 1626, 1627, 1630, 1663, 1669, 1683, 1684, 1685, 1750, 1756, 1757, 1760, 1762, 1763, 1764, 1765, 1829, 1855, 1917, 1918, 1929, 1961, 1963, 1985, 2001, 2002, 2027, 2049, 2053, 2055, 2068, 2091, 2094, 2151, 2163, 2164, 2165, 2166, 2167, 2169, 2172, 2186, 2187, 2191, 2209, 2210, 2213, 2215, 2233, 2235, 2253, 2264, 2273, 2334, 2335, 2337, 2340, 2353, 2354, 2357, 2360, 2362, 2363, 2364, 2365, 2366, 2371, 2408, 2410, 2459, 2461, 2482, 2491, 2514, 2515, 2516, 2570, 2647, 2648, 2649, 2652, 2654, 2661, 2690, 2702, 2703, 2704, 2705, 2709, 2710, 2711, 2712, 2713, 2714, 2715, 2719, 2751, 2804, 2805, 2854, 2864, 2866, 2868, 2873, 2877.5, 2920, 2952, 2953, 2957, 3015, 3022, 3029

2. Terminal supplements 24, 44, 50, 59, 74, 95, 183, 221, 241, 288, 289, 290, 291, 353, 367, 368, 370, 414, 425, 434, 435, 436, 437, 439, 440, 441, 470, 472, 473, 475, 497, 498, 499, 500, 527, 528, 529, 530, 532, 580, 581, 582, 616, 617, 620, 621, 624, 626, 627, 636, 669, 690, 693, 708, 710, 711, 712, 713, 714, 715, 716, 717, 718, 719, 720, 723, 734, 736, 740, 757, 759, 760, 761, 762, 763, 765, 766, 767, 769, 783, 893, 908, 1039, 1073, 1080, 1094, 1098, 1100, 1102, 1128, 1129, 1130, 1131, 1175, 1194, 1195, 1213, 1218, 1226, 1257, 1260, 1264, 1269, 1273, 1276, 1277, 1278, 1279, 1280, 1286, 1296, 1329, 1331, 1334, 1335, 1336, 1337, 1340, 1395, 1396, 1398, 1411, 1414, 1415, 1425, 1436, 1474.5, 1475, 1528, 1532, 1533, 1534, 1552, 1553, 1562, 1603, 1607, 1610, 1623, 1625, 1628, 1629, 1630, 1713, 1729, 1737, 1750, 1758, 1760, 1762, 1763, 1764, 1765, 1768, 1771, 1797, 1815, 1900, 1908, 1918, 1960, 1961, 1962, 1963, 1964, 1969, 1975, 1985, 2027, 2078, 2192, 2210, 2217, 2233, 2240, 2263, 2269, 2270, 2333, 2342, 2343, 2353, 2388, 2408, 2409, 2410, 2461, 2480, 2491, 2511, 2512,

2513, 2514, 2516, 2549, 2635, 2646, 2647, 2648, 2649, 2652, 2661,
2690, 2692, 2698, 2699, 2700, 2701, 2702, 2703, 2705, 2707, 2708,
2712, 2713, 2714, 2715, 2780, 2820, 2833, 2835, 2845, 2853, 2864,
2865, 2868, 2871, 2873, 2877.5, 2920, 2923, 2939, 2943, 2944, 2945,
2946, 2952, 2957, 3003, 3015, 3037

J. Polarized Light Effects

    1. *in vitro* 279, 496

    2. *in vivo* 182, 307, 520, 522, 623, 650, 661, 824, 825, 959, 980, 981,
983, 984, 987, 988, 989, 991, 999, 1000, 1006, 1007, 1008, 1011,
1014, 1015, 1016, 1017, 1024, 1221, 1222, 1223, 1417, 1705, 1706,
1724, 1807, 1941, 1973, 1974, 1984, 2351, 2417, 2418, 2419, 2421,
2422, 2423, 2424, 2426, 2430, 2432, 2470, 2471, 2613, 2614, 2615,
2620, 2625, 2626, 2628, 2629, 2630, 3118, 3119, 3120, 3121, 3122,
3123

K. Reciprocity studies 58, 70, 143, 144, 167, 215, 219, 260, 295, 388, 506,
537, 539, 553, 594, 630, 631, 662, 728, 978, 983, 989, 1013, 1020,
1099, 1275, 1321, 1330, 1417, 1526, 1541, 1665, 1692, 1804, 1891,
1941, 2011, 2016, 2055, 2199, 2243, 2328, 2329, 2332, 2345, 2374,
2375, 2377, 2418, 2419, 2430, 2501, 2521, 2614, 2643, 2704, 2757,
2912, 2914, 2996, 3018, 3083, 3099, 3100

SECTION II: PHYTOCHROME MOLECULAR PROPERTIES

A. Chromophore

    1. Biosynthesis 205

    2. Destruction 275, 348, 699

    3. Linkage 430, 743, 744, 1501, 1502, 2302

    4. Structure 86, 281, 295, 323, 324, 417, 419, 430, 1064, 1135, 1244,
1497, 1498, 1499, 1501, 1502, 2302, 2532, 2533, 2534, 2680, 2681,
2777

B. Effects of molecular environment

    1. Anaerobic spectrophotometric effects, *in vivo* 1368, 1371, 1482, 2101

    2. ATP interactions, *in vitro* 2751

    3. Inorganic ions, *in vitro* 785, 1580, 1581, 1582, 1583, 1707, 1708,
1709, 1710, 2081, 2082, 2084, 2162, 2751, 2752, 3073

    4. Organic chemicals, *in vitro* 699, 782, 785, 1501, 1502, 1581, 1582,
1583, 1709, 1949, 1950, 1951, 2081, 2082, 2083, 2129, 2280, 2281,
2284, 2285, 2734, 2752, 2777, 3073

e. Epicotyls 267, 271, 399, 400, 401, 402, 646, 647, 773, 774,
    1366, 1368, 1369, 1370, 1371, 1372, 1374, 1375, 1659, 1662,
    1731, 1732, 1733, 1735, 2153, 2315, 2579, 2580, 2582, 2594,
    2777, 2779

f. Flowers 900, 2152, 2153, 2593, 2594

g. Fronds 2267

h. Hypocotyls 195, 196, 197, 267, 271, 399, 697, 894, 898, 900,
    901, 1362, 1363, 1365, 1366, 1489, 1693, 1700, 1701, 1709,
    1710, 1895, 1898, 2155, 2156, 2157, 2159, 2160, 2281, 2284,
    2374, 2375, 2377, 2380, 2399, 2401, 2675

i. Leaves 267, 271, 272, 298, 387, 418, 421, 517, 576, 1370,
    1468, 2100, 2139, 2153, 2197, 2199, 2583, 2584, 2585, 2586,
    2590, 2597

j. Megagametophytes 901

k. Mesocotyls 267, 271, 272, 342, 387, 502, 574, 2135, 2590,
    2594, 2596

l. Mitochondria 863, 864, 1662

m. Nodes 271, 272, 387, 502, 1468, 2135

n. Roots 271, 773, 774, 783, 1731, 1732, 1733, 1735, 2100,
    2135, 2139, 2153, 2675

o. Seeds 900, 901, 1361, 1490, 1545, 1649, 1653, 1658, 1672,
    1733, 2588, 2589, 2590, 2776, 2777, 3104, 3105

p. Stems 271, 398, 773, 774, 900, 1489, 2234, 2583, 2584, 2585,
    2586, 2597

q. Tissue cultures 1333, 2999, 3000, 3001

ix. Ratio P_r to P_{fr} 25, 100, 140, 188, 189, 192, 194, 195, 197, 272,
298, 342, 350, 390, 398, 502, 517, 518, 574, 698, 704, 706, 778,
783, 814, 898, 907, 967, 1097, 1099, 1101, 1105, 1129, 1142,
1143, 1145, 1148, 1216, 1360, 1363, 1365, 1367, 1374, 1375, 1482,
1489, 1545, 1617, 1651, 1653, 1658, 1659, 1660, 1666, 1669, 1671,
1693, 1700, 1701, 1703, 1705, 1706, 1731, 1732, 1735, 1830, 1898,
2043, 2071, 2081, 2083, 2100, 2115, 2116, 2117, 2127, 2153, 2156,
2162, 2234, 2280, 2281, 2374, 2375, 2378, 2380, 2381, 2382, 2383,
2578, 2579, 2580, 2589, 2664, 2693, 2777, 2818.5, 2999, 3000,
3001, 3104, 3105

SECTION III: BIOLOGICAL RESPONSES

A.   Abscission   491, 936, 1247, 1427

B.   Angle of:

   1.   Branches   613, 1269, 3102

   2.   Petioles   2353, 2354

C.   Bioelectric potential   20, 886, 957, 1232, 1234, 1236, 1988, 1989, 1990, 2173, 2174, 2175, 2176, 2177, 2286, 2287, 2288, 2326, 2722, 2723, 2724, 2725, 2726, 2727, 2728, 2729, 2729.5, 2730, 2731, 2732, 2979, 3086, 3087

D.   Carbon dioxide (nonrespiratory/nonphotosynthetic)

   1.   Release   729, 730, 1688, 1689, 3021

   2.   Uptake   1353, 2061, 2892, 2897

E.   Cell (see also headings Q, Z and AA.)

   1.   Differentiation   211, 288, 291, 305, 308, 545, 573, 616, 617, 626, 672, 709, 712, 758, 776, 955, 958, 1040, 1152, 1411, 1413, 1475, 1520, 1528, 1544, 1713, 1717, 1718, 1802, 1836, 1841, 1860, 1862, 1863, 1873, 1878, 1917, 1964, 1967, 1984, 2015, 2027, 2032, 2033, 2180, 2181, 2213, 2223, 2226, 2306, 2340, 2387, 2388, 2402, 2511, 2514, 2569, 2600, 2610, 2636, 2702, 2703, 2704, 2705, 2707, 2709, 2746, 2772, 2932, 2975

   2.   Mitosis   1635

   3.   Wall properties   788, 789, 1574, 1716

F.   Chromosome protection/repair   332, 845, 846, 866, 867, 1341, 1342, 1343, 1344, 1345, 1346, 1347, 1348, 1349, 1350, 1351, 1377, 1416, 1635, 1636, 1831, 1832, 1833, 1834, 2514, 2684, 2685, 2686, 2687, 2688, 2689, 3050, 3057, 3058, 3082, 3083

G.   Compositional changes

   1.   Acetyl choline   693.5, 954, 956, 957, 1232, 1234, 1235, 1236, 1237, 1238, 1324, 2068, 2085, 2202, 2203, 2362, 2363, 2364, 2370, 2728, 3085, 3086, 3087

   2.   Alkaloids   2820

   3.   Amino acids   17, 31, 32, 33, 85, 292, 293, 460, 464, 493.5, 494, 790, 791, 891, 892, 896, 951, 955, 1028, 1029, 1030, 1031, 1032, 1033, 1119, 1146, 1147, 1303, 1334, 1354, 1389, 1454, 1455, 1456, 1503, 1525, 1540, 1575, 1678, 1697, 1742, 1744, 1781, 1821, 1823, 1826, 1827, 1828, 1943, 1993, 1994, 1995, 1998, 2024, 2025, 2026, 2031, 2061, 2062, 2063, 2064, 2119, 2203, 2276, 2312, 2325, 2432, 2618,

378

2619, 2624, 2815, 2892, 2896, 2901, 2920, 2972, 2974, 3025, 3089, 3122

4. Ascorbic acid   43, 144, 145, 152, 601, 614, 956, 1245, 1287, 1334, 1383, 1384, 1385, 1690, 1691, 1692, 1882, 1884, 1900, 2038, 2289, 2307, 2308, 2393, 2434, 2435, 2436, 2440, 2669, 2723, 2724, 2872, 2959

5. ATP   314, 492, 723, 863, 956, 1224, 1225, 1236, 1287, 1297, 1789, 2085, 2350, 2355, 2415, 2432, 2476, 2545, 2547, 2643, 2723, 2724, 2757, 3002, 3070, 3085, 3086, 3087, 3122

6. Caloric content   729, 730

7. Carbohydrates   17, 30, 31, 32, 33, 106, 292, 363, 445, 460, 683, 790, 791, 869, 870, 871, 883, 928, 955, 973, 1030, 1141, 1150, 1334, 1408, 1431, 1485, 1487, 1503, 1594, 1820, 1821, 1827, 1828, 1909, 1910, 1911, 1953, 1987, 1993, 1994, 1995, 2024, 2025, 2031, 2061, 2080, 2095, 2096, 2109, 2144, 2145, 2146, 2482, 2484, 2599, 2602, 2603, 2612, 2616, 2617, 2619, 2621, 2622, 2624, 2637, 2659, 2696, 2815, 2893, 2894, 2895, 2898

8. Carbohydrate/nitrogen ratio   106, 363, 1485, 1797, 2095, 2096, 2109, 2599, 2602, 2603, 2659, 2695, 2696, 2893, 2898

9. (of) chloroplasts   97, 251, 333, 949, 1152, 1569, 1754, 2179, 2184

10. Cyclic nucleotides   509, 807, 1241, 1551, 2085, 2974, 3073

11. Enzymes (also see following specific enzyme entries)   5, 6, 7, 8, 9, 11, 19, 31, 33, 60, 62, 63, 64, 65, 66, 87, 99, 100, 101, 102, 151, 152, 154, 251, 253, 254, 287, 293, 333, 372, 373, 374, 375, 376, 377, 378, 510, 514, 546, 547, 548, 549, 550, 551, 552, 554, 565, 569, 570, 571, 573, 593, 596, 597, 598, 600, 601, 603, 604, 605, 606, 607, 608, 609, 612, 614, 652, 653, 654, 660, 725, 739, 740, 741, 742, 754, 771, 855, 877, 878, 879, 880, 883, 884, 922, 926, 941, 949, 1077, 1083, 1138, 1160, 1161, 1162, 1163, 1164, 1165, 1237, 1246, 1254, 1255, 1310, 1311, 1356, 1382, 1414, 1415, 1433, 1434, 1579.5, 1658, 1662, 1694, 1695, 1698, 1699, 1738, 1739, 1777, 1827, 1828, 1891, 1893, 1895, 1898, 1906, 1907, 1999, 2016, 2017, 2018, 2019, 2020, 2021, 2022, 2023, 2026, 2046, 2066, 2067, 2068, 2069, 2071, 2105, 2163, 2164, 2165, 2166, 2167, 2169, 2172, 2228, 2289, 2295, 2312, 2324, 2370, 2396, 2397, 2443, 2444, 2449, 2451, 2452, 2465, 2556, 2558, 2568, 2575, 2599, 2606, 2607, 2675, 2677, 2748, 2751, 2752, 2843,

2844, 2888, 2904, 2964, 2965, 2966, 2986, 2988, 2989, 2992, 2993, 3060, 3070, 3071, 3073, 3085, 3087, 3097

    i. Acetyl cholinesterase [EC 3.1.1.7] 1237

   ii. Acid phosphatase [EC 3.1.3.2] 63, 66, 333, 1777

  iii. Adenosine triphosphatase [EC 3.6.1.3] 3085, 3087

   iv. Adenylate kinase [EC 2.7.4.3] 333, 739, 740, 741, 879

    v. Alanine aminotransferase [EC 2.6.1.21] 2169, 2172

   vi. Amino acid-activating enzymes 1077

  vii. δ-aminolaevulinate dehydratase [EC 4.2.1.24] 2607

 viii. α-amylase [EC 3.2.1.11] 547, 548, 549

   ix. Arginase [EC 3.5.3.1] 573

    x. Ascorbate oxidase [EC 1.10.3.3] 9, 63, 64, 87, 550, 551, 552, 1906, 1907, 2071, 2842

   xi. Aspartate aminotransferase [EC 2.6.1.1] 293, 2169, 2172

  xii. Carboxydismutase [EC 4.1.1.39] 253, 652, 653, 654, 660, 877, 878, 879, 880, 949, 1827, 2026, 2295, 2465

 xiii. Catalase [EC 1.11.1.6] 152, 546, 554, 1579.5, 2105

 xiv. Chalcone isomerase [EC 5.5.1.6] 2988, 2989, 2992

  xv. Chlorophyllase [EC 3.1.1.14] 2888

 xvi. Cinnamic acid hydroxylase 597

 xvii. Cytochrome oxidase [EC 1.9.3.1] 2289

xviii. 5-dehydroquinate dehydratase [EC 4.2.1.10] 19

 xix. Diaphorase [EC 1.6.4.3] 333

  xx. Diastase (starch degradation) [EC 3.2.1.1, 3.2.1.2] 883

 xxi. Enolase [EC 4.2.1.11] 880, 2465

 xxii. (β)-fructofuranosidase (sucrose hydrolysis) [EC 3.2.1.26] 31, 33

xxiii. Fructosebisphosphate aldolase [EC 4.1.2.13] 253

xxiv. Fructose-1,6-bisphosphate 1-phosphohydrolase (alkaline) [EC 3.1.3.11] 877, 878, 879, 880, 2465

 xxv. Glucose-6-phosphate dehydrogenase [EC 1.1.1.49] 293, 653, 660, 754, 879, 949, 2575, 2606, 2986

 xxvi. Glutamate dehydrogenase [EC 1.4.1.2] 1777

xxvii. Glutamic-oxaloacetate transaminase [EC 2.6.1.1] 2606

xxviii. Glutathione reductase (NADPH) [EC 1.6.4.2] 552

2036, 2037, 2087, 2088, 2096, 2119, 2178, 2179, 2180, 2181, 2204, 2206, 2276, 2291, 2435, 2464, 2465, 2487, 2556, 2563, 2653, 2670, 2759, 2814, 2902, 2923, 2958, 2959, 2960, 2961, 2962, 2963, 3025, 3054, 3069, 3073

14. Organic acids 17, 31, 32, 33, 292, 293, 363, 460, 790, 791, 951, 1028, 1030, 1031, 1032, 1033, 1079, 1235, 1238, 1334, 1354, 1389, 1503, 1689, 1779, 1823, 1827, 1828, 1909, 1910, 1911, 1986, 1987, 1993, 1994, 2016, 2024, 2025, 2026, 2163, 2164, 2165, 2166, 2167, 2169, 2172, 2355, 2356, 2357, 2366, 2368, 2413, 2416, 2619, 2631, 2632, 2643, 2818, 2896, 2904, 3089

15. pH of cells 2289

16. Phenolic compounds 19, 60, 88, 89, 99, 100, 101, 102, 572, 591, 592, 593, 594, 596, 597, 598, 600, 601, 602, 603, 604, 605, 606, 607, 608, 609, 724, 725, 726, 796, 837, 839, 840, 843, 855, 884, 922, 926, 950, 951, 1086, 1163, 1245, 1454, 1455, 1456, 1472, 1736, 1737, 2104, 2148, 2190, 2191, 2228, 2314, 2316, 2642, 2820, 2920, 2921, 2964, 3061

17. Pigments

   i. Anthocyanin 27, 48, 74, 99, 101, 102, 130, 131, 132, 144, 145, 167, 260, 297, 367, 425, 510, 534, 537, 539, 540, 553, 565, 604, 665, 670, 712, 714, 884, 888, 889, 890, 891, 892, 893, 894, 895, 896, 897, 898, 899, 922, 1039, 1052, 1128, 1129, 1209, 1269, 1287, 1288, 1289, 1290, 1305, 1308, 1324, 1415, 1494, 1505, 1506, 1519, 1524, 1538, 1539, 1540, 1541, 1575, 1642, 1643, 1674, 1677, 1736, 1812, 1837, 1840, 1870, 1879, 1881, 1882, 1884, 1885, 1887, 1891, 1895, 1900, 1905, 1922, 1991, 1992, 2014, 2065, 2066, 2067, 2080, 2148, 2211, 2396, 2397, 2412, 2413, 2414, 2415, 2416, 2435, 2440, 2478, 2481, 2502, 2503, 2519, 2520, 2521, 2522, 2523, 2551, 2552, 2623, 2631, 2632, 2633, 2634, 2642, 2643, 2697, 2780, 2781, 2782, 2829, 2845, 2870, 2872, 2915, 2916, 2917, 2918, 2919, 2989, 3039, 3040, 3041, 3043, 3075

  ii. Carotenes 58, 144, 251, 257, 397, 407, 510, 660.5, 702, 849, 850, 1076, 1190, 1243, 1306, 1385, 1386, 1388, 1437.5, 1569, 1678, 1715, 1909, 1910, 1911, 2014, 2103, 2196, 2198, 2199, 2323, 2344, 2403, 2404, 2405, 2406, 2602, 2603, 2657, 2818.5, 2883, 2884, 3003, 3043

H. Conditions which alter *in vivo* responses:
1. Anaerobiosis 31, 32, 33, 659, 751, 831, 839, 890, 992, 1180, 1186, 1224, 1225, 1680, 1828, 2012, 2101, 2125, 2355, 2357, 2359, 2360, 2691, 2692, 2757, 2901, 3089
2. Carbohydrates 124, 125, 200, 425, 594, 606, 829, 892, 951, 1144, 1225, 1262, 1287, 1339, 1450, 1473, 1551, 1799, 1800, 1806, 1924, 1953, 1955, 1972, 1992, 2340, 2350, 2351, 2391, 2440, 2441, 2641, 2853, 2920, 2972, 2974, 3054, 3055, 3060, 3081, 3122
3. Carbon dioxide 2, 92, 130, 132, 592, 619, 630, 824, 852, 876, 1299, 1301, 1579.5, 1686, 1780, 1781, 1782, 1924, 1939, 1978, 1979, 2028, 2031, 2047, 2351, 2402, 2972
4. Inorganic ions 124, 125, 128, 200, 400, 606, 607, 703, 720, 746, 771, 796, 802, 807, 810, 833, 904, 921.2, 931, 1045, 1085, 1087, 1092, 1098, 1111, 1113, 1115, 1118, 1141, 1159, 1236, 1292, 1297, 1300, 1301, 1302, 1364, 1367, 1429, 1450, 1451, 1484, 1522, 1557, 1660, 1725, 1781, 1813, 1906, 1924, 1954, 1955, 1977, 2030, 2040, 2081, 2175, 2176, 2337, 2355, 2356, 2357, 2359, 2360, 2361, 2362, 2363, 2365, 2366, 2368, 2369, 2413, 2416, 2425, 2427, 2441, 2466, 2474, 2475, 2484, 2576, 2643, 2673, 2674, 2692, 2721, 2723, 2724, 2728, 2729.5, 2732, 2735, 2743, 2852, 2925, 2926, 2972, 2973, 3081, 3085, 3087, 3122
5. Other organic chemicals 10, 29, 31, 32, 33, 44, 55, 62, 66, 102, 111, 114, 118, 123, 125, 126, 127, 128, 135, 144, 145, 154, 174, 256, 261, 299, 322, 332, 333, 360, 360.5, 372, 373, 374, 375, 376, 378, 386, 400, 401, 402, 443, 445, 457, 461, 464, 488, 490, 495, 504, 510, 514, 533, 540, 547, 548, 549, 569, 591, 592, 594, 596, 601, 606, 635, 644, 655, 656, 659, 660, 663, 693.5, 703, 724, 725, 728, 746, 753, 771, 796, 802, 830, 831, 832, 833, 837, 839, 840, 842, 843, 869, 871, 876, 886, 887, 888, 889, 890, 891, 895, 909, 914, 919, 933, 935, 942, 956, 957, 992, 1085, 1087, 1092, 1119, 1146, 1147, 1161, 1163, 1224, 1225, 1226, 1232, 1234, 1235, 1236, 1237, 1238, 1245, 1271, 1281, 1283, 1284, 1290, 1299, 1300, 1302, 1303, 1314, 1323, 1347, 1349, 1352, 1360, 1362, 1363, 1367, 1373, 1376, 1378, 1379, 1380, 1381, 1384, 1390, 1406, 1414, 1418, 1419, 1429, 1433, 1434, 1446, 1448, 1452, 1453, 1457, 1474, 1484, 1507, 1508, 1519, 1534, 1538, 1539, 1551, 1560, 1575, 1576, 1591, 1631, 1632, 1656, 1658, 1660, 1662, 1677,

1678, 1680, 1681, 1692, 1708, 1712, 1725, 1732, 1733, 1735, 1742, 1743, 1744, 1745, 1748, 1759, 1778, 1780, 1781, 1785, 1796, 1803, 1806, 1813, 1814, 1816, 1817, 1827, 1878, 1879, 1880, 1884, 1885, 1887, 1920, 1921, 1922, 1943, 1953, 1954, 1955, 1976, 1977, 1998, 2014, 2016, 2018, 2024, 2025, 2030, 2066, 2068, 2083, 2085, 2105, 2119, 2121, 2125, 2163, 2164, 2166, 2175, 2178, 2179, 2180, 2181, 2191, 2203, 2204, 2205, 2206, 2218, 2228, 2240, 2267, 2280, 2281, 2284, 2295, 2300, 2301, 2325, 2335, 2347, 2357, 2360, 2365, 2368, 2370, 2391, 2392, 2404, 2405, 2406, 2412, 2413, 2414, 2416, 2417, 2425, 2427, 2428, 2432, 2435, 2437, 2438, 2439, 2440, 2454, 2466, 2467, 2468, 2472, 2475, 2476, 2484, 2548, 2550, 2555, 2563, 2567, 2568, 2576, 2577, 2624, 2643, 2653, 2656.5, 2666, 2667, 2692, 2766, 2767, 2776, 2784, 2785, 2789, 2812, 2813, 2832, 2911, 2917, 2918, 2919, 2924, 2926, 2927, 2959, 2963, 2971, 2974, 3060, 3065, 3066, 3073, 3075, 3081, 3086, 3087, 3104, 3105, 3114, 3115, 3116, 3122

6. pH 317, 1144, 1303, 1748, 1778, 2175, 2176, 3122

7. Redox potential 1419

8. Temperature 26, 31, 32, 33, 43, 45, 54, 55, 56, 59, 62, 70, 85, 117, 118, 119, 133, 140, 168, 169, 199, 223, 295, 318, 397, 435, 436, 437, 438, 439, 461, 520, 523, 578, 579, 580, 581, 584, 585, 602, 604, 605, 619, 621, 622, 632, 634, 638, 662, 690, 695, 703, 725, 731, 733, 735, 737, 741, 748, 805, 810, 811, 824, 825, 832, 867, 882, 889, 890, 896, 905, 908, 999, 1002, 1020, 1041, 1115, 1139, 1184, 1186, 1197, 1198, 1200, 1208, 1246.5, 1256, 1258, 1259, 1260, 1276, 1281, 1282, 1315, 1359, 1391, 1392, 1393, 1399, 1425, 1426, 1432, 1461, 1462, 1463, 1473, 1506, 1514, 1548, 1554, 1555, 1556, 1557, 1610, 1637, 1658, 1665, 1667, 1668, 1671, 1676, 1720, 1726, 1733, 1746, 1750, 1811, 1830, 1841, 1908, 1918, 1940, 1941, 1984, 1985, 1998, 2011, 2028, 2040, 2108, 2116, 2120, 2146, 2231, 2240, 2241, 2242, 2277, 2318, 2355, 2357, 2366, 2368, 2369, 2390, 2391, 2394, 2500, 2611, 2628, 2649, 2665, 2687, 2688, 2709, 2712, 2713, 2735, 2737, 2739, 2740, 2741, 2742, 2744, 2783, 2784, 2785, 2787, 2788, 2789, 2797, 2800, 2801, 2803, 2804, 2806, 2855, 2856, 2857, 2921, 2972, 2976, 2977, 2978, 2980, 3015, 3017, 3018, 3022, 3048, 3054, 3062, 3063, 3077, 3079, 3105

I. Cytoplasmic:
   1. Streaming 1494, 2470, 2476
   2. Viscosity 2459, 2471, 2476, 3112
J. Dormancy 26, 386, 455, 512, 622, 882, 1248, 1380, 1589, 1750, 1835, 1959, 2010, 2011, 2107, 2235, 2488, 2540, 2541, 2577, 2833, 2859, 2906, 3022
K. Etiolation 179, 180, 495, 713, 716, 717, 718, 859, 1217, 1431, 1837, 1923, 1997, 1998, 2044, 2498
L. (in) excised:
   1. Buds 611, 1086, 1227
   2. Coleoptiles 15, 105, 157, 158, 160, 161, 162, 163, 164, 165, 166, 256, 330, 517, 518, 592, 788, 823, 834, 1099, 1142, 1143, 1144, 1145, 1146, 1147, 1148, 1149, 1170, 1187, 1366, 1370, 1457, 1551, 1579, 1660, 1705, 1706, 1965, 1990, 2081, 2083, 2099, 2100, 2127, 2281, 2284, 2407, 2547, 2640, 2641, 2773, 2774, 2972, 2974, 3005, 3007, 3010, 3016, 3017, 3018, 3099, 3100, 3103
   3. Cotyledons 888, 893, 967, 1365, 1519, 1658, 1693, 1919, 2023, 2453, 2643
   4. Epicotyls 32, 33, 124, 200, 400, 401, 402, 745, 794, 869, 870, 871, 951, 1097, 1099, 1149, 1366, 1367, 1370, 1372, 1457, 1784, 2036, 2037, 2203, 2301, 2315, 2316, 2370, 2580, 2582
   5. Flowers 1520, 2631, 2632
   6. Fronds 929
   7. Gametophytes 835, 3074
   8. Hypocotyls 591, 592, 593, 594, 597, 601, 604, 746, 874, 875, 876, 888, 893, 923, 957, 1101, 1143, 1245, 1299, 1301, 1365, 1366, 1473, 1474, 1619, 1693, 1859, 2072, 2284, 2298, 2299, 2300, 2301, 2441, 2453, 2501, 2547, 2732, 3048, 3049
   9. Leaf discs 46, 457, 887, 920, 921, 1141, 1159, 1417, 1450, 1587, 1590, 1591, 1592, 1790, 1920, 1921, 1987, 2118, 2121, 2122, 2123, 2124, 2466, 2467, 2468, 2670
   10. Leaves 24, 44, 70, 154, 491, 630, 683, 745, 879, 919, 973, 1078, 1080, 1132, 1134, 1189, 1216, 1303, 1370, 1450, 1544, 1573, 1614, 1632, 1748, 1755, 1787, 1789, 1813, 1814, 1821, 1825, 1987, 2080, 2119, 2142, 2143, 2145, 2146, 2165, 2166, 2167, 2169, 2204, 2208, 2356, 2357, 2358, 2360, 2365, 2366, 2420, 2459, 2482, 2498, 2547, 2556, 2612, 2756, 2815, 2879, 2881, 2882, 2883, 2884, 2885, 2892,

1246.5, 1256, 1258, 1259, 1263, 1265, 1282, 1283, 1284, 1313, 1314, 1315, 1316, 1359, 1361, 1377, 1378, 1379, 1381, 1383, 1384, 1394, 1420, 1421, 1459, 1461, 1462, 1466, 1478, 1491, 1492, 1493, 1514, 1535, 1543, 1550, 1554, 1555, 1557, 1560, 1618, 1620, 1621, 1623, 1624, 1634, 1648, 1651, 1657, 1658, 1664, 1665, 1666, 1667, 1668, 1670, 1672, 1676, 1679, 1680, 1681, 1712, 1717, 1718, 1727, 1728, 1729, 1730, 1740, 1741, 1742, 1744, 1745, 1751, 1752, 1790, 1920, 1921, 1953, 1954, 1955, 1958, 1959, 1975, 1976, 1978, 1979, 2009, 2010, 2012, 2028, 2029, 2030, 2040, 2041, 2043, 2049, 2050, 2051, 2052, 2097, 2105, 2106, 2107, 2108, 2120, 2214, 2216, 2218, 2231, 2237, 2238, 2239, 2241, 2242, 2245, 2253, 2255, 2256, 2260, 2277, 2278, 2322, 2392, 2394, 2420, 2438, 2454, 2455, 2479, 2481, 2490, 2500, 2506, 2509, 2517, 2518, 2543, 2544, 2550, 2555, 2567, 2568, 2573, 2574, 2576, 2577, 2588, 2589, 2608, 2609, 2638, 2653, 2655, 2672, 2673, 2674, 2682, 2683, 2735, 2736, 2737, 2738, 2739, 2740, 2741, 2742, 2743, 2744, 2766, 2767, 2775, 2776, 2777, 2783, 2784, 2785, 2787, 2788, 2791, 2792, 2797, 2798, 2799, 2800, 2801, 2803, 2804, 2805, 2806, 2840, 2846, 2851, 2852, 2855, 2856, 2857, 2858, 2859, 2906, 2907, 2935, 2971, 2981, 3031, 3062, 3063, 3066, 3067, 3076, 3077, 3078, 3079, 3080, 3091, 3092, 3104, 3105

   iii. Time course 75, 117, 319, 538, 615, 649, 828, 910, 911, 917, 1041, 1042, 1044, 1058, 1158, 1174, 1180, 1182, 1184, 1312, 1380, 1400, 1401, 1402, 1403, 1404, 1463, 1556, 1559, 1567, 1633, 1671, 1743, 1746, 1772, 1869, 2011, 2114, 2386, 2390, 2391, 2481, 2789, 3090

3. Spores 93, 304, 307, 321, 380, 663, 782.5, 1035, 1223, 1242, 1409, 1584, 1807, 1835, 1860, 1873, 1874, 2045, 2183, 2185, 2351, 2456, 2457, 2611, 2627, 2636, 2639, 2665, 2666, 2667, 2668, 2746, 2812, 2813, 2830

4. Turions 453, 455, 1548.5, 1549.5, 2539

Q. Growth of and/or size/shape of:

1. Buds 31, 32, 33, 209, 611, 622, 869, 871, 935, 936, 1086, 1227, 1245, 1269, 1286, 1383, 1384, 1387, 1457, 1565, 1566, 1756, 2541, 2556, 2559, 2866, 3022

2. Cells 73, 95, 105, 114, 115, 149, 163, 165, 199, 264, 302, 355, 361, 362, 380, 457, 458, 469, 472, 543, 545, 557, 558, 560, 561, 574, 593,

623, 627, 650, 672, 721, 745, 746, 756, 782.5, 786, 789, 793, 834, 852, 853, 856, 890, 923, 959, 970, 1040, 1121, 1144, 1201, 1210, 1211, 1247, 1299, 1300, 1309, 1355, 1409, 1412, 1429, 1470, 1485, 1486, 1551, 1562, 1601, 1606, 1716, 1780, 1782, 1802, 1803, 1806, 1816, 1817, 1836, 1837, 1842, 1846, 1847, 1848, 1849, 1855, 1859, 1861, 1863, 1878, 1884, 1888, 1892, 1924, 1960, 1984, 2008, 2034, 2096, 2099, 2103, 2104, 2121, 2122, 2126, 2180, 2181, 2194, 2217, 2226, 2243, 2276, 2296, 2298, 2299, 2300, 2317, 2389, 2402, 2407, 2438, 2439, 2441, 2445, 2537, 2570, 2600, 2636, 2642, 2649, 2746, 2773, 2871, 2882, 2914, 2915, 2962, 2972, 2974, 3007, 3018, 3042, 3043, 3044, 3048, 3049

3. Chloroplasts 107, 109, 112, 114, 115, 255, 689, 721, 925, 928, 949, 1132, 1339, 1754, 1836, 1984, 2118, 2610, 2636, 2637, 2831, 2898, 3112, 3115

4. Coleoptiles 14, 15, 16, 72, 73, 82, 105, 156, 159, 160, 161, 163, 164, 165, 271, 330, 350, 403, 421, 496, 517, 518, 557, 560, 561, 783, 786, 834, 844, 1001, 1099, 1142, 1144, 1145, 1146, 1147, 1148, 1149, 1170, 1171, 1187, 1210, 1211, 1216, 1251, 1355, 1383, 1457, 1470, 1515, 1542, 1551, 1585, 1586, 1716, 1780, 1781, 1782, 1808, 1942, 1943, 2060, 2086, 2099, 2100, 2101, 2141, 2232, 2389, 2407, 2537, 2600, 2640, 2641, 2773, 2816, 2891, 2953, 2972, 2973, 2974, 2996, 3005, 3006, 3007, 3008, 3009, 3010, 3017, 3103

5. Cotyledons 302, 593, 615, 775, 854, 991, 994, 1121, 1122, 1181, 1411, 1489, 1717, 1718, 1839, 1842, 1880, 1882, 2273, 2435, 2549, 2745

6. Epicotyls 31, 124, 148, 200, 400, 401, 402, 403, 482, 512, 525, 671, 672, 745, 775, 794, 797, 851, 852, 853, 869, 870, 871, 1097, 1099, 1149, 1227, 1367, 1453, 1457, 1616, 1732, 1733, 1784, 1785, 1914, 1915, 1942, 2036, 2037, 2203, 2301, 2315, 2316, 2324, 2325, 2332, 2768, 2819, 3043

7. Flowers 690, 766, 1263, 1269, 1286, 1475, 2213, 2333, 2649, 2660, 2945, 3033, 3034

8. Fronds 728, 1522, 1549, 2042, 2116, 2263, 2264, 2265, 2268, 2269, 2270, 3109

9. Fruits 1247, 1248, 1589, 1591, 1810, 3088

10. Gametophytes 111, 113, 114, 115, 493.5, 503, 543, 545, 650, 689, 959, 1191, 1201, 1223, 1339, 1409, 1561, 1641, 1798, 1799, 1800, 1803,

1804, 1805, 1811, 1815, 1817, 1878, 1971, 1972, 1973, 1974, 1998,
2032, 2180, 2181, 2402, 2569, 2613, 2614, 2615, 2620, 2625, 2626,
2628, 2629, 2630, 2636, 2967, 3029, 3074

11. Hypocotyls 5, 10, 99, 132, 136, 143, 144, 179, 180, 302, 381, 382,
383, 482, 524, 525, 593, 627, 641, 671, 672, 682, 714, 745, 746, 852,
874, 875, 876, 889, 890, 892, 952, 960, 961, 962, 963, 964, 965, 966,
970, 1001, 1045, 1058, 1101, 1120.5, 1121, 1122, 1182, 1184, 1269,
1321, 1324, 1411, 1415, 1418, 1419, 1423, 1424, 1425, 1427, 1428,
1429, 1432, 1473, 1474, 1489, 1493, 1524, 1575, 1597, 1622, 1627,
1629, 1713, 1721, 1758, 1759, 1761, 1762, 1763, 1767, 1768, 1771,
1837, 1842, 1847, 1849, 1855, 1859, 1863, 1882, 1884, 1888, 1892,
1895, 2008, 2016, 2077, 2114, 2273, 2276, 2298, 2299, 2300, 2301,
2324, 2389, 2404, 2435, 2437, 2439, 2441, 2442, 2445, 2481, 2616,
2617, 2618, 2621, 2622, 2624, 2697, 2708, 2745, 2746, 2823, 2824,
2915, 2959, 3003, 3038, 3040, 3041, 3043

12. Internodes 3, 125, 128, 129, 143, 148, 218, 248, 363, 371, 495, 500,
507, 519, 527, 528, 529, 532, 533, 572, 582, 585, 614, 660.5, 666,
697, 698, 712, 714, 756, 766, 796, 857, 859, 1010, 1013, 1020, 1051,
1084, 1090, 1097, 1099, 1219, 1249, 1269, 1278, 1335, 1352, 1387,
1441, 1450, 1489, 1494, 1521, 1522, 1528, 1553, 1562, 1571, 1574,
1600, 1610, 1614, 1622, 1640, 1717, 1718, 1758, 1759, 1761, 1762,
1763, 1914, 1960, 1967, 1982, 1983, 2002, 2056, 2058, 2273, 2312,
2313, 2314, 2315, 2316, 2320, 2327, 2328, 2329, 2330, 2332, 2348,
2364, 2495, 2542, 2647, 2648, 2649, 2745, 2746, 2753, 2768, 2769,
2770, 2772, 2819, 2848, 2860, 2865, 2871, 2889, 2932, 2944, 2945,
2946, 2951, 2996, 3013, 3014, 3038, 3039

13. Leaves 3, 31, 46, 133, 148, 199, 255, 297, 350, 363, 406, 421, 449,
457, 471, 478, 481, 495, 500, 512, 524, 525, 533, 587, 589, 613, 614,
666, 683, 711, 712, 745, 756, 761, 772, 803, 829, 844, 934, 1039,
1131, 1132, 1141, 1166, 1167, 1190, 1209, 1247, 1263, 1269, 1331,
1335, 1336, 1337, 1353, 1393, 1410, 1411, 1414, 1415, 1417, 1437,
1489, 1587, 1590, 1591, 1592, 1616, 1682, 1698, 1699, 1717, 1718,
1790, 1863, 1914, 1915, 1920, 1921, 1924, 1927, 2056, 2075, 2109,
2121, 2122, 2123, 2124, 2126, 2144, 2145, 2272, 2273, 2320, 2324,
2325, 2331, 2343, 2353, 2354, 2384, 2386, 2410, 2466, 2467, 2468,
2483, 2490, 2495, 2511, 2512, 2549, 2600, 2647, 2648, 2649, 2652,

2659, 2698, 2745, 2746, 2753, 2769, 2771, 2819, 2860, 2902, 2944, 2945, 2953, 2996, 3007, 3008, 3014, 3035, 3039, 3040, 3041, 3067, 3081

14. Mesocotyls 72, 73, 156, 159, 219, 271, 350, 501, 556, 557, 560, 564, 684, 856, 1170, 1171, 1251, 1467, 1490, 1542, 1617, 1780, 1781, 1782, 1783, 1808, 1924, 1990, 2003, 2049, 2076, 2317, 2345, 2346, 2347, 2348, 2349, 2407, 2600, 2816, 2841, 2968, 2969, 2970, 2973, 3017, 3040, 3068

15. Nodes 1614, 2770, 2973

16. Nuclei 108, 110, 112, 113

17. Nucleoli 113, 1399

18. Petioles 3, 143, 449, 499, 500, 525, 528, 582, 671, 672, 683, 756, 829, 1010, 1013, 1039, 1247, 1269, 1522, 1574, 1616, 1717, 1718, 2273, 2353, 2354, 2410, 2483, 2647, 2648, 2649, 2652, 2659, 2697, 2745, 2746, 2816, 2944, 2945, 2951, 2952, 2996, 3014, 3081, 3109

19. Rhizomes 1804

20. Roots 136, 149, 152, 381, 382, 383, 641, 783, 829, 854, 1082, 1121, 1182, 1184, 1209, 1263, 1294, 1324, 1445, 1522, 1575, 1682, 1732, 1733, 1753, 1966, 2011, 2034, 2075, 2086, 2224, 2306, 2307, 2311, 2391, 2392, 2463, 2481, 2483, 2490, 2492, 2493, 2511, 2638, 2658, 2698, 2723, 2745, 2747, 2810, 2811, 2822, 3003, 3034

21. Seeds 2240

22. Sporophytes 107, 307, 380, 623, 1521, 1522, 1584, 1801, 1836, 1860, 1862, 1970, 2045, 2637, 2639, 2967

23. Stems 31, 32, 33, 46, 123, 125, 126, 127, 128, 129, 148, 215, 245, 248, 363, 371, 406, 449, 495, 497, 498, 499, 500, 507, 526, 582, 585, 586, 588, 589, 613, 664, 668, 669, 690, 696, 697, 698, 756, 761, 795, 796, 797, 803, 854, 872, 878, 946, 1039, 1084, 1090, 1097, 1099, 1129, 1174, 1193, 1217, 1247, 1248, 1252, 1263, 1265, 1266, 1269, 1294, 1304, 1307, 1307.5, 1329, 1335, 1357, 1376, 1408, 1437, 1450, 1453, 1489, 1508, 1531, 1552, 1553, 1562, 1581, 1595, 1596, 1597, 1598, 1599, 1601, 1602, 1603, 1607, 1608, 1609, 1610, 1614, 1623, 1624, 1625, 1626, 1682, 1717, 1718, 1750, 1784, 1785, 1942, 1960, 1982, 1983, 2000, 2056, 2058, 2075, 2102, 2117, 2192, 2194, 2202, 2203, 2235, 2236, 2272, 2312, 2313, 2320, 2327, 2330, 2353, 2354, 2384, 2408, 2409, 2410, 2480, 2481, 2483, 2490, 2495, 2511, 2647,

925, 928, 1134, 1176, 1205, 1422, 1569, 1579.5, 1754, 2044, 2230, 2464

3. Flowers 1, 38, 59, 92, 137, 181, 232, 234, 245, 288, 289, 290, 291, 295, 305, 308, 357, 358, 359, 366, 367, 368, 369, 370, 371, 405, 406, 412, 413, 414, 435, 436, 437, 439, 441, 443, 445, 449, 466, 498, 507, 508, 582, 617, 620, 624, 626, 628, 664, 690, 708, 709, 712, 714, 731, 732, 734, 735, 736, 737, 766, 769, 986, 904, 931, 932, 933, 939, 943, 944, 947, 1039, 1088, 1089, 1092, 1094, 1095, 1098, 1100, 1102, 1113, 1129, 1130, 1139, 1174, 1188, 1194, 1195, 1212, 1213, 1220, 1247, 1257, 1261, 1262, 1264, 1266, 1267, 1269, 1270, 1271, 1272, 1275, 1278, 1279, 1280, 1286, 1292, 1297, 1313, 1326, 1327, 1330, 1389, 1391, 1392, 1395, 1396, 1397, 1398, 1406, 1410, 1435, 1437, 1440, 1474.5, 1475, 1528, 1532, 1533, 1544, 1552, 1623, 1624, 1625, 1628, 1630, 1663, 1669, 1713, 1756, 1757, 1760, 1762, 1763, 1764, 1765, 1916, 1917, 1918, 1925, 1927, 1929, 1931, 1932, 1935, 1961, 1962, 1963, 1964, 1967, 2002, 2015, 2027, 2049, 2053, 2068, 2091, 2094, 2151, 2209, 2210, 2213, 2233, 2272, 2273, 2321, 2334, 2335, 2337, 2338, 2340, 2371, 2408, 2410, 2458, 2482, 2483, 2491, 2512, 2513, 2514, 2515, 2516, 2549, 2635, 2646, 2647, 2648, 2649, 2652, 2660, 2661, 2662, 2699, 2700, 2701, 2702, 2703, 2704, 2705, 2706, 2707, 2708, 2709, 2710, 2711, 2712, 2713, 2714, 2715, 2719, 2825, 2826, 2839, 2853, 2854, 2860, 2864, 2866, 2868, 2873, 2877.5, 2932, 2944, 2945, 2946, 2951, 2953, 2957, 2984, 3015, 3032, 3059, 3091

4. Fronds 1296, 1549

5. Fruits 2102, 3088

6. Gametophytes 1223, 1641, 1815, 1878, 2225, 2387, 2388

7. Hairs 672, 1209, 1399, 1838

8. Leaves 756, 1257, 1713, 1720, 1863, 2769

9. Rhizoids 1957, 1984, 2461, 2832

10. Rhizomes 1191

11. Roots 149, 658, 672, 745, 777, 1265, 1269, 1324, 1522, 1571, 1720, 2073, 2307, 2311, 2453, 2488, 2658, 2822, 2994, 3101

12. Runners 1269, 1270, 3102

13. Spores 361, 541, 837, 2035, 2215, 2720

14. Stems 133, 353, 386, 621, 1335, 1720, 1915

15. Turions 507

V. Interactions with growth regulators (also see following specific entries)

1, 2, 10, 18, 26, 31, 38, 71, 90, 95, 96, 98, 104, 118, 119, 123, 124, 125, 129, 134, 135, 139, 140, 141, 143, 163, 164, 165, 178, 261, 262, 264, 265, 299, 302, 315, 316, 317, 318, 330, 360.5, 381, 382, 386, 393, 400, 424, 449, 455, 464, 504, 509, 510, 519, 528, 533, 547, 548, 549, 560, 561, 567, 601, 606, 612, 634, 638, 641, 654, 655, 656, 660.5, 663, 671, 673, 703, 728, 747, 753, 771, 772, 776, 777, 786, 793, 794, 796, 803, 823, 830, 837, 839, 840, 841, 847, 851, 852, 853, 855, 856, 868, 869, 871, 874, 875, 876, 887, 916, 917, 936, 954, 955, 956, 1080, 1083, 1084, 1085, 1086, 1087, 1090, 1147, 1152, 1157, 1179, 1181, 1183, 1187, 1193, 1227, 1232, 1234, 1241, 1242, 1245, 1246.5, 1248, 1282, 1284, 1299, 1300, 1301, 1302, 1303, 1304, 1305, 1306, 1307, 1307.5, 1308, 1309, 1314, 1352, 1355, 1357, 1359, 1378, 1380, 1381, 1385, 1386, 1388, 1418, 1425, 1429, 1439, 1446, 1447, 1448, 1449, 1450, 1452, 1454, 1455, 1456, 1467, 1472, 1473, 1474, 1478, 1479, 1491, 1492, 1508, 1515, 1521, 1522, 1524, 1551, 1555, 1559, 1566, 1579, 1581, 1583, 1585, 1586, 1589, 1591, 1592, 1595, 1596, 1597, 1598, 1599, 1600, 1602, 1603, 1606, 1607, 1608, 1610, 1614, 1621, 1622, 1623, 1624, 1626, 1631, 1632, 1634, 1716, 1721, 1726, 1728, 1729, 1743, 1744, 1748, 1749, 1759, 1778, 1784, 1785, 1790, 1791, 1798, 1803, 1806, 1808, 1814, 1816, 1855, 1859, 1905, 1913, 1920, 1921, 1922, 1924, 1942, 1943, 1961, 1964, 1965, 1966, 1976, 1978, 1979, 1980, 1981, 1982, 1983, 1987, 2008, 2027, 2029, 2030, 2036, 2037, 2040, 2067, 2072, 2076, 2079, 2085, 2086, 2104, 2107, 2112, 2113, 2119, 2121, 2122, 2123, 2124, 2125, 2141, 2186, 2187, 2202, 2203, 2213, 2218, 2232, 2238, 2240, 2241, 2242, 2245, 2263, 2267, 2268, 2269, 2270, 2295, 2296, 2298, 2300, 2301, 2310, 2312, 2314, 2316, 2324, 2345, 2346, 2347, 2348, 2349, 2350, 2359, 2362, 2363, 2365, 2367, 2390, 2391, 2407, 2454, 2466, 2467, 2468, 2469, 2480, 2482, 2542, 2550, 2554, 2567, 2568, 2574, 2577, 2641, 2653, 2656.5, 2682, 2692, 2723, 2724, 2726, 2727, 2729, 2730, 2731, 2752, 2766, 2767, 2774, 2799, 2821, 2832, 2841, 2849, 2850, 2871, 2873, 2875, 2880, 2881, 2889, 2906, 2972, 2973, 2974, 2975, 2994, 3023, 3031, 3042, 3044, 3066, 3067, 3068, 3073, 3081

1. Abscissic acid 31, 38, 98, 178, 299, 315, 360.5, 519, 847, 876, 1245, 1300, 1303, 1314, 1381, 1385, 1386, 1388, 1478, 1632, 1778, 1983, 1987, 2119, 2203, 2359, 2362, 2726, 2729, 2730, 2731, 2821

2. Cytokinins 31, 90, 95, 96, 98, 118, 135, 178, 299, 386, 393, 455, 464, 504, 638, 641, 654, 660.5, 728, 753, 830, 839, 840, 841, 847, 868, 871, 876, 887, 955, 1080, 1085, 1087, 1090, 1181, 1193, 1227, 1242, 1245, 1300, 1303, 1378, 1380, 1381, 1385, 1429, 1454, 1455, 1456, 1508, 1521, 1559, 1566, 1583, 1626, 1632, 1726, 1778, 1790, 1791, 1814, 1816, 2027, 2030, 2067, 2079, 2119, 2121, 2122, 2123, 2124, 2125, 2218, 2263, 2268, 2269, 2270, 2295, 2324, 2391, 2454, 2466, 2467, 2468, 2550, 2653, 2726, 2730, 2731, 2752, 2766, 2821, 2849, 2850, 2973, 2980, 2981, 3031, 3073

3. Ethylene 1, 2, 316, 318, 424, 612, 663, 851, 852, 853, 874, 875, 876, 1152, 1187, 1299, 1301, 1302, 1304, 1305, 1306, 1307, 1307.5, 1308, 1309, 1388, 1474, 1632, 1806, 1808, 1905, 1920, 1921, 1922, 1978, 1979, 2040, 2072, 2362, 2365, 2577, 2726, 2730, 2731, 2766, 2875, 3081

4. Gibberellins 10, 18, 26, 31, 98, 118, 119, 123, 124, 129, 134, 135, 139, 140, 141, 163, 178, 209, 262, 299, 316, 317, 360.5, 381, 382, 449, 455, 504, 509, 528, 533, 547, 548, 549, 567, 601, 638, 641, 654, 655, 656, 703, 747, 796, 830, 847, 853, 869, 871, 874, 916, 917, 1084, 1090, 1157, 1179, 1181, 1183, 1193, 1242, 1245, 1246.5, 1248, 1282, 1284, 1300, 1302, 1307.5, 1309, 1352, 1355, 1357, 1359, 1385, 1388, 1418, 1429, 1446, 1447, 1448, 1449, 1450, 1452, 1473, 1478, 1479, 1491, 1492, 1508, 1521, 1522, 1524, 1551, 1555, 1581, 1583, 1589, 1591, 1595, 1596, 1597, 1598, 1599, 1600, 1602, 1603, 1606, 1607, 1608, 1610, 1614, 1621, 1622, 1623, 1624, 1626, 1631, 1632, 1721, 1726, 1728, 1729, 1743, 1744, 1748, 1778, 1784, 1785, 1855, 1859, 1924, 1942, 1943, 1976, 1980, 1981, 1982, 1983, 2008, 2027, 2029, 2030, 2036, 2037, 2040, 2076, 2107, 2119, 2122, 2125, 2186, 2187, 2203, 2204, 2205, 2206, 2207, 2208, 2232, 2238, 2240, 2241, 2242, 2245, 2312, 2314, 2316, 2324, 2345, 2346, 2347, 2348, 2349, 2350, 2390, 2454, 2467, 2468, 2480, 2542, 2550, 2567, 2568, 2574, 2577, 2653, 2656.5, 2682, 2692, 2726, 2730, 2731, 2766, 2767, 2799, 2832, 2859, 2871, 2889, 2906, 2972, 3023, 3066, 3067, 3073, 3081

5. Indoleacetic acid 10, 31, 71, 95, 96, 123, 124, 125, 129, 163, 164, 165, 261, 264, 265, 302, 330, 360.5, 393, 400, 510, 560, 561, 593, 601, 606, 634, 671, 673, 771, 772, 776, 777, 786, 793, 794, 796, 803, 823, 837, 853, 855, 868, 871, 876, 936, 1083, 1084, 1086, 1090, 1147,

1193, 1242, 1245, 1299, 1300, 1301, 1302, 1303, 1307, 1307.5, 1308,
1309, 1355, 1425, 1429, 1439, 1467, 1472, 1508, 1551, 1579, 1581,
1583, 1585, 1586, 1592, 1598, 1614, 1716, 1748, 1749, 1759, 1778,
1798, 1803, 1913, 1924, 1942, 1943, 1961, 1964, 1965, 1966, 1980,
2072, 2076, 2086, 2104, 2113, 2125, 2141, 2202, 2203, 2240, 2245,
2267, 2295, 2296, 2298, 2300, 2310, 2312, 2314, 2316, 2324, 2345,
2348, 2359, 2362, 2363, 2365, 2407, 2469, 2493, 2494, 2554, 2641,
2656.5, 2723, 2724, 2726, 2727, 2729, 2730, 2731, 2766, 2774, 2832,
2889, 2973, 2974, 2975, 3023, 3042, 3044, 3068, 3073, 3081

W. Leaf sheaths 199, 1640, 2698

X. Localization of photoperception by phytochrome (in terms of biological
    responses):
    1. In organs 31, 70, 143, 148, 248, 302, 329, 387, 450, 458, 476, 477,
        478, 479, 480, 481, 482, 485, 486, 487, 489, 528, 564, 594, 622, 687,
        786, 874, 875, 1034, 1178, 1189, 1300, 1483, 1508, 1551, 1571, 1572,
        1637, 1658, 1988, 1989, 2200, 2203, 2299, 2300, 2312, 2335, 2360,
        2488, 2641, 2747, 2816, 2885, 2914, 2918
    2. Subcellular 182, 520, 623, 824, 825, 959, 981, 984, 987, 1007, 1011,
        1015, 1016, 1017, 1024, 1222, 1223, 1724, 1973, 1974, 1985, 2486,
        3120, 3121, 3122, 3123

Y. Metabolism of:
    1. Buds 31, 32, 33, 60, 249, 250, 251, 869, 950, 951, 1086, 1229, 1234,
        1254, 1255, 1306, 1451, 1452, 1453, 1457, 1581, 1980, 1996, 2085,
        2125, 2464, 2465, 2559, 3002
    2. Chloroplasts 333, 1152, 2087, 2088, 2295
    3. Coleoptiles 43, 77, 350, 517, 560, 592, 823, 861, 1143, 1187, 1518,
        1924, 1942, 1943, 1965, 1986, 1988, 1989, 1990, 2081, 2083, 2127,
        2161, 2494, 2545, 2547, 2556, 2575, 2591, 2774
    4. Cotyledons 64, 65, 99, 102, 131, 167, 179, 180, 302, 372, 373, 374,
        375, 376, 377, 378, 458, 492, 512.5, 513, 514, 546, 547, 549, 550,
        551, 552, 554, 597, 598, 610, 655, 742, 775, 888, 889, 892, 893, 896,
        897, 899, 924, 925, 967, 1045, 1120, 1120.5, 1122, 1161, 1162, 1163,
        1164, 1182, 1205, 1206, 1207, 1239, 1240, 1321, 1325, 1433, 1434,
        1472, 1519, 1524, 1526, 1541, 1575, 1655, 1656, 1658, 1715, 1818,
        1847, 1879, 1882, 1884, 1892, 1905, 1906, 1961, 1963, 2014, 2016,
        2018, 2020, 2021, 2022, 2023, 2071, 2073, 2125, 2148, 2276, 2405,

2435, 2440, 2443, 2449, 2451, 2452, 2453, 2616, 2617, 2634, 2643, 2675, 2677, 2678, 2748, 2751, 2759, 2780, 2781, 2827, 2828, 2843, 2917, 2918, 2959, 2960, 2961, 2962, 2963, 2989, 3054, 3071

5. Epicotyls 30, 31, 32, 33, 43, 99, 102, 482, 745, 775, 794, 851, 871, 950, 951, 1045, 1120, 1306, 1364, 1367, 1453, 1457, 1826, 1942, 1944, 2037, 2325, 2370, 2464, 2465 2598, 2694

6. Flowers 85, 1482, 2623, 2631, 2632, 2633

7. Fronds 929, 1909, 1910, 1911

8. Fruits 540, 926, 1243, 1385, 1386, 1388, 2148, 2520, 2522

9. Gametophytes 112, 114, 115, 493.5, 543, 544, 1322, 1878, 1997, 2061, 2062, 2063, 2064, 2178, 2179, 2180, 2181, 2184, 2831

10. Hypocotyls 6, 7, 11, 66, 99, 100, 102, 131, 167, 373, 514, 550, 551, 552, 554, 591, 592, 593, 594, 596, 597, 598, 600, 601, 602, 603, 604, 605, 606, 607, 608, 609, 714, 725, 742, 745, 888, 889, 892, 893, 896, 897, 899, 957, 1045, 1120, 1120.5, 1122, 1143, 1161, 1245, 1301, 1415, 1519, 1524, 1540, 1541, 1558, 1575, 1826, 1870, 1882, 1888, 1895, 1907, 2014, 2016, 2021, 2022, 2023, 2073, 2396, 2435, 2440, 2443, 2451, 2453, 2502, 2545, 2547, 2616, 2617, 2621, 2622, 2624, 2634, 2729.5, 2732, 2780, 2781, 2782, 2843, 2917, 2959, 2960, 2966

11. Leaves 22, 23, 24, 31, 43, 44, 49, 68, 69, 77, 85, 154, 163, 250, 253, 254, 257, 293, 297, 333, 350, 360.5, 363, 457, 458, 460, 471, 474, 475, 476, 477, 478, 479, 480, 481, 482, 486, 488, 489, 491, 507, 614, 626, 683, 726, 789, 790, 791, 826, 879, 883, 885, 919, 920, 921, 948, 973, 975, 1045, 1076, 1077, 1078, 1080, 1119, 1132, 1134, 1150, 1159, 1190, 1204, 1334, 1354, 1356, 1431, 1450, 1503, 1518, 1544, 1553, 1564, 1572, 1573, 1579.5, 1592, 1614, 1631, 1646, 1678, 1689, 1691, 1692, 1694, 1695, 1698, 1699, 1737, 1755, 1779, 1787, 1788, 1789, 1813, 1814, 1820, 1821, 1823, 1825, 1826, 1929, 1986, 1987, 2039, 2046, 2047, 2068, 2069, 2080, 2087, 2088, 2119, 2142, 2143, 2145, 2146, 2154, 2164, 2165, 2166, 2167, 2169, 2172, 2186, 2187, 2188, 2189, 2196, 2197, 2198, 2199, 2204, 2205, 2206, 2207, 2208, 2295, 2305, 2308, 2310, 2323, 2325, 2326, 2344, 2356, 2357, 2360, 2361, 2362, 2363, 2364, 2365, 2373, 2393, 2482, 2494, 2498, 2499, 2538, 2546, 2547, 2556, 2591, 2603, 2606, 2607, 2612, 2619, 2644, 2645, 2657, 2670, 2695, 2696, 2754, 2755, 2756, 2757, 2814, 2815, 2818, 2820, 2879, 2881, 2883, 2884, 2885, 2888, 2892, 2893, 2894, 2895,

4. Cells 691, 692, 693, 693.5, 694

5. Coleoptiles 156, 157, 158, 160, 161, 162, 163, 166, 264, 265, 272, 387, 388, 450, 1442, 1579, 2600, 3006, 3016, 3017, 3018, 3098, 3099, 3100

6. Cotyledons 261, 329, 2244, 2438

7. Cotyledon epinasty 261, 1493

8. Epicotyls 745, 797, 869, 870, 1732

9. Epicotyl hooks 360, 482, 489, 745, 797, 870, 994, 1319, 1328, 1508, 1574, 1861, 1913, 1914, 1915, 2252, 2301, 2364, 2420

10. Flowers 81, 762, 1318, 1408

11. Fronds 1494

12. Hypocotyls 1299, 1534, 1848

13. Hypocotyl hooks 84, 143, 302, 360, 479, 480, 482, 489, 501, 525, 574, 970, 1101, 1299, 1300, 1301, 1302, 1418, 1419, 1423, 1424, 1425, 1428, 1429, 1432, 1509, 1531, 1534, 1575, 1619, 1846, 1919, 1922, 2072, 2125, 2243, 2244, 2252, 2296, 2298, 2299, 2300, 2301, 2389, 2435, 2438, 2481, 2501, 2823, 2875, 3038, 3042, 3044, 3045, 3048, 3049

14. Leaves 20, 44, 103, 121, 245, 248, 259, 300, 301, 306, 313, 325, 329, 462, 507, 630, 666, 686, 687, 690, 711, 756, 802, 805, 807, 810, 816, 868, 930, 1123, 1126, 1226, 1273, 1276, 1320, 1393, 1475, 1483, 1484, 1494, 1615, 1616, 1637, 1748, 1756, 1759, 2006, 2177, 2229, 2318, 2355, 2356, 2357, 2358, 2359, 2360, 2361, 2362, 2363, 2364, 2365, 2366, 2368, 2369, 2408, 2411, 2485, 2486, 2601, 2649, 2654, 2691, 2692, 2745, 2882, 2946, 3030, 3081

15. Leaf epinasty 3, 98, 360, 360.5, 505, 506, 756, 994, 1189, 1303, 1408, 1632, 1778, 1779, 2119, 2146, 2206, 2420, 2619, 2698, 2860, 2913, 2914

16. Nuclei 1753

17. Petioles 20, 687, 802, 1494, 2411, 2860, 2946, 3081

18. Rhizomes 104, 1192

19. Roots 1228, 1753, 2392, 2492, 2493

20. Sporophytes 623

21. Stems 206, 665, 795, 797, 1307, 1309, 1508, 1509, 1531, 2098, 2202, 2203, 3101

22. Tendril coiling 1224, 1225, 1233, 2098, 3101

AA. Number of:

1. Branches   1269, 1984

2. Buds   616, 1816, 1817, 2320

3. Cells   72, 73, 111, 114, 115, 149, 252, 255, 292, 361, 362, 380, 457, 458, 464, 545, 655, 672, 700, 721, 782.5, 856, 867, 923, 1040, 1158, 1201, 1202, 1304, 1387, 1395, 1409, 1412, 1485, 1486, 1487, 1488, 1562, 1635, 1641, 1780, 1782, 1783, 1798, 1802, 1836, 1859, 1924, 1960, 1984, 2020, 2011, 2012, 2034, 2095, 2096, 2103, 2104, 2121, 2122, 2126, 2181, 2291, 2292, 2402, 2407, 2569, 2570, 2600, 2610, 2636, 2639, 2642, 2649, 2764, 2871, 2908, 2909, 2910, 2911, 2912, 2960, 3057, 3058

4. Chloroplasts   255, 469, 721, 928, 1338, 1810, 1836, 2118, 2351, 2831

5. Flowers   46, 311, 357, 358, 414, 441, 499, 589, 590, 628, 709, 712, 759, 766, 769, 873, 904, 939, 947, 1089, 1092, 1094, 1095, 1098, 1100, 1102, 1113, 1247, 1257, 1269, 1278, 1313, 1391, 1392, 1398, 1408, 1410, 1441, 1474.5, 1475, 1544, 1625, 1810, 1916, 1961, 1962, 1963, 1964, 2027, 2236, 2273, 2321, 2333, 2386, 2410, 2491, 2515, 2516, 2699, 2700, 2701, 2702, 2703, 2704, 2705, 2706, 2707, 2708, 2709, 2710, 2711, 2712, 2713, 2714, 2715, 2825, 2854, 2865, 2932, 3033

6. Fronds   620, 727, 728, 1085, 1087, 1296, 2264, 2265, 2268, 2269, 2270, 3109

7. Fruits   414, 532, 666, 710, 873, 1591, 1810, 2102, 2272, 2273, 2333

8. Gametophytes   2387, 2388

9. Leaves   3, 414, 466, 512, 563, 582, 589, 613, 614, 733, 873, 1190, 1257, 1261, 1269, 1335, 1340, 1408, 1437, 1682, 1713, 1717, 1718, 1756, 1757, 1760, 1763, 1863, 2273, 2386, 2483, 2549, 2647, 2648, 2649, 2652, 2698, 2769, 2772, 2860, 2865, 2871, 2894, 2932, 2944, 2945, 2946, 2957

10. Nodes   2860

11. Rhizomes   1191

12. Roots   672, 745, 777, 794, 1045, 1209, 1626, 2073, 2075, 2306, 2307, 2822

13. Seeds   410, 704, 766, 1174, 1269, 2043, 2240, 2899, 3059

14. Stems   386, 504, 507, 613, 665, 1294

BB. Organ Interactions 31, 143, 148, 163, 179, 180, 261, 302, 458, 474, 476, 477, 478, 479, 480, 481, 482, 485, 486, 487, 489, 518, 528, 592, 594, 597, 598, 601, 654, 655, 672, 684, 856, 888, 893, 898, 1086, 1101, 1121, 1181, 1182, 1450, 1519, 1553, 1571, 1614, 1658, 1693, 1784, 1785, 1847, 1892, 1924, 2021, 2022, 2023, 2034, 2076, 2099, 2125, 2276, 2296, 2299, 2300, 2301, 2390, 2391, 2435, 2439, 2441, 2973, 3010, 3054, 3081

CC. Phosphorylation (see respiration and photosynthesis subheadings)

DD. Photoperiodic effects on:

1. Buds 183, 449, 511, 611, 1387, 1565, 3022

2. Chloroplasts 477, 1338, 1985, 2464

3. Flowers 38, 44, 59, 92, 137, 173, 181, 214, 215, 221, 232, 234, 237, 238, 241, 305, 308, 357, 359, 364, 366, 368, 369, 370, 405, 406, 435, 436, 437, 439, 445, 449, 498, 499, 507, 511, 515, 524, 526, 529, 530, 532, 582, 590, 616, 617, 620, 624, 626, 628, 708, 709, 711, 712, 714, 731, 732, 734, 735, 736, 738, 759, 761, 763, 765, 766, 767, 886, 904, 931, 933, 934, 939, 943, 947, 1039, 1088, 1089, 1092, 1094, 1095, 1098, 1100, 1102, 1113, 1128, 1129, 1130, 1139, 1194, 1195, 1212, 1213, 1217, 1220, 1257, 1261, 1262, 1264, 1267, 1269, 1271, 1272, 1278, 1279, 1280, 1297, 1326, 1327, 1330, 1389, 1395, 1396, 1397, 1398, 1406, 1435, 1436, 1437, 1440, 1441, 1474.5, 1475, 1528, 1532, 1533, 1544, 1552, 1623, 1625, 1628, 1630, 1663, 1669, 1713, 1757, 1760, 1762, 1763, 1764, 1765, 1918, 1925, 1928, 1929, 1931, 1932, 1933, 1934, 1935, 1936, 1961, 1962, 1964, 1967, 2002, 2015, 2027, 2049, 2053, 2054, 2055, 2058, 2068, 2091, 2151, 2192, 2209, 2210, 2213, 2233, 2273, 2333, 2334, 2335, 2340, 2371, 2388, 2410, 2482, 2491, 2512, 2513, 2514, 2515, 2516, 2635, 2646, 2647, 2648, 2649, 2652, 2660, 2661, 2662, 2699, 2700, 2701, 2702, 2703, 2704, 2705, 2706, 2707, 2708, 2709, 2710, 2711, 2712, 2713, 2714, 2715, 2719, 2826, 2839, 2853, 2864, 2865, 2866, 2868, 2873, 2877.5, 2922, 2032, 2944, 2945, 2957, 2984, 3015, 3034, 3035, 3037, 3047, 3051

4. Fronds/thalli 472, 473, 710, 713, 715, 716, 717, 718, 719, 720, 1296, 1797, 2042, 2266, 2267, 2268, 2269, 2270, 2388, 2461, 2570, 2845, 3029

5. Gametogenesis 958, 2388

6. Leaves 3, 24, 449, 471, 477, 511, 512, 563, 582, 611, 672, 1039,

1226, 1269, 1276, 1277, 1320, 1331, 1336, 1337, 1411, 1472, 1615, 1616, 1925, 2001, 2002, 2233, 2331, 2342, 2343, 2353, 2354, 2360, 2361, 2362, 2363, 2364, 2365, 2366, 2368, 2369, 2410, 2459, 2480, 2511, 2692, 2698, 2946, 2957

7. Metabolism 443, 474, 475, 477, 482, 507, 511, 601, 603, 671, 693, 717, 718, 719, 720, 723, 740, 741, 849, 1039, 1108, 1109, 1110, 1111, 1112, 1115, 1118, 1237, 1331, 1334, 1385, 1472, 1829, 1900, 2068, 2069, 2163, 2164, 2165, 2166, 2167, 2169, 2172, 2186, 2187, 2333, 2360, 2361, 2362, 2365, 2368, 2369, 2464, 2690, 2820, 2833, 2845, 2902, 3021

8. Petioles 3, 582, 672, 2353, 2952

9. Roots 658, 1269, 1294, 2306, 2311, 2511

10. Seed germination 141, 168, 169, 438, 440, 580, 581, 695, 740, 748, 749, 750, 751, 753, 908, 1198, 1199, 1313, 2052, 2278, 2767, 2804, 2805, 3062

11. Spore germination 1860, 2611, 2627

12. Sporulation 541, 2215, 2223

13. Stems 3, 499, 507, 511, 512, 563, 582, 618, 619, 621, 627, 671, 672, 957, 1039, 1219, 1269, 1277, 1294, 1329, 1335, 1411, 1553, 1625, 1629, 1925, 1960, 2001, 2002, 2008, 2233, 2235, 2329, 2353, 2354, 2409, 2410, 2480, 2511, 2946, 2957, 3015, 3022

14. Stoma 1685, 1686

EE. Photosynthesis
1. General 130, 132, 393, 445, 471, 652, 653, 659, 663, 826, 842, 886, 1029, 1296, 1787, 1788, 1789, 2034, 2095, 2292, 2354, 2412, 2413, 2414, 2415, 2416, 2427, 2472, 2643, 2754, 2755, 2756, 2757, 2893, 2898, 3114, 3115

2. Oxygen release measured 132, 826, 956, 1787, 1788, 1789, 2754, 2755, 2756, 2757, 2758

3. Photosynthetic phosphorylation 471, 567, 1787, 1788, 1789

FF. Phototaxis 693.5

GG. Plant:
1. Size 3, 18, 315, 394, 414, 511, 563, 566, 567, 589, 614, 621, 660.5, 666, 667, 668, 672, 757, 759, 760, 762, 769, 793, 797, 844, 872, 1174, 1190, 1209, 1249, 1269, 1313, 1340, 1377, 1408, 1446, 1447, 1633, 1634, 1638, 1682, 1749, 1794, 1923, 1927, 2001, 2002, 2102,

2114, 2217, 2233, 2244, 2263, 2272, 2273, 2385, 2386, 2391, 2511, 2512, 2635, 2698, 2834, 2902, 2905, 3000, 3043

2. Weight   3, 46, 47, 50, 144, 363, 393, 394, 466, 507, 528, 545, 560, 566, 567, 582, 589, 614, 666, 729, 730, 759, 1045, 1121, 1122, 1125, 1174, 1190, 1209, 1249, 1269, 1340, 1437, 1516, 1518, 1522, 1682, 1810, 1863, 1925, 1927, 2114, 2273, 2490, 2511, 2512, 2635, 2649, 2698, 2769, 2847, 2860, 2899, 2902, 2946, 2986, 3033, 3043, 3059

HH. Polarity of growth   1807

II. Pollen chromosomes   1636, 2686, 2687, 3083

JJ. Respiration:

1. General   24, 70, 125, 130, 256, 350, 486, 487, 636, 659, 729, 730, 789, 927, 942, 956, 1108, 1109, 1110, 1111, 1112, 1115, 1118, 1120, 1120.5, 1121, 1122, 1175, 1236, 1301, 1560, 1564, 1688, 1689, 1823, 1825, 1826, 1829, 1998, 2010, 2011, 2012, 2146, 2240, 2290, 2291, 2323, 2354, 2357, 2360, 2482, 2619, 2672, 2673, 2674, 2743, 2785, 3085, 3086, 3087, 3114

2. Oxidative phosphorylation   31, 32, 33, 488, 490, 659, 863, 866, 1185, 1809, 2547, 2672, 2673, 2674, 2676, 3085

KK. Rhythms (endogenous)   4, 20, 38, 44, 82, 103, 211, 300, 301, 311, 313, 329, 357, 358, 362, 441, 572, 590, 603, 630, 644, 659, 685, 687, 693, 738, 739, 740, 741, 794, 807, 810, 930, 931, 932, 939, 958, 1095, 1104, 1108, 1109, 1110, 1111, 1112, 1115, 1118, 1123, 1126, 1200, 1276, 1312, 1318, 1395, 1396, 1397, 1398, 1475, 1494, 1552, 1594, 1615, 1616, 1637, 1655, 1684, 1685, 1687, 1738, 1829, 1929, 1931, 1932, 1934, 1935, 1936, 1985, 2042, 2053, 2069, 2096, 2150, 2163, 2164, 2165, 2166, 2167, 2169, 2172, 2210, 2318, 2353, 2359, 2360, 2361, 2362, 2365, 2366, 2368, 2369, 2430, 2458, 2515, 2516, 2611, 2627, 2654, 2690, 2692, 2702, 2703, 2704, 2705, 2709, 2710, 2711, 2712, 2713, 2714, 2715, 2920, 2921, 2923, 3021, 3023

LL. Senescence   21, 22, 23, 472, 473, 484, 491, 919, 1750, 1808, 1813, 1814, 1987

MM. Sex expression   958, 1984, 2070

NN. Spore release (also see other specific spore responses)   286

OO. Stoma   49, 459, 493, 630, 683, 689, 758, 920, 921, 921.2, 921.5, 948, 1078, 1204, 1317, 1337, 1353, 1412, 1444, 1507, 1572, 1594, 1683, 1684, 1685, 1686, 1755, 1937, 1939, 2005, 2047, 2154, 2188, 2189, 2372, 2373, 2538, 3012, 3096

PP. Subcellular structures:

1. Chloroplasts (see specific response headings)

2. Dictyosomes 1753, 2493

3. Membranes 198, 1497, 1710, 2066, 2174, 2175, 2176, 2276, 2288, 2383, 2729.5, 2831, 2922, 2926, 3085

4. Microbodies 789, 1579.5

5. Microtubules 2974

6. Mitochondria 411, 860, 861, 863, 1185, 1236, 1662, 1753, 1809, 1938, 2179, 2606, 2831, 3067

QQ. Time of development of:

1. Buds 1816, 1817, 2865

2. Flowers 59. 81, 137, 288, 289, 290, 291, 371, 414, 499, 508, 511, 582, 589, 611, 666, 709, 712, 731, 732, 733, 759, 760, 761, 763, 765, 767, 769, 873, 1098, 1128, 1129, 1265, 1269, 1278, 1280, 1340, 1408, 1410, 1435, 1436, 1475, 1516, 1533, 1625, 1810, 1925, 1927, 1931, 1932, 2015, 2094, 2109, 2192, 2273, 2384, 2386, 2495, 2513, 2514, 2635, 2649, 2662, 2825, 2853, 2865, 2866, 2877.5, 2905, 2932, 2944, 2945, 2953, 2984, 3033, 3034

3. Fruits 1810, 2102, 2109, 2272, 2495, 3088

4. Gametophytes 1641, 2388

5. Leaves 459, 2109, 2495, 2512, 2769, 2944

RR. Tissue:

1. Redox potential 2326

2. Water status (including turgor) 165, 259, 355, 756, 807, 920, 921, 1300, 1314, 1473, 1558, 1606, 1618, 1620, 1750, 1939, 1953, 1954, 1955, 1956, 2202, 2203, 2231, 2318, 2355, 2358, 2365, 2366, 2390, 2882, 2932, 2979

SS. Tissue cultures 27, 95, 96, 116, 384, 464, 555, 572, 573, 756, 849, 867, 884, 953, 954, 955, 956, 1176, 1332, 1416, 1519, 1523, 2103, 2104, 2182, 2211, 2212, 2551, 2642, 2975, 2985, 2986, 2987, 2988, 2992, 2993

TT. Tissues:

1. Cortex 923, 1753, 1956, 2173, 2772

2. Endosperm 2391

3. Epidermis 48, 756, 789, 924, 925, 1159, 1494, 1507, 1717, 1718, 1810, 1841, 1960, 2034, 2135, 2173, 2649, 2745, 2772, 2871, 2917, 2989

9. Hypocotyls 99, 593, 745, 852, 875, 1045, 1121, 1122, 1575, 1713, 1882, 1888, 2114, 2435, 2697, 2959, 3003, 3038, 3041, 3043

10. Leaves 3, 22, 50, 253, 254, 350, 363, 406, 418, 421, 458, 471, 511, 582, 589, 655, 745, 873, 1076, 1077, 1132, 1141, 1166, 1167, 1190, 1331, 1334, 1335, 1336, 1337, 1356, 1427, 1437, 1450, 1489, 1574, 1682, 1754, 2046, 2118, 2192, 2198, 2199, 2236, 2343, 2353, 2354, 2480, 2495, 2511, 2603, 2649, 2659, 2695, 2697, 2820, 2893, 2898, 2902, 3035, 3038, 3041, 3043

11. Mesocotyls 350

12. Petioles 3, 582, 2697

13. Roots 99, 149, 152, 582, 666, 1121, 1122, 1190, 1209, 1335, 1437, 1575, 1682, 1732, 2236, 2307, 2463, 2490, 2511, 2512, 2659, 2698, 2847, 2959, 3003, 3038

14. Seeds 729, 766, 1269, 1620, 2109, 2192, 2240, 2899, 3059

15. Sporophytes 1522, 2033

16. Stems 50, 125, 126, 363, 582, 589, 873, 877, 878, 880, 1090, 1174, 1190, 1252, 1307, 1334, 1335, 1437, 1450, 1451, 1453, 1581, 1682, 2109, 2192, 2236, 2353, 2354, 2480, 2495, 2511, 2603, 2649, 2695, 2697, 2820, 2847, 3035, 3038, 3059

SECTION IV: REVIEWS

A. Action spectra 216, 217, 225, 227, 229, 233, 331, 341, 562, 784, 804, 971, 990, 1055, 1056, 1060, 1061, 1062, 1066, 1067, 1613, 1843, 1895, 2007, 2057, 2254, 2505, 2530, 2531, 2718

B. Biological rhythms 142, 309, 310, 312, 444, 629, 804, 806, 933.5, 938, 939, 940, 1093, 1107, 1114, 1151, 1588, 1611, 1968, 2074, 2171, 2258, 2462, 2564, 2941.5, 3004, 3020, 3021.5

C. Carbohydrate effects 784, 800, 1822, 2013, 2900, 2903

D. Chloroplast development 155, 184, 185, 1405, 1570, 2553, 3106

E. Chloroplast movement/orientation 972, 979, 982, 985, 986, 990, 993, 995, 996, 998, 1005, 1009, 1012, 1018, 1021, 1023, 1026, 1026.5, 1027, 2429, 2431, 2473, 2477, 2763, 2886, 2928, 2956, 2979.5, 3110, 3116

F. Chromosome protection/repair 1747, 3056

G. Distribution taxonomically 204, 233, 1103, 2504 (see Taxonomic Index)

H. Dormancy/vernalization 918, 1107, 1952, 2004, 2149, 2271, 2790, 2795, 2933, 2934, 2941, 2941.2, 2942

I. Enzyme induction/levels 155, 595, 599, 784, 1696, 1895, 1896, 1898, 1899

1901, 1904, 2168, 2170, 2171, 2447, 2448, 2450, 2527, 2562.5, 3072, 3106

J. Flowering 94, 94.5, 142, 204, 207, 208, 213, 216, 217, 222, 224, 225, 227, 230, 231, 232, 233, 368, 379, 516, 531, 625, 629, 764, 770, 804, 937, 938, 939, 940, 1046, 1049, 1065, 1066, 1068, 1074, 1107, 1151, 1177, 1465, 1537, 1588, 1611, 1613, 1625, 1714, 1719, 1933, 1952, 1968, 2258, 2274, 2336, 2339, 2460, 2462, 2716, 2717, 2718, 2838, 2861, 2874, 2876, 2941.5, 2950, 2983, 3093, 3094, 3095

K. Fungal effects 1711

L. General reviews 47, 116.5, 142, 204, 222, 228, 233, 235, 236, 243, 246, 247, 285, 320, 327, 335, 340, 341, 343, 345, 396, 536, 625, 779, 780, 784, 787, 798, 804, 808, 809, 902, 1003, 1025, 1050, 1053, 1054, 1069, 1071, 1074, 1075, 1091, 1103, 1117, 1168, 1250, 1291, 1293, 1295, 1407, 1438, 1471, 1496, 1504, 1511, 1512, 1536, 1593, 1644, 1766, 1770, 1773, 1786, 1845, 1850, 1854, 1857, 1864, 1902, 1903, 1930, 1939.5, 2093, 2110, 2111, 2309, 2319, 2352, 2557, 2761, 2763, 2836, 2837, 2862, 2869, 2877, 2878, 2880, 2950, 2997, 2998, 3051, 3052

M. Geotropism 996, 997, 3019

N. High irradiance reaction (HIR) 94, 142, 175, 233, 1021, 1037, 1055, 1060, 1061, 1066, 1068, 1295, 1588, 1611, 1613, 1843, 1857, 1868, 1872, 1894, 1895, 2149, 2246, 2247, 2254, 2258, 2259, 2504, 2867

O. Hormone interactions 11.5, 175, 177, 263, 328, 365, 629, 784, 800, 801, 827, 906, 1107, 1298, 1465, 1604, 1605, 1611, 1612, 1613, 1792, 1968, 2004, 2048, 2508, 2561, 2760, 2942, 2995, 3095

P. *In vitro* properties 142, 204, 276, 280, 283, 284, 349, 351, 784, 902, 1063, 1066, 1067, 1071, 1103, 1568, 2136, 2258, 2304, 2504, 2530, 2531, 2535, 2536

Q. Leaf movement 688, 804, 806, 1151, 1230, 2367

R. Localization within a cell 283, 986, 1018, 1021, 1026, 1895, 1896, 2258, 2446, 2504

S. Localization within a plant 224, 225, 233, 283, 784, 2258, 2504

T. Membrane interactions 94.5, 804, 1070, 1230, 1495, 2258, 2381.5, 2504, 2561, 2928, 2955, 2979.5

U. Nucleic acid effects 784, 2508

V. Photomorphogenesis and its mechanism 142, 204, 217, 222, 224, 225, 226, 228, 229, 233, 239, 240, 283, 294, 303, 328, 331, 341, 404, 463, 483, 535, 559, 625, 643, 722, 779, 780, 781, 784, 787, 800, 902, 968, 969,

971, 972, 1037, 1049, 1050, 1055, 1057, 1061, 1067, 1068, 1070, 1071,
1074, 1103, 1116, 1169, 1173, 1231, 1298, 1388, 1430, 1438, 1510, 1512,
1536, 1549.5, 1593, 1604, 1605, 1613, 1766, 1769, 1770, 1776, 1786, 1792,
1822, 1843, 1844, 1850, 1852, 1853, 1856, 1857, 1858, 1866, 1868, 1872,
1875, 1883, 1889, 1890, 1894, 1895, 1896, 1897, 1899, 1901, 2057, 2074,
2092, 2110, 2111, 2149, 2246, 2247, 2250, 2254, 2258, 2259, 2271, 2275,
2319, 2504, 2508, 2510, 2530, 2557, 2565, 2650, 2651, 2679, 2763, 2822,
2838, 2862, 2863, 2867, 2878, 2947, 2948, 2949, 2950, 2954, 3026, 3027,
3051

W. Photoperiodism 94, 142, 204, 207, 208, 213, 216, 217, 222, 224, 225, 226,
227, 229, 230, 231, 232, 233, 240, 244, 303, 309, 310, 312, 368, 379, 444,
467, 468, 516, 531, 542, 599, 625, 629, 764, 770, 804, 906, 937, 938, 939,
940, 1046, 1047, 1048, 1053, 1061, 1065, 1066, 1067, 1068, 1072, 1093,
1107, 1117, 1151, 1177, 1476, 1477, 1537, 1563, 1588, 1611, 1613, 1625,
1714, 1819, 1926, 1933, 1952, 1968, 2007, 2059, 2074, 2089, 2092, 2168,
2171, 2258, 2274, 2275, 2279, 2294, 2336, 2339, 2460, 2462, 2551, 2716,
2717, 2718, 2838, 2861, 2863, 2874, 2933, 2934, 2936, 2937, 2941.5, 2983,
3051, 3093, 3094

X. Phototropism 266, 268, 451, 559, 562, 792, 997, 1037, 1844, 1850, 2507,
2762

Y. Photosynthetic effects 468, 2758, 2900, 2903, 2928

Z. Pigment production 142, 155, 185, 210, 233, 595, 784, 800, 1056, 1061,
1062, 1067, 1068, 1388, 1819, 1850, 1851, 1876, 1895, 1896, 1899, 1901,
1912, 2258, 2527, 2560, 2562.5, 2838, 2887, 3053

AA. Physical/chemical responses of phytochrome *in vivo* following irradiation
204, 283, 346, 707, 784, 1003, 1066, 1067, 1103, 1116, 1568, 1895,
1939.5, 2136, 2258, 2446, 2504, 2530, 2531

BB. Physical/chemical responses of phytochrome *in vivo* to irradiation 204,
276, 283, 336, 341, 345, 707, 784, 1066, 1067, 1103, 1895, 2136, 2254,
2258, 2446, 2504, 2530, 2531, 2536, 2562, 2595

CC. Polarotropism 982, 986, 990, 996, 1009, 1018, 1021, 1027, 2956

DD. Protein synthesis 175, 184, 354, 784, 1822, 2900, 2903

EE. Purification of phytochrome 142, 204, 282, 283, 349, 784, 1067, 1071,
2303, 2530, 2531, 2536

FF. Respiration effects 175, 784, 866, 1469, 2900, 2903

☆ U. S. GOVERNMENT PRINTING OFFICE : 1977 O - 232-506